$14.95

A THEORY OF DATA

Clyde H. Coombs, THE UNIVERSITY OF MICHIGAN

A THEORY OF DATA

JOHN WILEY & SONS, INC., NEW YORK · LONDON · SYDNEY

to Lo

Preface

In 1948 Samuel A. Stouffer invited me to spend a year at Harvard's Laboratory of Social Relations with him, Paul F. Lazarsfeld, and Frederick Mosteller. The intent was to spend the year developing and exchanging our ideas in the area of psychological measurement and scaling. Some new ideas were just beginning to stir,* and I was delighted with the opportunity.

During that year the idea of the scale grid and of unfolding theory emerged, but it was several more years before a general framework for psychological measurement and scaling was developed. This framework appeared in Festinger and Katz† in a chapter entitled "Theory and Methods of Social Measurement," and was called *a theory of data*. I now refer to that formulation as the "old" theory of data because in 1957 a sudden insight led to a thorough revision‡ and finally to this book.

This theory of data is offered as an analysis of the foundations of psychological measurement. The theory extends from behavior—where psychological measurement begins—to the inferential classification of stimuli and people—where it ends. Psychological measurement models may be thought of as logical systems to arrive at such inferential classifications. Any such logical system is not necessarily thought of as a scaling model, however. Scaling models have come to be associated with the particular logical systems that lead to geometrical representa-

---

* C. H. Coombs, Some hypotheses for the analysis of qualitative variables, *Psychol. Rev.*, **55**, 167–74 (1948).
† L. Festinger and D. Katz, *Research methods in the behavioral sciences*, Dryden Press, New York, 1953.
‡ C. H. Coombs, A theory of data, *Psychol. Rev.*, **67**, 143–59 (1960).

tions of inferential classification—for example, unidimensional scales and multidimensional spaces. This book is concerned exclusively with geometrical models for the inferential classification of stimuli and people.

All scaling models are concerned with the analysis of data, but each model has been designed for some particular kind of data and, indeed, usually associated with one particular behavioral context. Here, in the theory of data, we are concerned with a comprehensive system for distinguishing and relating all the types of data with which measurement and scaling theories deal, regardless of the behavioral context of the data or their sources. It should not be surprising, then, that a distinction between data and behavioral observations has to be drawn; data and behavior may be closely related but they are not necessarily the same thing.

Though a countless variety of behavior may be observed and recorded, we shall see that the varieties of data are remarkably limited. Therein lies the service that the theory of data renders. In the real world context of behavior there seems no limit to the variety of models which might be constructed for inferential classification. In the abstract context of data, however, we can develop quite a simple system which displays and clarifies the similarities and differences among such models. Such a system has several advantages, including facilitating transfer of training on one model to the other models and making visible the variety of alternative models which might be appropriate for any given set of data.

The classification system for behavioral data provided by this theory is used as the framework for organizing the book. I report in some detail the research done at Michigan in this area of scaling and data theory. In summary form the related work of Guttman, Lazarsfeld, Luce, Stevens, Thurstone, Torgerson, and others is reported, to integrate the domain of psychological measurement and scaling. I regard Torgerson's *Theory and Methods of Scaling* as a companion volume and have tried to avoid duplication wherever possible.

The first chapter is an overview of the classification system in which I try to make intuitively reasonable the abstractions underlying this theory of data. It introduces the four basic quadrants corresponding to the four kinds of data for which inferential classification systems have been built. These four quadrants, in numerical order, I have called preferential choice data, single stimulus data, stimuli comparison data, and similarities data. The second chapter is a systematic discussion of methods of collecting data, including a number of new procedures. Certain measures are constructed, using information theory, which provide criteria helpful in deciding what method to use in a particular instance. These two chapters, but particularly Chapter 1, are prerequisite to the rest of the book.

Parts 2 to 5 each comprise a cluster of chapters concerned respectively with the four basic kinds of data. Each part begins with an introductory chapter (or section of a chapter) which discusses the kind of data treated in the rest of that part of the book. As a rule, the remaining chapters in each part deal with successively more complex models. Further, where appropriate, the models leading to weaker inferential classifications like nominal or ordinal scales are discussed first. To a considerable extent each of the four parts of the book can stand alone, but I have indicated important dependencies by cross references. The last part of the book, Part 6, is a cluster of chapters dealing with interrelations among the various kinds of data and with matters which are of common concern to them all.

Occasionally sections of chapters or whole chapters are devoted to extrapolations to and speculations about what I think are important ideas illuminated by the theory of data. Chapters 13, 16, 18, and 25 are examples.

There is more material than readers with specialized interests will want or need. Consequently, each chapter is concluded with a rather complete summary which serves as a guide to the substantive content of the chapter. A preliminary reading of the summary of a chapter is recommended.

My professional colleagues concerned with basic theoretical problems of measurement in psychology constitute the principal audience. Scaling technology, however, is of interest to all behavioral scientists who do research, so new methods developed at Michigan are presented in some detail.

The formal mathematical level is quite low; algebra, geometry, and some elementary set theory and calculus are sufficient for the most part. I have tried to present all important ideas in verbal terms without dependence on formal mathematics but on a willingness to think abstractly. A case in point is the introductory paragraphs of Chapter 7 on multi-dimensional unfolding. This chapter is somewhat more mathematically demanding than most of the others. Consequently, the beginning is an extended introduction which is a heuristic discussion intended to serve the needs of those who only want a general understanding of what multidimensional unfolding is all about.

As Margenau has said,* measurement lies at the juncture of theory and experience—the first contact of reason and nature. This juncture is my concern and the immediate subject matter of this theory of data.

Ann Arbor, Michigan   C. H. COOMBS
January 1964

---

* Henry Margenau, "Philosophical problems concerning the meaning of measurement in physics," in *Measurement: definitions and theories*, edited by C. W. Churchman and P. Ratoosh, John Wiley and Sons, New York, 1959.

Acknowledgments

From the beginning, in 1947, the research on which this book is based was encouraged, supported, and criticized by Donald G. Marquis. It is a pleasure to acknowledge my debt to him. I wish also to thank Robert M. Thrall of the Department of Mathematics at The University of Michigan with whom I worked closely in the early stages of the mathematical formulation and Richard C. Kao, now of RAND Corporation, with whom I had extended interaction during recent years.

I wish it were possible to acknowledge individually the support I found in the atmosphere created by my colleagues at Michigan. They were always willing to listen and to criticize ideas. It is often the many intangibles that ease the task and indeed make it possible in the first place. In particular I would like to mention Daniel Katz. I would also like my many students over the years to know that I am deeply grateful for their support and their substantial contributions.

Throughout the text there are occasional references to instances in which I have been guided or instructed by others. For several individuals, however, this is a totally inadequate indication of my debt. They include Robert P. Abelson, Robyn M. Dawes, and John W. Tukey, whose penetrating critical comments taught me much about my own work.

I have also received from Lee J. Cronbach, R. Duncan Luce, S. S. Stevens, and Warren S. Torgerson very thoughtful comments and criticism which led to substantial changes in parts of the book.

Of considerable import also were comments and criticisms from Norman Feather, John A. Keats, Roderick M. MacDougall, Donald W. McElwain in Australia, and Jan Vastenhouw in The Netherlands.

Philip J. Runkel, whose particular interest is in interpersonal communication and understanding, read all of two drafts, and while he is not to be blamed for any failures of the book to communicate, he is to be credited with vast improvements over my first attempts. I also benefited greatly from many sessions with Joseph L. Zinnes during the preparation of the first draft.

For the protection of those I have named I should add that advice was not always heeded, sometimes for intellectual reasons and sometimes because it would have led me afield. So, while I owe much to others, the use I have made of their suggestions and contributions is my own responsibility.

For a careful reading and considerable editoral assistance in the final stages I am indebted to Dr. Thomas G. G. Bezembinder and Myron Wish. For typing and secretarial assistance in the early draft of the book I wish to thank Mrs. Julie Raventos at the Center for Advanced Study in the Behavioral Sciences; for preparation of the final draft and for bibliographical assistance I owe thanks to my secretary at The University of Michigan, Mrs. Suzanne Maine. For assistance in proofreading the final copy, I am indebted to Mrs. Joan Barth.

All of my research reported in this book was made possible by a number of successive research grants over the years. These have been suitably acknowledged elsewhere except the two most recent: an NSF grant, No. 65820, 1958–1961, and an NIMH grant, No. M4236. The latter provided an initial year at the Center for Advanced Study in the Behavioral Sciences during which the first draft of the book was prepared. Without the facilities and freedom provided by the Center I would probably never have undertaken the task.

C. H. C.

Contents

A THEORY OF DATA

PART 1
_____

BASIC CONCEPTS

Data may be viewed as relations between points in a space. This geometric viewpoint, which we shall develop and explore, leads to a simple classification of types of data. One consequence of this classification is the development of new scaling models; another is the highlighting of certain similarities among data and models from different areas in psychology.

Other viewpoints are possible. For the purposes of this book, however, we use the term data in this restricted geometric sense.

The material contained in this part is generally prerequisite to most of the rest of the book, in that the concepts and vocabulary introduced in these chapters are used freely throughout the remainder. The first chapter is designed to give an overview of this theory of data and explains the organization of the book. The second chapter assembles in one unit a variety of related material on collecting and analyzing data relevant to each of the several parts of the book that follow.

CHAPTER 1

An Overview of a Theory of Data

This book is a report of fourteen years of research into the foundations of psychological measurement. Our orientation to the subject is basically geometrical, and from this viewpoint we find that psychological measurement models, normally dressed in specific and different behavioral languages, may reveal interesting and suggestive interrelations when perceived in a common abstract language.

This consideration of data as relations between points in space leads to a simple classification system of the basic kinds of data which should prove useful (1) to the teacher of psychological measurement and scaling, (2) to the experimenter deciding what method to use in collecting and analyzing data, and (3) to the theoretician in psychological measurement.

To the teacher the value lies in the order and structure introduced to a field which has been developing very rapidly and somewhat chaotically. The similarities among scaling methods are a major feature of this system, and it thereby facilitates learning through generalization and transfer. To the experimenter the value lies in the logical structure placed on methods of collecting and analyzing data, in that the repertoire is increased and some criteria for evaluation and selection are provided. To the theoretician the value lies in the generation of new problems at the same time that possible lines of solution are suggested.

1. SCOPE OF THE THEORY

Behavioral scientists follow a great variety of methods under the general rubrics of collecting and analyzing data. We propose to introduce order into this abundance by formulating in a universal language the processes by which behavioral data are made, of what they are made, and how they become measurements. In the course of doing this the term *data* itself will take on a restricted (not *different*) meaning, and we become persuaded that the data are in part a product of the mind of the observer.

The restricted meaning that is given here to the term *data* arises from the fact that it has two common uses in behavioral science. The term is commonly used to refer both to the recorded observations and to that which is analyzed. These are not necessarily the same thing, and a distinction is imperative. This distinction seems a subtle and difficult point to some on initial contact with the theory of data; the third section of this chapter is designed to clarify it.

The term data is used here to refer only to that which is analyzed. As will be evident, the same observations may frequently be interpreted as one of two or more different kinds of data. The choice is an optional decision by the scientist and represents a creative step on his part in collecting the data he analyzes. It is the different kinds of data and their interrelations with which this theory is concerned. It might help to clarify the scope of the theory of data if we turn to the diagram of Fig. 1.1.

At the extreme left is the universe of potential observations, all of the things the behavioral scientist might choose to record. If an individual is asked whether he would vote for candidate A, the observer usually records his answer, yes or no; but we might ask why the time it took him to answer is not of interest, or whether there was a change in respiration, or in his galvanic skin response, or what he did with his hands, and so on. From this richness the scientist must select some few things to record, and this step is called phase 1 in the diagram.

These recorded observations, however, are not yet data in the sense of this theory of data; an interpretive step on the part of the scientist, called phase 2 in the diagram, is required to convert the recorded observations into data. Phase 2 involves a classification of observations in the sense

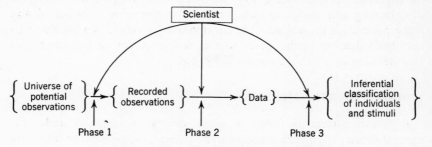

Fig. 1.1 Flow diagram from the real world to inferences.

that individuals and stimuli are identified and labeled, and the observations are classified in terms of a relation of some kind between individuals and stimuli, or perhaps just between stimuli.

Then, given this prior classification, phase 3 involves the detection of relations, order, and structure which follow as a logical consequence of the data and the model used for analysis.

The scientist enters each of these three phases in a creative way in the sense that alternatives are open to him and his decisions will determine in a significant way the results that will be obtained from the analysis. Each successive phase puts more limiting boundaries on what the results might be. At the beginning, before phase 1, there are, perhaps, no limits on the potential conclusions; but each phase then constrains the universe of possible inferences that can ultimately be drawn from the analysis.

For example, suppose an experimenter has subjects judge which of two policies is more beneficial to society. He might use such judgments to study the statements or to study the individuals. If the experimenter decides to interpret the behavior he observed as relations between an individual and a stimulus, he will ultimately come to different conclusions than if he interprets the observed behavior as relations between stimuli. This is an example of a decision which has to be made in phase 2. The decision then restricts the variety of models among which choice must be made in phase 3.

I am not deploring these creative roles of the scientist but merely trying to detail explicitly the processes by which conclusions are drawn about individuals and stimuli from behavioral observations. The basic point is that our conclusions, even at the level of measurement and scaling (which seems such a firm foundation for theory building), are already a consequence of theory. A measurement or scaling model is actually a theory about behavior, admittedly on a miniature level, but nevertheless theory; so while building theory about more complex behavior it behooves us not to neglect the foundations on which the more complex theory rests.

This illustrates the general principle that all knowledge is the result of theory—we buy information with assumptions—"facts" are inferences,* and so also are data and measurements and scales.

The theory of data, then, is concerned with behavioral theory at the initial level that provides the foundation for psychological measurement and scaling. It is concerned only with phase 2 and phase 3, that is, the mapping of the recorded observations into data and the choice of models for making inferences from the data. Phase 1, perhaps the most important of all, the decision as to what to observe, is beyond the scope of this theory.

---

* In this regard see Hanson (1958), who maintains that even the observations are inferences (or see Putnam's 1959 review of his book).

The kind of analysis in which we are interested has been referred to somewhere as the internal productivity of data—the structure or the relations within the a priori classification system—as distinct from external productivity—the relation of this classification system to that associated with some other set of data.

In still other terms, the entire process of measurement and scaling may be said to be concerned with data reduction. We have, perhaps, an overwhelming number of observations, and their comprehensibility is dependent on their reduction to measurements and scales. This is a mechanical process, but only after buying a (miniature) theory of behavior. It is the universe of these behavior theories, their structure and the relations among them, with which the theory of data is concerned.

Unfortunately, the distinction between the recorded behavior and the data makes exposition difficult. The desirability of illustrations in the course of exposition is obvious. The danger lies in the possibility of inferring that what is done in analyzing a particular behavioral example is in some sense "right" or what should be done. On the contrary, *there is no necessary interpretation of any behavioral example as some particular kind of data.* On the other hand, there are many instances of conventions so nearly universal that an identity appears to exist between the observations and the data. Instances of such conventions abound in the physical sciences and in experimental psychology; for example, when a recorded observation is itself a measure, as the number of drops of saliva, the amplitude of a galvanic skin response, or the number of items right in a test. In such instances the convention seems so natural and reasonable that we are almost unable to make a different interpretation, a different mapping, of the behavior into data.

One of the objectives of this exposition is to loosen these bonds or at least bring about a full awareness of them. To accomplish this, each kind of data will be illustrated by a variety of behavioral examples, following convention in most instances. In other instances the same behavioral examples will be used in less conventional ways to illustrate different kinds of data and the different kinds of results obtained as a consequence. This is done more freely in Parts 2–6.

2. BASIC CONCEPTS

One of the consequences of the formal analysis of what constitutes behavioral data is its classification into four basic kinds of data called *preferential choice* data, *single stimulus* data, *stimulus comparison* data, and *similarities* data. Parts 2 to 5 of the book deal with these in turn and in some detail. The purpose of this section is to introduce on a verbal and intuitive level the basic concepts of data theory that lead to this classification. This discussion provides the motivation for the formal statement of the theory of data presented in the next section and also serves as an introduction to the next four parts of the book.

To introduce the basic concepts for each of the four kinds of data, we take an imaginary sample of subjects and stimuli and assume that certain observations have been made. The observations we shall consider first are of a kind that maps the most naturally into what we have called preferential choice data. Then, in turn, we consider other kinds of observations that map easily into each of the other three kinds of data. In each instance we map the observations into data by making an interpretation which is extremely common but by no means necessary. In the rest of the book the mapping of observations into data is taken up again in greater detail, and alternatives to the interpretations made here are discussed.

Suppose we have the preferential choices of each of a number of individuals with respect to a number of stimuli. Although it does not matter who the individuals are or what the stimuli are, it is more interesting to imagine that the stimuli are drawn from a reasonably homogeneous class and that the individuals are drawn from a relevant homogeneous class. The stimuli may be candidates, colors, or candies, but not all three or even two. It seems complicated enough at this stage to observe whether an individual prefers a chocolate cream to peanut brittle without asking if he likes the color blue even more. If the stimuli are candidates, the individuals would presumably have some cultural commonality with the candidates. If the stimuli are colors, we might at least want to know if any of the individuals were color blind. If the stimuli are candies, anyone with normal taste perception would do. Finally, for no very important reason, imagine that the stimuli are presented in pairs and the individual indicates his preference in each pair.

We are not surprised to observe that the choices individuals make are not alike. Some of the individuals will yield a set of preferential choices which are transitive, and hence each one's preferences may be completely represented by a rank order of the stimuli from most to least preferred. These rank orders will certainly not all be alike, however. Other individuals will yield preferential choices that are not transitive and so cannot be completely represented by a rank order. What do these individual differences mean? How might they have come about?

We might hypothesize that the stimuli were "really" different stimuli for different individuals. Of course this may not be so from an objective (the experimenter's?) point of view—peanut brittle is peanut brittle, red is red, and candidate A is always candidate A—but subjectively this might be the case. To one person the only salient characteristic of peanut brittle is that it is brittle; to another the only thing that matters is that it is sticky. Red is red unless the individual is color blind, and candidate A is trying to be different things to different people. If we take this point of view, an intuitively reasonable one sometimes, we should not have wasted time collecting preferential choice data. An anchor point is needed, and the same stimulus being presented to different individuals provides such an anchor. If a stimulus differs in a significant way from one individual to the next, absolutely nothing can be done with just these observations, and with this point of view, to try to find out anything about the stimuli or about the individuals.

Having abandoned this hypothesis—that individuals differ in their preferences because they perceive the stimuli differently—we concede that each stimulus is more or less the same thing for everyone, not just in its physical dimensions but in whatever its subjective characteristics might be. Peanut brittle is crunchy, sticky, and sweet; red is—well, red; and candidate A is a liberal, internationally minded, inexperienced politician. In fact, we might conveniently imagine that each stimulus can be represented by an appropriately selected point in a space of one, two, three, or more dimensions. At this stage we do not know yet how many dimensions this space should have nor where the points would be that correspond to the stimuli. These, in fact, are questions we would consider asking the data to answer. So the notion of a psychological space with stimuli mapped into points in it is introduced.

If each stimulus point, however, has the same location in this space for all the individuals, how might differences in preferences have arisen? We suspect that the individuals themselves are somehow different, and hence their differences must be captured in the model in order that it may generate their different preferences. We intuitively accept the idea that one individual likes some particular thing more than another individual does, and furthermore, that if this thing were changed somewhat, one individual's preference for it might increase and the other's decrease. It is as if there were, perhaps, an ideal choice for each individual, a stimulus that he would prefer to all the possible alternatives of that kind. We conceive, then, of representing an individual by a point in the same space containing the stimulus points, in such a way that the point corresponding to the individual is a point of his maximum preference in this domain of stimuli.

Consider, for example, a set of statements of opinion about athletic scholarships ranging from for to against. An informed individual will feel that some of these statements reflect his opinion better than others. In fact, we could conceive of some hypothetical statement that just exactly expresses how he feels about athletic scholarships. This would be a statement he would endorse in preference to all other statements and would correspond to an ideal point.

We immediately leap to the further hypothesis that the individual's preference ordering reflects how near the corresponding stimulus points are to his ideal point. We now have a psychological space with both stimuli and individuals mapped into points in such a way that the mutual relations among the points in the space reflect, by some rule, the observed preference orderings of the various individuals. Now we try to account for individual *differences* in preference orderings in terms of the location of ideal points in a common frame of reference with the stimuli.

This theory of preferential choice behavior leads to an algorithm, called the unfolding technique, for constructing a psychological space from such data. Most of Part 2 is concerned with the theory of this technique. A space such as this in which there are points corresponding to individuals and to stimuli is called a *joint space* in this book.

One further step in the process of abstraction should be taken. The important distinction is not that the points correspond to individuals and to stimuli in themselves, but rather to elements of two different sets of real world objects. For example, if we observed in a concept formation experiment the rank order in which each stimulus matched the several concepts, the data could be analyzed by unfolding to arrive at a joint space of stimuli and concepts.

We have introduced some of the basic concepts associated with the theory of preferential choice, but we considered only a limited portion of our hypothetical observations. Let us return to them and recall that some individuals had pairwise preferences which were intransitive. Such observations make it incumbent upon us to show how the relations among these points in the joint space could somehow generate intransitivities. We may choose to construct the model so that intransitive choices occur only as a consequence of fluctuations. The argument would be that in some fundamental, basic sense individuals' preferences are "really" transitive but that some random component blurs this basic picture. In line with this, it might be imagined that the ideal point corresponding to an individual in the joint space has a certain random oscillation and so also have the points corresponding to the stimuli. In fact, most individuals do not have a sharp point of maximum preference with respect to candy, color, candidates, or anything else. Furthermore, the same physical stimulus appears somewhat differently at different times. We might hope, however, that in relation to the total space these regions of oscillation or uncertainty for a point are reasonably small.

If this were the case, collecting data by the method of pair comparison would yield intransitive sets of preferential choices not by virtue of any inherent intransitivity but by virtue of a random component. How might we distinguish between such a random component and a more fundamental "true" intransitivity? By repeated independent observations a random component could be controlled enough to reveal the predominant, more usual, and hence characteristic preference. Then the question could be raised whether these stochastic preferences satisfied transitivity or whether there was some significant degree of intransitivity. If intransitivity of the predominant stochastic preferences was obtained, then the unfolding model would be violated and a different theory would be called for— one that can accommodate significant intransitivities.

Since there may be random oscillation of a point there is a need for methods of collecting data that yield what might be called redundancy. The term redundant data is used here to refer to experimentally independent replications of an observation. There exists a systematic way of looking at most methods of collecting data which structures and relates them with respect to their capacity to generate information and with respect to how much of the information is redundant under certain assumptions. Since these matters are relevant and are used throughout the rest of the book, they are taken up in the next chapter. They are not an intrinsic part of this theory of data but a very useful parallel development. They have to do with certain abstract properties of the recorded observations from which the theory of data springs.

Before we leave this discussion of preferential choice data, we summarize what has been abstracted as their essential character. Individuals and stimuli are regarded as points in a psychological space. The preferential choice of an individual between two stimuli is interpreted to mean one stimulus point is nearer the individual's ideal point than is the other stimulus point. The model is saying that there is a distance, as yet undefined, between every pair of points, and in particular, between an individual's ideal point and a stimulus point. Here the data consist of pairs of points, sometimes called *dyads* or *couples*, in which the elements of a pair correspond, in order, to an individual and to a stimulus; such pairs of points are referred to as being from distinct sets. The data consist of more than that, however; they consist of the information that the elements of one pair of such points are nearer each other than are the elements of another pair. So, we might describe such data in general terms as comprising order relations on pairs of dyads whose elements are from distinct sets.

In this particular set of hypothetical data, in which an individual indicates a preference between a pair of stimuli, an important question is whether the point corresponding to the individual is one and the same point in both dyads, whether the two points might differ by virtue of just a random component, or whether they might be points drawn from entirely different multivariate distributions. For example, if some of the stimuli are candies and some are cigarettes, then an individual judging whether he prefers peanut brittle to Camels may correspond to one ideal point for the candy and to another one for the cigarette. The unfolding theory may be used to test hypotheses of this kind against the data.

We turn now from preferential choice data to single stimulus data. Suppose our hypothetical individuals are presented with the same stimuli as before, but this time each is asked whether he would approve of that candidate, or whether he would like that color for his living room, or whether he would buy that kind of candy. In generic terms the individual merely responds positively or negatively to some degree to each of the stimuli in turn or makes an absolute judgment about each. The previous model was deliberately constructed for preferential choice behavior; the kind of observation being made here is what is called single stimulus observation. How may the previous model for preferential choice be adapted to handle single stimulus data?

The individual is identified with his ideal point in the same space with all the stimulus points. He says "yes" to some and "no" to the others. A reasonable hypothesis is that he likes those stimuli whose points are not too far distant from his ideal point. We might hypothesize that for each individual there is a critical neighborhood at the moment he responds to a particular stimulus which provides that he will respond positively if the stimulus is within it, otherwise not. The essential character of such data may be stated in abstract terms analogous to that for preferential choice data. Individuals and stimuli are mapped into points in a psychological space, and the individual's positive response to a stimulus is taken to signify that the stimulus point is in some sense "near" the ideal point. Here the data consist of pairs of points in which the elements of a pair correspond, in order, to an individual and a stimulus. So the dyads are made up of points from distinct sets. The information in the data indicates whether the distance between a pair of such points is or is not greater than some threshold or critical distance. Such data may be described in abstract terms as a *proximity* relation on a pair of points from distinct sets.

The value of an abstract formulation lies in its generality. A great variety of real world observations may be mapped into the same kind of data. Clinical diagnosis, rating scale behavior, and magnitude estimation (to run some kind of a gamut) are examples. To diagnose is to attach a syndrome label, such as "schizophrenic," to a patient. Supervisors asked to rate the efficiency of foremen associate a descriptive adjective with each foreman. Individuals asked to estimate the weight of a stimulus associate a number with it. In each case the real world consists of two distinct sets of elements—patients and syndromes, foremen and adjectives, weights and numbers. Each element is assumed to correspond to a point in a space. There is a point corresponding to each syndrome, the textbook description, and the point corresponding to the characteristics of the patient as perceived by the clinician. If the clinician answers "yes" to the question, "Is this patient schizophrenic?," his answer may be interpreted as a proximity relation on the corresponding pair of points. In the case of rating scales and magnitude estimation, the objects of judgment (foremen or weights) and the response categories (adjectives or numbers) are assumed to be points on a line, and again the judgment is interpreted as a proximity relation on a pair of points from distinct sets.

The fact that these very different kinds of observations may be looked on as generating the same kind of data means that the models constructed for the analysis of these several kinds of real world observations are intimately related and, at least potentially, there is a certain interchangeability among them. As we proceed we shall perceive more clearly the similarities and differences among models in terms of the assumptions they make about such things as the information in the data. For some, coarse grain data like "near-far" are sufficient, and for others the interpoint distances must be measured on a ratio scale. Hence we can sometimes observe a hierarchical relation among models in terms of the information they require over and above the elementary proximity relation.

Up to this point two kinds of observations have been illustrated and given a formal interpretation; the first was an instance of preferential choice data, the second an instance of single stimulus data. The formal character of the data in these instances may be seen to differ in two respects. One difference is that a relation exists on a pair of dyads for preferential choice data, whereas it is on a pair of points for single stimulus data. A second difference is that for the preferential choice data it is an order relation, and for single stimulus data it is a proximity relation.

The question which naturally leaps to mind is whether there are observations that might be interpreted as proximity relations on pairs of dyads and whether there are other observations that might be interpreted as order relations on pairs of points. The answer is "yes." We leave these variations for later detailed discussion, however, and pursue instead another basic concept, which has to do with a third dimension in which data may differ.

Returning once more to the candidates, colors, or candies, let us present them in pairs to our subjects and ask each individual to judge which member of each pair is the more liberal candidate, the warmer color, or the more subtle blend of flavors. Usually when we make such observations we find that, by and large, the various judges tend to agree with each other. There is a significant degree of conformity. In fact, when it is absent, the experimenter tends to separate the subjects into two or more groups, each group containing subjects who are more homogeneous. The objective of the experimenter in making such observations is to "measure" the stimuli on the subjective attribute in question. The individuals are replicated to control a random component in the judgment. The point here is that judgments are presumed to reflect differences among the stimuli, not the individuals. If the individuals are presumed to be different, they are put in separate groups and their judgments analyzed independently.

The elemental observation here is the judgment of an individual that of the two stimuli presented one has more of the specific attribute in question than the other. How might such observations be abstracted? We might hypothesize that each stimulus may be represented by an appropriate point on a line which is a continuum to be interpreted as the attribute in question. Furthermore, when an individual judges one stimulus to have more of this attribute than the other, this corresponds to the statement that the point for that stimulus is to the right of the other on this continuum. The same individual at different times might contradict himself, or different individuals might not always agree, but this is accounted for by the random "oscillations" of each point within a more or less restricted neighborhood.

When we make such an interpretation of the observations, the essential character of the data may be stated in abstract terms similar to those for preferential choice data and for single stimulus data. In this case there are pairs of points in which both points have been drawn from the same set, as both points correspond to stimuli. The individual in such an interpretation is not a point in the space. Finally, the observation has been interpreted as an order relation on that pair of points. To put it succinctly, we have order relations on pairs of points from the same set— data that might be called *stimulus comparison data* in contrast to preferential choice data and to single stimulus data.

Such data introduce a new dimension in which data may differ. We have already seen that data may differ with respect to *whether a relation exists on a pair of points or on a pair of dyads*, and with respect to *whether the relation is an order or a proximity relation*. In the previous examples of preferential choice data and of single stimulus data, the elements of a pair of points were drawn from distinct sets, that is, individuals and stimuli, or objects of judgment and response categories. In the case of stimulus comparison data the elements of a pair of points are seen to be from the same set; the pairs of points all correspond to pairs of stimuli.

This is perhaps one of the oldest kinds of data in the history of experimental psychology, and it is not surprising to find that there are a variety of models for analyzing such data to arrive at measures of the stimuli on the attribute in question. These models differ in ways that are discussed in Part 4.

This overview of the theory of data has now introduced the three fundamental dichotomies in terms of which I propose to categorize all behavioral data. Before turning to more abstract exposition, however, we need to describe one more kind of data in order to complete this survey. In the discussion of preferential choice behavior at the beginning of this section, we considered the hypothesis that individual differences in preferences might have arisen because a stimulus was not subjectively the same thing to all judges. We now turn to this problem of finding out in what terms different individuals perceive a stimulus that to the experimenter is unchanging.

It might seem that stimulus comparison data of the kind just discussed would serve this purpose, because we could "measure" how liberal the candidates are, how warm the colors, and how subtle the blend of flavors in the candies. There is no apparent limit, however, to the variety of attributes on the basis of which we might coerce the subjects into comparing the stimuli. And the question naturally arises: If we permit the subject freedom of choice in evaluating or comparing stimuli, in what terms does he do it?

To see how this type of problem may be approached, let us return to our now overworked subjects and ask them to perform one more task. All pairs of stimuli will be formed, and the individuals will be presented with these pairs and asked in which pair the members are more alike. This, of course, might be done in a great variety of ways; to be concrete let it be done by pair comparisons, that is, pairs of dyads are presented and the individual says which one of the dyads contains the more similar stimuli. How might such behavior be represented in terms of the type of model that we used in discussing the other kinds of data?

The individual might be presumed to perceive each stimulus as a union or coalition of certain characteristics or attributes. Once again the stimulus may be represented by a point in a space in which the coordinates of the point correspond to the projections of the stimulus on the various dimensions (characteristics) which are the relevant ones in the individual's perception of the stimulus. In fact, all the stimuli may be presumed to be represented by points in a common space of relevant dimensions. Note that no constraint has been placed on the individual about which or how many dimensions there might be. In fact the object in making these observations is to attempt to determine just that.

The individual's judgment that one pair of such stimuli are more alike than another may then be interpreted to mean that the distance between the one pair of points is less than that between the other pair of points. In formal terms, such data are order relations on pairs of dyads in which all the points are from the one set of stimulus points. In verbal terms, what the data consist of are comparisons between stimulus differences, and hence such data are called *similarities data*. The individual is not here conceived of as corresponding to a point, but rather as being characterized by the structure of the entire space. Information about this structure is what we hope to extract from the data. A model designed to obtain this needs to make further specifications, such as what is meant by distance in the space. Then, given these assumptions, a calculus that will construct a space which can reproduce the data to some significant degree may be built. Such data and the models designed for their analysis are discussed in Part 5.

Some of the interrelations among these four different kinds of data are discussed in the chapters of Part 6, which concludes with a chapter relating this formulation of a theory of data to an earlier formulation.

3. THE FORMAL BASIS OF DATA

The formal axioms and definitions that comprise this theory of data are contained in an appendix to this chapter. Some models would require more axioms, and some would require less. The compromise I have made is to provide as limited a number as would still have sufficient breadth and scope to span the variety of models with which this book is concerned. In this section we discuss these axioms from a primarily heuristic point of view in order to familiarize the reader with much of the notation used throughout the book.

In all behavioral observations converted into data, something plays the role of an acting, deciding, responding organism and something plays the role of a stimulus. The acting organism may be a worm, an organ, a colony, or a social group. The stimulus varies over a gamut from the highly controlled excitation of an end organ to the stimulus complex an individual responds to in social interaction. It is sometimes said that psychology is concerned with the problem of what is the nature of the stimulus. Data theory does not have this problem, however. Data theory merely says that whenever behavior has been mapped into data to be analyzed, someone has labeled something as a stimulus and something else as a behaving organism. Data theory neither approves nor disapproves of this labeling.

Of course, responses also exist. What characterizes measurement situations is that the repertoire of responses is strictly limited. Only in certain projective instruments is the effort made to free the response of any restraints. The repertoire of responses which lead to data and measurement has, generically speaking, a very limited variety. The responses reflect either consonance or dominance. This consonance or dominance relation may be between an individual and a stimulus, as when an individual endorses a candidate or solves an arithmetic problem, respectively, or between stimuli, as when he judges them similar or says one is greater than another. The objective of these observations is to measure the individuals and/or the stimuli on the one or more relevant attributes or traits.

These remarks provide some insight into the particular axioms that constitute the basis of this theory of data. It is evident that individuals and stimuli can be thought of as points in a space of one or more dimensions in such a way that the relations among the points will reflect the observed behavior, and hence the space is called a psychological space. When the space is one-dimensional it is frequently called a subjective scale.

The first three axioms and the first definition are concerned with the existence and some of the properties of the space a measurement or scaling model is designed to construct. Axiom 1 postulates a space the dimensions of which are segments of the real line. This axiom is stronger than necessary for some measurement models in that it postulates more than is needed. Some measurement models, for example, lead only to ordinal scales or to ordered metric scales, and some multidimensional scaling models only require spaces whose dimensions are represented by ordinal scales. Rather than have a different axiom in the basis for each level of scaling, however, we postulate as much as is ever necessary and then speak of weaker measurement models as "recovering" this space only at lower levels of scales.

The space is assumed to be a metric space, but the distance function is not specified. Most psychological scaling models assume a multidimensional psychological space to be Euclidean, to incorporate the familiar everyday notion of distance. Some do not even require a metric space, whereas others specify a distance function other than Euclidean, such as the "city block" model in which the distance from one point to another is measured along perpendicular paths and there are no diagonal routes.

With this machinery, then, we have the notion of a space with points in it in relatively fixed locations and having one or more dimensions. Our purpose is to use this space as a representation of the behavior of individuals responding to stimuli. For many kinds of behavior or interpretations of behavior such a representation may not be suitable or other kinds of representations may be more useful. Such behavior or inter-pretations of it are not of concern in this book.

We turn, then, to the matter of how to utilize these metric spaces for the representation of behavior in terms sufficiently general to cover the range and variety of models in psychological scaling. For notational purposes we have the following label sets:

$$D = \{1, 2, \ldots, d, \ldots, r\}; \qquad H = \{1, 2, \ldots, h, \ldots, t\};$$
$$I = \{1, 2, \ldots, i, \ldots, m\}; \qquad J = \{1, 2, \ldots, j, k, l, j', \ldots, n\}$$

The set D is used to designate the dimensions of an r-dimensional space. The set H designates trials, or another appropriate temporal variable, as when an individual responds to the same stimulus more than once.

The sets I and J are for the designation of two distinct sets of real world objects. An illustration might be a set of individuals and a set of stimuli, in which case the convention is adopted of using the label set I for the individuals and the label set J for the stimuli. In some instances the stimuli being responded to may be other individuals, as occurs when an individual is asked who in a group influences him most. Here the members of the group serve both as individuals responding to stimuli and as stimuli to the other individuals of the group. If the experimenter, in mapping these observations into data, desires to distinguish between an individual as a respondent and the same individual when being re-sponded to (that is, as a stimulus), the label set I is used for respondents and the label set J for the individuals as response objects (stimuli). If the experimenter decides not to distinguish between these two roles, then the individuals constitute only one set of objects.* When there is only one set of objects either label set may be used, of course, but the convention of using the set J is followed. Finally, one other convention is followed in the use of these label sets I and J. Suppose individuals are identifying silhouettes of aircraft. The silhouettes constitute one set of objects, and the identifying labels, the response alternatives, are another set of objects. The label sets I and J would then be used for these two distinct sets, the label set I for the objects of judgment and the label set J for the response alternatives. This occurs in any instance of rating or absolute judgment in which one set of objects is mapped into another set.

Some very critical distinctions made by the theory of data rest on the composition of pairs of points, so we spell out these distinctions in some detail.

We sometimes have one set of objects and sometimes two sets of objects to be mapped into points in a psychological space in such a way that

---

* This is an example of the creative role the experimenter plays in making data out of the behavioral observations.

observed relations between the real world objects will be represented by abstract relations among the points in the space. If we have only a single set of objects, then the set of points which correspond to these objects is called the set Q, and the objects are called stimuli. If we wish to talk about a second set of distinct objects in the real world, then we need to refer to the set of points which corresponds to them, so we designate that set of points as the set C. The set of objects corresponding to the points in the set C is not uncommonly a set of individuals.

Data sometimes involve a relation between an individual and a stimulus, a heterogeneous pair, and we refer to the corresponding pair of points as a heterogeneous pair or heterogeneous dyad. Such a pair of points, then, is made up of one point from the set C and one point from the set Q. The set of all such pairs we call A. If we imagine a matrix with elements of the set C designating rows and elements of the set Q designating columns, then each cell of this matrix correspond to a pair (c_i, q_j) and all the cells of this matrix constitute the set A. The set A is known as the Cartesian product of the sets C and Q and may be designated $A = C \times Q$. Individuals passing and failing arithmetic problems or endorsing and rejecting candidates may readily be interpreted as A data.

Data sometimes involve a relation between a pair of stimuli, a homogeneous pair, and so we may refer to the corresponding pair of points as a homogeneous pair or homogeneous dyad. Such a pair of points is made up of two points from the set Q. The set of all such pairs we call B, and it is formed from the Cartesian product of the set Q with itself, that is, $B = Q \times Q$. Judgments as to which candidate is more liberal, which candy is sweeter, and which color is brighter may readily be interpreted as B data.

We also have a need for supersets consisting of pairs of dyads. They are needed for data which involve a relation between two homogeneous pairs of points, that is, all four points are stimuli. The set of all the pairs of homogeneous dyads we designate as $B \times B$ data. Observations to the effect that the "confusions" between one pair of stimuli are greater than the "confusions" between another pair of stimuli may readily be interpreted as $B \times B$ data.

Another superset of interest is that for data involving a relation between two heterogeneous pairs of points, that is, each pair of points is a heterogeneous pair. The set of all the pairs of heterogeneous dyads we designate as $A \times A$ data. Judgments to the effect that Mr. X is a better president than Mr. Y is a governor could be examples of $A \times A$ data. Such data have not been given any serious attention by either collectors or analyzers of data but a proper subset has. This subset, which is of some interest, is the superset of pairs of heterogeneous dyads which have one point in common, that is, each pair of points is a heterogeneous pair but one member is the same in each pair. Judgments to the effect that Mr. X would make a better governor than president could be an example of such data.

Because an individual's point is typically the common element in a pair of heterogeneous dyads, we designate the set of all dyads involving some particular point in common A_i. The set of all the pairs of heterogeneous dyads involving a particular individual is, then, $A_i \times A_i$; and the set of all the pairs of heterogeneous dyads which have a point in common is the union of the $A_i \times A_i$ for all i, which we designate $\bigcup_i (A_i \times A_i)$.

A possible example of $\bigcup_i (A_i \times A_i)$ data would be the pair comparison preferences of a number of individuals for various kinds of candies. A heterogeneous dyad is made up of an individual's point and a candy point; and the individual's point is common to the pairs of such dyads which are compared.

The important axiom that generates the basic kinds of data is Axiom 4. It states that all psychological data may be viewed as an interpretation of behavior in which three dichotomies are satisfied, as stated in the appendix.

The first two dichotomies generate the various sets which have just been constructed, as is shown in the next section. In effect, what the first two dichotomies assert is that all data may be viewed as a relation on a pair of points or on a pair of dyads. To each dyad corresponds a distance between the member points, and a distance may itself be regarded as a point, so we might say that all data may be viewed as relations on pairs of points; it is convenient, however, to segregate data which consist of relations on distances between points from data which consist of relations on the points themselves, because the models for scaling points may need to be different from those for scaling distances.

The third dichotomy specifies that the relation is either an order relation or a proximity relation. For example, a judgment as to which of two candidates is more liberal may be interpreted as an order relation on the corresponding pair of points. The judgment that a particular candidate is liberal may be interpreted as a proximity relation on the corresponding pair of points—one representing the candidate and the other representing the concept "liberal." As alternatives to these names for the relations the terms *dominance* and *consonance* relation, respectively, might sometimes capture the real world implication more adequately.

In its most summary form, then, the theory of data asserts that behavior may be interpreted as a relation on a pair of points and the relation may be either a dominance or a consonance relation.

We come then to Axiom 5 and the final four definitions. These are all concerned with the concept of *relevant dimensions*. The point is that although an individual and the stimulus he is responding to have many characteristics, at the moment that he responds only certain of these characteristics may be relevant in mediating that response. Thus, one of the characteristics of a candidate for office is his religious affiliation, and, similarly, the voter also has a religious affiliation. This characteristic or dimension, however, may or may not be relevant in that voter's evaluation. In general we might anticipate that not all the characteristics of an individual and a stimulus would mediate his response to it. It is important to make these considerations explicit because they are implicit in all models from the point of view of this theory of data, in that all models require a unique identification between a set of relevant dimensions and a stimulus when individuals respond to it.

Definitions 2 and 3 designate the projection of a stimulus point and an individual point respectively into the subspace of relevant dimensions. Thus c_{hij}, for example, is the point corresponding to individual i at the moment h when responding to stimulus j. Similarly q_{hij} is the point corresponding to stimulus j at the moment h when individual i is responding to it.

The last two definitions designate the value of the function $p(a, b)$ for a heterogeneous pair and a homogeneous pair, respectively, in the space of relevant dimensions. Thus the quantity $|p_{hij}|$ is the distance between an individual point and a stimulus point when projected into the space of relevant dimensions.

With this set of axioms and definitions, the variety of psychological data that are recognized may now be constructed and related to various psychological measurement and scaling models.

4. THE STRUCTURE OF DATA

Axiom 4 offers three dichotomies and asserts that all behavioral observations may be so interpreted as to satisfy each of these three dichotomies. This suggests the possibility of their being, in principle at least, $2^3 = 8$ different kinds of data. This cube can be oriented in any of three different ways, and it seems to make the most general psychological sense to subordinate the third dichotomy somewhat to the first two. The cross partition of the first two dichotomies, then, yields four classes called quadrants, each of which is dichotomized by the third condition of Axiom 4. The quadrants are numbered from QI to QIV and each is divided into an "a" and a "b" half. Their organization is portrayed in Fig. 1.2.

I suggest that these eight classes represent the eight kinds of primitive

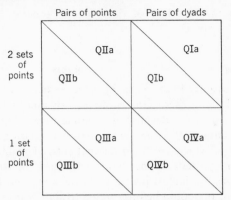

Fig. 1.2 The eight kinds of data.

data from which all psychological measurement arises. A psychological measurement model is designed to take the data of one of these classes and make inferences about a psychological space.

The reason for the subordination of the third dichotomy to the other two lies in the fact that, in some instances, observations are made which, taken together, are a mixture of the two classes of data in a single quadrant. This occurs most commonly when an individual is allowed an intermediate category of response. This point is illustrated in several instances as we once more range over the varieties of data, somewhat as before but more compactly, to illustrate the abstractions involved and to define the information in each class of data.

Quadrant Ia

This class of data consists of order relations on pairs of dyads, the elements of which are from distinct sets. The preferential choices of an individual over a set of alternative stimuli offer a natural illustration. The stimuli and the individuals are mapped into a joint space, and the preferential choice is interpreted as an order relation on the relative distances of the two stimulus points from their respective ideal points.

Formally, the information in the data may be defined as

$$|p_{hij}| - |p_{hik}| \leq 0 \Leftrightarrow j \cdot\rangle k$$

where the symbol $\cdot\rangle$ signifies "preferred to." That is, if and only if, at the moment h, the point corresponding to alternative j is at least as near the ideal point of individual i as the point corresponding to alternative k, the individual says he prefers alternative j to alternative k. The definition of the information in this class of data readily generalizes to ranking more than two alternatives.

Quadrant Ib

Data of this class, to my knowledge, have never been collected in their own right exclusively, and there are no models for analyzing them. This class is important, however, because it is sometimes obtained in combination with QIa data. QIb data are proximity relations on pairs of dyads, the elements of which are from distinct sets. To obtain such data exclusively, we might present an individual with pairs of stimuli and ask him if he does or does not have a preference—but not what his preference is. His answer, yes or no, could be interpreted to signify that the *difference* between the distance of one stimulus and the distance of the other stimulus, each from their respective ideals, is greater or less than some critical threshold quantity.

It would seem silly in this context to collect such data, because it would be so much more informative, if the subject has a preference, to have him name it—which would be QIa data. QIb data would occur, though, if the subjects were permitted an intermediate category of response, such as indifferent, uncertain, or "can't decide."

The information in QIb data may be defined as

$$\left| \, |p_{hij}| - |p_{hik}| \, \right| \leq \epsilon_{hi,jk} \Leftrightarrow j \, \dot{M} \, k$$

where the symbol $j \, \dot{M} \, k$ signifies "j matches k in preference" and ϵ is a nonnegative real number corresponding to some idiosyncratic difference in distances which bounds the individual's willingness to choose. The information in the data has the interpretation that, if and only if, at the moment h, the distances of the two stimulus points from the ideal points are similar (within $\pm\epsilon$), the individual says he cannot choose between them.

Quadrant I

QIa data require that an individual always indicate his preference, QIb that he never indicate his preference but merely whether or not he has one. Obviously, if sometimes he indicates a preference and sometimes he does not, we have a mixture, which is called QI data. The information in such data may be defined as:

$$|p_{hij}| - |p_{hik}| < - \, \epsilon_{hi,jk} \Leftrightarrow j \cdot \rangle k$$
$$\left| \, |p_{hij}| - |p_{hik}| \, \right| \leq \epsilon_{hi,jk} \Leftrightarrow j \, \dot{M} \, k$$
$$|p_{hij}| - |p_{hik}| > \epsilon_{hi,jk} \Leftrightarrow k \cdot \rangle j$$

That is, if and only if, at the moment h, the difference in the distances to the two alternative points from the ideal point exceeds some value, the individual indicates a preference and the choice reflects the nearer alternative.

Quadrant IIa

Formally, the data in this class consist of order relations on pairs of points from distinct sets, and the information may be defined as

$$p_{hij} \geq 0 \Leftrightarrow i \rangle j$$

where the symbol $\rangle$ signifies "i dominates j," for example, passes, exceeds, or says yes. That is if, and only if, at the moment h, the point corresponding to the individual dominates the point corresponding to the stimulus, the individual responds positively to the stimulus. This kind of data, a dominance relation between a pair of points from distinct sets, is very common. It may be represented by the conventional interpretation of an individual's passing or failing an arithmetic item as in the well-known Guttman scalogram model. The individual may be conceived of as being mapped into a point corresponding to a measurement of his arithmetic ability, the item as being mapped into a point corresponding to its difficulty on the same continuum, and the individual's passing or failing as an order relation on the two points.

Quadrant IIb

In Section 2 of this chapter this class of data was illustrated by the interpretation given to whether an individual would approve of a particular candidate, whether he would like a particular color for his living room, or whether he would buy a particular kind of candy. Formally, such data are proximity relations on pairs of points from distinct sets, and the information in such data is defined as

$$|p_{hij}| \leq \epsilon_{hij} \Leftrightarrow i \, \dot{M} \, j$$

That is, if and only if, at the moment h, the absolute distance of the point corresponding to individual i from the point corresponding to stimulus j is sufficiently small, the individual responds positively to the stimulus by approving, endorsing, agreeing, or saying yes, as the case may be. The quantity ϵ, a nonnegative real number, corresponds here to a limiting difference which bounds the individual's willingness to respond affirmatively. Other examples of this class of data have been mentioned in the previous discussion.

Quadrant II

By QII we indicate data which are in part QIIa and in part QIIb. In these data, then, the relation may be either an order or a proximity relation on a pair of points from distinct sets. Such data could be obtained if an individual in responding to a statement of opinion were permitted to say (1) he endorsed it, (2) he did not endorse it, it is too radical, (3) he did not endorse it, it is too conservative. The first response is an instance of a proximity relation, the latter two are instances of order relations.

The information in the data may be defined as

$$p_{hij} > \epsilon_{hij} \Leftrightarrow i \rangle j$$

$$|p_{hij}| \leq \epsilon_{hij} \Leftrightarrow i \dot{M} j$$

$$p_{hij} < -\epsilon_{hij} \Leftrightarrow j \rangle i$$

That is, if and only if, at the moment h, the difference between the two points exceeds a certain quantity, the response indicates one is greater than the other; otherwise the response indicates they are matched.

Quadrant IIIa

Typical of the behavior mapped into the data of QIIIa is the judgment of an individual as to which of two stimuli has more of some attribute. Each stimulus is mapped into a point on a line corresponding to measures of the attribute, and the observation is interpreted as an order relation on this pair of points from the same set.

The information in such data is defined as

$$p_{hi,jk} \geq 0 \Leftrightarrow j \rangle k$$

where $j \rangle k$ signifies the observation "j dominates k." That is, if and only if, at the moment h, for an individual i the point corresponding to stimulus j exceeds the point corresponding to stimulus k, the observation is made that j dominates k.

Examples of the observations mapped into such data are the judgments of individuals as to which of a pair of weights is heavier or which of a pair of statements of opinion is more conservative. The intent of such data is to arrive at a scale of subjective magnitude of the stimuli, called a stimulus scale. The points being measured are all members of one and the same set, and hence are called stimuli. The individuals are not mapped into points on the scale, in contrast to QI and QII.

Quadrant IIIb

The data of QIIIb are proximity relations on pairs of points from the same set. An example would be the behavior of an individual in judging whether pairs of stimuli do or do not match each other.

The formal definition of the information in such data is

$$|p_{hi,jk}| \leq \epsilon_{hi,jk} \Leftrightarrow j \, M \, k$$

where $j \, M \, k$ signifies the observation that "stimulus j matches stimulus k." That is, if and only if, at the moment h, the apparent difference between two stimuli is no more than some prescribed positive quantity, the response indicates that they match each other.

This kind of data is just beginning to be useful in the scaling of distances between pairs of stimulus points. The interpoint distances may then be used to recover the stimulus points themselves.

Quadrant III

As before, the data identified with an entire quadrant is a mixture. In this case the data may be either order or proximity relations on pairs of points from the same set. If in judging which of two stimuli has more of some attribute the individual is permitted an intermediate category of judgment, such as "I don't know," some of the judgments will reflect an order relation and some a proximity relation on a pair of points from the same set.

The information in such data is

$$p_{hi,jk} > \epsilon_{hi,jk} \Leftrightarrow j \rangle k$$
$$|p_{hi,jk}| \leq \epsilon_{hi,kj} \Leftrightarrow j \, M \, k$$
$$p_{hi,jk} < -\epsilon_{hi,jk} \Leftrightarrow k \rangle j$$

That is, if and only if, at the moment h, the difference between two stimuli exceeds a certain minimum, the individual judges one to be greater than the other; otherwise he responds with the intermediate category.

Quadrant IVa

The behavior of individuals when presented with two pairs of stimuli and asked which pair is more alike is representative of behavior typically mapped into QIVa. Each of the stimuli is mapped into a point, and the individual is presumed to be responding to the comparative distances

between pairs of points. The response is interpreted as an order relation
on pairs of dyads whose points are all from the same set.

The information in such data may be defined as

$$|p_{hi,jk}| - |p_{hi,j'k'}| \leq 0 \Leftrightarrow (j,k) \langle (j',k')$$

where $(j,k) \langle (j',k')$ signifies the response "the pair (j,k) is more alike
than the pair (j',k')." That is, if and only if, at the moment h, the difference between the stimuli j and k appears less than the difference between
the pair j' and k', the response is made that the pair (j,k) are more alike.

The recent development of models for the analysis of such data reflects
a developing recognition of their importance for the study of the perceptual
and cognitive space of an individual. This area, called multidimensional
psychological scaling, has a very promising future.

Quadrant IVb

The type of behavior that can be mapped into QIVb is the response of
an individual to two pairs of stimuli where the response is interpreted as
indicating that one pair is no more alike (or different) than the other pair.
Each of the stimuli is presumed to be mapped into a point, and the individual is responding to the differences between pairs of points. The
response is interpreted as a proximity relation on a pair of dyads in which
all points are from the same set.

The information in such data is

$$\left| \, |p_{hi,jk}| - |p_{hi,j'k'}| \, \right| \leq \epsilon_{hi,jk,j'k'} \Leftrightarrow (j,k) \, M \, (j',k')$$

where $(j,k) \, M \, (j',k')$ signifies a response of the form "the pair of stimuli
(j,k) is no more alike or different than the pair (j',k')." That is, if and
only if, at the moment h, the difference between the stimuli j and k is
within a prescribed positive magnitude of the difference between the pair
of stimuli j' and k', the individual indicates that the differences match
each other.

The method of bisection for constructing stimulus scales is an example
of this kind of data in that the subject adjusts a stimulus to be midway
between two others. In effect he manipulates a stimulus until he is unable
to distinguish the distance between it and the one above from the distance
between it and the one below.

Quadrant IV

If in judging the relative similarity of two pairs of stimuli an individual
is permitted to respond by saying that one pair is more alike than another
or that he cannot decide, the data could be interpreted as QIV data.

The information in such data may be defined as

$$|p_{hi,jk}| - |p_{hi,j'k'}| < -\epsilon_{hi,jk,j'k'} \Leftrightarrow (j, k) < (j', k')$$
$$\left| |p_{hi,jk}| - |p_{hi,j'k'}| \right| \leq \epsilon_{hi,jk,j'k'} \Leftrightarrow (j, k) \, M \, (j', k')$$
$$|p_{hi,jk}| - |p_{hi,j'k'}| > \epsilon_{hi,jk,j'k'} \Leftrightarrow (j', k') < (j, k)$$

That is, if and only if, at the moment h, the difference between one pair of stimuli is sufficiently less than the difference between the other pair, the subject indicates which pair is more alike; otherwise he says their differences match.

5. THE FOUR KINDS OF DATA

Because an intermediate category of judgment has the effect of yielding data some of which fall in the a class of a quadrant and some in the b, the dichotomy of an order versus a proximity relation has been somewhat subordinated to the other two dichotomies. On the level of real world behavior there is a similarity between the behaviors that get mapped into the two classes of a quadrant. Giving a name to each of the quadrants which, at least partially, reflects the kind of real world behavior that is typically mapped into it attempts to capture this similarity. This, of course, is contrary to the earlier distinction insisted on, the distinction between the behavioral observations and the data that are analyzed; hence this step is taken with some trepidation. My experience has been that these real world referents help students in acquiring an understanding of the theory of data. The step is taken, however, with the suggestion that reasoning should proceed from the formal properties of the data rather than from these real world labels. No real world behavior necessarily belongs in any particular quadrant.

In QI the relation observed is on a pair of distances where each distance is the distance between a pair of points from distinct sets. A possible, but by no means universal, source of such data is the preferential choices of an individual over a set of stimuli in which he is comparing the distances of stimulus points from an ideal point. Hence the data may be called individual-stimulus differences comparison or *preferential choice* data.

In QII the relation observed is on a pair of points in which the points are identified with elements from distinct sets. This interpretation may be given to mental test behavior, rating scale behavior, and absolute judgment. We may refer to it as an individual-stimulus comparison or by the familiar term of *single stimulus* data.

It is in this quadrant that the recorded observations and the data *may* merge into one. Ordinary physical measurements are observations which are QII data; as, for example, the number of drops of saliva produced or the amplitude of the excursion of a recording pen. One set of points corresponds to the real numbers and the other set of points corresponds to the observations. The classification and structure in the data follow directly from those in the real number system, and psychological scaling methods are not required.

In QIII the relation observed is on a pair of points that are from the same set—all stimuli. Such data may be called *stimulus comparison* data.

In QIV the relation observed is on a pair of distances where each distance is between a pair of stimuli. This may be referred to as stimuli-differences comparison or *similarities* data.

These names are portrayed in Fig. 1.3.

These four kinds of data are taken up in turn in the next four parts of the book. In each case an introduction precedes the discussion of models for analyzing that particular kind of data. The introduction will discuss the nature of the data, some of the kinds of behavioral observations that are mapped into that kind of data, and something about the organization of the chapters in that part of the book.

Part 6, the last part, is concerned with interrelations among quadrants and other matters that pertain to the system as a whole.

Single stimulus data or Individual-stimulus comparison or A data	Preferential choice data or Individual-stimulus differences comparison or $A \times A$ data
Stimulus comparison data or B data	Similarities data or Stimuli-differences comparison or $B \times B$ data

Fig. 1.3   The four kinds of data.

6. SUMMARY

This chapter offers an overview of the theory of data and explains the organization of the rest of the book. To introduce the basic concepts of the system a vital distinction is drawn between behavior and data, and the latter term is given a highly restricted meaning. The term data is used here to refer to formal relations on points—because these relations are what are analyzed, not the behavior itself. Although the data are an offspring of behavior, the scientist has a much more intimate and creative relation to the process than that of midwife. Behavior does not yield data by parthenogenesis. The role of the scientist in the process is to choose the genus; the behavior then chooses the species. Behavior never acts or speaks for itself in creating data; it only speaks when spoken to, when asked a question. The experimenter selects the repertoire, a particular alphabet of messages, and then the behavior chooses from these alternatives what to play, what the message is to be. Answers are in terms of the questions asked, and to map behavior into a particular kind of data and to analyze this class of data by a particular model is to ask particular questions.

A circuit, on a verbal and intuitive level, is then made through the varieties of data by means of detailed discussion of various kinds of behavior and how they may be mapped into data. This discussion leads up to the abstraction of the universal characteristics of data which form the basis of the theory of data. The axioms and definitions, contained in the appendix to this chapter, are discussed heuristically in some detail. These lead naturally to the organization or structuring of the varieties of data in the form of the four quadrants of a fourfold table, each of the quadrants being further divided in two. The four quadrants represent the four fundamental, qualitatively distinct, kinds of data and, by indirection, four basic kinds of behavior. Their real world characteristics are, somewhat hazardously, captured in the labels assigned to them. From QI to QIV, in turn, they are preferential choice data, single stimulus data, stimulus comparison data, and similarities data. The information in each of these kinds of data is formally defined.

7. APPENDIX

The following are label sets:

$$D = \{1, 2, \ldots, d, \ldots, r\}; \quad H = \{1, 2, \ldots, h, \ldots, t\};$$
$$I = \{1, 2, \ldots, i, \ldots, m\}; \quad J = \{1, 2, \ldots, j, k, l, j', \ldots, n\}$$

Axiom 1: To each element d in D there corresponds a segment of the real line $K^{(d)}$.

Definition 1: Let $K = \{x \mid x = (x^{(1)}, x^{(2)}, \ldots, x^{(d)}, \ldots, x^{(r)})\}$, where $x^{(d)}$ is in $K^{(d)}$, in which the elements x are vectors in r-dimensional space.

We have the following sets of points in K:

$$C \subset K \quad \text{in which} \quad C = \{c_i \mid i \text{ in } I\}$$
$$Q \subset K \quad \text{in which} \quad Q = \{q_j \mid j \text{ in } J\}$$

so the points in C and Q correspond respectively to the elements of the label sets I and J.

We construct the following dyads:

$$A = C \times Q \qquad A = \{(c_i, q_j)\}$$
$$A_i \subset A, \qquad A_i = \{(c_i, q_j) \mid i \text{ fixed}\}$$
$$B = Q \times Q \qquad B = \{(q_j, q_k)\}$$

where A is the set of heterogeneous pairs and B is the set of homogeneous pairs.

We construct the following sets of pairs of dyads: $A \times A$, $\bigcup_i(A_i \times A_i)$, and $B \times B$.

The set $A \times A$ is the set of pairs of heterogeneous dyads, and the set $\bigcup_i(A_i \times A_i)$ is a subset of $A \times A$ consisting of the pairs of heterogeneous dyads that have a point in common. The set $B \times B$ is the set of homogeneous pairs of dyads.

Axiom 2: There exists a real-valued function $p(a, b)$ defined for a and b in K, such that $|p(a, b)|$ satisfies

$$|p(a, b)| = |p(b, a)|$$
$$p(a, b) = 0 \Leftrightarrow a = b$$
$$|p(a, b)| \leq |p(a, c)| + |p(b, c)|$$

where $\Leftrightarrow$ signifies "implies and is implied by."

Axiom 3: Given two vectors differing only in one component, the sign of p is determined by that one component.

Axiom 4: All psychological data may be viewed as an interpretation of behavior in which

   i. a relation exists on a pair of points (a dyad) or on a pair of dyads;
   ii. the elements of a pair of points are drawn from two distinct sets or from one set; and
   iii. the relation is either an order relation ($>$) or a proximity relation ($\bigcirc$).

Axiom 5: To each triple (h, i, j) and to each quadruple (hi, jk) there corresponds a subset $D' = D'(h, i, j)$ or $D'' = D''(hi, jk)$ of D, that is $D' \subset D$, $D'' \subset D$. The subset D' or D'', as the case may be, is called the *set of relevant dimensions.*

Definition 2: q_{hij} is the projection of the vector q_j in the set of relevant dimensions, D' or D'', as the case may be.

Definition 3: c_{hij} is the projection of the vector c_i in the set of relevant dimensions D'.

Definition 4: $p_{hij} = p(c_{hij}, q_{hij})$ is the value of $p(a, b)$ for the ordered pair (c_{hij}, q_{hij}), which will play the role of a "signed distance" between the pair of points in the space of the relevant dimensions D'.

Definition 5: $p_{hi,jk} = p(q_{hij}, q_{hik})$ is the value of $p(a, b)$ for the ordered pair (q_{hij}, q_{hik}), which will play the role of a "signed distance" between the pair of points in the space of relevant dimensions D''.

REFERENCES

Hanson, N. R., 1958, *Patterns of discovery*, Cambridge University Press, Cambridge, England.
Putnam, Hilary, 1959, Review of Hanson's Patterns of discovery, *Science*, **129**, 1666–67.

CHAPTER 2

On Methods of Collecting Data

This chapter is concerned with methods of collecting data in any of the quadrants, in which a subject indicates his choices among a set of alternatives. He may indicate his choices by picking some of the alternatives or by rank ordering some. Examples include the method of pair comparisons, in which a subject is presented with two stimuli at once and is instructed to pick one of them, the method of triads in which the subject is presented with three stimuli at a time and instructed to rank order his choices, and the method of rank order in which the subject is presented with all n stimuli and is instructed to rank order them. In using a rating scale the subject is presented with a set of response alternatives (for example, adjectives, categories, labels, numbers) from which he picks one. In the area of sociometric choice still other methods are not uncommonly used. For example, in a sixth grade class of twenty children, each child might be asked who his best friends are, or who his first, second, and third best friends are, or who are the two he likes the least, and so on.

These methods are all obviously interrelated, and equally obviously many others are not mentioned. The desirability of enumerating and organizing this variety of methods is clear, and a system, here called the searchingness structure, is designed for this purpose. After we have enumerated explicitly a great number of possible methods for collecting data, it seems only proper that we provide the experimenter with some criteria to serve as guide lines in making a choice. Information theory provides a measurement model useful for this purpose. Abstract dimensions of methods, called channel capacity and redundancy, are constructed. Such measures are inadequate and are certainly an incomplete set of criteria. The reader is warned of the need to consider additional criteria in Section 3.

Many of the methods enumerated in the searchingness structure are very powerful and useful in statistically controlling and measuring inconsistency of behavior. Models are then needed to separate out the momentary fluctuations in behavior which may obscure the behavior's more persistent and organized character. Such models are discussed in Section 4.

1. THE SEARCHINGNESS STRUCTURE

If we consider methods of choice for a moment, it is obvious that they have at least two dimensions. One is the number of stimuli presented at a time, which can range from presenting all of them at once down to subsets of just a few at a time, such as two (pair comparisons) or three (triads). The second dimension is a dichotomy having to do with whether the subject has been asked to pick or to rank order his choices.

We may express these ideas succinctly by stating that a set of n stimuli may be presented in subsets of p at a time, and the subject may be asked to pick or order k of them in each presentation.* Clearly $1 \leq k < p \leq n$. Figure 2.1 portrays the variety of possibilities in a form called the searchingness structure.† Of all these possible methods, of which there are $(n - 1)^2$, only four are well known:

(1) Method of single stimuli:‡ $p = n$, pick 1; that is, 'pick $1/n$.'
(2) Method of rank order: $p = n$, order $(n - 1)$; that is, 'order $(n - 1)/n$.'
(3) Method of pair comparisons: $p = 2$, pick 1; that is, 'pick $1/2$' = 'order $1/2$.'
(4) Method of triads: $p = 3$, order 2; that is, 'order $2/3$.'

These four are identified in Fig. 2.1 by the four cells numbered correspondingly. Looking at the array of methods in the entire structure the saliency of three of these particular four methods would seem to reside in the fact they represent "corners" of the structure. Only the method of triads moves "inside" the structure, but even it stays immediately adjacent to a corner. We naturally wonder about all the other methods—how they might differ among themselves, which purposes each may serve best, and just what their respective strengths and weaknesses are.

* There is a formal identity between asking a subject to pick k of p stimuli or to reject k', $k + k' = p$. Consequently, all the properties of the method 'pick k of p' are identically properties of the method 'reject $(p - k)$.' Whether such an identity holds for behavior is an empirical question. S. S. Komorita (1958), using a probability learning situation, made several comparisons between *logically* equivalent methods and found equivalent empirical results.
† This general form was first suggested by James Chabot (personal communication).
‡ The method of single stimuli also includes the method 'pick any $/n$' which is not included in the searchingness structure; see Chapter 14.

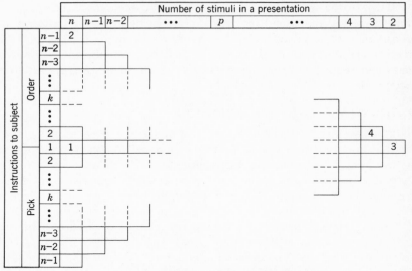

Fig. 2.1 The searchingness structure.

This chapter is concerned with some of the ways these methods differ among themselves. The relevance of these differences to the strengths and weaknesses of the methods in application is taken up in the successive parts of the book dealing with the analysis of data.

Certain general characteristics of the methods are presented in this chapter. In particular, the two general characteristics of these methods for which measures are developed here are their *channel capacity* and their amount of *redundant information*. Channel capacity indicates how much information a method might carry and thereby provides a measure of relative power. Redundancy indicates how much of this capacity is allocated to measuring and controlling inconsistency of behavior. Information theory provides a measurement model well suited to evaluating these.*

Channel Capacity†

The number of different ways k stimuli can be picked out of p is $\binom{p}{k}$, and the number of ways a subset of size k can be ordered is $k!$.

---

* This was first suggested to me by J. E. Keith Smith (personal communication).
† I am particularly indebted to John Tukey for many valuable suggestions throughout this chapter. He is, of course, not to be held responsible for the use I made of them.

So the total number of possible orderings of k out of p is

$$k!\binom{p}{k} = \frac{p!}{(p-k)!}$$

The maximum channel capacity of a method is achieved if its alphabet of alternatives is used by the respondent with constant and equal probabilities and if the responses to successive presentations are independent. Under these conditions, then, the amount of information from any one presentation of p stimuli, when the individual orders k of them, would be[*]

$$\log \frac{p!}{(p-k)!}$$

If the individual, instead of ordering k, merely picks k, the maximum amount of information that is possible is

$$\log \frac{p!}{(p-k)!\,k!}$$

The difference, then, between the channel capacities of 'pick k/p' and 'order k/p' methods is that 'order k/p' increases the capacity by $\log k!$ bits.

The number of presentations is $\binom{n}{p}$. The maximum capacity of a method is obtained by accumulating the information from successively independent presentations. Thus the channel capacity of 'order k/p,' designated $C_{\text{order }k/p}$, is

$$C_{\text{order }k/p} = \binom{n}{p} \log \frac{p!}{(p-k)!} \tag{2.1}$$

and for 'pick k/p'

$$C_{\text{pick }k/p} = \binom{n}{p} \log \frac{p!}{(p-k)!\,k!} \tag{2.2}$$

As an illustration, Table 2.1 gives the channel capacity for the searchingness structure methods when $n = 10$ and all presentations are made. We see, for example, that the method of triads, 'order 2/3,' has almost seven times the channel capacity of the method of pair comparisons, whereas the method of rank order, 'order 9/10,' has somewhat less than half.

The maximum capacity of a method would be utilized if there were no redundancy in it—if each successive response were new and unpredictable. Such behavior would be random and is not characteristic of what is usually found, leading us to seek a measure of the redundancy of a method.

---

[*] All logarithms are to the base 2. For a general reference on information theory see Garner (1962).

Table 2.1   Channel Capacity ($n = 10$) in Bits

p

		10	9	8	7	6	5	4	3	2
	9	21.8								
	8	20.8	184.7							
	7	19.2	174.7	688.5						
Order	6	17.2	158.8	643.5	1475.9					
	5	14.3	138.8	572.1	1355.9	1993.3				
	4	12.3	115.6	482.1	1165.7	1783.3	1740.5			
	3	9.5	89.8	377.6	925.7	1450.4	1488.5	962.8		
	2	6.5	61.7	261.3	647.1	1030.4	1089.1	725.8	310.2	
	1	3.3	31.7	135.0	336.9	542.8	585.1	420.0	190.2	45.0
	2	5.5	51.7	216.3	527.1	820.4	837.1	542.8	190.2	
	3	6.9	63.9	261.3	615.5	907.6	837.1	420.0		
	4	7.7	69.8	275.8	615.5	820.4	585.1			
Pick	5	8.0	69.8	261.3	527.1	542.8				
	6	7.7	63.9	216.3	336.9					
	7	6.9	51.7	135.0						
	8	5.5	31.7							
	9	3.3								

Redundancy

The problem of constructing a measure of the redundancy of a method revolves around the definition of what is new or basic information. The total amount of information must be partitioned into new information and redundant information. The manner of doing this reflects a point of view as to what basic information is and what redundant information is.

If an individual chooses A over B and then B over C, is his choice of A over C redundant or is it new information? If we assume that the behavior is transitive, the last judgment is redundant. If we are asking whether the behavior is transitive, the last judgment is not redundant. The individual's response to the pair of stimuli A and C in this case is either new and basic information or it is a replication in that it yields information already known.

The point of view adopted here is that transitivity of judgmental behavior is an empirical question. Hence, the distinct pairwise comparisons are regarded as basic or new information, and a replication of a pair is regarded as yielding redundant information useful for the purpose of statistically controlling or measuring inconsistency of the judgments.

I shall use as a measure of redundancy, then, the number of bits of channel capacity in method "x" per pair comparison, implicitly included in method x, beyond the one bit for each pair allotted by the method of pair comparisons, 'order 1/2.' The symbol for this measure will be $\mathcal{R}$ to distinguish it from redundancy as ordinarily defined in information theory. Hence

$$\mathcal{R}_{x:\text{order } 1/2} = \frac{C_x}{C_{\text{order } 1/2}} - 1 \quad (2.3)$$

In general, however, if any method a is used to define the basic information, the relation between $\mathcal{R}_{x:a}$ and C_x is given by

$$\mathcal{R}_{x:a} = \frac{C_x}{C_a} - 1 \quad (2.4)$$

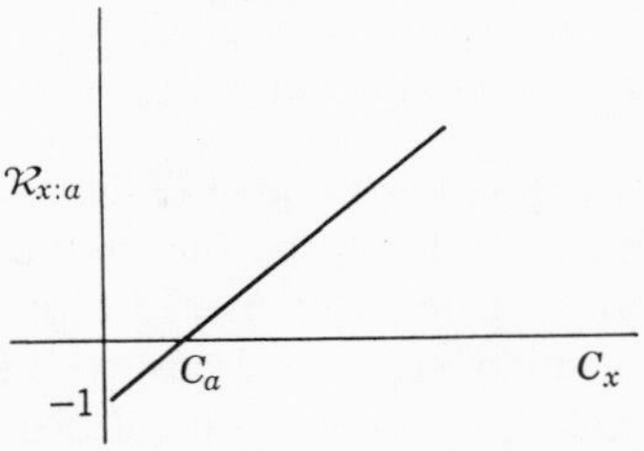

which is linear, as illustrated in Fig. 2.2.

Fig. 2.2 Redundancy of method x with method a used to define the basic information.

The intercept is -1 and changing the definition of basic information merely changes the slope, which is $1/C_a$.

Table 2.2 gives the redundancy in the methods of the searchingness structure for $n = 10$ measured against the information in the method

Table 2.2 Redundancy of Methods of Collecting Data Expressed as an Excess over Pair Comparisons ($n = 10$)

		p								
		10	9	8	7	6	5	4	3	2
	9	−0.51								
	8	−0.54	3.10							
	7	−0.57	2.88	14.31						
	6	−0.62	2.53	13.30	31.82					
Order	5	−0.68	2.08	11.70	29.11	43.28				
	4	−0.73	1.58	9.71	24.89	38.61	37.69			
	3	−0.79	1.00	7.39	19.59	31.20	32.11	20.39		
	2	−0.85	0.37	4.81	13.39	21.89	23.21	15.70	5.89	
	1	−0.92	−0.30	2.00	6.49	11.10	12.00	8.33	3.23	0
	2	−0.88	0.15	3.81	10.71	17.20	17.60	11.00	3.23	
	3	−0.84	0.42	4.81	12.70	19.19	17.60	8.33		
	4	−0.83	0.55	5.13	12.70	17.20	12.00			
Pick	5	−0.83	0.55	4.81	10.71	11.10				
	6	−0.83	0.42	3.81	6.49					
	7	−0.84	0.15	2.00						
	8	−0.88	−0.30							
	9	−0.92								

of pair comparisons. To aid in interpreting this table, we see that the method of triads, 'order 2/3,' has 5.89 bits of redundant capacity with respect to pair comparisons. This means that when this method is used with $n = 10$ stimuli, 6.89 bits of channel capacity are allotted to each pair comparison, of which 5.89 are redundant, i.e., in excess of the 1 bit allotted by the channel capacity of the method of pair comparisons, 'order 1/2.'

The Interpretation of Redundancy. Any method x which has an information capacity less than the method a, which is used as the base method, will yield a negative measure of redundancy. There is some question as to whether negative measures of redundancy have any meaning, and a possible interpretation is offered here.

The negative redundancy of a method x is the number of bits of channel capacity that would have to be added *to each implicit pair comparison* to bring the method up to the channel capacity of the method of pair comparisons. Thus in Table 2.2 we see that the method of rank order for $n = 10$ has -0.51 bits of redundant channel capacity. This means that the channel capacity of the method of rank order, when $n = 10$, allots 0.49 bits to each pair comparison. This falls short of the channel capacity of the method of pair comparisons by 0.51 bits per pair comparison.

Consider another example. Let us measure the redundancy of the method of rank order against the method of pair comparisons for $n = 3$.

The number of ways we may rank order three stimuli is 6, and the channel capacity of this method, $C_{\text{order } 2/3}$, then, is log $6 = 2.58$ bits.

By definition, the redundancy of this method is

$$\mathscr{R} = \frac{2.58}{3} - 1 = -0.14$$

This means that if an experimenter decomposes the rank order of three stimuli into the three implicit pair comparisons he could be* adding as much as 0.14 bits to each pair. In the case of $n = 10$, the rank order decomposes into 45 pair comparisons, and as much as 0.51 bits could be created in this manner for each pair of stimuli.

These figures, based on channel capacity, are lower bounds to the redundancy. They are only reached if the experimenter's a priori probabilities for the pairwise choices are all one-half and he does not assume transitivity of judgment.

* The reason for saying "could be" is that the true capacity and the true redundancy of a method depend on the respondent's probabilities, which are not known a priori. Hence I have used limiting values by assuming he responds randomly. I suspect that in the majority of applications the actual capacity would be less and the redundancy greater.

At the other extreme, suppose the individual's pairwise probabilities are all 1.0 and transitivity is assumed. Then for n stimuli there are only $n - 1$ essential pair comparisons for which the experimenter has a priori probabilities of one-half, so the method of pair comparisons would yield $n - 1$ bits of information. The method of rank order provides $n!$ alternative response patterns among which the experimenter is equally uncertain. So the information in this method would be log $n!$.

In general, then, under these conditions, the method of rank order for $n > 2$ would have positive redundancy relative to the method of pair comparisons. This excess positive redundancy is due to the implicit pair comparisons between nonadjacent elements in the rank ordering which are implied by the transitivity of the pair comparisons.

For example, for $n = 3$, if pairwise probabilities are 1.0 and the individual is transitive in his judgments, the method of pair comparisons would yield 2 bits of information, assuming the experimenter is maximally uncertain of the pairwise choices. If, under these same conditions, the method of rank order is used, the information would be log $3! = 2.58$ bits. The excess redundancy of 0.58 bits is contained in the implicit pair comparison between the individual's first and third choice among the three stimuli.

In the case of $n = 10$, under these same conditions, the information in pair comparisons is 9 bits, whereas in the method of rank order it is log $10! = 21.8$. The excess redundancy of 12.8 bits is contained in the many implicit pair comparisons between the nonadjacent elements of the rank order.

These figures are upper bounds to the redundancy of these methods, obtained by imposing conditions perhaps as extreme as those imposed for obtaining the lower bounds. Most of the interesting psychological data are obtained under conditions of less than perfect reliability; in fact, the inconsistency may itself be a subject of some interest, as the development of stochastic models bears witness.

Incidentally, the efficiency of the method of pair comparisons under these extreme conditions could not in general be achieved, because the presentation of a particular subset of $n - 1$ pairs is called for, and it cannot in general be known beforehand. The relevant subset could, however, be sequentially approximated for a given individual.

A table for the upper bounds on the redundancy of methods of collecting data may be readily obtained by using $n - 1$ for C_a in equation 2.4, which merely increases the slope of the function relating redundancy to C_x.

We see then that, in actual application, both the information yield and the actual redundancy of any given method are not known because they are dependent on the state of mind of the experimenter and on certain unknown properties of the subject's behavior. The bounds provided here serve merely as guide lines.

An Experimental Comparison of Three Methods

If we are interested in determining the pairwise probabilities of choice, an obvious procedure for collecting the data is to present all the pair comparisons repeatedly, provided this can be done in such a way as to ensure experimental independence of the responses to a given pair when it is repeated. Because this method is tedious, resort may be made to one of the more powerful methods of the searchingness structure, in which we present at least 3 stimuli at a time and have the subject order k of them, provided that the condition of "independence from other alternatives" is satisfied.

For example, for $n = 12$ there are 66 pairs, and 100 replications of the 66 pairs are required for 100 bits of channel capacity on each pair, a total of 6600 presentations of pairs.

If these stimuli are presented in triads and rank ordered in each triple, the result is 220 triples with log 6 bits of channel capacity for each. The rank order of the three stimuli in each triple may be decomposed into 3 pair comparisons with 0.86165 bits allotted to each pair. With $n = 12$ there are 10 replications of each pair of stimuli in the set of 220 triples, yielding 8.6165 bits for each pair. If the 220 triads are replicated 12 times the total number of bits accumulated on each pair is 103.398. So the 2640 presentations of triads allot approximately the same number of bits of channel capacity on each pair as the 6600 presentations of pairs do alone. Of course it may be that each presentation of a triad requires more effort of a subject than a presentation of a pair comparison does. As will be seen, however, it is doubtful that the effort required by the triad versus that required by the pair comparison is in the ratio of 6600 to 2640, at least for some kinds of stimuli.

If the $n = 12$ stimuli are presented in sets of 4 and rank ordered, the channel capacity of a presentation is log 24, which, when distributed equally over the decomposition into 6 pairs, allots 0.76415 bits per pair. Each pair occurs 45 times in a single replication of the 495 sets of 4, and hence 34.387 bits are accumulated on each pair. Three experimentally independent replications then yield 103.160 bits on each pair. So the $3 \times 495 = 1485$ presentations of 4 stimuli at a time allot approximately the same number of bits of channel capacity on each pair as the 6600 presentations of pairs do alone.

Whether there is any real increase in efficiency depends on whether the subject generates more information per unit of experimental time in these more powerful methods. A pilot study* of this was carried out on two subjects using twelve color patches. For subject A (a male) the color patches were desaturated reds and judgments were made as to which was a better "rust" color. For subject B (a female) the color patches were shades of purple and the judgments were preferential choice. The methods compared were pair comparisons, triads, and quadruples, with order k where $k = p - 1$. The sequence of presentations within each method was balanced for any trend effects, and the three methods were distributed over the sequence of sessions to balance out any trend effects among them.

The results are reported in Table 2.3.

Table 2.3 Comparative Efficiency of Three Methods of Collecting Data

		Aver. No. of Min. for 1 Complete Replication	Total No. of Bits in 1 Complete Replication	Average No. of Bits/Min.	Gain over Pair Comparisons
Subject A	pair compar.	11.01	66.00	6.00	
	triads	52.67	568.69	10.80	80%
	quadruples	160.00	2269.53	14.18	136%
	pair compar.	9.79	66.00	6.74	
Subject B	triads	47.42	568.69	11.99	78%
	quadruples	144.33	2269.53	15.72	133%

The results indicate that the more powerful methods were also more efficient† in the sense of utilizing the greater channel capacity available, with experimental time held constant.‡

It is to be anticipated that with more complex stimuli, where each stimulus is a larger "chunk" of information in its own right, the comparative efficiency of these methods may not be the same as found here.

* This study was carried out by Sally Sperling, Percival Tomlinson, David Cross, Clint Fink, and John Dwyer, and was primarily designed to be a replication study of the laterality effect in preferential choice. See Chapter 5, Sections 9 and 10 and Chapter 24, Section 4.
† This, of course, refers to the efficiency of the experiment itself and not necessarily to the efficiency of the subject's performance.
‡ This conclusion is subject to the reservation that the increased information output of the subjects was not merely a consequence of unconsidered judgments and a shift toward random behavior. This reservation is not substantiated, however, by the internal structure of the data in which laterality effects were clearly evident. (See Chapter 5, Section 9.)

2. SPECIAL MODIFICATIONS OF THE SEARCHINGNESS STRUCTURE

Balanced Incomplete Block Designs

As is evident from Tables 2.1 and 2.2, some methods have great capacity and hence great redundancy as compared to the method of pair comparisons. In fact the capacity of some of them for a reasonable size n is so great that their use might well overload the subject. For example, for $n = 10$, to use 'order 5/6' would require the subject to rank order the six stimuli in the 210 presentations of all sets of six. The effects of boredom and fatigue might lead to random behavior or some form of stereotypy, either of which would vitiate the value of using the more powerful method. On the other hand, we might take advantage of the power of some of these methods by using a subset of the total set of possible presentations. If we may obtain more information from a subject on a single presentation without taxing him, fewer presentations are called for to obtain the same amount of information than are called for by a less powerful method.

One useful kind of subset of presentations is known as a balanced incomplete block design (BIBD). "Taste preference testers" (for example, see Terry, Bradley, and Davis, 1952; and also R. A. Bradley, 1954) and other mathematical statisticians have provided a good deal of technical literature on them. BIBD's have also been utilized in psychology at least as early as 1951 (Durbin, 1951), and most recently Gulliksen and Tucker (1961) have provided a computer program for their analysis.

A BIBD in this context* is a subset of presentations from the searchingness structure in which n stimuli are presented in b blocks of p at a time so that each stimulus occurs in r of the blocks and every pair of stimuli occurs λ times in all.

Some necessary conditions for the existence of BIBD's are given by the following two expressions:

$$\lambda = \frac{r(p - 1)}{n - 1} \tag{2.5}$$

$$rn = bp$$

where b = number of presentations (blocks)
$\quad n$ = total number of stimuli
$\quad r$ = number of replications of each stimulus
$\quad p$ = number of stimuli in a presentation
$\quad \lambda$ = number of replications of each pair of stimuli.

---

* The relevance of the literature on BIBD's to our problem was first brought to my attention by J. E. Keith Smith in 1952.

A method for generating a subset of triads in the special case where n is an odd multiple of 3 and $\lambda = 1$ is given by Schucker (1959); see also Bose (1960).

Hanani (1961) provides the sufficient conditions for the existence of BIBD's for $p = 3$ and 4 (and every λ) and also for $p = 5$ with $\lambda = 1, 4,$ or 20. He proves that $\lambda(n - 1) = 0 \pmod 2$ and $\lambda n(n - 1) = 0 \pmod 6$ are necessary and sufficient for the existence of BIBD's for n stimuli presented 3 at a time and any λ. He also proves that $\lambda(n - 1) = 0 \pmod 3$ and $\lambda n(n - 1) = 0 \pmod{12}$ are necessary and sufficient for the existence of BIBD's for n stimuli presented 4 at a time and any λ. His proofs "enable effective construction of the designs" (1961, p. 362).

The channel capacity of a BIBD allotted to each pair comparison if the subject rank orders all the stimuli in the presentation is

$$\frac{\lambda \log p!}{\binom{p}{2}}$$

and the total capacity in the design is

$$b \log p!$$

Perhaps the most efficient method of all would be the use of incomplete block designs without perfect balance so that data could be collected and information concentrated where most needed. Such designs are discussed in Chapter 9 of Cochran and Cox (1957), but their use in this context has not been explored.

Cartwheel Designs

A special problem arises in the case of collecting similarities data in which comparisons are made on distances between stimuli, as when stimuli A, B, and C are presented and the subject is asked to judge whether A or B is more like C. With n stimuli there are $n' = \binom{n}{2}$ distances between pairs of stimuli. If the data of interest are order relations on pairs of these distances, then we must enter the searchingness structure with n' rather than n, because the effective stimulus is a distance. With $n = 10$ there are $n' = 45$ distances, and it is obvious that only the weakest methods would be feasible in their complete form. The situation is made even more difficult if we want redundancy on pairs of distances, as when the probability that one distance is judged less than another is to be estimated. This case arises not uncommonly in multidimensional scaling.

If this information is needed for all the pairs of distances, then a balanced incomplete block design on the n' distances is convenient because it provides the same number of bits of information on each pairwise comparison, and all pairs of distances are compared. Even this, however, may be an exorbitant requirement.

Fortunately, however, all this information may not be needed. Instead of requiring order relations on all the pairs of distances, models exist which require comparisons only between those pairs of distances which have a common terminus (called *conjoint distances*). The unfolding technique adapted to similarities data requires order relations on pairs of distances such as $\overline{AB}$ against $\overline{BC}$, in which these two distances have the point for stimulus B as a common terminus. A very subordinate role* is played by order relations on pairs of distances such as $\overline{AB}$ and $\overline{CD}$, which have no common terminus and are called *disjoint* distances. Consequently, it is useful to have a system of designs particularly suitable for collecting information about pairs of conjoint distances and de-emphasizing pairs of disjoint distances. Such designs enable an experimenter to utilize the channel capacity of his method for collecting data and at the same time concentrate the subject's effort to obtain the most relevant and important information.

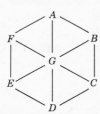

Fig. 2.3 A cartwheel.

A presentation in this general system may be abstractly considered as an arrangement with the stimuli on the "rim" of a wheel and connected by "spokes" to a stimulus at the "hub" (see Fig. 2.3). The term "cartwheel" is used for these designs because it provides a natural vocabulary for descriptive purposes.

The subject is asked to rank order all the distances indicated by lines in the presentation. Thus, in Fig. 2.3 there are twelve distances among these seven stimuli which are to be rank ordered.

In the figure G is called the hub and all the other stimuli are on the rim. A line between the hub stimulus and a stimulus on the rim is called a spoke, and a line between adjacent stimuli on the rim is called a rim.

A great variety of presentation designs is possible, but the most practical ones are the five illustrated in Fig. 2.4.

Case 1 was perhaps first used by M. W. Richardson (1938). I (1954) called it the method of similarities, and Torgerson (1958) called it the method of triadic combinations. The name I gave it is hereby withdrawn, and the same fate is recommended for the name given by Torgerson. The term *method of similarities* is appropriate for any method making

* See the analysis of conditional proximity matrices in Chapters 17 and 22.

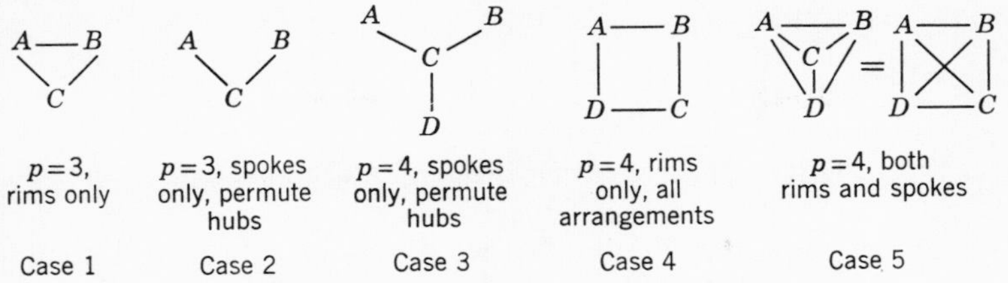

$p=3$, rims only	$p=3$, spokes only, permute hubs	$p=4$, spokes only, permute hubs	$p=4$, rims only, all arrangements	$p=4$, both rims and spokes
Case 1	Case 2	Case 3	Case 4	Case 5

Fig. 2.4 Five special cases of cartwheels.

comparisons of differences and should not be wasted by limiting it to this special case. The term *method of triadic combinations* refers only to the fact that stimuli are presented in sets of three, and this does not distinguish between cases 1 and 2, or whether the effective stimuli are points or distances.

Case 2 is the pair comparison of all distances with a common terminus.* "Permute hubs" in the definition of the method means that each set of three stimuli must be presented three times, each stimulus being placed at the hub in turn. This method is called by Torgerson (1958) the complete method of triads. It is recommended that this name be dropped also. It is correct that all sets of three stimuli are presented, but the distances between points are the effective stimuli, and not all triples of distances are presented. In fact, no disjoint pairs of distances are ever compared, as this requires four stimuli in a presentation. A complete method of triads for similarities data should properly refer to the presentation of all sets of three distances from the total of n' distances.

Case 3 is also a kind of triadic method in the sense that sets of three distances are presented at one time and the individual orders them in magnitude. The sets of distances, however, just as in case 2, consist of distances with a common terminus, the stimulus point corresponding to the hub stimulus. Each set of four stimuli must be presented four times so that each stimulus may be placed at the hub in turn. Note that in this case, even though there are four stimuli in a presentation, no disjoint distances are ever directly compared, only conjoint distances. Intuitively it is to be anticipated that case 3 will bear the same relation to case 2 that the method of triads does to the method of pair comparisons in the searchingness structure.

In case 4 disjoint distances are compared as well as conjoint distances. Each set of four stimuli must be presented in three arrangements, rotating (over the other three) the element diagonally opposite any one stimulus. Thus, the three arrangements for $p = 4$, rims only, are displayed in Fig. 2.5.

* The use of this method is described in some detail in Dember (1960.)

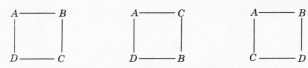

Fig. 2.5 The three arrangements for $p = 4$, rims only.

Case 5 is perhaps near the limit of what may be expected of a subject because he is being asked to rank order the six distances among four stimuli. The feasibility of these methods, however, is dependent on the nature of the stimuli.

Information theory provides a convenient and suitable measurement system for the purpose of comparing these methods.

Channel Capacity of Cartwheels. If all response patterns are equally probable and successive presentations are experimentally independent so

Table 2.4 Channel Capacity of Cartwheel Designs in Bits

	No. of Possible Response Patterns to a Presentation	No. of Presentations	Channel Capacity
Spokes only, permute hubs	$(p-1)!$	$p\binom{n}{p}$	$p\binom{n}{p}\log(p-1)!$
Rims only, all arrangements	$p!$	$\dfrac{(p-1)!}{2}\binom{n}{p}$	$\dfrac{(p-1)!}{2}\binom{n}{p}\log p!$
Both rims and spokes	$\binom{p}{2}!$	$\binom{n}{p}$	$\binom{n}{p}\log\binom{p}{2}!$

that information is cumulative, then maximum capacity is achieved. Table 2.4 contains the necessary expressions to compute the information capacity of any cartwheel design.

For the five special cases of cartwheels in Fig. 2.4 the information capacity for various values of n is given in Table 2.5. It is evident that their capacities increase rapidly with increasing n.

Redundancy of Cartwheels. The problem of measuring the redundancy of cartwheels is more complicated than that of measuring the redundancy of the complete methods in the searchingness structure. In the latter the method of pair comparisons was used as the base in order that the measure of redundancy might reflect the power of a method to measure inconsistency. That is, redundancy was defined as the number of bits of channel capacity per pair of stimuli beyond the one bit per pair allotted by the method of pair comparisons.

In the cartwheel methods all pairs of distances are not compared equally often. Cases 1, 2, and 3, for example, present no pairs of disjoint distances, but only pairs of conjoint distances. Cases 4 and 5 compare disjoint distances as well as pairs of conjoint distances, but each makes

Table 2.5 Channel Capacity (in Bits) of Five Cartwheel Designs for Various Values of n

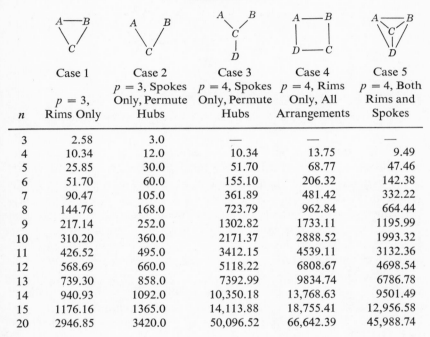

n	Case 1 $p = 3$, Rims Only	Case 2 $p = 3$, Spokes Only, Permute Hubs	Case 3 $p = 4$, Spokes Only, Permute Hubs	Case 4 $p = 4$, Rims Only, All Arrangements	Case 5 $p = 4$, Both Rims and Spokes
3	2.58	3.0	—	—	—
4	10.34	12.0	10.34	13.75	9.49
5	25.85	30.0	51.70	68.77	47.46
6	51.70	60.0	155.10	206.32	142.38
7	90.47	105.0	361.89	481.42	332.22
8	144.76	168.0	723.79	962.84	664.44
9	217.14	252.0	1302.82	1733.11	1195.99
10	310.20	360.0	2171.37	2888.52	1993.32
11	426.52	495.0	3412.15	4539.11	3132.36
12	568.69	660.0	5118.22	6808.67	4698.54
13	739.30	858.0	7392.99	9834.74	6786.78
14	940.93	1092.0	10,350.18	13,768.63	9501.49
15	1176.16	1365.0	14,113.88	18,755.41	12,956.58
20	2946.85	3420.0	50,096.52	66,642.39	45,988.74

more comparisons of conjoint distances than of disjoint distances. Consequently there is a complication in measuring the redundancy of cartwheels in that there is more redundancy on certain pairs than on others.

Insofar as the pair comparison of conjoint distances is concerned, case 2 is the method that collects the basic information. Case 2 plays the identical role among cartwheel methods that the method of pair comparisons plays in the complete searchingness structure. Case 2 calls for the presentation of only those pairs of distances that are conjoint, and each pair is presented once. Hence case 2 is an appropriate base for evaluating redundancy of cartwheel methods in that the redundancy measures so obtained reflect the contribution to channel capacity from replication. This is clearly true for cases 1, 2, and 3 in that the redundancy so measured is equally distributed over all pairs of distances presented. This is not so for cases 4 and 5, which need more careful interpretation of the redundancy measure.

The measure of redundancy proposed for a cartwheel method x is

$$\mathscr{R}_x = \frac{C_{\text{case } x}}{C_{\text{case } 2}} - 1 \qquad (2.6)$$

From Table 2.4 it is apparent that the channel capacity of case 2 ($p = 3$ spokes only, permute hubs) is $C_{\text{case } 2} = 3\binom{n}{3}$, and hence

$$\mathscr{R}_x = \frac{C_{\text{case } x}}{3\binom{n}{3}} - 1$$

The redundancy of case 1 (rims only, $p = 3$), then, reduces to

$$\mathscr{R}_{\text{case } 1} = \frac{\log 3!}{3} - 1 = -0.14$$

This negative redundancy is a consequence of the fact that the decomposition of the rank order of the three distances in each presentation allots only 0.86 bits of channel capacity to each pair comparison. This reduction in channel capacity relative to that of pair comparisons is a consequence of the transitivity of judgment imposed by the method of collecting data. The value -0.14 is a constant in case 1 and not a function of n. This independence of redundancy of case 1 from n is in contrast to the method of triads in the searchingness structure, for which redundancy is a function of n. Thus we have another reason for distinguishing case 1 from the method of triads. The method of triads, if used to obtain similarities data, would require presentation of *all triples of distances*, because distances are the stimuli in similarities judgments, and this rapidly becomes impractical with increasing n.

These considerations now make clearer my objection to the use of the name method of triads for either case 1 or case 2. The method of triads in the searchingness structure has positive redundancy which increases with n. Cases 1 and 2 have negative and zero redundancy, respectively, which is independent of n.

The redundancy of case 3 ($p = 4$, spokes only, permute hubs) is

$$\mathscr{R}_{\text{case } 3} = \frac{4\binom{n}{4} \log 3!}{3\binom{n}{3}} - 1 = 0.862(n - 4.161)$$

Redundancy figures for case 3 for various values of n are given in the first column of Table 2.6.

The redundancy of case 4 ($p = 4$, rims only, all arrangements) needs to be partitioned into redundancy on pairs of disjoint distances and redundancy on pairs of conjoint distances. Each presentation yields a rank order of 4 distances which decompose into 6 pairs. Two of these pairs are between disjoint distances and 4 are between conjoint distances.

There is a channel capacity of log 4! $= 4.58$ bits for each presentation, which may be allotted over the 6 pairs equally, giving 0.763 bits per pair. The 2 pairs of disjoint distances in a set of 4 are presented exactly twice in the 3 arrangements of each set of 4. Hence 1.53 bits of channel capacity are obtained on each pair of disjoint distances, and hence the redundancy on such pairs is 0.53 bits, a constant for case 4 and therefore omitted from Table 2.6.

Since each pair of conjoint distances is presented once with each remaining stimulus (that is, $n - 3$ times in all), the accumulated bits of channel capacity for each of these pairs are $0.763(n - 3)$. Hence the redundancy on pairs of conjoint distances is

$$\mathcal{R}_{\text{case 4}} = 0.763(n - 3) - 1 = 0.763(n - 4.310)$$

A similar partition of the redundancy of case 5 needs to be made. In each presentation the subject rank orders 6 distances which decompose into 15 pairs. This allots (log 6!)/15 $= 0.633$ bits per pair per presentation.

Each set of 4 stimuli is presented exactly once in case 5, in contrast to the 3 arrangements of each set in case 4. Hence each pair of disjoint distances is presented exactly once, and so each pair is allotted -0.362 bits of redundancy, a constant for all n and omitted from Table 2.6.

Each pair of conjoint distances occurs once in the 1 presentation of each set of 4 stimuli in case 5, and there are $n - 3$ sets of 4 in which each such pair occurs. This yields an accumulated channel capacity for pairs of conjoint distances of $0.633(n - 3)$, and hence the redundancy is

$$\mathcal{R}_{\text{case 5}} = 0.633(n - 3) - 1 = 0.633(n - 4.580)$$

Computations of the redundancy in the channel capacity of cases 4 and 5 for pairs of conjoint distances for various values of n are given in Table 2.6.

These figures for redundancy are really just another way to describe the channel capacity of a method. The numbers in Table 2.5 on channel capacity represent the maximum total number of bits that could be obtained by each method for a given number of stimuli. The numbers in Table 2.6 on redundancy represent the channel capacity (reduced by one bit) allotted to each pair comparison of conjoint distances.

As n increases, the percentage of channel capacity allotted to redundancy increases. It is significant to note, however, that although case 4 has a higher channel capacity than case 3 it has less redundant channel capacity allotted to pairs of conjoint distances. Therefore this method, case 4, actually has less power for controlling and measuring inconsistency on pairs of conjoint distances than does case 3.

Table 2.6 Number of Redundant Bits of Channel Capacity per Conjoint Pair for Cases* 3, 4, and 5 for Various Values of n

n	Case 3	Case 4	Case 5
4	−0.14	−0.24	−0.37
5	0.72	0.53	0.27
6	1.59	1.29	0.90
7	2.45	2.05	1.53
8	3.31	2.82	2.17
9	4.17	3.58	2.80
10	5.03	4.34	3.43
11	5.90	5.10	4.06
12	6.76	5.87	4.70
13	7.62	6.63	5.33
14	8.48	7.39	5.96
15	9.34	8.16	6.60
20	13.65	11.97	9.76

* Case 1 has a constant redundancy of −0.14 per pair comparison, and case 2 has zero redundancy by definition.

This difference comes about, of course, because so much of the channel capacity of case 4 is allotted to pairs of disjoint distances. The total number of pairs of distances is $\left(\binom{n}{2} \atop 2 \right)$, and the number of pairs of conjoint distances is $n \binom{n-1}{2}$, so the difference, $3 \binom{n}{4}$, is the number of pairs of disjoint distances. Hence $3 \binom{n}{4}(0.763)$ is the amount of channel capacity of case 4 allotted to pairs of disjoint distances.

It is instructive to compare cases 3 and 5 also. Case 5 is case 3 with the rims added. The result is that more information needs to be processed in each presentation but there are fewer presentations; case 5 bears the relation to case 3 that case 1 does to case 2. In particular we note that case 5 has less channel capacity and less redundancy for all values of n than does case 3; this is in spite of the fact that case 5 would be more likely to overload a subject's ability to process information than would case 3.

3. CHOOSING A BEST METHOD

The difficult problem of which method to use in any particular instance will not be solved here, but some of the principal issues involved will be discussed. For this purpose we might regard a psychological experiment as a communication system between a subject and an experimenter in which the method of collecting data is the channel and the method of analyzing data is a transducer between the channel and the experimenter (see Fig. 2.6). This analogy between experimentation and communication is not a new one, having been suggested at least as early as 1950 by MacKay (1950).*

On a priori grounds, we would expect that the higher the channel capacity the better, but this is certainly not true. A price is paid for data, not only in financial terms but in wear and tear on the organism at the source. A method with too high a channel capacity may, through boredom and fatigue, result in a decrease in information transmitted, through stereotypy of behavior.

Furthermore, the potential variety of messages from the organism may not be great, in which case a more powerful method is inefficient. In some instances, for example, when a subject is consistent and transitive, nothing more powerful than the method of rank order is called for.

Ideally, a method of collecting data should be selected which matches the information content in the source but is not such a burden as to generate noise. These criteria may be in conflict with each other, or with constraints imposed by the stimulus material or by the method of analysis to be used, or with practical considerations like time and money.

Fig. 2.6 Analogy between a psychological experiment and a communication channel.

* Brought to my attention by George Miller.

The final choice must be a compromise and must be made by the experimenter. The facts provided about these methods are useful, but they are not sufficient or decisive.*

4. DATA REDUCTION MODELS

The problem here is how to analyze redundant data in order to arrive at a scale of the stimuli. We have, for example, 'order k/p' data, and the data are at worst chaotic and at best perhaps overwhelming. Models designed to introduce at least an intermediate stage of intelligibility into such data I have here called data reduction models—primarily because their intent is merely to condense the original observations.

Figure 2.7 illustrates the role these models play. Paths 1 and 2 in the figure represent the two kinds of data reduction models that are discussed here. Path 1 refers to what I have called decomposition models and path 2 to the method of expected matrices. These two paths represent two different approaches to the problem of constructing a stimulus scale from the redundant data.

Path 1 is perhaps the most common way. Data collected by the method of triads, or an even more powerful method, are used to estimate the pairwise probabilities by applying a decomposition model. Then the pairwise probabilities are utilized to construct a stimulus scale.

Path 2, involving the use of an expected matrix, is a generalization of the procedure of using an average rank order or total vote count.

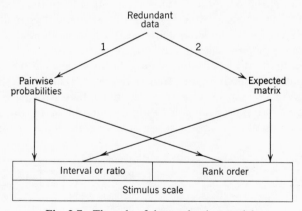

Fig. 2.7 The role of data reduction models.

* See Chapter 4 for some further characteristics of these methods relevant to selecting a best method.

A Decomposition Model

A problem with the more powerful methods of collecting data is that of translating the observations into the presumed equivalent observations that would have been obtained if the pair comparisons had been replicated. That is, having collected data by a complete 'order 2/3,' how do we process them to determine the pairwise probabilities? Those who have used these methods of collecting data have customarily counted the number of times one stimulus is chosen over another in all presentations in which that pair is embedded. For example, the pair of stimuli A and B is embedded in $n - 2$ triads if the complete 'order 2/3' method is used. To estimate the probability that A will be chosen over B, the customary practice has been to determine the proportion of times A has been chosen over B in those $n - 2$ presentations in which both A and B appeared.

There is a model implicit in this procedure which for the method of triads may be constructed as follows:

Consider two fixed stimuli A and B and a third stimulus X, which may be any of a number of other stimuli. The joint probability that an individual will make the three judgments $A > B$, $B > X$, $A > X$, corresponds to the probability that he will rank the stimuli in the order $A\ B\ X$. We use $p(ABX)$, then, as a shorthand notation for the joint probability of the implicit pair comparison judgments. The notation for a conditional probability is a vertical bar; that is, $p(AB \mid AX)$ is the probability the individual chooses A over B having already chosen A over X. The following identities may be written:

$$p(ABX) = p(AB)\, p(AX \mid AB)\, p(BX \mid AB, AX)$$
$$p(AXB) = p(AB)\, p(AX \mid AB)\, p(XB \mid AB, AX) \qquad (2.7)$$
$$p(XAB) = p(AB)\, p(XA \mid AB)\, p(XB \mid AB, XA)$$

Summing these three equations gives

$$p(ABX) + p(AXB) + p(XAB) = p(AB)\{p(AX \mid AB)\, [p(BX \mid AB, AX)$$
$$+ p(XB \mid AB, AX)] + p(XA \mid AB)\, p(XB \mid AB, XA)\}$$

But $p(BX \mid AB, AX) + p(XB \mid AB, AX) = 1$. Also $p(XB \mid XA, AB) = 1$ by virtue of the imposition of transitivity within each triple by the method of collecting the data. Assuming that $p(AB)$ is independent of X, we have

$$p(AB) = p(ABX) + p(AXB) + p(XAB) \qquad (2.8)$$

The assumption that $p(AB)$ is independent of X is a strong form of the "independence from other alternatives" axiom that continually crops up in choice theory and decision making.

This is only one of a number of possible models for decomposition that might be considered. For example, we might assume that an individual required to order a triple makes the three component pair comparisons independently and according to their respective probabilities. If the result is intransitive we might then assume that the intransitivity is resolved at random, or that the entire process is repeated, and so on. The variety of possible models is limited only by man's ingenuity. It might be true, of course, that more than one model holds for the different individuals in a sample. If this is the case, the problem of analyzing data collected by the more powerful methods of the searchingness structure becomes more complex. The model developed here is offered only as an explicit formulation of the assumption underlying the procedure usually followed.

Having obtained the pairwise probabilities directly, or from redundant data by the decomposition model presented here, or by some other decomposition model, the next step is to construct a stimulus scale. An important condition here is weak stochastic transitivity, which is

$$p(AB) \geq 0.5 \text{ and } p(BC) \geq 0.5 \Rightarrow p(AC) \geq 0.5 \qquad (2.9)$$

If this condition is satisfied, it yields an ordinal scale immediately. If this condition is not satisfied, an ordinal scale does not exist, because the data imply a denial of transitivity. A ranking arrived at by virtue of weak stochastic transitivity is a maximum likelihood estimate of the correct ordering.

It might be supposed that the imposition of transitivity on each triad imposes weak stochastic transitivity on the pairwise probabilities. This is not so, however, as an example will show. Suppose a subject rank orders the stimuli in the triads from a set of five stimuli as follows:

BCA	BCD	ACE
ABD	CBE	—
ABE	DCA	—

The condition of weak stochastic transitivity is not satisfied by these data as it may readily be observed that $p(AB) = \frac{2}{3}$, $p(BC) = \frac{2}{3}$, but $p(AC) = \frac{1}{3}$.

A variety of models, many of which have not been explored by psychologists, are discussed by Brunk (1960) for constructing a ranking from paired comparisons.

Equation 2.8 says that the proportion of triads in which A has been chosen over B is an estimate of $p(AB)$. These pairwise probabilities may then be employed in such measurement models as Thurstone's model for comparative judgment or the Bradley-Terry-Luce (BTL) model of choice behavior to construct an interval or ratio scale of the stimuli, respectively.

The Method of Expected Matrices

In applying a decomposition model, the data come only from those presentations in which both stimuli occur together. Each pairwise probability, and hence the ordering on each pair, is based only on the presentations in which the pair is embedded. It would seem desirable, under some circumstances, to use more of the data to determine the order of the stimuli. In particular, we might consider using all the presentations in which a stimulus occurs to determine its order among the others. The method of expected matrices is designed to do just this.

Suppose that we wish to construct a stimulus scale and proceed to collect QIIIa data, using a complete method from the searchingness structure in which p stimuli are presented at a time and the individual is asked to order k of them. The data obtained may be tabulated in a data matrix in which the columns correspond to stimuli and the rows from top to bottom correspond to the rankings from 1 to k. In each cell is recorded the number of times the stimulus of that column was accorded the ranking of that row, counted over all the presentations in which that stimulus appears.

A transcendent or predominant ordering, obscured by inconsistency, is assumed to exist for the individual. The method of expected matrices consists of two steps: (1) calculating what the data matrix would be expected to look like if the predominant ordering were not obscured by inconsistency and the columns were in order, and (2) permuting the columns of the observed matrix to match the expected matrix as closely as possible, by some criterion.

An expected data matrix may be calculated, assuming no inconsistency, as follows. Let γ designate the number of a column and ρ designate the number of a row. Then the general term $e_{\rho\gamma}$ of the expected matrix for order k of p is

$$e_{\rho\gamma} = \binom{\gamma - 1}{\rho - 1}\binom{n - \gamma}{p - \rho} \tag{2.10}$$

The first factor on the right is the number of ways stimuli can have a higher rank than γ in a presentation, and the second factor is the number of ways stimuli can have a lower rank.

As an illustration, the expected matrix for $n = 10$, 'order 4/5,' is given in Table 2.7, in which the assumed correct ordering is alphabetical.

Stimulus E in the table, for example, will be ranked first in only five of all the presentations in which it appears—in those presentations in which the other four are selected from the five lower than E in the predominant ordering. There are five different ways in which this can be done.

Table 2.7   The Expected Matrix for $n = 10$, 'Order 4/5'

Rank in the Predominant Ordering, γ

		1	2	3	4	5	6	7	8	9	10
		A	B	C	D	E	F	G	H	I	J
Rank in a presenta-tion, ρ	1	126	70	35	15	5	1	0	0	0	0
	2	0	56	70	60	40	20	6	0	0	0
	3	0	0	21	45	60	60	45	21	0	0
	4	0	0	0	6	20	40	60	70	56	0
	5	0	0	0	0	1	5	15	35	70	126

The expected matrix for 'pick k/p' may be readily obtained from the corresponding matrix for 'order k/p' by simply summing the first k rows in each column. Thus, the expected matrix for 'pick 2/5' is given in Table 2.8, in which the entries are the column sums of the first two rows from Table 2.7.

Table 2.8   The Expected Matrix for $n = 10$, 'pick 2/5'

Predominant Ordering, γ

	1	2	3	4	5	6	7	8	9	10
	A	B	C	D	E	F	G	H	I	J
No. of times picked	126	126	105	75	45	21	6	0	0	0

The obtained data matrix may then be compared with the expected matrix to seek the permutation of the columns of the data matrix that yields a "best" match between corresponding cells. Just what is meant by "best" is an independent decision. Minimizing a χ^2 suggests itself, that is, seek that permutation of the columns of the observed matrix for which the χ^2 based on corresponding cells is a minimum.

The method of expected matrices requires that the data satisfy a strong form of the axiom of independence from other alternatives. In addition, it is preferable that the data be collected by balanced designs to improve discriminability among columns of the expected matrix. The method is not recommended for QIa preferential choice data for the first reason,* nor for QIVa cartwheel data for both reasons. If the first reason applies to QIa preferential choice data it also applies to cartwheel data, in that a hub is a temporary ideal. The second reason applies because the columns of an expected matrix for cartwheels are much less discriminable, and hence inconsistent data may readily fail to yield a unique ordering of the distances.

* This is discussed in Section 10 of Chapter 5.

The method of expected matrices, then, is recommended only for QIIIa data, for which it as yet yields only an ordinal scale. No model currently exists for transforming the observed data matrix into an interval scale of the stimuli beyond the level of such procedures as getting the vote count for each stimulus, that is, how many times each stimulus has been chosen over others.

5. SUMMARY

A logical extension of well-known methods of collecting data like the methods of single stimuli, rank order, pair comparisons, and triads leads to the searchingness structure, in which any subset of $p \leq n$ stimuli is presented at a time and the subject picks or orders $k < p$ in each presentation. The channel capacity and the channel redundancy of the methods are evaluated using information theory, and an experimental comparison of three of the methods is reported.

Two special modifications of the searchingness structure are incomplete block designs and cartwheel designs. The value of the former lies in making possible the use of powerful methods to obtain more information from the subject in each presentation and accumulating the same total amount of information as is obtained from the many presentations required in a less powerful method. The value of the cartwheel designs lies in collecting similarities data, in that these designs concentrate the effort on conjoint distances and relatively neglect those pairs of distances which are disjoint. Such data are particularly valuable for certain methods of analysis of QIVa data (for example, methods for analyzing conditional proximity data; see Chapters 17 and 22).

Some comments about choosing a best method are made, and an analogy is drawn in which the collection and analysis of data are regarded as a communication network between organism and experimenter.

Certain models for analyzing data discussed in later chapters require either pairwise probabilities or an ordering of the stimuli for each individual. Powerful methods of collecting data that do not yield such information directly need to undergo a process of data reduction. Two models for such purposes are discussed: (1) a decomposition model which is proposed for arriving at pairwise probabilities and, if weak stochastic transitivity is satisfied, at an ordering for each individual, and (2) expected matrices, which use more of the data to arrive at an ordering, but require a certain independence of context in the response tendencies.

It is by no means proposed that the searchingness structure exhausts the possible variety of methods of collecting data. An obvious omission, for example, is the ordering of the stimuli into k categories, as in category scaling and in the Q-sort technique. Such methods could be subjected to a similar analysis if there were some expected distribution of the number of stimuli assigned to each category. Such methods are all versions of the method of single stimuli (for example, 'pick $1/n$') as is also the case with such methods as S. S. Stevens' magnitude estimation. An informational analysis of the general method, 'pick $1/n$,' tells a very incomplete story because a great deal of information lies in various other assumptions that usually go along with the use of the method; for example, whether the response categories are elements of a simple order, an interval scale, or a ratio scale. An informational analysis such as was carried out here assumes the responses are only elements of a nominal scale.

REFERENCES

Bose, R. C., 1960, "On a method of constructing Steiner's triple systems," Chapter 11 in *Contributions to probability and statistics*, edited by I. Olkin et al., Stanford University Press, Stanford.

Bradley, R. A., 1954, Incomplete block rank analysis: on appropriateness of the model for a method of paired comparisons, *Biometrics*, **10**, 375–90.

Brunk, H. D., 1960, Mathematical models for ranking from paired comparisons, *J. Amer. statist. Ass.*, **55**, 503–20.

Cochran, W. G., and G. M. Cox, 1957, *Experimental designs*, second edition, John Wiley and Sons, New York.

Coombs, C. H., 1954, A method for the study of interstimulus similarity, *Psychometrika*, **19**, 183–94.

Dember, W. N., 1960, *The Psychology of Perception*, Holt, Rinehart and Winston, New York.

Durbin, J., 1951, Incomplete blocks in ranking experiments, *British J. Psychol., Statist. Section*, **4**, 85–90.

Garner, W. R., 1962, *Uncertainty and structure as psychological concepts*, John Wiley and Sons, New York.

Gulliksen, H., and L. Tucker, 1961, A general procedure for obtaining paired comparisons from multiple rank orders, *Psychometrika*, **26**, 173–83.

Hanani, Haim, 1961, The existence and construction of balanced incomplete block designs, *Ann. math. Statist.*, **32**, 361–86.

Komorita, S. S., 1958, Probability learning under equivalent data collection methods, *J. exp. Psychol.*, **55**, 115–20.

MacKay, D. M., 1950, Quantal aspects of scientific information, *Phil. Mag.*, **41**, 289–311.

Richardson, M. W., 1938, Multidimensional psychophysics, *Psychol. Bull.*, **35**, 659–60 (abstract).

Schucker, R. E., 1959, A note on the use of triads for paired comparisons, *Psychometrika*, **24**, 273–76.

Terry, M. E., R. A. Bradley, and L. L. Davis, 1952, New designs and techniques for organoleptic testing, *Food Technology*, **6**, 250–54.

Torgerson, W. S., 1958, *Theory and methods of scaling*, John Wiley and Sons, New York.

PART 2

PREFERENTIAL CHOICE DATA

The first two chapters have provided an overview of the theory of data and a systematic analysis of methods of collecting data. With these chapters as background, we take up each of the four quadrants in turn and discuss in greater detail the data and some of the appropriate models for this analysis. In this part we take up QI, preferential choice data. After an introduction to the nature of QIa data, we begin with the analysis of data collected by the least powerful methods and with the simplest form of the unfolding technique and progress to more complicated analyses.

CHAPTER 3

Introduction to QI

The purpose of this introductory chapter is (1) to discuss in greater detail the variety of behavior that may be mapped into QI, both on a formal level and in real world terms, and (2) to indicate the organization of this part of the book.

On the abstract level, QI involves relations on pairs of dyads in which the members of each pair of points are identified with elements of distinct classes in the real world. As an illustration, consider the Müller-Lyer illusion involving feathers and arrows, as in Fig. 3.1.

Suppose an individual is asked whether the pair of lines on the left or on the right is more nearly the same length and his judgment that the pair on the left is more alike is interpreted to mean that the difference between the lengths of the two lines on the left is less than the difference between the two lines on the right. Let us further suppose that there are more of such pairs of lines, always made up of a feathered line and an arrowed line, and hence no pair of lines in which both are arrowed or both are feathered. By virtue of such pairing, the "feathers" are members of one class, and the "arrows" members of another class, and the pairs are always made up of a member from each. If we identify each feathered line and

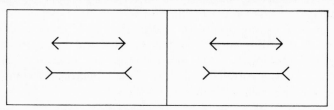

Fig. 3.1 The Müller-Lyer figures.

each arrowed line with a point, then, in this particular instance, we may speak of having order relations on pairs of pairs of points from distinct sets.*

Let the arrows be mapped into elements of the point set $C = \{c_i\}$ and the feathers be mapped into elements of the set $Q = \{q_j\}$ and form all pairs $A = C \times Q = \{(c_i, q_j)\}$; then the data are order relations on the elements of the Cartesian product $A \times A$. Such data constitute the general case of QIa. No model has been constructed to recover the psychological space K from precisely such data. Models have been developed, however, for analyzing a particular subset of these data, the case in which one of the lines, say the arrow, is the same in the two pairs.

We first form the pairs of points $A_i = \{(c_i, q_j) \mid i \text{ fixed}\} \subset A$. The Cartesian product $A_i \times A_i$ constitutes the pairs of dyads with the same arrow as a common member. The $\bigcup_i (A_i \times A_i)$ is then the set of all such pairs of dyads taken over the arrows. In effect, then, we have a pair comparison of the similarity of every pair of feathers to each arrow.

This is the kind of data the unfolding technique is designed to analyze and with which the chapters of Part 2 are concerned. The reason this limited set of data is of interest is that it is a possible interpretation of preferential choice behavior. If individuals are asked to make preferential choices among a set of alternative stimuli, the individuals and the stimuli may be conceived as elements of the two point sets C and Q respectively, and the data obtained are on the set $\bigcup_i (A_i \times A_i)$.

The more general case of QIa, $A \times A$ data, in the context of preferential choice behavior would require such observations as "individual 1 preferred stimulus a more than individual 2 preferred stimulus b." Such data are not usually obtained, because they require an assumption of *inter*personal comparability of utility, an assumption generally to be avoided. $A_i \times A_i$ data, in the case of preferential choice, requires the assumption of *intra*personal comparability of utility, a considerably weaker and more reasonable requirement.

We could obtain $A \times A$ data in the case of two kinds of stimuli, such as feathers and arrows or tones and lights, as discussed in Chapter 24, and it would seem desirable to extend the unfolding technique to the analysis of such data. As yet it has not been so extended. We might take the further step of pairing up arrows and pairing up feathers and collecting data on *all* pairs of dyads. Such data are $B \times B$ data, since the pairing process generates only one set, and therefore they constitute QIVa data for which models are available. Some of these interrelations among data matrices are discussed more fully in Chapter 24.

---

* This manner of speaking is not precise, as it is not the *points* which are from distinct classes but the real world objects with which they are identified.

No model has ever been constructed for data that are exclusively QIb. Such data are a proximity relation on a pair of dyads from distinct sets. This could be the interpretation given to the following observation. An individual is presented with a pair of stimuli and asked whether or not he has a preference, and the individual is to respond only with "yes" or "no." The interpretation of a "no" response is that the two points corresponding to the stimuli are not distinguishably different in their absolute distances from the individual's ideal point, that is, a proximity relation on a pair of distances.

Such observations have never been collected in their own right as far as I am aware, nor are there other behavioral observations which are mapped exclusively into QIb. Perhaps the lack of any ordinary behavior which "naturally" maps into QIb accounts for the lack of models for analyzing this kind of data; or conversely, perhaps the lack of models for them discourages us from deliberately seeking out such behavior. These data, however, are sometimes collected in conjunction with QIa data when an intermediate category of judgment ("can't decide") is permitted the subject. Then a preference would be an instance of QIa data and a lack of preference QIb data. The analysis of such mixed data is not considered at this stage of the development of these models. All the rest of Part 2 is concerned exclusively with the analysis of QIa data.

In the rest of Part 2 the real world context of individuals making preferential choices among stimuli will be used in most of the discussion and illustration of $\bigcup_i (A_i \times A_i)$ data and models. The methods which are discussed, however, are by no means restricted to such a real world context, as already indicated. In addition, behavioral observations in such areas as conditioning, generalization, and transfer may be mapped into identically the same data. These are discussed in Chapter 9.

Methods of analyzing QIa data will be presented; the analysis of QIa data that can be fitted by a one-dimensional model is dealt with before the analysis of data that require multidimensional analysis. In the discussion of unidimensional data, the analysis of data in the form of 'pick k/n' is presented in the next chapter on parallelogram analysis, and the analysis of data of the form 'order k/n' follows. The final chapter in Part 2 is concerned with opening gates and widening horizons to alternative approaches, some of which are frankly speculative.

SUMMARY

The data with which Part 2 is concerned are order relations on pairs of dyads from distinct sets. Whenever the relative similarity of the elements of one set to an element of another set is compared the data are

QI. Preferential choice behavior may be interpreted as QIa data, but other varieties of behavior may also be so interpreted. In a formal sense there are three degrees of "completeness" of QI data, distinguished here as $\bigcup_i(A_i \times A_i) \subset A \times A \subset B \times B$.

To illustrate these three, imagine that we have two sets of objects—a list of psychological journals, and a list of articles suitable for publication in them. If the observations only tell us which of every pair of journals a given article is more suited for, we have $\bigcup_i(A_i \times A_i)$ data. If the observations tell us in addition whether one article is more appropriate for one journal than some other article is for some other journal, the data are $A \times A$ data. If, finally, in addition, the observations contain the information that any given pair of articles is more or less similar than any given pair of journals, then we have $B \times B$ data.

The first two are QIa data and the latter, $B \times B$, is QIVa data. Models have been constructed explicitly for the analysis of $\bigcup_i(A_i \times A_i)$ data and for the analysis of $B \times B$ data. Part 2 deals only with the analysis of $\bigcup_i(A_i \times A_i)$ data; Part 5 deals with the analysis of $B \times B$ data.

If an individual who is asked to state his preferences between alternatives indicates indifference, his behavior may readily be mapped into QIb. QIb data seem never to appear "naturally," and as far as I know have never deliberately been collected exclusively in their own right. No model has ever been constructed for the analysis of such data. Hence the chapters of Part 2 are concerned exclusively with the analysis of QIa data.

The organization of chapters in Part 2 proceeds from the simplest unidimensional analysis of the simplest data on preferential choice to the multidimensional analysis of the most complete information about individuals' preferential choices. The last chapter is concerned with the frontiers and the generality of QIa research.

CHAPTER 4

Parallelogram Analysis

We shall now begin the discussion of methods of analyzing preferential choice data. This chapter introduces a method called parallelogram analysis, which is concerned with the construction of ordinal scales from data collected by the methods in the left-hand column of the searchingness structure, 'pick k/n' and 'order k/n.' The latter methods, 'order k/n,' yield information about the relative order of magnitude of distances between stimuli, as well as order relations on the stimuli themselves, if $k \geq 3$. The analysis of this kind of data to obtain the metric information is done by the unfolding technique, which is a natural extension of parallelogram analysis and is presented in the next chapter.

In the discussion of data for parallelogram analysis or unfolding analysis we assume either that the individual responded only once to the set of n stimuli, or, if more than once, that the data have been reduced to a form equivalent to responding only once. As an illustration, suppose that the stimuli are a half-dozen cigarettes of different brands, that in a blindfold test the subject is asked to pick the two he likes best, and that this is replicated a number of times for each subject on the six brands of cigarettes.

We might expect that at different times an individual will not always pick the same ones but that overall, some will be chosen more often than others. Such data can be reduced to a form suitable for analysis by parallelogram methods by specifying a value of k such that, for each individual, k of the stimuli can be said to be preferred over the remaining $n - k$.

This kind of data could also be reduced to a form suitable for analysis by the unfolding technique by using the percentage of times each brand was chosen by an individual to rank order the stimuli from most to least preferred. All the stimuli do not need to be ranked for each individual, but if at least three of them $(k \geq 3)$ are, the unfolding technique is applicable and metric information may be obtained if certain conditions are satisfied.

Whether the data are collected in a single trial or with replication, the essential point is that the behavior is represented by a 'pick k' or an 'order k' of the n stimuli for each individual. The individual is represented by a single point c_i, and each stimulus by a point q_j, and the two sets of points C and Q are assumed to be in the same space of relevant dimensions D'.

The next section begins the study of 'pick k/n' data in the simple case in which D' is one-dimensional. The multidimensional analysis of 'pick k/n' data has not been developed.

As a matter of notation throughout this chapter, consider a J scale to be a segment of the real line, on which stimuli have distinct values $q_j = A, B, C$, and so on, successively labeled alphabetically in their natural order.

1. ORDINAL ANALYSIS OF 'PICK k/n' DATA

We assume that each individual has a hypothetical ideal stimulus which would be preferred to any other alternative and that he prefers, among other alternatives, the one nearest his ideal. If the individuals and the stimuli are represented by points c_i and q_j, respectively, along a common one-dimensional continuum, the absolute distance of a stimulus point from the ideal is

$$|p_{ij}| = |c_i - q_j| \tag{4.1}$$

If, for example, we let $k = 3$, the individual will select the three stimuli for which the quantity $|p_{ij}|$ is the smallest. A data matrix may be constructed with the individuals as rows and the stimuli as columns and with an x in the cell (i, j) to indicate that individual i chose stimulus j. The data matrix will have k x's in each row. It is usually convenient to work with the reduced data matrix in which duplicate rows and duplicate columns are eliminated.

A rearrangement of the columns and rows is sought that will make the x's form a solid diagonal band (a parallelogram) across the data matrix, as illustrated in Table 4.1.

This procedure is called *parallelogram analysis** and is to be distinguished from the closely related procedure of Guttman's *scalogram analysis* for QIIa data.

---

* This is closely similar to a procedure proposed by Fredrick Mosteller, "A theory of scalogram analysis using noncumulative types of items," Reprint 9, Laboratory of Social Relations, Harvard University, 1949, unpublished manuscript.

Table 4.1 The Parallelogram Pattern for 'Pick 3/7' Data

Stimuli

		A	B	C	D	E	F	G
Response	1	x	x	x				
Patterns	2		x	x	x			
	3			x	x	x		
	4				x	x	x	
	5					x	x	x

If the parallelogram pattern can be found, the hypothesis that the stimuli and individuals may be represented by points on a common unidimensional J scale is supported. The order of the columns corresponds to a rank order of the stimulus points and the order of the rows to a rank order of the individuals.*

2. CHARACTERISTICS OF 'PICK k/n' DATA

Working Midpoints

To each individual there corresponds a subset k of the n stimuli which is called his response pattern. Each distinct response pattern is associated with a segment of the J scale. These segments are generated by the midpoints between certain pairs of stimuli. Although, of course, there is a midpoint between every pair of stimulus points, a 'pick k/n' method "activates" a proper subset, unique to that value of k, and these "activated" ones are called the *working midpoints*. This may be illustrated as follows.

The stimuli in a response pattern must always be contiguous in order on the J scale. For example, if $k = 2$, and the stimuli are labelled alphabetically in order from left to right (see Fig. 4.1), individuals at the extreme left† must choose the pair (AB). The next admissible response pattern is the pair (BC), and the point that divides the continuum between these two response patterns is the midpoint between stimuli A and C.

---

* It is hardly necessary to point out that the ordering on the J scale from left to right is not distinguishable in the matrix from the reverse ordering.

† This sentence reflects a manner of speaking which is not precise, but is very convenient when there is no danger of confusion. The danger lies in the failure to distinguish between the real world objects and the points to which they correspond. It is not the stimuli which are "in order from left to right" nor are there "individuals at the extreme left." The alternatives seem to be very cumbersome sentences or an even more specialized vocabulary, like "j points" and "i points." The slight danger of confusion seems to me the lesser evil.

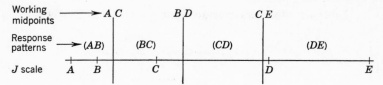

Fig. 4.1   The J scale under 'pick $2/n$.'

The next admissible response pattern is (CD), and it corresponds to a segment of the continuum separated from the preceding by the midpoint between B and D.   In general, for $k = 2$, the *working midpoints* are those between a stimulus j and the *second* stimulus from it, $j + 2$.

If $k = 3$, the first two admissible response patterns are (ABC) and (BCD).   The point that divides the segments of the continuum corresponding to these patterns is the AD midpoint.   In general, for any k, the working midpoints are those between the stimulus j and the stimulus $j + k$. Clearly, different midpoints are working for different k's, with the consequence that each k yields different information because it partitions the continuum differently.   It seems useful, then, to try to construct some criteria for comparing these 'pick k/n' methods in addition to those developed in Chapter 2 for the entire set of methods in the searchingness structure.

Discriminability

The degree to which a method like 'pick k/n' discriminates among individuals depends on the number of working midpoints.   In any particular application, the discriminability also depends on the distribution of the individuals and the relation of this distribution to the midpoints, but these factors are neglected here in order to construct what might be called general or universal characteristics of the methods.

The number of working midpoints for 'pick k/n' is easily seen to be $n - k$, and so the number of segments on the continuum, corresponding to classes of individuals, is $n - k + 1$.   Clearly, the smaller k is, the more discrimination, and the relation is linear.   'Pick $2/n$' yields $n - 1$ classes; at the other extreme, 'pick $(n - 1)/n$' divides the population into only two classes.   In the case of 'pick $(n - 1)/n$' there is only one working midpoint, the one between the first and the last stimulus, and the continuum is divided into only two segments.   In brief, then, 'pick k/n' divides a one-dimensional continuum into $n - k + 1$ segments which are ordered on the continuum.   A unique response pattern is associated with each of these segments, and hence the corresponding subset of individuals who emitted the pattern is also associated with it.   To each value of k there corresponds a unique set of midpoints generating the segments into which the continuum is partitioned.

In addition to affecting the discriminability among individuals, the particular value of k chosen for a 'pick k/n' method also affects the discriminability among the stimuli. This may be seen as follows. The first response pattern contains the first k stimuli on the left of the continuum. Each successive response pattern drops the leftmost stimulus in the previous response pattern and adds the next stimulus to the right on the continuum. Clearly, if k is too large relative to n, the stimuli will be simply ordered only at the ends of the continuum and there will be a subset of undifferentiated stimuli in the middle of the continuum. More precisely, the number of classes of stimuli formed under a 'pick k/n' method is $2(n - k) + 1$; and to order all stimuli the number of classes of stimuli must be as great as n, from which we may write

$$2(n - k) + 1 \geq n$$

and hence

$$k \leq \frac{n + 1}{2} \qquad (4.2)$$

If the value of k exceeds this quantity, the number of stimuli left in the undifferentiated central subset is $n - [2(n - k)] = 2k - n$. For example, if $n = 7$ and 'pick 5' were used, the first two and last two stimuli would be ordered on the J scale with a subset of three stimuli unordered between them. This is perhaps brought out more clearly by the parallelogram pattern illustrated in Table 4.2, in which it may be seen that stimuli C, D, and E are undifferentiated in the sense that they cannot be ordered by the data as given in the matrix.

Table 4.2   The Parallelogram Pattern for 'Pick 5/7' Data

	Stimuli						
	A	B	C	D	E	F	G
Response	x	x	x	x	x		
Patterns		x	x	x	x	x	
			x	x	x	x	x

To summarize with respect to discriminability among stimuli, we find that given enough individuals 'pick k/n' yields a simple order of the stimuli unless k is greater than $(n + 1)/2$, in which case there are $2k - n$ undifferentiated stimuli in a central subset on the J scale.

One further aspect of the discriminability of 'pick k' methods needs to be pointed out. Although discrimination between stimuli and between individuals is better for smaller than for larger k, the working midpoints $(j, j + k)$ are more and more centrally located on the J scale as k increases because they are midpoints between stimuli which are further apart in rank order on the J scale. Hence as k increases, discriminability between individuals is increased in the central region of the J scale. Just the reverse is true for discriminability between stimuli, because as k increases beyond $(n + 1)/2$ the undifferentiated subset of stimuli in the central region is increased.

An obvious variant on 'pick k/n' as a method of collecting data is to ask the subject to 'reject k'/n.' No analysis of 'reject k'/n' as a method is necessary here because it is evident that to each 'pick k/n' there corresponds a 'reject k'/n' with $k + k' = n$, and hence the analysis of 'pick k/n' applies identically to 'reject k'/n.' This, of course, is a formal equivalence and does not imply that real world observations of 'pick k/n' and 'reject k'/n,' with $k + k' = n$, would be psychologically equivalent, but merely that the method of analysis would be. The 'reject k'' method is merely converted into the equivalent 'pick k.'

Reproducibility

In any practical application of these 'pick k/n' methods perfect parallelogram patterns are not usually obtained. To obtain an index which represents a measure, in some sense, of just how adequate a scale has been obtained from the data, the concept of reproducibility is useful. This index, first introduced by Guttman (1944), is simply the percentage of the choices that are reproduced by the scale, the complement being the percentage of errors. It was applied by Guttman to the complete data matrix, but Milholland (1955) has pointed out that there are several different reproducibility measures possible with somewhat different implications.

Unfortunately certain mathematical properties of the index make it difficult to interpret. These limitations are discussed in some detail by Green (Lindzey, 1954, Chapter 9), White and Saltz (1957), and by Torgerson (1958), and stem from the fact that the lower bound for the index is dependent on the marginal popularity of the alternatives, and the expected value of the index, even for chance responses, is often high. In spite of these limitations, however, the index has been widely used, in conjunction with auxiliary criteria, to determine whether a scale is acceptable or not, perhaps because no better alternative index is available.

The most recent work on statistical methods for various coefficients of reproducibility has been published by Sagi (1959) and Goodman (1959). Goodman provides methods for testing whether an observed coefficient differs significantly from that expected if the responses to items are independent, and he also provides methods for estimating the variance of coefficients of reproducibility when responses to different items are dependent. This estimate permits us to set up confidence intervals for these coefficients. These methods, however, are only clearly appropriate *before* a set of items have been purified, and as Goodman suggests, a significant coefficient of reproducibility under the assumption of independence may not signify that there is, in some sense, a scale.

Guttman's index of reproducibility and, in fact, the variety of measures suggested by Milholland, all have their counterpart applicable to the data matrices of 'pick k/n' data. The same limitations still hold, however, and statistical properties, such as expected values, would be different for 'pick k/n' data from the properties for the QIIa data for which the coefficients were originally designed. So it is not possible to say at this point what constitutes acceptable values. It should be pointed out that if the coefficient is computed by counting the number of blank cells in each row that fall between two x's, the effect is to weight each error by the number of cells the error deviates from perfect reproducibility. The coefficient that would correspond to Guttman's would be based only on a count of the number of gaps (regardless of size) between the x's in each row.

Decomposability

Another characteristic of 'pick k/n' data matrices that can arise may be called *decomposability*. In this condition the stimuli may be partitioned

Table 4.3   A Decomposable Matrix for 'Pick 2/7' Data

Stimuli

	A	B	C	D	E	F	G
Response Patterns	x	x					
		x	x				
				x	x		
					x	x	
						x	x

into subsets or blocks such that they are ordered within the blocks but the blocks are not ordered. An example of a decomposable matrix is presented in Table 4.3, where the dashed lines show a partitioning between two blocks.

The stimuli A, B, C form one block, and the remaining stimuli form another. Obviously the blocks can be permuted, which would yield an equally good representation of the data with corresponding appropriate permutations of the rows. Such data do not provide a unique solution to a scale.

Decomposability may arise from either of two conditions: (1) The working midpoints may be so close together relative to the density of the individuals' ideals that there is a segment of the continuum to which no individuals in the sample correspond; (2) a kind of multidimensionality in which the individuals are partitioned into blocks and the stimuli into corresponding blocks; this would occur if the individuals were partitioned into Democrats and Republicans and the stimuli were candidates for office also partitioned into Democrats and Republicans. Then if the individuals did not jump party lines the result would be a decomposable data matrix.

For convenience, the first condition will be called a lack of *relative compactness* and the second one a *disjunctive multidimensionality*. Unfortunately a matrix for 'pick k/n' data does not permit distinguishing between these two sources of decomposability if either obtains.

Vulnerability

Another characteristic of these methods, called *vulnerability*, is worthy of consideration when an experimenter is deciding which method of data collection to choose. The purpose of constructing such a concept is to offer a temporary substitute in the absence of a statistical theory of reproducibility. The basic idea is that the methods differ intrinsically in their sensitivity to error, relative compactness, and disjunctive multidimensionality.

The idea may be illustrated in the following way. For a given sample of subjects and a set of stimuli, let us suppose that data collected by 'pick $3/n$' did not satisfy a perfect parallelogram, and that a certain coefficient of reproducibility was obtained. If the data had been collected by 'pick $2/n$' or by 'pick $4/n$' instead of 'pick $3/n$,' coefficients of reproducibility could also have been computed, and the question arises, how would these various coefficients of reproducibility compare? If some methods generally yielded lower coefficients of reproducibility than others, we would call them more vulnerable.

The method of pair comparisons, unreplicated, provides a reference point of maximum vulnerability on a scale. This point is so defined because, of the total variety of ways an individual can respond under a given method, the method of pair comparisons has a larger proportion which would violate perfect unidimensional scalability.

Thus, if there are n stimuli, then under the method of pair comparisons there are $2^{\binom{n}{2}}$ possible response patterns. Only $n!$ of these are transitive, and the subset of those which satisfy unidimensional scalability* is $\binom{n}{2} + 1$. Hence under the method of pair comparisons for a given J scale, a scalable response pattern must be one of $\binom{n}{2} + 1$ out of $2^{\binom{n}{2}}$ possible. In contrast to this, under 'pick k/n' there are $n - k + 1$ admissible response patterns for a given J scale out of $\binom{n}{2}$ possible response patterns. As an illustration, for the case of $n = 5$, there are 11 admissible response patterns out of the possible 1024 under the method of pair comparisons, whereas under 'pick $2/n$' there are 4 admissible patterns out of a possible 10. For larger n the vulnerability of the method of pair comparisons relative to 'pick k/n' increases further.

To complete the story, consider the 'order k/n' methods. Here there are $1 + nk - k(k + 1)/2$ admissible response patterns out of a total possible variety of $k! \binom{n}{k}$. As an illustration, if 'order k/n' is 'order 2/5' there are 8 admissible response patterns out of a possible 20. Under 'order 4/5,' which is the method of rank order and the most vulnerable of the 'order k/n' methods, there are 11 admissible response patterns out of a possible 120, which is far more vulnerable than any 'pick k/n' but still far less than the method of pair comparisons.

In other words, there are more ways for things to go wrong under the method of pair comparisons than under any other. Consequently, if there is a random component the method of pair comparisons would be the most sensitive to it.

For the 'pick k/n' methods the nearer the redundancy of the method is to the redundancy of pair comparisons (see Table 2.2) the more vulnerable it is. It is evident from Table 2.2 that the vulnerability of 'pick k/n' methods is maximal for k in the neighborhood of $n/2$ and decreases symmetrically as k departs from this region; and for a given 'pick k/n' vulnerability increases with n.

The coefficient of reproducibility may be regarded as a statistic used to test the hypothesis of unidimensionality in the data. The concept of vulnerability is related to this coefficient in that the probability of "an error of the first kind" increases with vulnerability and the probability of "an error of the second kind" decreases. This is a poor substitute for the development of the statistical properties of the coefficient of

* See Chapter 5.

reproducibility; their development is much to be desired both for 'pick k/n' data and for Guttman-type scales.

3. CHOOSING A BEST 'PICK k/n' METHOD

Discriminability and vulnerability are two characteristics of a method that must be considered in choosing a 'pick k/n.' A small value of k yields more discrimination among individuals, which diminishes linearly as k increases, because there is a loss of discrimination at the ends of the continuum. For values of k up to approximately $n/2$, a simple ordering of the stimuli is obtained; above this value, a central subset of stimuli is unordered. Vulnerability increases with k up to an integral value of approximately $n/2$ and then decreases.

Both discriminability and vulnerability, however, are also functions of n, so the experimenter must juggle both k and n to obtain the amount of discriminability he wants, where he wants it, and the degree of vulnerability he desires for his particular purposes. The choice is the experimenter's, who must also consider other relevant factors such as feasibility.

4. 'PICK $1/n$'—A SPECIAL CASE

At the point of juncture in the searchingness structure between the 'pick k/n' and 'order k/n' methods is 'pick $1/n$.' It is a curious method in that it represents an exception in the searchingness structure methods. The parallelogram method for analyzing 'pick k/n' data discussed in the previous pages is completely helpless in analyzing 'pick $1/n$' data. There is exactly one x in each row of the data matrix, and hence for each permutation of the columns there is a permutation of the rows so that the x's all fall on the main diagonal and form a parallelogram. Because the matrix is maximally decomposable, however, there is no way to use the data to order both the stimuli *and* the individuals, as is possible for any other values of k.

If, however, the order of the stimuli on the J scale (*or* the order of the individuals) is known, the order of the individuals (*or* the stimuli) immediately follows. Rating scale data is a typical example in which the order of the alternatives is already known and not required from the data. Hence to locate the individuals it is quite sufficient to collect 'pick $1/n$' data.

'Pick $1/n$' data, then, is single stimulus data, including what is called absolute judgment data. In each such instance the individual is presented with a stimulus and a range of alternative responses from which he selects one. The analysis of this kind of data is taken up in Part 3.

5. ORDINAL ANALYSIS OF 'ORDER k/n' DATA

The analysis of a data matrix obtained by an 'order k/n' method is a natural extension of the procedure for analyzing 'pick k/n' data. As in the case of the complete data matrix for 'pick k/n' data, let the rows correspond to individuals and the columns to stimuli. In each cell of the data matrix, the x of the 'pick k/n' data matrix is replaced by an integer between 1 and k inclusive, representing the individual's first, second, . . . , kth choice among the stimuli. It is again possible and usually more convenient to work with the reduced data matrix in which the rows are reduced to the distinct response patterns of individuals over stimuli and the columns reduced to the distinct response patterns of stimuli over individuals.

Keeping in mind that for QIa data the individual's preference ordering is determined by the distances of stimulus points from his ideal point, it is evident that, if the order of the columns corresponds to the order of the stimulus points on the J scale, the integers in any row should decrease strictly monotonically to 1 and then increase strictly monotonically. Hence we seek a permutation of the columns of the data matrix that satisfies this condition. The integer 1 in any row is found in the column that corresponds to the stimulus nearest that individual's ideal point. To order the individuals, then, we seek a permutation of the rows such that in each column the integers descending the column weakly monotonically decrease until the integer 1 is reached after which the integers must weakly monotonically increase. An illustration of the pattern sought in the case of 'order 3/6' is presented in Table 4.4, which is one of a number that are possible.

A comparison of Table 4.4 with Table 4.1 shows that each response pattern for 'pick $3/n$' data corresponds to a block of three or four distinct response patterns in 'order $3/n$' data.

If there is an arrangement of the 'order k/n' data matrix which satisfies the conditions given, the hypothesis that the stimuli and individuals can be represented by points on a common ordinal J scale is supported. Furthermore, the order of the columns corresponds to the rank order of the stimulus points, and the order of the rows to the rank order of the classes of individuals identified with the corresponding response patterns.

This is as much information as can be obtained in the case of 'order $2/n$' data. For $k \geq 3$, however, the data contain information about the order relations on distances between pairs of stimuli, yielding what is called an ordered metric J scale. This metric information is not readily obtained from the matrix method of parallelogram analysis. The analysis of the data to obtain such information is discussed in full in Chapter 5.

Table 4.4   A Parallelogram Pattern for 'Order 3/6' Data

Stimuli

		A	B	C	D	E	F
Response	1	1	2	3			
Patterns	2	2	1	3			
	3	3	1	2			
	4		1	2	3		
	5		2	1	3		
	6		3	1	2		
	7			1	2	3	
	8			2	1	3	
	9			3	1	2	
	10			3	2	1	
	11				2	1	3
	12				3	1	2
	13				3	2	1

6. CHARACTERISTICS OF 'ORDER k/n' DATA

Working Midpoints

It is obvious that every 'order k/n' response pattern corresponds to a 'pick k/n' response pattern with further differentiation. In fact, to an individual's 'order k/n' response pattern there formally corresponds an implicit 'pick $1/n$' response pattern, a 'pick $2/n$' response pattern, and so on up to 'pick k/n.' This reveals that the working midpoints for an 'order k/n' method are those for all these pick methods combined (see Fig. 4.2). In contrast to the 'pick k/n' methods in which the working midpoints are different for each k, the working midpoints of an 'order

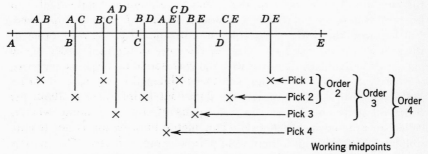

Fig. 4.2   Working midpoints for 'pick' and 'order' methods.

k/n' method are included among those for any higher k. Hence, as the k of 'order k/n' increases, the subset of midpoints successively added are less in number and are between stimuli further apart in the rank order on the J scale. This, of course, is relevant to the degree of discrimination of the methods and to the point on the J scale at which that discrimination is being made, and hence to such matters as sensitivity to error or inconsistency, that is, vulnerability.

Discriminability, Reproducibility, and Vulnerability

From the fact that an 'order k/n' method accumulates the working midpoints of the pick methods from 'pick $1/n$' to 'pick k/n,' it is clear that the discriminability of an 'order k/n' method considerably exceeds that for the corresponding 'pick k/n.' Each response pattern corresponds uniquely to a segment of the J scale continuum bounded by adjacent working midpoints. The number of response patterns is the number of working midpoints plus 1. The midpoints between all pairs of k stimuli are working, as well as those between each of the k stimuli and each of the remaining $n - k$ stimuli, so the total number of response patterns is

$$1 + \binom{k}{2} + k(n - k) = 1 + nk - \frac{k(k + 1)}{2} \qquad (4.3)$$

The maximum number of response patterns is obtained when $k = n - 1$, which of course is the well-known method of rank order, in which all the midpoints are working and the number of response patterns is $\binom{n}{2} + 1$.

Almost nothing has been done on the reproducibility and vulnerability of this kind of data. It is intuitively evident that the methods are highly vulnerable and increasingly so as the k of 'order k/n' increases. This is exemplified in a study by Kamenetzky and Schmidt (1957), who, in order to measure students' attitudes toward draft deferment, had them rank order five statements of opinion in order of endorsement. They observe that

When *pretest* (italics original) preferences were scaled by the unfolding technique, only 87 per cent of the observed rank orders were found to be deducible from the best fitting joint scale. However, when only the first *two* ranks ['order 2/5'] were considered, the unfolding analysis classified 98 per cent of the rank orders on the joint scale. Accordingly, the latter scale, which provided eight distinguishable levels of favorableness toward abolition of student deferments, was used in the subsequent analysis.*

An analogy might prove useful. We might think of the discriminability of the methods in the left-hand column of the searchingness structure

---

* Kamenetzky and Schmidt (1957, p. 201).

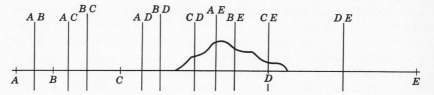

Fig. 4.3 How midpoints truncate an individual's distribution of ideals.

(Fig. 2.1) as analogous to the power of a microscope, and ascending the column as analogous to increasing the power of the microscope. If the object we are looking for is a point that randomly fluctuates, a lower power will fix the point in a larger field (segment of the continuum), whereas a higher power, providing a view of a smaller region, will reveal only a blur. It was this analogy which led to the name "searchingness structure" in the first place.

In order to overcome the blurring under a high-power microscope we may "fix" the object. This is precisely analogous to what the more powerful methods of the searchingness structure seek to do by their redundancy. The techniques discussed under data reduction models (see Chapter 2) seek an ordering of the stimuli which would in some sense "best" represent the individual's randomly varying ideal. In fact it is obvious that if an individual's ideal point is randomly varying, the condition of weak stochastic transitivity applied to redundant data will yield the rank order of the stimuli from the *median* of the distribution of ideals. This follows from the fact that the midpoint between any pair of stimuli will truncate the distribution of the individual's ideal, and the median of the distribution will always be included in the larger portion. This is illustrated in Fig. 4.3, which shows a hypothetical distribution of an individual's ideal point and how it may be truncated by midpoints between stimuli. Therefore, when the ideal point is varying but the stimulus points are not, the ordering obtained by weak stochastic transitivity is the ordering from the ideal fixed at its median point.

7. SUMMARY

A method of analysis called parallelogram analysis is presented, first in the context of analyzing 'pick k/n' data and then 'order k/n' data, all methods in the left-hand column of the searchingness structure. The method of analysis requires manipulation of a data matrix, much in the manner of Guttman's scalogram analysis of QIIa data. The technique applied to data collected by the various methods yields a J scale or information about the scalability of the data. As we proceed up the left-hand column of the searchingness structure we obtain increasing discriminability of stimuli and individuals. When 'order $3/n$' is reached, metric information appears in the form of order relations on the intervals between stimuli. At the top of the column of methods we have the method of rank order which yields maximum discriminability and has the most vulnerability among these methods of collecting data.

Characteristics of the methods of collecting data, such as discriminability and vulnerability, determine the characteristics of the resulting data matrix, such as reproducibility and decomposability. These concepts are discussed in the context of choosing a best method. An analogy is drawn between the power of the methods in the searchingness structure and the power of a microscope.

'Pick $1/n$' is mentioned briefly as the case of the searchingness structure that corresponds to the method of single stimuli.

The complete analysis of 'order k/n' data including extraction of metric information is taken up in the next chapter.

REFERENCES

Goodman, L. A., 1959, Simple statistical methods for scalogram analysis, *Psychometrika*, **24**, 29–43.

Guttman, L., 1944, A basis for scaling qualitative data, *Amer. sociol. Rev.*, **9**, 139–50.

Kamenetzky, J., and H. Schmidt, 1957, Effects of personal and impersonal refutation of audience counterarguments on attitude change, *J. abnorm. soc. Psychol.*, **54**, 200–03.

Lindzey, G., editor, 1954, *Handbook of social psychology*. Vol. II. *Special fields and applications*, Addison-Wesley Publishing Co., Cambridge, Mass.

Milholland, J., 1955, Four kinds of reproducibility in scale analysis, *Educ. psychol. Measmt.*, **15**, 478–82.

Sagi, P. C., 1959, A statistical test for the significance of a coefficient of reproducibility, *Psychometrika*, **24**, 19–27.

Torgerson, W. S., 1958, *Theory and methods of scaling*, John Wiley and Sons, New York.

White, B. W., and E. Saltz, 1957, Measurement of reproducibility, *Psychol. Bull.*, **54**, 81–99.

CHAPTER 5

The Unfolding Technique
in One Dimension

The basic assumptions of the theory of preferential choice on which the unfolding technique in one dimension is based are as follows. Each individual and each stimulus may be represented by a point on a common dimension called a *J scale*, and each individual's preference ordering of the stimuli from most to least preferred corresponds to the rank order of the absolute distances of the stimulus points from the ideal point, the nearest being the most preferred. The individual's preference ordering is called an *I scale* and may be thought of as the *J* scale folded at the ideal point with only the rank order of the stimuli given in order of increasing distance from the ideal point (see Fig. 5.1). The data consist of a set of *I* scales from a number of individuals, and the analytical problem is how to unfold these *I* scales to recover the *J* scale.

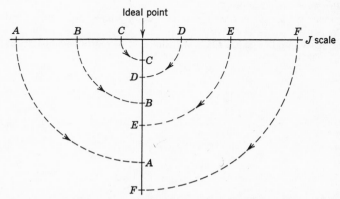

Fig. 5.1 An *I* scale preference ordering *C D B E A F*, obtained by folding a *J* scale.

The problems the psychologist may be interested in include those of discovering whether a common latent attribute may be underlying the preferences of individuals among the alternatives, measuring such an attribute, determining the degree to which such a common attribute exists, or determining for what subpopulations such a common attribute exists.

The unfolding technique, as well as the method of parallelogram analysis, may be regarded both as a scaling criterion and as a scaling method in the same sense as Guttman scalogram analysis. This distinction between a scaling criterion and a scaling method is one of relative emphasis. On the one hand the technique may be used to test the hypothesis that a unidimensional latent attribute can account for the observed behavior, in which case it is a scaling criterion. On the other hand it may be used to construct such a unidimensional scale, in which case it is a scaling method.

All scaling techniques have such dual capabilities, but they differ in their relative capability for the two purposes. Some are more effective as scaling methods than as scaling criteria; for others the reverse is true. The concept of vulnerability, previously introduced, is relevant to the effectiveness of a method as a scaling criterion. In general, these two capabilities are intimately related, their relation being similar to that between "errors of the first kind" and "errors of the second kind" in the statistical testing of hypotheses.

Unfolding theory is an assumption about a reality, the nature of the judgment process in preferential choice behavior. The unfolding technique, then, may be used to test this assumption *and* the assumption that a common unidimensional scale obtains. The high vulnerability of the method increases the likelihood of an "error of the first kind" as against an "error of the second kind." So-called weaker methods of scaling have this property of vulnerability and tend to be regarded as scaling criteria. A so-called stronger method of scaling is less vulnerable, tends always to yield a unidimensional solution to data, and is one for which the likelihood of an "error of the second kind" has increased relative to an "error of the first kind."

There is a shadow area in which scale criteria are not strictly met, but we may want to go ahead and construct a scale anyway. Guttman calls them quasi-scales; we shall meet an analogous situation in the application of unfolding theory.

The unfolding technique as developed here in Part 2 is more effective as a scaling criterion than as a scaling method in view of its vulnerability. One way to strengthen a technique as a scaling method is to introduce probabilistic versions, as Lazarsfeld did with Guttman scalogram analysis by his latent distance model. This has also been done for the unfolding technique and is discussed in Part 6. The effect of strengthening a technique as a scaling method is to reduce its capability as a scaling criterion.

When we are interested in scaling from the point of view of a scaling criterion we are interested in psychological theory; when we are interested in scaling from the point of view of a scaling technique we have already adopted some theory (that which led to the data and their conversion to measurements) and are interested in constructing tools for further research.

The unfolding technique is presented here in its dual capacity as a scaling criterion and a scaling method. Such progress as has been made on these problems is given in detail. Progress has been made on the necessary conditions a set of data must meet to satisfy a common J scale, the scaling criterion problem, and substantial progress has been made on the problem of recovering the J scale at the level of an ordered metric* scale.

Before proceeding with the unfolding technique in detail, a broader perspective on it may be obtained from a mathematical interpretation.

1. A MATHEMATICAL INTERPRETATION OF THE UNFOLDING TECHNIQUE

The fundamental observational equation in the theory of data is

$$p_{hij} = c_{hij} - q_{hij} \tag{5.1}$$

For the unfolding technique the subscript h may be dropped, because we assume that experimentally independent replications of the stimuli have reduced the preferences to a simple rank order (see the data reduction models discussed in Chapter 2).

The absolute distance between the jth stimulus point and the ith individual's ideal point is

$$|p_{ij}| = |c_{ij} - q_{ij}| \tag{5.2}$$

and his preference for stimulus j over stimulus k denotes that

$$|p_{ij}| - |p_{ik}| \leq 0 \tag{5.3}$$

The data consist of a set of simultaneous inequalities of the form of statement 5.3, where $i = 1, \ldots, m$ and $j, k = 1, \ldots, n$. The mathematical problem is to solve these inequalities for the unknowns, the c_{ij} and the q_{ij}.

The unfolding technique is essentially an algorithm for this purpose; it recovers the q's on an ordered metric scale, orders the classes in which

---

* An ordered metric scale is a simple order of elements with a transitive order relation on at least some pairs of intervals between elements.

the c's may be put, and, as these classes correspond to segments of the J scale, provides ordered metric information on the size of these segments.

2. BASIC CONCEPTS

The basic concepts of unfolding in one dimension are introduced here by a reasonably complete treatment of the case of $n = 4$, the simplest case in which metric relations may be obtained. Consider the case of a J scale, a segment of the real line, on which the four stimuli have distinct values A, B, C, and D, successively labeled* alphabetically in their order on the J scale.

Some notational conventions are that (1) the midpoint between any pair of stimuli is represented by the corresponding pair of letters, for example, the midpoint between stimuli A and C is AC, always written in alphabetical order; and (2) the absolute distance between any pair of stimuli is represented by the corresponding pair of letters with a bar over them, for example, the absolute distance between stimuli A and C is $\overline{AC}$.

There is a midpoint between each pair of stimuli on the J scale and an individual's preference between two stimuli reflects on which side of their midpoint his ideal is located. If the J scale has 4 stimuli on it there are 6 midpoints which, if they are distinct, divide the J scale into 7 segments. All the individuals whose ideals lie in the same segment have identical preference orderings on all pairs of stimuli. The pairwise preferences of each individual are necessarily transitive, according to this model, except for fluctuations in c and q's, to be introduced in Section 9. Hence the pairwise preferences reduce to a rank order which is the same I scale for all individuals in the same segment. As a consequence, there is a one-to-one correspondence between the rank order of the midpoints on the J scale and the set of I scales.

From a set of I scales it is a simple matter to arrive at the rank order of the midpoints from which metric relations are deduced. Information about the metric relations is contained in the midpoint order, as may be seen from the following argument.

The rank order of the stimuli on a J scale generates a necessary partial order on the order of the midpoints. For example, stimulus A's midpoints are necessarily ranked in the order AB, AC, and AD. Similarly the rank order of B's midpoints is AB, BC, and BD.

---

* The unfolding technique involves the manipulation of sequences of alphabetical symbols, and it is convenient to utilize capital letters rather than lower-case letters for this purpose. Because of the context there is no likelihood of confusion with other aspects of data theory in which some of these symbols are used for other purposes.

The order of the two midpoints BC and AD is not implied, however, by the rank order of the stimuli themselves. In fact it is evident that the order of the midpoints BC and AD is determined by the relative magnitudes of the distances $\overline{AB}$ and $\overline{CD}$ and vice versa. For if A, B, C, and D represent the scale values of four stimuli in order of increasing magnitude and if the midpoint BC precedes AD, then

$$\frac{B+C}{2} < \frac{A+D}{2}, \qquad B + C < A + D, \qquad B - A < D - C$$

and clearly the converse holds.

Therefore, the midpoint order BC, AD implies and is implied by the fact that the distance between C and D is greater than that between A and B, that is, BC, $AD \Leftrightarrow \overline{CD} > \overline{AB}$ in shorthand form. Of course AD, $BC \Leftrightarrow \overline{AB} > \overline{CD}$. So the necessary partial order on the midpoints generated by the simple order on the stimuli is converted into a simple order on the midpoints by the metric relations.

The one-to-one correspondence between the rank order of the midpoints and the set of I scale preference orderings permits reasoning from the set of preference orderings to the metric relations on the J scale. To illustrate these correspondences, the two cases (where the midpoint AD precedes BC and vice versa) are presented here in detail. Consider the J scale in Fig. 5.2.

All individuals to the left of the midpoint AB are in interval I_1 and have the same preference ordering or I scale, $A\,B\,C\,D$. Individuals in interval I_2 are nearer stimulus B than A but in all other respects are like those in I_1, so their preference ordering is $B\,A\,C\,D$. Individuals in interval I_3 differ from those in I_2 only in being nearer C than A, having crossed the AC midpoint, so their preference ordering on this and only this pair is reversed from that of I_2, giving $B\,C\,A\,D$. Continuing along the J scale, as each midpoint is crossed an *adjacent* pair of stimuli in an I scale is reversed to yield the next I scale, until finally in I_7 the preference ordering obtained is $D\,C\,B\,A$. The complete set of I scales generated by such a J scale is given in Table 5.1.

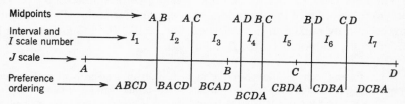

Fig. 5.2 J scale of four stimuli with $\overline{AB} > \overline{CD}$.

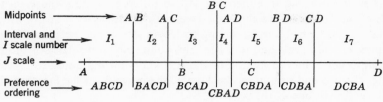

Fig. 5.3   *J* scale of four stimuli with $\overline{CD} > \overline{AB}$.

Now consider the *J* scale in Fig. 5.3, in which $\overline{CD} > \overline{AB}$. Note that it differs from the preceding one only in the order of the midpoints *BC* and *AD*, which bound the interval I_4. Consequently the *I* scales in these two sets are respectively identical except for I_4, which in the one instance is *B C D A* and in the other *C B A D*.

Table 5.1   The Set of *I*
Scales for Fig. 5.2

I Scale and Interval No.	Preference Ordering
I_1	*A B C D*
I_2	*B A C D*
I_3	*B C A D*
I_4	*B C D A*
I_5	*C B D A*
I_6	*C D B A*
I_7	*D C B A*

With four stimuli on a *J* scale there are only two possible midpoint orders, as illustrated, and depending on which of the two sets of *I* scales comprises the data, the corresponding inference as to which ordered metric scale obtains may be made.

It is simple enough, given a *J* scale, to generate the corresponding set of *I* scales. The problem of interest to the experimenter is the converse one of constructing the *J* scale from a set of *I* scales.

3. ANALYTICAL PROCEDURE

Our concern here, given a set of *I* scales, is how to extract all the information about the *J* scale. The assumption is made that nothing is already known about the *J* scale, and the questions to be asked of the data are: Does a unidimensional *J* scale solution exist? If so, what is it?

The first step is to determine the rank order of the stimuli on the *J* scale. It may be determined immediately. If an *I* scale is a folded *J* scale, the I scale must end in either one of two different stimuli, those on the ends of the J scale. If we think of the J scale as a length of string with a series of knots on it corresponding to where the stimuli are, and then if we pick up the J scale and fold it at any point, the knot furthest from the folding point is inevitably one of the end knots on the unfolded J scale. Hence the two end stimuli on the J scale are known from the fact that all I scales end with one of them.

Knowing the two end stimuli on the J scale, there must be two and only two I scales beginning with one of these and ending with the other, and these two I scales must be mirror images of each other. No other pairs of I scales which are mirror images are admissible in a set of I scales generated by a unidimensional J scale. The occurrence of more than one pair of mirror image I scales among the set of observed I scales is sufficient to permit rejection of the hypothesis of a unidimensional latent attribute common to that set of subjects with respect to their preferences for that set of stimuli, according to this model.

Table 5.1 provides a simple example: Each I scale ends in either A or D; there exists an I scale beginning with A and ending with D and another beginning with D and ending with A; and these two I scales are mirror images of each other. Either of these two I scales may be taken to be the rank order of the stimuli on the J scale, and this immediately permits advantage to be taken of the order of the alphabet in labeling the stimuli. The J scale recovered at the level of an ordinal scale is spoken of as a *qualitative* J scale to distinguish it from the *quantitative* J scale which is at least an ordered metric scale.

Having the qualitative J scale, the next step is to determine the order of the I scales within the set in order to determine the order of the midpoints and hence arrive at metric information. The I scales in a set are correctly ordered only if in passing from one to the next a pair of adjacent stimuli is reversed in order. When the I scales are arranged in order, as in Table 5.1, then as we pass from I_1 to I_7 and follow the ordinal position of any one stimulus from I scale to I scale, we find that the stimulus moves completely to the left before it moves to the right. Another way to visualize it is to think of an individual walking along a J scale from left to right and to note that he approaches each stimulus before going away from it. This, of course, may be recognized as the condition given for the parallelogram pattern of 'order k/n' to the effect that the integers in a column must decrease strictly monotonically to 1 and then increase.

The order of the I scales immediately yields the order in which the midpoints have been crossed on the J scale, because crossing a midpoint reverses a pair of adjacent stimuli in an I scale. Since the first two midpoints crossed must always be AB and AC, the second and third I scales are known merely from the qualitative J scale. Similarly the last three I scales are always known because the last two midpoints are given by the qualitative J scale. The order of the midpoints which fall between the first two and last two, however, is not implied by the qualitative J scale, and hence this order provides new information. The new information is metric information.

4. A HYPOTHETICAL EXAMPLE

In this example it is assumed that the hypothetical preference ordering of each of a number of individuals has been obtained for $n = 6$ stimuli and it is assumed that (1) there are no more than $\binom{n}{2} + 1 = 16$ distinct I scales; (2) the I scales all end in either one of only two different stimuli, labeled A and F; (3) an I scale exists which begins with A and ends with F and which is the mirror image of one beginning with F and ending with A; and (4) that the remainder of the I scales may be ordered between the first and last in such a manner as to satisfy the condition that an adjacent pair of stimuli is reversed in adjacent I scales. A set of I scales which satisfy all these conditions is illustrated in Table 5.2.

Table 5.2   A Set of I Scales for $n = 6$

I Scale No.	I Scale	Lower Bounding Midpoints	Metric Information
1	$A\ B\ C\ D\ E\ F$		
2	$B\ A\ C\ D\ E\ F$	AB	
3	$B\ C\ A\ D\ E\ F$	AC	
4	$B\ C\ D\ A\ E\ F$	AD	$AD,\ BC \Rightarrow \overline{AB} > \overline{CD}$
5	$C\ B\ D\ A\ E\ F$	BC	
6	$C\ D\ B\ A\ E\ F$	BD	$BD,\ AE \Rightarrow \overline{DE} > \overline{AB}$
7	$C\ D\ B\ E\ A\ F$	AE	
8	$C\ D\ E\ B\ A\ F$	BE	$BE,\ AF \Rightarrow \overline{EF} > \overline{AB}$
9	$C\ D\ E\ B\ F\ A$	AF	$BE,\ CD \Rightarrow \overline{BC} > \overline{DE}$
10	$D\ C\ E\ B\ F\ A$	CD	$AF,\ CD \Rightarrow \overline{AC} > \overline{DF}$
11	$D\ C\ E\ F\ B\ A$	BF	$CD,\ BF \Rightarrow \overline{DF} > \overline{BC}$
12	$D\ E\ C\ F\ B\ A$	CE	$BF,\ CE \Rightarrow \overline{BC} > \overline{EF}$
13	$E\ D\ C\ F\ B\ A$	DE	$DE,\ CF \Rightarrow \overline{EF} > \overline{CD}$
14	$E\ D\ F\ C\ B\ A$	CF	
15	$E\ F\ D\ C\ B\ A$	DF	
16	$F\ E\ D\ C\ B\ A$	EF	

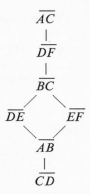

Fig. 5.4   Metric relations from Table 5.2.

The extreme left-hand column of Table 5.2 contains the I scale numbers which are the ordinal numbers of the successive segments of the J scale generated by the successive midpoints. To each such segment there corresponds a unique preference ordering, given in the second column. The midpoint that bounds the lower (left) end of each segment is given in the third column of the table. The last column contains the metric information implied by the order of midpoints. The metric information may be compactly portrayed by a partial order as shown in Fig. 5.4, in which most of the metric relations implicit* in the rank order of the stimuli on the J scale are omitted for clarity.

Given the simple order of the midpoints on a J scale the question arises as to which pairs of midpoints should be looked at to arrive most economically at the significant metric relations. A glance at the third and fourth columns of Table 5.2 reveals that only some pairs of midpoints were used to read off metric relations; the basis for this selection is as follows. Those order relations between midpoints which are implied merely by the *order of the stimuli* on the J scale have no metric information. Thus the fact that the midpoint CD comes before the midpoint EF is of no interest, as it contains no new information. The order relations between midpoints which are of interest because they contain new information are those order relations not implied by the qualitative J scale. Those pairs of midpoints whose order relations are of interest are readily identified from the following considerations.

Besides defining a midpoint, a pair of stimuli are also the end points of a segment of the J scale. If the terminal points of one segment are both

---

* By "implicit" metric relations is meant the fact that knowing that three points are in the order A, B, C on the real line implies that $\overline{AC} = \overline{AB} + \overline{BC}$ and hence is larger than either alone.

contained within the terminal points of another segment, then the order of their respective midpoints contains metric information. For example, the segment of the continuum defined by the stimuli C and E is completely contained within the segment defined by B and F, and hence the order of the midpoints BF and CE contains metric information (see Fig. 5.5).

We might say that if one pair of stimuli *envelops* another on the J scale the order of their respective midpoints has metric implications. Such pairs of midpoints as BE and CF represent segments which overlap each other, but one of the segments does not envelop the other, and hence the order of their midpoints is implied by the rank order of the terminal points of their respective segments of the J scale.

Although the order of midpoints between enveloping pairs of stimuli contains metric information, not all such pairs of midpoints need to be examined, because some of them contain metric information implicit in the metric information contained in other pairs. In Table 5.2, for example, we find that the midpoint AE is preceded by both BC and BD. Stimuli A and E envelop B and C and also envelop B and D, so there is metric information in the midpoint order BC, AE and also in the midpoint order BD, AE. If the midpoint BD precedes AE, however, then BC must also, because BC must precede BD. The consequence of this is that the midpoint order BC, AE contains no information beyond that implied by the order BD, AE, as is readily shown. The metric implications are

$$BC, AE \Rightarrow \overline{CE} > \overline{AB}$$
$$BD, AE \Rightarrow \overline{DE} > \overline{AB}$$

but
$$\overline{CE} = \overline{CD} + \overline{DE}$$

so
$$\overline{CE} > \overline{DE}$$

and hence $\overline{CE} > \overline{AB}$ may be inferred from the fact that $\overline{DE} > \overline{AB}$. It is sufficient then to compare only the BD and AE midpoints in this instance.

To pick out the critical pairs of midpoints to be examined we begin with the first midpoint and compare it with each successive midpoint in turn unless their order relation is already implied by a prior comparison. An easy way to compare them is to write down the sequence of all the

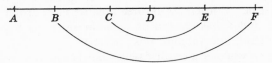

Fig. 5.5 Enveloping pairs of stimuli.

midpoints in order, mark the divisions between sequences of necessary order, and make the comparisons between the midpoint at the end of each sequence and the midpoint at the beginning of each following sequence unless the relation is already implied by a prior comparison.

As an illustration, consider the sequence of midpoints from Table 5.2: AB, AC, AD, $\cdot BC$, BD, $\cdot AE$, BE, $\cdot AF$, $\cdot CD$, $\cdot BF$, $\cdot CE$, DE, $\cdot CF$, DF, EF. The first three midpoints in this sequence are in their necessary order, but a dot has been placed between AD and BC because their order is not implied by the natural partial order. Similarly, each of the following dots indicates the interruption of a natural sequence. The end of the first natural sequence, AD, should then be compared with the beginning of all the other sequences unless the relation is implied either by their natural order or by a prior comparison. Thus AD is compared with BC but no other comparison with AD is necessary because the order relation of AD with the beginning of each of the other sequences, AE, AF, CD, BF, CE, and CF, is given as an immediate consequence of their natural order.

The end of the next natural sequence, BD, is compared with AE only, for the same reason. The end of the third natural sequence, BE, is compared with AF and also with CD but no other comparisons are necessary. This procedure is continued through all the natural sequences and usually eliminates a considerable amount of unnecessary work, especially as n increases.

Another "computing" short-cut is the following procedure for reading off metric implications from the order of two midpoints. Write the two midpoints in order, as, for example, CD, BF from Table 5.2, then form two new pairs by associating in order the first member of each midpoint and the second member of each, giving in this case CB and DF. One of these new pairs will always be in alphabetical order and the other not (if there are metric implications) and the pair in alphabetical order bounds the greater distance. So here the pair DF is in alphabetical order and the pair CB is not; hence $\overline{DF} > \overline{BC}$.

A useful procedure to determine the I scale number of an isolated I scale, when the qualitative J scale is known, is to count the number of midpoints crossed and add *one*. For example, to determine the I scale number of the preference ordering $D\,C\,E\,B\,F\,A$, we note that A has crossed five (all) of its midpoints because there are five stimuli to the left of A in the I scale; B has crossed three because there are three stimuli to the left of it; and C has crossed one, making nine in all. Hence this I scale is in the tenth interval and so is I scale 10.

The answer to whether a set of I scales satisfies all the conditions for a common J scale requires an examination of the metric information to see if a partial order such as that of Fig. 5.4 can be constructed, which is only possible if the metric relations are transitive. If there are metric relations which are intransitive, obviously a necessary condition for a common quantitative J scale is violated.

As a case in point, suppose that I scale 13 in Table 5.2 is $D E F C B A$. All the conditions for a common qualitative J scale are met, but not those for a common quantitative J scale. If I scale 13 is $D E F C B A$, the midpoint CF precedes DE because the midpoint CF has been crossed but

Table 5.3 Relation between Number of Quantitative and Qualitative J Scales

n	Number of Distinct Qualitative J Scales	Upper Bound to the Number of Distinct Quantitative J Scales for Each Qualitative One
4	12	2
5	60	12
6	360	286
7	2,520	33,592
8	20,160	23,178,840

DE has not. But $CF, DE \Rightarrow \overline{CD} > \overline{EF}$, which contradicts the transitivity of the metric relations $\overline{EF} > \overline{AB}$ and $\overline{AB} > \overline{CD}$ implied by the order of other midpoints in the sequence. This makes clear the fact that constructing a J scale is a matter of piecing it together from different individuals, and the inference that a common quantitative J scale exists is sustained only if all these pieces of information are mutually compatible.

Although no adequate statistical procedures for testing significance levels are available it is suggested by the following figures that common qualitative and quantitative J scales are not likely by chance. For n stimuli the number of distinct qualitative J scales is $n!/2$ and an upper limit* to the number of distinct quantitative J scales for *each* qualitative J scale is given by Thrall (1952) as

$$\frac{\left[\dfrac{n(n-1)}{2}\right]!\,(n-2)!\,(n-3)!\cdots 2!}{(2n-3)!\,(2n-5)!\cdots 3!}$$

The values of this function for the first few values of n are given in Table 5.3.

---

* This is an upper limit because it includes instances with an intransitive metric, as illustrated, which may occur for $n \geq 6$.

The product of the two numbers in a row of this table gives, for that value of n, an upper limit to the number of sets of I scales which will unfold and yield a quantitative J scale. Such sets of I scales are called *admissible* sets. Now the total number of *possible* sets of I scales is

$$\left(\begin{matrix} n! \\ \binom{n}{2} + 1 \end{matrix} \right)$$

which for $n = 4$ is 346,104 and for $n = 5$ is on the order of 1.16×10^{18}. As n increases, this figure for the number of possible sets of I scales continues to increase more rapidly than does the number of admissible sets. The ratio of the number of admissible to the number of possible sets is the probability that a set of $\binom{n}{2} + 1$ I scales chosen at random will satisfy a common quantitative J scale. For $n = 4$ this probability is on the order of 6.9×10^{-5} and decreases as n increases, so the probability of getting a set of I scales by chance which will unfold to yield a common quantitative J scale is infinitesimal.

5. A REAL EXAMPLE

This example is from the grade expectations of the students in an introductory course in mathematical psychology given in the fall of 1959, the summer of 1960, and the fall of 1961. This is an elementary course required of all the graduate students in psychology at The University of Michigan who are *not* planning to do any further work in mathematical psychology. Students interested in mathematical psychology skip this course and begin with a more technical one.

Early in the course the students were given a dittoed form containing all pair comparisons of the letter grades A+, A, A−, B+, B, B−, C+, in a random sequence. For each pair comparison the students were instructed to indicate which grade was more nearly the grade they expected to get in the course. Each subject then tabulated his own pair comparisons and, if they were transitive, converted them into a rank order I scale. At this point in the course no instruction had been given pertaining to scaling theory in general or to the unfolding technique in particular.

The I scales obtained are presented in Table 5.4 in which the letter grades from A+ to C+ are represented respectively by the symbols A to G in order. The total number of subjects is 62, of whom 58 gave transitive I scales and 4 did not. These latter are indicated in the table with the intransitive stimuli contained in parentheses. These stimuli in parentheses are to be read clockwise, that is, the I scale $(F^E G) D\ C\ B\ A$ indicates that this subject "preferred" F to E, E to G, and G to F.

When the I scale number for each I scale is determined we find, among others, that I scale numbers 5, 9, and 10 are represented by more than one I scale. This reflects the fact that the order of midpoints and hence the metric relations are not the same for the subjects with different I scales with the same I scale number. It is clear that the same qualitative J scale satisfies all subjects which is, of course, not surprising, but what would be of psychological interest is the metric relations.

Table 5.4 Data on Grade Expectations

I Scale Number	I Scales and Their Respective Frequencies of Occurrence			
1	$A B C D E F G$ 6			
2	$B A C D E F G$ 4			
3	$B C A D E F G$ 5			
4	$C B A D E F G$ 1			
5	$C B D A E F G$ 8	$B C D E A F G$ 2		
6	$C B D E A F G$ 2	$C D B A E F G$ 1		
7	$C D B E A F G$ 2	$C B D E F A G$ 1	$D C B A E F G$ 1	
8	$C D B E F A G$ 0			
9	$D C B E F A G$ 2	$C D B E F G A$ 1	$D C E B A F G$ 1	
10	$D C E B F A G$ 5	$D C B E F G A$ 1	$D E C B A F G$ 2	$C D (B^E F) G A$ 1
11	$D C E F B A G$ 1			
12	$D E C F B A G$ 1	$D E C B F G A$ 1		
13				
14	$D E F C B G A$ 1			
15		$E D C F G B A$ 1		
16	$E D F C G B A$ 2	$E D F (B^C G) A$ 1	$F E D C B A G$ 1	
17	$E D F G C B A$ 3			
18	$E F D G C B A$ 0			
19		$F (E^D G) C B A$ 1		
20	$F E G D C B A$ 2			
21	$F G E D C B A$ 0	$(F^E G) D C B A$ 1		
22	$G F E D C B A$ 0			

Although no single set of metric relations satisfies all the I scales, we might be interested in that particular set of metric relations which satisfies the most data. This is not too difficult to determine by trial and error, and the I scales listed in the first column are the ones which satisfy this dominant quantitative J scale. Because this set of I scales is incomplete, some metric information is unobtainable, but such information as can be obtained is given in Table 5.5. The metric information is presented in the form of a partial order in Fig. 5.6 with the symbols converted back into the letter grades.

Three psychological inferences may be drawn from the metric relations pictured in Fig. 5.6. (1) The spread of the A's on this subjective scale is

**Table 5.5 Midpoint Order and Metric Implications
for Data in Table 5.4**

Midpoint Order*	Metric Implications
AB	
AC	
BC	$BC, AD \Rightarrow \overline{CD} > \overline{AB}$
AD	
AE	$AE, BD \Rightarrow \overline{AB} > \overline{DE}$
BD	
AF	$BD, AF \Rightarrow \overline{DF} > \overline{AB}$
CD	$CD, BE \Rightarrow \overline{DE} > \overline{BC}$
BE	$CD, AG \Rightarrow \overline{DG} > \overline{AC}$
BF	$BF, CE \Rightarrow \overline{BC} > \overline{EF}$
CE	$BF, AG \Rightarrow \overline{FG} > \overline{AB}$
CF, AG	$CF, DE \Rightarrow \overline{CD} > \overline{EF}$
DE, BG	$CF, BG \Rightarrow \overline{FG} > \overline{BC}$
CG	$AG, DE \Rightarrow \overline{AD} > \overline{EG}$
DF, EF, DG	$DE, CG \Rightarrow \overline{EG} > \overline{CD}$
BG	$CG, DF \Rightarrow \overline{CD} > \overline{FG}$
FG	

* The weak ordering is due to the incompleteness
of the set of I scales.

greater than the spread of the B's, that is, $\overline{A+A-} > \overline{B+B-}$. (2) Changing the letter grade has more psychological effect than adding a plus or minus, i.e., the largest single interval is from A— to B+ and the second largest is from B— to C+. (3) Adding a plus to a grade adds a larger psychological increment than a minus subtracts, that is, $\overline{A+A} > \overline{AA-}$ and $\overline{B+B} > \overline{BB-}$.

The metric relations and hence these inferences drawn from them are a composite from the relations between the different I scales. There is no evidence from an analysis of preferential choice data that all these metric relations hold for all individuals on the J scale. Furthermore, we do not know the extent to which generalizations may be drawn. It would not be surprising if these same individuals had a different metric for their grade expectations in another course or even a different metric for this same course after a midterm examination. In fact such research might contribute to the literature on motivation and level of aspiration.

The results of this analysis are quite typical, in my experience, of the findings in an unfolding analysis of the data generated by what is

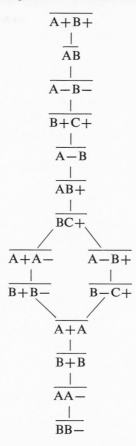

Fig. 5.6 Metric relations for grade expectations.

presumed to be a unidimensional J scale on a priori grounds—a dominant J scale may usually be found satisfying a majority of the cases, 72% in this instance; there will be some I scales which require a different metric and others which even require a different qualitative J scale; and there will be some intransitive I scales (if the data are collected by unreplicated pair comparisons).

Whether the cases that do not fit the dominant J scale merely represent unreliability in the data or are significant departures can best be determined by using more powerful methods of collecting the data in the first place, for example, methods with redundancy which permit control of inconsistency. An instance of this is contained in the Coombs-Pruitt study (see Chapter 6) of variance and skewness preferences.

6. CONVERSION OF AN ORDERED METRIC SCALE TO AN INTERVAL SCALE

It is very useful to have some reasonable method by which numbers can be assigned to the stimuli on a J scale so as to satisfy the given metric relations. There are, of course, an infinite number of such representations, so we have the further problem of selecting a particular one. Frank Goode* of The University of Michigan has developed and explored a method for assigning a reasonable set of numerical scale values to stimuli on an ordered metric scale. His method has potentialities beyond the use made of it here.

We begin with a partial order on the distances between stimuli. The general idea is to set the smallest interval equal to some positive but unknown quantity Δ_1, and successively larger distances are obtained by introducing additional unknown positive Δ's. A matrix equation may be set up which expresses the scale values of the stimuli as a linear function of these Δ's. Values assigned to the Δ's lead to interval scale values for the ordered metric scale.

We illustrate the procedure with an example worked out in detail.† We take the partial order on the metric for grade expectations, as given in Fig. 5.6, and construct an interval scale. For the purpose we restore the letters from A to G in alphabetical order to represent the grades from A+ to C+.

The procedure is best carried out using a worksheet, as illustrated in Table 5.6, for this problem. On the left-hand side of the table is the partial order as recoded from Fig. 5.6. Each element in the partial order of distances is made up of one or more contiguous single intervals, and this relation is indicated in the second column of the worksheet. The rest of the worksheet indicates the sequence of steps in working out a solution for this particular case, the little arrows indicating footnotes to the table.

Beginning at the bottom of the partial order we see that $\overline{EF}$ is the smallest interval, and it is, of course, a single interval. We set it equal to some positive but unknown quantity, Δ_1. The distance $\overline{BC}$ is the next largest, so it is as great as Δ_1 plus some positive unknown quantity Δ_2. By similar reasoning, $\overline{DE}$ is equal to $\Delta_1 + \Delta_2 + \Delta_3$ and $\overline{AB}$ is equal to $\Delta_1 + \Delta_2 + \Delta_3 + \Delta_4$.

At this point the partial order is seen to divide. Both $\overline{DF}$ and $\overline{FG}$ are larger than $\overline{AB}$ but are themselves not comparable. We may proceed by

---

* Personal communication, 1957. His work is still in progress.

† A simple version of the method is illustrated in Section 4 of Chapter 17.

$$\overline{AD} = \overline{AB} + \overline{BC} + \overline{CD} = 2\Delta_2 + \Delta_3 + 3\Delta_4 + 2\Delta_5 + \Delta_6 = 4\Delta_2 + 2\Delta_3 + 2\Delta_4 + \Delta_6 + 4\Delta_7 + 3\Delta_8$$

$$-\overline{BE} = \overline{BC} + \overline{CD} + \overline{DE} = 2\Delta_2 + \Delta_3 + 2\Delta_4 + \Delta_5 + \Delta_6 + \Delta_7 = 4\Delta_2 + 2\Delta_3 + \Delta_4 + \Delta_6 + 4\Delta_7 + 3\Delta_8$$

$$-\overline{CF} = \overline{CD} + \overline{DE} + \overline{EF} = 2\Delta_2 + \Delta_3 + 2\Delta_4 + \Delta_5 + \Delta_6 = 3\Delta_2 + 2\Delta_3 + \Delta_4 + \Delta_6 + 4\Delta_7 + 3\Delta_8$$

$$-\overline{DG} = \overline{DE} + \overline{EF} + \overline{FG} = 2\Delta_2 + \Delta_3 + 3\Delta_4 + 2\Delta_5 = 3\Delta_2 + 2\Delta_3 + \Delta_4 + \Delta_6 + 3\Delta_7 + 3\Delta_8$$

$$-\overline{CE} = \overline{CD} + \overline{DE} = 2\Delta_2 + \Delta_3 + 2\Delta_4 + 2\Delta_5 = 3\Delta_2 + 2\Delta_3 + \Delta_4 + \Delta_6 + 3\Delta_7 + 2\Delta_8$$

$$-\overline{BD} = \overline{BC} + \overline{CD} = 2\Delta_2 + \Delta_3 + 2\Delta_4 + \Delta_5 = 3\Delta_2 + \Delta_3 + \Delta_4 + \Delta_6 + 3\Delta_7 + 2\Delta_8$$

$$-\overline{EG} = \overline{EF} + \overline{FG} = 2\Delta_2 + \Delta_3 + \Delta_4 + \Delta_5 + \Delta_6 = 2\Delta_2 + \Delta_3 + \Delta_4 + \Delta_6 + 2\Delta_7 + 2\Delta_8$$

$$= 2\Delta_2 + \Delta_3 + \Delta_4 = 2\Delta_2 + \Delta_3 + \Delta_4 + \Delta_6 + 2\Delta_7 + \Delta_8$$

$$= \Delta_2 + \Delta_3 = 2\Delta_2 + \Delta_3 + \Delta_4 + \Delta_6 + \Delta_7 + \Delta_8$$

$$-\overline{AB} = \overline{AB} = \Delta_1 + \Delta_2 + \Delta_3 + \Delta_4 = \Delta_2 + \Delta_3 + \Delta_4 + 2\Delta_7 + 2\Delta_8$$

$$-\overline{DE} = \overline{DE} = \Delta_1 + \Delta_2 + \Delta_3 = \Delta_2 + \Delta_3 + \Delta_4 + 2\Delta_7 + 2\Delta_8$$

$$-\overline{BC} = \overline{BC} = \Delta_1 + \Delta_2 = \Delta_2 + \Delta_3 + \Delta_4 + 2\Delta_7 + \Delta_8$$

$$-\overline{EF} = \overline{EF} = \Delta_1 = \Delta_4 + \Delta_5 = \Delta_2 + \Delta_3 + \Delta_4 + \Delta_7 + \Delta_8$$

$$= \Delta_2 + \Delta_3 + \Delta_7 + \Delta_8$$

$$= \Delta_2 + \Delta_7 + \Delta_8$$

$$= \Delta_7 + \Delta_8$$

Tree diagram:

```
   EG ────── CD ────────── FG
     \                      /
      AC                 DF
          AB ── DE ── BC ── EF
```

(1) $\overline{DF} > \overline{AB} \Rightarrow \Delta_1 > \Delta_4$, so (2) let $\Delta_1 = \Delta_4 + \Delta_5$.   (3) $\overline{EG} > \overline{AC} \Rightarrow \overline{EG} = \overline{AC} + \Delta_6$.   (4) $\overline{FG} = \overline{EG} - \overline{EF}$.
(5) $\overline{EG} > \overline{CD} \Rightarrow \Delta_4 + \Delta_5 > \Delta_7$, so (6) let $\Delta_4 + \Delta_5 = \Delta_7 + \Delta_8$.

going up either branch of the partial order, and it makes no difference in the ultimate outcome, although one usually turns out to be easier than the other. We note that one side of the partial order involves $\overline{DF}$, a sum of two single intervals, and the other involves $\overline{FG}$, a single interval alone, and we suspect that it is generally easier in the long run to take first the side of the partial order that involves sums of single intervals. This is what we do here.

The distance $\overline{DF} = \overline{DE} + \overline{EF}$ and hence is equal to $2\Delta_1 + \Delta_2 + \Delta_3$. However, $\overline{DF} > \overline{AB}$, so $2\Delta_1 + \Delta_2 + \Delta_3 > \Delta_1 + \Delta_2 + \Delta_3 + \Delta_4$, and hence

$$\Delta_1 > \Delta_4$$

So we let

$$\Delta_1 = \Delta_4 + \Delta_5$$

In the next column of the worksheet, then, we rewrite $\overline{DF}$ as $\Delta_2 + \Delta_3 + 2\Delta_4 + 2\Delta_5$, and for all the elements of the partial order below $\overline{DF}$ we substitute $\Delta_4 + \Delta_5$ for Δ_1. We then continue up the partial order:

$$\overline{AC} = \overline{AB} + \overline{BC}$$
$$= (\Delta_2 + \Delta_3 + 2\Delta_4 + \Delta_5) + (\Delta_2 + \Delta_4 + \Delta_5)$$
$$= 2\Delta_2 + \Delta_3 + 3\Delta_4 + 2\Delta_5$$

and we must check to see that $\overline{AC}$ is at least as great as $\overline{DF}$ for every component and greater in at least one, that is, $\overline{AC}$, as a vector, must dominate $\overline{DF}$. To illustrate the procedure in detail, the coefficients of the components for $\overline{AC}$ are, in order, (2, 1, 3, 2) and for $\overline{DF}$, (1, 1, 2, 2). We see then that $\overline{AC}$ will necessarily be greater than $\overline{DF}$, as required by the partial order.

We come next to $\overline{EG}$, which must be larger than $\overline{AC}$, so we add a positive but unknown quantity Δ_6 to $\overline{AC}$ and we obtain $\overline{EG} = 2\Delta_2 + \Delta_3 + 3\Delta_4 + 2\Delta_5 + \Delta_6$.

At this point we go back and check the other branch of the partial order that leads up to $\overline{EG}$, that is, $\overline{FG} < \overline{CD} < \overline{EG}$. Because $\overline{EG} = \overline{EF} + \overline{FG}$, we may solve for $\overline{FG}$ directly by subtracting $\overline{EF} = \Delta_4 + \Delta_5$ from $\overline{EG}$; and we obtain $\overline{FG} = 2\Delta_2 + \Delta_3 + 2\Delta_4 + \Delta_5 + \Delta_6$. We must check, then, to make sure that $\overline{FG}$ dominates $\overline{AB}$. The $\overline{FG}$ vector is (2, 1, 2, 1, 1) and the $\overline{AB}$ vector is (1, 1, 2, 1, 0), so dominance is assured.

The partial order shows $\overline{CD}$ to be greater than $\overline{FG}$, so we introduce a new positive quantity Δ_7 and set $\overline{CD} = \overline{FG} + \Delta_7$. But because

$$\overline{EG} > \overline{CD}$$

$$2\Delta_2 + \Delta_3 + 3\Delta_4 + 2\Delta_5 + \Delta_6 > 2\Delta_2 + \Delta_3 + 2\Delta_4 + \Delta_5 + \Delta_6 + \Delta_7$$

and hence

$$\Delta_4 + \Delta_5 > \Delta_7$$

So we let

$$\Delta_4 + \Delta_5 = \Delta_7 + \Delta_8$$

and now Δ_5 may be eliminated from all expressions.

We may then continue up the partial order, which is now a simple procedure because all the remaining elements of the partial order are compounded from elements we have already determined. For example,

Table 5.7 Worksheet for Scale Values of Stimuli

Successive Single Intervals		In Vector Notation	Scale Values of Stimuli
$\overline{AB} = \Delta_2 + \Delta_3 + \Delta_4$	$+ \ \Delta_7 + \Delta_8$	$(1, 1, 1, 0, 1, 1)$	$B = (1, 1, 1, 0, 1, 1)$
$\overline{BC} = \Delta_2$	$+ \ \Delta_7 + \Delta_8$	$(1, 0, 0, 0, 1, 1)$	$C = (2, 1, 1, 0, 2, 2)$
$\overline{CD} = 2\Delta_2 + \Delta_3 + \Delta_4 + \Delta_6 + 2\Delta_7 + \Delta_8$		$(2, 1, 1, 1, 2, 1)$	$D = (4, 2, 2, 1, 4, 3)$
$\overline{DE} = \Delta_2 + \Delta_3$	$+ \ \Delta_7 + \Delta_8$	$(1, 1, 0, 0, 1, 1)$	$E = (5, 3, 2, 1, 5, 4)$
$\overline{EF} =$	$+ \ \Delta_7 + \Delta_8$	$(0, 0, 0, 0, 1, 1)$	$F = (5, 3, 2, 1, 6, 5)$
$\overline{FG} = 2\Delta_2 + \Delta_3 + \Delta_4 + \Delta_6 + \ \Delta_7 + \Delta_8$		$(2, 1, 1, 1, 1, 1)$	$G = (7, 4, 3, 2, 7, 6)$

the next element in the partial order is $\overline{BD} = \overline{BC} + \overline{CD}$. This process is completed to insure that no further changes are necessary in the vector components of the single intervals.

The next step is to obtain the scale values of the stimuli in terms of the Δ's. We arbitrarily assign the scale value of zero to stimulus A, then the scale value of stimulus $B = \overline{AB}$, $C = \overline{AB} + \overline{BC}$, and so on. A worksheet for this is shown in Table 5.7. On the left-hand column of the worksheet are the successive single intervals expressed in terms of the final Δ components, $(\Delta_2, \Delta_3, \Delta_4, \Delta_6, \Delta_7, \Delta_8)$, as determined in Table 5.6. The middle column of the worksheet expresses the single intervals in vector notation. The column on the right of the worksheet contains the scale values of the stimuli in vector notation, each succeeding stimulus vector being a component-wise sum of the single interval vectors.

The scale values of the stimuli in the last column of Table 5.7 may be written as the successive rows of a matrix, V, which postmultiplied by a column vector Δ generates a new column vector S, which is a feasible solution to the scale values of the stimuli, with stimulus A at zero.

The column vector Δ may be any set of numbers greater than zero. One simple solution is the "equal Δ" solution for which the column vector Δ is a unit vector. This solution is

$$\begin{bmatrix} 1 & 1 & 1 & 0 & 1 & 1 \\ 2 & 1 & 1 & 0 & 2 & 2 \\ 4 & 2 & 2 & 1 & 4 & 3 \\ 5 & 3 & 2 & 1 & 5 & 4 \\ 5 & 3 & 2 & 1 & 6 & 5 \\ 7 & 4 & 3 & 2 & 7 & 6 \end{bmatrix} \begin{bmatrix} 1 \\ 1 \\ 1 \\ 1 \\ 1 \\ 1 \end{bmatrix} = \begin{bmatrix} 5 \\ 8 \\ 16 \\ 20 \\ 22 \\ 29 \end{bmatrix}$$

$$V \qquad\qquad \Delta \; = \; S \qquad\qquad (5\cdot4)$$

An infinite number of solutions satisfy the same metric relations, of course, and this "equal Δ" solution is only one. We face the problem, then, of selecting a particular scale from among these many. The following comments are offered to assist in resolving this problem.

Table 5.8   General Expressions and Scale Values for the Stimuli

Stimuli

	A	B	C	D	E	F	G
General Expression	0	$\Delta_1 + 3$	$2\Delta_1 + 4$	$3\Delta_1 + 10$	$4\Delta_1 + 12$	$5\Delta_1 + 12$	$6\Delta_1 + 17$
$\Delta_1 = 2$	0	5	8	16	20	22	29
$\Delta_1 = 10$	0	13	24	40	52	62	77

It will be recalled that $\Delta_1 = \Delta_7 + \Delta_8$ and is the smallest single interval. We may keep all the other Δ's constant and equal to *one* while we set $\Delta_8 > 1$ (that is, $\Delta_1 > 2$). This is equivalent to keeping certain *differences* between distances constant while we otherwise stretch or contract the scale, and has the corresponding effect of depressing or dramatizing the differences in distances between stimuli.

An easy way to see what is going on is to write a new expression for each scale value in terms of Δ_1 as the only unknown. Thus, the scale value of stimulus B, where $\Delta_1 = \Delta_7 + \Delta_8$ and all other Δ's are equal to *one*, is

$$B = \Delta_2 + \Delta_3 + \Delta_4 + \Delta_7 + \Delta_8 = \Delta_1 + \Delta_2 + \Delta_3 + \Delta_4 = \Delta_1 + 3$$

and the scale value of C is

$$C = 2\Delta_2 + \Delta_3 + \Delta_4 + 2\Delta_7 + 2\Delta_8$$
$$= 2\Delta_1 + 2\Delta_2 + \Delta_3 + \Delta_4 = 2\Delta_1 + 4$$

A table of these values for all the stimuli, with Δ_1 fixed at the value 2 and at the value 10, is contained in Table 5.8.

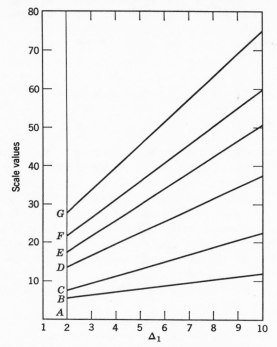

Fig. 5.7 Stimulus scale values as a function of Δ_1.

The effect of increasing the value of Δ_1 is to depress the differences in metric relations, that is, to tend toward equally spaced stimuli. This may be seen in Fig. 5.7; setting a value for Δ_1 defines a vertical line with Δ_1 as its intercept on the abscissa. Its intersections with the fan of straight lines determine the respective scale values of the stimuli. The two vertical lines for $\Delta_1 = 2$ and $\Delta_1 = 10$ are shown in the figure. We note that *when Δ_1 is given its minimal integral value* ($\Delta_1 = 2$) the scale obtained is the same as that obtained with the equal Δ assumption in equation 5.4.

Frank Goode did this for a given ordered metric scale, with the first and last stimuli fixed at the ends of the scale, and allowing the various Δ's to take on all admissible integral values. Fixed boundaries were obtained for each stimulus, with unimodal distributions of admissible scale values for each stimulus. He observed that if the Δ's are all set equal, the scale values of the several stimuli are all close to the modes of their respective distributions.

It is not yet known under what conditions it would be true in general that the equal Δ assumption would yield such a "highly representative" scale. It is correct in this instance, and it is certainly a simple and practical method. It also is a solution in which the metric relations are highly dramatized, as is evidenced by Fig. 5.7.

Abelson and Tukey (1959) have developed another method for converting nonmetric information into metric information. Abelson says of their method, in a personal communication, that it is rather too complex to apply often by hand to the ordered metric situation with more than five or six stimuli. On the other hand, he actually did apply it to the ordered metric scale of seven stimuli in this example. Their method seeks that set of scale values for which the minimum correlation (squared) with whatever the true values might be is a maximum. This method insures that the best will be done in the worst possible circumstances.

The set of scale values Abelson obtained, rounded off to a simple integer scale, is as follows, for stimuli A to G respectively: 0, 5, 10, 29, 34, 39, 58. The squared maximin correlation is .959, which means that the "true" scale, no matter how different it is so long as it satisfies the same ordered metric relations, must correlate at least .98 with this one.

He computed the minimum squared correlation for the $\Delta_1 = 2$ solution with constant Δ, as obtained by this simple version of Frank Goode's method, and the value obtained is .944. Hence this solution must correlate at least .97 with the true one.

There is little difference, of course, between .98 and .97, but, on the other hand, there is no assurance that Goode's method with a constant Δ assumption would always do almost as well as the Abelson-Tukey method. The great advantage of the constant Δ method is its simplicity.

Shepard (1962) also has a method, but it is impossible to perform without a computer. There are also uniqueness problems with small n, and partial orders give trouble because they must be converted into simple orders. His method, however, is much more than a method for assigning numbers to stimuli on an ordered metric scale; rather, it is a method for multidimensional scaling of QIVa data, but the method is at least potentially applicable to this simpler case.

The fact that seems to be emerging from these developments is that ordered metric information places rather strong constraints on the admissible scale representations and that there are reasonable criteria for choosing among them. I expect a convention of constructing a numerical representation of ordered metric data to develop very rapidly.

7. METRIC ANALYSIS OF 'ORDER k/n' DATA

The analytical procedure that has been described and illustrated in some detail has been applied to data in which each I scale is a complete rank order of all n stimuli, that is, 'order k/n' where $k = n - 1$.

Modifications of the procedure required for $3 \leq k < n - 1$ are obvious and immediate. These incomplete I scales have the first k elements ordered with the remaining elements unordered in the tail of each I scale. The principal difference lies in the fact that there is less information about the order of midpoints since the ordering is a weak ordering, and hence less information about metric than could have been obtained from complete I scales.

8. WIDTH OF I SCALE INTERVALS

We have seen that the distribution of individuals' ideal points on a J scale is divided into a series of intervals to each of which corresponds a unique I scale. These I scale intervals are generated by the midpoints between stimuli, and hence we may derive information about the relative widths of these I scale intervals from knowledge about the relative distances between stimuli.

Assuming that the J scale is a segment of the real line, we may, with no loss of generality, let the scale be translated so that the first stimulus has the scale value $A = 0$. The scale value, then, of the midpoint between the stimuli at A and B is $\overline{AB}/2$, and the scale value of the midpoint AC is $(\overline{AB} + \overline{BC})/2$. Hence the size of the second I scale interval, which is always bounded by these two midpoints on the left and right respectively, is clearly $\overline{BC}/2$, that is, its width is half the distance between the second and third stimuli. Proceeding in this manner it is very simple to arrive at the metric relations among I scale intervals given the metric relations among stimuli. The scale values of the midpoints among six stimuli on a J scale are given in Table 5.9.

On any particular J scale, the order of the midpoints determines the boundaries of any particular I scale interval, so to illustrate the use of Table 5.9 the grade expectation data of Table 5.4 will be used. For $n = 7$ there are 22 I scale intervals, each of which, except the first and last, is bounded by two successive midpoints. These I scale intervals are listed in Table 5.10 with their bounding midpoints, and the consequent width of the interval obtained by subtracting the scale value of the lower bounding midpoint from the higher bounding midpoint.

A number of interesting relations among the magnitudes of these I scale intervals follow directly from the ordered metric given in Fig. 5.6 for this same J scale. Designating an I scale interval by its corresponding I scale number, the metric relations among the I scale intervals are portrayed in Fig. 5.8, in which the magnitudes of the I scale intervals are related to the magnitudes of the stimulus intervals as given in Fig. 5.6.

Table 5.9 Scale Values of the Midpoints of Six Stimuli

Midpoints	Scale Values
AB	$\overline{AB}/2$
AC	$(\overline{AB} + \overline{BC})/2$
AD	$(\overline{AB} + \overline{BC} + \overline{CD})/2$
AE	$(\overline{AB} + \overline{BC} + \overline{CD} + \overline{DE})/2$
AF	$(\overline{AB} + \overline{BC} + \overline{CD} + \overline{DE} + \overline{EF})/2$
BC	$(2\overline{AB} + \overline{BC})/2$
BD	$(2\overline{AB} + \overline{BC} + \overline{CD})/2$
BE	$(2\overline{AB} + \overline{BC} + \overline{CD} + \overline{DE})/2$
BF	$(2\overline{AB} + \overline{BC} + \overline{CD} + \overline{DE} + \overline{EF})/2$
CD	$(2\overline{AB} + 2\overline{BC} + \overline{CD})/2$
CE	$(2\overline{AB} + 2\overline{BC} + \overline{CD} + \overline{DE})/2$
CF	$(2\overline{AB} + 2\overline{BC} + \overline{CD} + \overline{DE} + \overline{EF})/2$
DE	$(2\overline{AB} + 2\overline{BC} + 2\overline{CD} + \overline{DE})/2$
DF	$(2\overline{AB} + 2\overline{BC} + 2\overline{CD} + \overline{DE} + \overline{EF})/2$
EF	$(2\overline{AB} + 2\overline{BC} + 2\overline{CD} + 2\overline{DE} + \overline{EF})/2$

Table 5.10 Width of I Scale Intervals for the Dominant J Scale of Table 5.4

I Scale No.	Lower Midpoint	Higher Midpoint	Width of I Scale Interval
1	—	AB	Indeterminate
2	AB	AC	$\overline{BC}/2$
3	AC	BC	$\overline{AB}/2$
4	BC	AD	$(\overline{BD} - \overline{AC})/2 = (\overline{CD} - \overline{AB})/2$
5	AD	AE	$\overline{DE}/2$
6	AE	BD	$(\overline{AD} - \overline{BE})/2 = (\overline{AB} - \overline{DE})/2$
7	BD	AF	$(\overline{FB} - \overline{AD})/2 = (\overline{DF} - \overline{AB})/2$
8	AF	CD	$(\overline{AD} - \overline{CF})/2 = (\overline{AC} - \overline{DF})/2$
9	CD	BE	$(\overline{CE} - \overline{BD})/2 = (\overline{DE} - \overline{BC})/2$
10	BE	BF	$\overline{EF}/2$
11	BF	CE	$(\overline{BE} - \overline{CF})/2 = (\overline{BC} - \overline{EF})/2$
12–20			Indeterminate
21	EG	FG	$\overline{EF}/2$
22	FG	—	Indeterminate

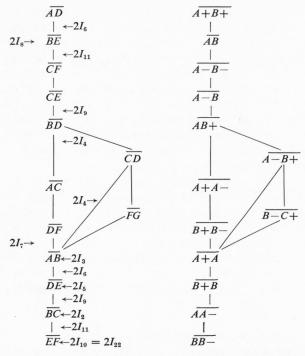

(a) Notation as in Table 5.9   (b) Grade notation restored

Fig. 5.8 Metric relations of I scale intervals.

This figure points up the great differences among the magnitudes of the I scale intervals. I_9, for example, is only half as wide as the difference between the stimulus intervals $\overline{DE}$ and $\overline{BC}$; I_2 is half as wide as the width of $\overline{BC}$; and I_5 is as wide as I_2 and I_9 added together.

The fact that I scale intervals differ so much in width has implications for data collection. The wider an interval the more variability of an ideal point* may be tolerated with the individual still yielding a transitive I scale which folds the J scale. This is evident from the fact that if an individual's ideal point remains in one and the same I scale interval on the J scale throughout all replications, his judgments are completely consistent regardless of how much his ideal may vary within that I scale interval. So the smaller that interval the more sensitive it is to a given amount of inconsistency and the more likely some inconsistency is to lead to intransitive I scales.

* This idea of variability of an ideal point, and of a stimulus point, is important in unfolding theory and is the concern of Section 9, where it is discussed in some detail.

Experimentally independent replications or, in general, a method of collecting data that has redundant information, offers a way of controlling or measuring this inconsistency so that we can work with the stochastically dominant I scales. Unfortunately, not all I scale intervals need the same degree of redundant data, but how much is needed is not known until the data have been collected. It would seem that sequential data collection methods would offer a practical solution to this problem in that pairs of stimuli which are responded to consistently could be dropped earlier than pairs with a higher degree of inconsistency. The danger here, however, is the difficulty of maintaining experimentally independent replications as the repertoire of stimulus pairs diminishes.

Another possible solution to the problem is to drop down in the left-hand column of the searchingness structure to an "order k/n" method somewhat below that of the method of rank order. As pointed out in the chapter on the searchingness structure, this would cut out the heavy accumulation of the more centrally located midpoints, which tends to generate the smaller I scale intervals associated with higher sensitivity to inconsistency. If the data are collected by the method of rank order, we may analyze them as any 'order k' or 'pick k' data at will (for example, see Kamenetzky and Schmidt, 1957).

9. INCONSISTENCY OF PREFERENCES: A TEST OF UNFOLDING THEORY

The best test I have been able to devise, as yet, of the unfolding theory of preferential choice revolves around its implications for the stochastic properties of choice behavior. The usual, "reasonable" assumption is that the more consistent the pairwise choice, the more different the two stimuli, that is, the further apart the stimulus points should be. This corresponds to saying that pairwise probabilities of choice should satisfy strong stochastic transitivity. The condition of strong stochastic transitivity is

$$p(AB) \geq .5, \quad p(BC) \geq .5 \Rightarrow p(AC) \geq \text{maximum } [p(AB), p(BC)]$$

There are two other levels or degrees of stochastic transitivity known as moderate and weak stochastic transitivity. Moderate stochastic transitivity may be defined as

$$p(AB) \geq .5, \quad p(BC) \geq .5 \Rightarrow p(AC) \geq \text{minimum } [p(AB), p(BC)]$$

and weak stochastic transitivity as

$$p(AB) \geq .5, \quad p(BC) \geq .5 \Rightarrow p(AC) \geq .5$$

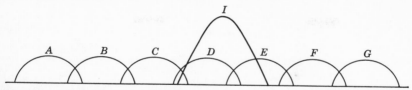

Fig. 5.9 *J* scale with variable stimuli ($A, \ldots, G$) and an individual with a variable ideal (I).

To illustrate these, suppose an individual prefers *A* over *B* 80% of the time and *B* over *C* 70% of the time; then the three levels of stochastic transitivity would require that he prefer *A* over *C* strongly, at least 80% of the time, moderately at least 70%, and weakly at least 50%.

An implication of unfolding theory is that strong stochastic transitivity will not hold in general but that moderate stochastic transitivity will. Indeed, the theory makes more detailed predictions.

The basic idea is that variability of an ideal point affects consistency of choice on certain pairs and not on others, depending on whether the pair of stimuli are on opposite sides of it on the *J* scale or on the same side. Consider an individual on a *J* scale, as in Fig. 5.9, in which each stimulus is represented by a probability distribution as is the individual's ideal. When an individual evaluates any pair of stimuli, let us assume that he chooses an ideal point at random out of the distribution of ideals and also a pair of stimulus points from their respective distributions.

We now introduce a variable called *laterality*. Let the term *unilateral* pair signify a pair of stimuli whose distributions are both on the same side of the *J* scale relative to the distribution of the individual's ideals (for example, *A* and *B* or *F* and *G*) and let the term *bilateral* pair signify a pair of stimuli whose distributions are on opposite sides of the distribution of ideals (for example, *B* and *F* or *A* and *G*). The maximum range of the effect of laterality is found in the comparison between the unilateral and the bilateral conditions; stimuli whose distributions significantly overlap the distribution of ideals have an effect that falls between these two extremes.

It is evident from the unfolding theory of preferential choice* that the inconsistency of the individual's preference on a unilateral pair of stimuli will be unaffected by the variability of the ideal; only the overlap of the stimulus distributions will generate inconsistency. In the case of bilateral pairs, however, the varying ideal will contribute to the inconsistency of judgment. This may be visualized more clearly with the aid of Fig. 5.10.

---

* A formal development is presented in Chapter 23. See also Zinnes (1959) and Coombs, Greenberg, and Zinnes (1961).

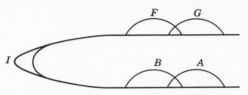

Fig. 5.10   The *J* scale of Fig. 5.9 partially folded.

In each replication on a pair a folding point is chosen out of the *I* distribution, and a pair of stimulus points out of their respective distributions. It is evident that if a pair of points is drawn at random, one from stimulus *A*'s distribution and one from *B*'s (a unilateral pair of stimuli), then the one that falls nearer an ideal point drawn from the *I* distribution is a matter independent of the variability of the ideal, and only dependent on the relation between the stimulus distributions. The same would be true for any other unilateral pair of stimuli such as *F* and *G*.

In contrast to unilateral pairs of stimuli, consider the case of a bilateral pair, such as *A* and *F*. Here the variability of the ideal is a very significant factor in the inconsistency of judgment. If from one replication to the next the ideal shifts toward the *A* distribution, it necessarily shifts away from the *F* distribution and of course vice versa. Using Fig. 5.10 we may picture the two bilateral distributions rolling over each other in opposite directions as the ideal varies, whereas a pair of unilateral distributions slides back and forth locked tightly together. We would predict, therefore, that the variance of an ideal would enter into the inconsistency of judgment on a bilateral pair of stimuli and have no effect on the inconsistency of judgment on a unilateral pair.

An experimental study of this predicted effect of laterality (Coombs, 1958) was carried out at the University of Amsterdam using 12 shades of gray, presenting all sets of 4 stimuli and asking the subject to rank order them from the best representative of what he meant by the label "gray" to the poorest ('order 3/4' from the searchingness structure). These instructions were used to try to make sure that the subjects' ideals would be in the middle of the *J* scale in order to provide a reasonable number of both unilateral and bilateral pairs for each subject.

The 495 presentations of 4 stimuli at a time were sequentially arranged to insure reasonable control of any sequential or trend effect in the course of the experiment. The complete set of 495 presentations was run on each of 2 successive nights with the same 4 subjects. Each subject, of course, is a completely separate experiment, as the *J* scales and the distributions of ideals may be expected to be different for each of them.

Each pair of stimuli occurs in $\binom{n-2}{2}$ presentations, in this case

$\binom{10}{2} = 45$; so the 2 evenings yield a total of 90 replications on a pair. These are obtained by decomposing the rank order on each presentation according to the decomposition model discussed in Chapter 2. These 90 replications, however, do not have the channel capacity of 90 experimentally independent pairwise replications. An estimate of their channel capacity compared with pairwise presentations may be obtained as follows.

A presentation of 4 stimuli may be rank ordered in $4! = 24$ different ways. The number of bits of channel capacity, assuming equal probabilities of the alternative orderings, is $\log 24 = 4.58$ bits per presentation. Decomposing the rank order into 6 pair comparisons and allotting these 4.58 bits over them equally, on the average yields 0.763 bits of channel capacity on each pair. Experimentally independent replications accumulate the 0.763 bits on each pair, and so for 90 replications we have 68.67 bits on each pair.

We do not know whether channel capacity has any bearing on our interest here, that is, reliability of the estimates of the probabilities, but it is the best guess we can make at present. Undoubtedly some probabilities are estimated with better reliability than others but we do not know enough to provide more than a reasonable estimate of the number of degrees of freedom on which each estimate is based. For each individual we arrive at a pairwise probability for each pair of stimuli based on the 90 replications which is estimated to have a reliability equivalent to about 69 experimentally independent replications.

A pairwise probability is based on the number of times each member of a pair was ranked higher, in accordance with the decomposition model discussed in Chapter 2. The data for each individual may be placed in a square data matrix with each stimulus identifying a corresponding row and column and each cell indicating the percentage of times the row stimulus was preferred to the column stimulus. Table 5.11 contains the data of the four subjects in the original report. The identification of the rows and columns of this matrix is different for each subject and corresponds to the rank order of the stimuli on each subject's I scale given below the table. The labels of the stimuli are in alphabetical order from the lightest gray to the darkest.

The decomposition model used to arrive at the pairwise percentages does not impose even weak stochastic transitivity, as pointed out in the discussion of the model, so it is interesting to observe whether the data for each of the 4 subjects indicate that his preferences are essentially transitive underneath the fluctuations.

A necessary and sufficient condition for weak stochastic transitivity is

Table 5.11   Inconsistency of Preferences for Each of the Four Subjects

	1	2	3	4	5	6	7	8	9	10	11	12
1		52 51 / 70 53	67 59 / 91 63	72 61 / 87 66	64 68 / 74 86	76 84 / 80 79	91 88 / 94 97	89 94 / 93 92	99 90 / 100 94	100 94 / 100 97	100 100 / 100 99	100 100 / 100 99
2			83 52 / 68 62	83 77 / 78 62	74 96 / 52 87	80 97 / 73 87	98 96 / 94 90	99 82 / 99 96	100 100 / 97 99	100 99 / 100 93	100 100 / 100 99	100 100 / 100 100
3				50 86 / 53 54	67 93 / 51 63	64 99 / 60 68	92 100 / 89 94	97 87 / 87 80	97 100 / 100 89	100 100 / 93 97	100 100 / 99 99	100 100 / 100 97
4					61 93 / 53 64	63 98 / 57 61	90 99 / 93 98	100 80 / 83 80	91 100 / 100 82	100 100 / 97 100	100 98 / 100 100	100 100 / 100 99
5						68 96 / 63 51	50 99 / 76 60	72 67 / 97 93	100 100 / 99 99	99 99 / 99 87	100 100 / 100 96	100 100 / 100 99
6							54 59 / 80 71	66 50 / 92 94	97 88 / 88 99	99 99 / 100 84	100 50 / 100 96	100 100 / 100 99
7								92 56 / 54 57	94 93 / 90 63	100 99 / 82 94	100 96 / 89 100	100 100 / 100 91
8									83 53 / 64 93	100 67 / 94 68	94 99 / 99 93	99 99 / 100 100
9										83 92 / 52 58	99 93 / 76 84	100 100 / 100 100
10											62 97 / 97 100	97 100 / 100 73
11												100 80 / 99 53

Note: The upper left-hand corner of each cell is subject 1; the upper right, subject 2; the lower left, subject 3; and the lower right, subject 4. The labels of the rows and columns from 1 to 12 are as follows for each of the four subjects: Subject 1: *GFEDHICBJAKL.* Subject 2: *JIHGFEDKCBLA.* Subject 3: *FGEDHICJBKLA.* Subject 4: *GFHIDEJCBKLA.*

that a permutation of the data matrix exists such that all the entries on one side of the diagonal are at least 50%. The order of the rows (or columns) then corresponds to the stochastically dominant I scale.* It is an interesting observation that such a permutation of the data matrix existed for each of the four data matrices. In the case of subject 1 the I scale was found in this way to be $G\ F\ E\ D\ H\ I\ C\ B\ J\ A\ K\ L$, which is the J scale folded in the neighborhood of stimulus G.

The effect of laterality on the inconsistency of preferences should be revealed in the testing of strong stochastic transitivity versus moderate stochastic transitivity, which may be done by examining all the ordered triples of stimuli embedded in the I scale ordering. The unfolding theory leads to a distinction between different kinds of triples of stimuli and correspondingly different predictions as to whether strong stochastic transitivity or moderate stochastic transitivity can be expected to be satisfied.

Ordered triples from the I scale of subject 1 are used here to illustrate the three different kinds of triples. The three kinds of triples are defined as (1) *unilateral triples*, in which all three stimuli are unilateral to the distribution of the ideal, for example, D, C, and B; I, J, and K; (2) *bilateral adjacent triples*, in which two stimuli are from one side of the J scale and are adjacent in the ordered triple, as embedded in the I scale order, and the third is from the other side of the J scale and is either first or last in the ordered triple, for example, H, I, and B; C, J, and K; (3) *bilateral split triples*, in which two stimuli are from one side of the J scale and are separated in their I scale rank order by the stimulus from the other side, for example, C, J, and A; H, B, and K.

These three kinds of triples are illustrated in Fig. 5.11.

Since the laterality effect does not enter into unilateral triples, the

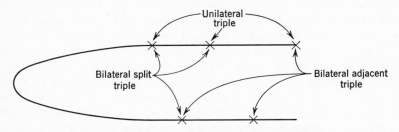

Fig. 5.11 Illustrating the three kinds of stimulus triples.

* If the distributions of the stimuli and of the ideals are all symmetric distributions, and the stimulus distributions have constant variance, then the stochastically dominant I scale gives the rank order of the means of the stimulus distributions in order of increasing distance from the mean of the distribution of ideals.

Table 5.12   Effect of Laterality on Strong Stochastic Transitivity*

	Subject 1		Subject 2		Subject 3		Subject 4	
	SST Sat.	SST Not Sat.	SST Sat.	SST Not Sat.	SST Sat.	SST Not Sat.	SST Sat.	SST Not Sat.
Bilateral pairs bounding bilateral adjacent triples	9	11	2	10	6	13	1	19
Unilateral pairs bounding unilateral triples	11	1	19	2	10	2	7	5
p	$<.01$		$<.001$		$<.01$		$<.001$	

* The figures reported in this table are different from those reported in Coombs (1958). David Cross, working on a replication study for me, reanalyzed the previous data and found some egregious errors due entirely to me. Fortunately, the corrected figures even more strongly supported the conclusions drawn from the original analysis.

variance of the ideal being irrelevant, we would expect strong stochastic transitivity to be satisfied by such triples to a statistically significant degree.

For bilateral adjacent triples (for example, H, I, and B in the I scale of subject 1) the first and last members of the triple always constitute a bilateral pair (for example, H and B), and there is always a unilateral pair embedded between them (for example, H and I). The inconsistency on the bilateral pair tends to be of a higher degree (that is, closer to 50%), than the inconsistency on the unilateral pair, because the latter inconsistency is not affected by the varying ideal. Hence the laterality effect would tend to counteract the effect of distance and should lead to a significant degree of violation of strong stochastic transitivity. Moderate stochastic transitivity, however, should be satisfied to a statistically significant degree.

Finally, for bilateral split triples (for example, C, J, and A in subject 1's I scale) the effect is just the opposite. The unilateral pair (C and A) consists of the first and third elements of the ordered triple and there are two bilateral pairs embedded between them (C and J, and J and A) so the effect of laterality is added to the effect of psychological distance, and violation of strong stochastic transitivity for such triples should almost never occur.

For each of the four subjects, the number of bilateral pairs bounding bilateral adjacent triples and the number of unilateral pairs bounding unilateral triples which satisfied and which failed to satisfy strong stochastic transitivity were counted, leaving out the first two stimuli on the I scale. These two stimuli are omitted because the location of the ideal point with respect to them is uncertain and hence the determination of laterality is uncertain too. The results are presented in Table 5.12 with χ^2 tests of significance.

It is clear that a very substantial proportion of bilateral adjacent triples fails to satisfy the condition of strong stochastic transitivity in contrast to the case for unilateral triples.

A more detailed analysis of some interest is the number of triples of each kind satisfying the different levels of stochastic transitivity. The results for each subject are reported separately in Table 5.13.

Triples of stimuli embedded in an I scale are not independent, so a suitable statistical test does not seem to be available. The qualitative

Table 5.13   Number of the Various Kinds of Triples Satisfying the Three Different Levels of Stochastic Transitivity

| | | Highest Level of Stochastic Transitivity Satisfied | | | |
		SST	MST	WST	Total Number of Triples
$S\,1$ Triples	bilateral adjacent	48	16	2	66
	unilateral	19	0	1	20
	bilateral split	34	0	0	34
$S\,2$ Triples	bilateral adjacent	16	19	5	40
	unilateral	54	2	0	56
	bilateral split	24	0	0	24
$S\,3$ Triples	bilateral adjacent	32	28	2	62
	unilateral	18	2	0	20
	bilateral split	38	0	0	38
$S\,4$ Triples	bilateral adjacent	14	48	0	62
	unilateral	12	8	0	20
	bilateral split	38	0	0	38

results, however, are clearly very close to those predicted by unfolding theory: that bilateral adjacent triples would violate strong stochastic transitivity to a substantial degree but not violate moderate stochastic transitivity; that unilateral triples would not substantially violate strong stochastic transitivity; that bilateral split triples would rarely, if ever, violate strong stochastic transitivity.

One further layer of analysis remains to be pursued. Unfolding theory not only predicts that a substantial number of bilateral adjacent triples will violate strong stochastic transitivity, but that when it occurs the violation will be of a particular kind, as follows. Each bilateral adjacent triple is bounded by a bilateral pair and so has another bilateral pair and a unilateral pair in between.

Consider, for example, the triple *HIB*, embedded in that order in subject 1's *I* scale. The pair *HB* is a bilateral pair with the pair *HI*, a unilateral pair, and the pair *IB*, a bilateral pair, in between. If such a triple violates strong stochastic transitivity, this should occur, according to unfolding theory, because the probability on the bounding bilateral pair, *HB*, is less than the probability on the embedded unilateral pair, *HI*.

We may examine, then, those bilateral adjacent triples in each subject's *I* scale which violate strong stochastic transitivity and see if the violation is of the particular kind predicted by the theory. The results are as follows:

(1) For subject 1 there is one triple, *DCJ*, which violates strong stochastic transitivity in a manner contrary to the theory: *D* is preferred over *C* 90% of the time, *C* over *J* 94%, *D* over *J* 91%. The situation may be portrayed as follows:

$$\overbrace{D_{.90}C_{.94}J}^{.91}$$

Clearly strong stochastic transitivity is violated, but the theory says that this violation should occur because the probability on the bounding bilateral pair, *DJ*, is less than that on the embedded unilateral pair, *DC*, that is, .91 is greater than .90, contrary to unfolding theory.

The corresponding analyses for the other three subjects may be summarized briefly.

(2) For subject 2 there are two such triples:

$$\overbrace{G_{.93}F_{1.00}L}^{.98}$$ and .98 is greater than .93

$$\overbrace{C_{.92}B_{.97}L}^{.93}$$ and .93 is greater than .92

(3) For subject 3 there are three such triples:

$$\overset{.93}{\overbrace{E_{.53}D_{.97}K}} \quad \text{and} \quad .93 \text{ is greater than } .53$$

$$\overset{.76}{\overbrace{H_{.63}I_{.80}C}} \quad \text{and} \quad .76 \text{ is greater than } .63$$

$$\overset{.99}{\overbrace{E_{.53}D_{1.00}L}} \quad \text{and} \quad .99 \text{ is greater than } .53$$

(4) For subject 4 there are two such triples:

$$\overset{.61}{\overbrace{I_{.64}D_{.51}E}} \quad \text{and} \quad .61 \text{ is greater than } .51$$

$$\overset{.60}{\overbrace{D_{.51}E_{.71}J}} \quad \text{and} \quad .60 \text{ is greater than } .51$$

Taken all together we have 8 instances of triples that do not conform to prediction plus an *additional* 9 which only satisfy weak stochastic transitivity, making a total of 17 triples out of the total of 480, about 3.5%; and this is a penetration into the rather fine structure of the data. The evidence for the laterality effect predicted by unfolding theory is quite strong.

Luce (1959) has criticized this experiment on the grounds that the determination of the pairwise probabilities is based on the intermediate step involving the decomposition model of Chapter 2, and alternative decomposition models are conceivable. This legitimate criticism motivated me to conduct a replication study* in which pairwise probabilities were determined by replication of pairs directly. The results of the previous study were confirmed for each of the two subjects run (see Table 5.14). Subject B was highly inconsistent, as was subject 4 in the original experiment.

A study involving pairwise presentations of gambles is reported by Coombs and Pruitt (1961) in which the effect of laterality is again evident. This was a study of the psychophysics of gambling in which gambles differing only in variance or only in skewness (odds) were presented. On the average, about 25% of all triples of bets failed to satisfy strong stochastic transitivity.

---

* This study was carried out by Sally Sperling, with the assistance at various times of David Cross, Percival Tomlinson, Clint Fink, and John Dwyer. See Chapter 2, Section 1 for a description of the study and a report of additional results.

**Table 5.14   Replication Study of Effect of Laterality
on Strong Stochastic Transitivity**

	Subject A		Subject B	
	SST Sat.	SST Not Sat.	SST Sat.	SST Not Sat.
Bilateral pairs bounding bilateral adjacent triples	5	12	6	18
Unilateral pairs bounding unilateral triples	22	6	10	8
p	$< .005$		$< .05$	

In the theoretical analysis of the effect of laterality at the beginning of this section the assumption was made that an individual chose *one and only one* ideal point from his distribution of ideals when he evaluated a *pair* of stimulus points. Such an assumption appears gratuitous and ad hoc and demands supporting evidence. There is certainly no a priori ground for such an assumption as opposed to assuming that an individual chooses a new ideal point with each stimulus point. Two lines of evidence support the former assumption. The first lies in the fact that if the latter assumption were true, the laterality effect would not exist; and it apparently does, as predicted by the assumption of a single ideal point for a pair of stimuli.

The second line of evidence lies in a further analysis of this experimental data, which has not previously been reported. It will be recalled that in this experiment the stimuli were presented in sets of four at a time, not pairwise, and there is evidence for the stability of an ideal point during the interval the individual responded to the entire presentation. The relevant data are the individual's responses to those sets of four stimuli in which two of the stimuli are from distributions on one side of the individual's distribution of ideal points and the other two stimuli are from the other side, schematically illustrated in Fig. 5.12, in which stimuli 1 and 2 are from one side and stimuli 3 and 4 are from the other side and the individual's distribution of ideal points is on the "bend" of the J scale.

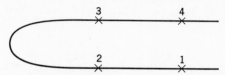

Fig. 5.12   Presentations used to test stability of an ideal point.

Of interest in such sets of four is the individual's ordering on the pair of stimuli 1 and 4 in the figure in relation to his ordering on the stimuli 2 and 3. If the individual's ideal point is relatively stable when responding to such sets of four stimuli, then if he is nearer stimulus 2 than stimulus 3, according to his preference ordering, he should, in general, tend to be nearer stimulus 1 than stimulus 4. Similarly, if he prefers stimulus 3 over stimulus 2, there should be a significant tendency to prefer stimulus 4 over stimulus 1. Such an effect, of course, is moderated by the other factors involved in making his choice but should be evident statistically over a large sample of such sets of four.

Table 5.15   Test of the Stability of the Ideal Point Within a Presentation

	Subject 1		Subject 2		Subject 3		Subject 4	
	$2 > 3$	$3 > 2$	$2 > 3$	$3 > 2$	$2 > 3$	$3 > 2$	$2 > 3$	$3 > 2$
$1 > 4$	237	31	69	26	122	107	116	37
$4 > 1$	146	83	62	53	79	141	116	158
p	$<.001$		$<.01$		$<.001$		$<.001$	

The results for each of the four subjects separately are presented in Table 5.15 in which the numbers in the cells are the number of presentations in which the preference orderings are as specified for that row and column. The p's reported are for χ^2 tests of significance.

There is evidence here, then, that the individual's ideal point was stable during the interval in which he responded to an entire presentation of four stimuli. This is the second line of evidence that supports the assumption that his ideal point is stable in pairwise presentations.

The significance of the effect of laterality on preferential choice lies in the application of such models as Thurstone's model for comparative judgment to convert the pairwise probabilities into measures of psychological distance in order to scale the stimuli. Pairwise probabilities of preferential choice should not be put in a common data matrix and transformed into psychological distance. Instead two separate data matrices are called for, one for probabilities for unilateral pairs and one for probabilities for bilateral pairs. The transformation of the probabilities into psychological distance must then take account of the effect of laterality on the inconsistency on bilateral pairs. These implications for Thurstone's model for comparative judgment are developed in Chapter 23.

Another implication in the effect of laterality should be pointed out. There is a certain a priori, intuitive reasonableness to the idea that individuals nearer the center of a J scale may hold their position less firmly, feel less intense about their position, and perhaps be more readily influenced or induced to change. These conclusions may be correct in themselves but they do not follow merely from greater inconsistency in judgment on the part of the more centrally located subjects. According to the laterality effect, subjects with the same variability of their ideal point will *behave* more inconsistently (whatever their susceptibility to influence and so forth) the nearer the distribution (of their ideal) is to the middle of the J scale. This is simply a consequence of their having to make a larger number of bilateral comparisons than do individuals more extreme than they are on the J scale.

10. USE OF EXPECTED MATRICES

The effect of laterality on inconsistency of QIa data is the reason that the method of expected matrices was rejected (see Chapter 2) as a data reduction model for such data and a decomposition model preferred.

Table 5.16 Dependence of Total Vote Count Methods on Other Alternatives

(a)	C	B	G	Total Vote Count		(b)	C	B	G	H	Total Vote Count
C	—	90	80	170		C	—	90	80	90	260
B	10	—	60	70		B	10	—	60	75	145
G	20	40	—	60		G	20	40	—	90	150
						H	10	25	10	—	45

The expected matrix is based on all presentations in which each stimulus occurs. If a new stimulus were added it would be unilateral to some and bilateral to others, and because of the laterality effect it could reverse the ordering on some pairs of stimuli. Consider the hypothetical data in Table 5.16.

If only stimuli C, B, and G were used with 100 replications on each pair, data such as those in Table 5.16a would be completely reasonable if C and B were a unilateral pair with G bilateral to them. Stochastically, the preference ordering is $C\,B\,G$ and the total vote count yields the same ordering. Table 5.16b introduces a new stimulus, H, which is bilateral to C and B and unilateral to G. The additional data in this table are again compatible with these conditions. We now observe that the stochastic ordering is $C\,B\,G\,H$, but the ordering by total vote count is $C\,G\,B\,H$. Introducing the stimulus H, generally unpreferred to the others (sometimes called an irrelevant alternative), has reversed the ordering of B and G from their stochastic ordering. H, being unilateral to G, has contributed substantially to its vote count, whereas, being bilateral to B, it has contributed less to B's vote.

A final example may be drawn from the laterality experiment reported earlier. These data were collected on $n = 12$, 'order 3/4,' with 2 replications, so the expected matrix may be readily computed and is given in Table 5.17. In 2 replications of the 495 presentations of 4 stimuli at a time, each stimulus would have appeared 330 times, and for perfectly consistent behavior would have been ranked first, second, third, and

Table 5.17 Expected Matrix for 'Order 3/4', $n = 12$, with Two Replications, as in the Amsterdam Study of Laterality

Rank Order in Presen- tation	Rank Order on I Scale											
	1	2	3	4	5	6	7	8	9	10	11	12
1	330	240	168	112	70	40	20	8	2	0	0	0
2	0	90	144	168	168	150	120	84	48	18	0	0
3	0	0	18	48	84	120	150	168	168	144	90	0
4	0	0	0	2	8	20	40	70	112	168	240	330
Expected total vote count	990	900	810	720	630	540	450	360	270	180	90	0

fourth the number of times given in the table according to its rank in the I scale. The bottom row of the table gives the number of times each stimulus would have been preferred to other stimuli, that is, the total vote count. This is obtained for each column by multiplying the number of first rank votes by 3, the number of second rank votes by 2, and the number of third rank votes by 1 and adding the products together.

The observed matrix can be tabulated for each subject; as an illustration, the observed matrix for subject 4 (the most inconsistent of all the four subjects) is given in Table 5.18 with the columns ordered according to the stochastic dominance of the stimuli determined from the decomposition model.

If the ordering on the I scale were based on the total vote count, stimuli D and E would be interchanged in order and so would stimuli A and L. Interestingly enough the interchange of D and E would bring this I scale into conformity with the J scale from A to L. As it is, according to weak stochastic transitivity, the ordering DE violates the folded J scale. Stimulus D is preferred to E 51 % of the times, however, and this is not a significant deviation.

Table 5.18 Observed Matrix for Subject 4 in the Amsterdam Experiment on the Laterality Effect

Rank Order in Presentation	Rank Order on I Scale Based on WST											
	G	F	H	I	D	E	J	C	B	K	L	A
1	215	199	165	155	81	86	44	20	8	15	1	1
2	81	98	102	100	149	144	93	111	58	46	6	2
3	27	29	39	55	76	82	130	134	151	129	64	74
4	7	4	24	20	24	18	63	65	113	149	259	253
Total vote count	834	822	738	720	617	628	448	416	291	266	79	81

These data illustrate the fact that the expected matrix (using the total vote count) will not necessarily yield the same ordering as the decomposition model. The effect of laterality leads to the recommendation that the method of expected matrices in general, and the total vote count in particular, is not suitable for arriving at an I scale of preference from redundant data. The I scale obtained by weak stochastic transitivity, on the other hand, has the sense of a maximum likelihood representation of the pairwise probabilities, and, if the distributions of stimuli and of ideals are symmetric distributions and the stimulus distributions have constant variance, the resulting rank order may be characterized as the ordering of the means of the stimulus distributions in order of increasing distance from the mean ideal. It is not apparent what would characterize a rank order obtained from the total vote count.

11. SUMMARY

The unfolding technique may be viewed as an algorithm for the solution of a system of simultaneous inequalities with certain properties and with limited information. The basic concepts of unfolding theory are discussed and the analytical procedure is presented in detail, including several "computing" shortcuts. The procedure is illustrated with the analysis of a hypothetical example and with real data on course grade expectations.

The ordered metric scale obtained by unfolding analysis may be converted into an interval scale by a method being developed by Frank Goode. A simplified version is presented and illustrated by application to the partially ordered metric obtained on the grade expectation study.

The unfolding technique is seen as continuous with, and as an extension of, parallelogram analysis, introducing the further concept of metric relations. The analysis of 'order k/n' data for any $k < n - 1$ is seen as an abbreviated case of the analysis of complete rank order I scales ($k = n - 1$), and the procedures are identical.

Information about distances between stimuli leads to information about the widths of the I scale intervals on the J scale. The manner in which this information may be obtained is worked out in detail. As a matter of theoretical interest it is observed that there is great variability in the widths of I scale intervals, and the implications of this for the selection of a method of collecting data are pointed out.

The unfolding model of preferential choice may be tested through its implications for the stochastic properties of choice behavior. In particular, moderate stochastic transitivity is expected to hold and strong stochastic transitivity is not. In fact, the theory specifies the particular triples of stimuli in which strong stochastic transitivity may be expected to (1) surely hold, (2) hold except for insignificant random departures, and (3) significantly not hold. An experiment is reported in which these implications were tested and supported.

One consequence of these stochastic properties of preferential choice data is that the method of expected matrices is inappropriate for the reduction of redundant preferential choice data. Just how this comes about is discussed and illustrated.

REFERENCES

Abelson, R. P., and J. W. Tukey, 1959, Efficient conversion of non-metric information into metric information, a paper presented at the American Statistical Association Social Sciences Section, December, 1959.

Coombs, C. H., 1958, On the use of inconsistency of preferences in psychological measurement, *J. exp. Psychol.*, **55**, 1–7.

Coombs, C. H., M. Greenberg, and J. Zinnes, 1961, A double law of comparative judgment for the analysis of preferential choice and similarities data, *Psychometrika*, **26**, 165–71.

Coombs, C. H., and D. G. Pruitt, 1961, Some characteristics of choice behavior in risky situations, *Ann. New York Acad. Sci.*, **89**, 784–94.

Kamenetzky, J., and H. Schmidt, 1957, Effects of personal and impersonal refutation of audience counterarguments on attitude change, *J. abnorm. soc. Psychol.*, **54**, 200–03.

Luce, R. D., 1959, *Individual choice behavior*, John Wiley and Sons, New York.

Shepard, R., 1962, The analysis of proximities: multidimensional scaling with an unknown distance function I, *Psychometrika*, **27**, 125–40.

Thrall, R. M., 1952, A combinatorial problem, *Michigan math. J.*, **1**, 81–88.

Zinnes, J., 1959, A probabilistic theory of preferential choice, unpublished Ph.D. dissertation, University of Michigan.

CHAPTER 6

Applications of Unfolding Theory

Since Chapters 3–5 are almost exclusively concerned with technical details and the mechanics of unfolding, several instances in which the theory has been utilized significantly might be instructive. Three such instances are reported here, one in social psychology, one in animal and child behavior, and one in decision processes.

1. RUNKEL'S STUDY OF COGNITIVE SIMILARITY AND COMMUNICATION

This study is reported in detail in Runkel's thesis (1956a) and has been published in abbreviated form (Runkel, 1956b). The basic idea is that the meaning of a communication to an individual is dependent on the communication's fitting into the individual's cognitive structure. Communication is not regarded as a process of exchanging packets of information in which one person merely adds to the belongings of another by giving him information. Rather, it is a kind of guessing game. Each person carries with him his cognitive field as a map of the world. He responds not to the world but to the map. When he receives a communication, the meaning it has is a consequence of how it can be fitted into the map.

The notion is entertained that the efficacy of a communication in imparting what it was intended to impart is dependent on the similarity of the cognitive maps of the communicators. The general hypothesis is that similarity of structure between two cognitive fields increases the efficacy of communication between them.

Runkel offers the following illustration. Suppose that a clothing salesman is communicating with a customer about suits. "Try on this size 40," the salesman suggests. "Not quite right? Well, let's try a size 42. There, that looks just fine, doesn't it? You'd like to try a size 44? All right, here you are. Yes, I agree, this one is a little too large. The size 42 is just right for you."

Let us now ask the customer what the salesman would say about a size 38 or a size 36, or about a size 46 or a size 48. Obviously the customer can predict very well what sizes the salesman would consider too small and too large. The point is that in providing the customer with an attribute in terms of which his judgments are being made, the salesman is giving the customer his opinions about stimuli which are not mentioned explicitly. From a sample of observed stimuli, the customer obtains information about other stimuli which can be judged according to the same attribute as that underlying the judgments among the sampled stimuli. The important qualification here is that both communicators must be making their judgments, and interpreting the communication which occurs, according to the same attribute. If this is the case, each person can make correct predictions about responses the other would make to stimuli not yet communicated about explicitly.

If the customer is purchasing a suit to wear to a costume ball, the order of sizes might not be at all the relevant attribute in terms of which he judges how funny the suits are. If the customer with such a purpose does not let the salesman know what attribute is underlying his judgments, we can only pity the salesman when we imagine the communication which might take place.

If two communicating individuals are not utilizing the same J scale, their respective I scales are said to be noncollinear. Two I scales can sometimes be said to be certainly noncollinear, but unfortunately two I scales may be generated from different J scales and not be detected as noncollinear. Hence the opposite of definitely noncollinear I scales will be called *compatible*.* Certainly all pairs of I scales generated by a common J scale are in this class, but it may also contain some pairs which have been generated from different J scales.

If two individuals form orientations which are compatible, communication from one to the other may transmit information about stimuli in addition to those stimuli which are explicitly mentioned in the communication. The general hypothesis then may be restated as follows: Communication about a sample of stimuli will convey more information about the stimuli from which the sample is drawn if the orientations of the communicators are compatible, and less information if they are noncollinear.

* Runkel uses the term collinear for this class, but it might be taken to say a little more than it should.

The index of compatibility, then, is merely the yes-no dichotomy of whether a pair of I scales, Runkel sometimes calls them orientations, *could* or *could not* be obtained by folding the same qualitative J scale. For the case of five stimuli where the ordering of one of the individuals is used to relabel the stimuli $A\,B\,C\,D\,E$ (not necessarily the J scale ordering), Runkel presents a table of the other orderings of the stimuli

Table 6.1   Noncollinearity Table for Five Stimuli

A B E D C	C E D B A
A C E D B	D A C B E
A D C B E	D A C E B
A D C E B	D A E C B
A D E C B	D B C A E
A E B D C	D B C E A
A E C B D	D B E C A
A E C D B	D E A C B
A E D B C	D E B C A
A E D C B	E A B D C
B A E D C	E A C B D
B C E D A	E A C D B
B D C A E	E A D B C
B D C E A	E A D C B
B D E C A	E B A D C
B E A D C	E B C A D
B E C A D	E B C D A
B E C D A	E B D A C
B E D A C	E B D C A
B E D C A	E C A D B
C A E D B	E C B D A
C B E D A	E C D A B
C E A D B	E C D B A
C E B D A	E D A C B
C E D A B	E D B C A

which would be noncollinear (Table 6.1). To compare two rank orders by means of the table, relabel the stimuli of one order $A\,B\,C\,D\,E$, respectively. Then label each stimulus of the second order with the letter assigned to that stimulus in the first order. If the resulting second rank order appears in Table 6.1, the two given rank orders are noncollinear.

There are fifty orderings in this table; none of them could be obtained by folding any qualitative J scale which also gave the ordering $A\,B\,C\,D\,E$, regardless of the order of the stimuli on the J scale. Not listed are the seventy orderings which are compatible.

Experimental Procedure

Runkel tested his theory by comparing the performance of students who were noncollinear with the instructor, with the performance of students who could be using the same J scale as the instructor. Students in the introductory course in psychology at The University of Michigan were presented with five statements which could be seen as related to the content of the course but which were not assertions of the kind that would be made as part of the course or given in tests. The five statements used were:

(1) The conditions of living in the United States tend to narrow the range of things we are able to do, think about, etc.
(2) People who have a firm moral code are in general better adjusted than those who have not.
(3) The biggest weakness of present day psychology is that it is too theoretical.
(4) Individuals could be changed in practically any way one might wish if the environment could be appropriately controlled.
(5) The strongest influence in shaping a person into the kind of person he becomes is his mother.

The statements were chosen so that it would be possible for one subject to judge them on the basis of one attribute, and for another subject to judge them on the basis of another attribute. With such stimuli, the order of preference given by the subject can reflect the attributes, and his weighting of them, that he brings to the stimulus situation.

In selecting the set of stimuli a long list of statements was first put together in which each statement, in the judgment of the experimenter, seemed interpretable from more than one viewpoint. These statements were then presented to a number of teachers of the introductory course in psychology, and each teacher was asked to state reasons students might have for agreeing or disagreeing with the statements. The objective was to find a set of statements that (1) could be judged on the basis of a variety of reasons or viewpoints and (2) could be discriminated from each other in regard to degree of agreement or disagreement with the statement. It will be seen that the search was for a highly heterogeneous rather than homogeneous set of items. The final selection rested on the judgments of the experimenter and the teachers. (A similar procedure was used in an earlier pilot study done with classes in zoology, which gave results substantially the same as those to be reported here.) According to the theory, any set of stimulus statements which was representative in the sense indicated, and discriminable, would have done as well as the set chosen.

The data were collected by the method of triads ('order 2/3'). The subject was instructed to mark, in each triad, the statement with which he most agreed and the statement with which he least agreed. Data were collected in this way from the classes of five instructors during the first week of the semester, and the identical procedure was repeated during the next to the last week of the semester. The same questionnaire given to the students was also given to each of the five teachers. The preferences of teacher and student among the five statements were analyzed by the decomposition model of Chapter 2, and if weak stochastic transitivity was satisfied rank orders of preference were constructed. Each teacher's rank order was then compared with the rank order given by each of his students by means of the noncollinearity table, and the teacher-student pair was then categorized as compatible or noncollinear.

Since it is asserted that noncollinear pairs of persons should exchange information less efficiently, and since quizzes on the course work can be taken as a measure of the degree to which the student has received the information which the teacher has given, the hypotheses may be stated in operational terms.

Hypothesis 1: Among students who yield reliable rank orders of attitude items pertinent to the course, those who from pretest to posttest maintain rank orders compatible with that of the instructor will receive higher grades on quizzes than those whose rank orders remain noncollinear with that of the instructor.

Hypothesis 2: The difference in quiz grades predicted by hypothesis 1 will be at least as pronounced when only those students are considered whose pretest and posttest rank orders are compatible.

The successive steps in processing the data for analysis were as follows:

(1) Out of seven classes in introductory psychology (taught by five teachers), some students responded only to the pretest or only to the posttest. The number responding to both administrations of the questionnaire was 145.

(2) Of 145 subjects responding at both pretest and posttest, 15 gave responses at one time or the other which were intransitive, indicating that they were "unwilling" to compose the stimuli into a simple order. This left 130.

(3) The 130 transitive subjects gave responses which contained varying degrees of inconsistency. The method 'order 2/3' presents each pair of stimuli to the subject 3 times when 5 stimuli are used. It is therefore possible for the subject to express a preference for stimulus A over stimulus B at one moment and for B over A at a later moment. If a subject is highly inconsistent, there is some ponderable possibility that the set of his responses would have yielded an intransitive relation among the stimuli, had he responded a moment later than he did. In this sense, inconsistency

may be interpreted as "uncertainty" on the part of the subject about putting a simple order on the stimuli. An arbitrary criterion was established at 70% of the paired comparisons. Subjects who gave inconsistencies in 30% or more of the pairs of stimuli were dropped from consideration. This removed 54 subjects, leaving 76. All 5 teachers gave transitive responses containing at least 80% consistency.

(4) Hypothesis 1 makes explicit the next step. Once the noncollinearity index is applied to two rank orders, it provides in itself evidence for change of viewpoint between the two responses. (The term "viewpoint" is used as a synonym for the cognitive structure underlying a rank ordering.) Subjects whose pretest responses were compatible with the teacher's, but whose posttest responses were noncollinear, or vice versa, would have been exposed to one condition and then to the other in some unknown proportion and could not reliably be used to test the hypothesis. Using only those subjects who were compatible at both, reduced the number of subjects by 34 of the 76, leaving 42. At this level of purity, so to speak, the noncollinearity index was judged effective enough to distinguish between the two classes of subjects.

(5) Hypothesis 2 requires a further step in selection. If the noncollinearity index is applied to the subject's own two responses, one at pretest and one at posttest, noncollinearity "pre to post" would imply that the subject has changed his viewpoint in the interim, even though the viewpoints at both times are compatible (or noncollinear) with that of the teacher. Of the 42 students used in testing hypothesis 1, 6 gave noncollinear pre-to-post responses, leaving 36 subjects for the test of hypothesis 2.

Results

Noncollinearity, then, applied in the manner described, is the independent variable for hypotheses 1 and 2. The dependent variable is the mean grade made by the subject on quizzes written and graded by his teacher. Within each of the seven classes, each quiz was given equal weight in the total score. In order to compare quiz grades across classes, z scores were then computed from each class. The z scores were used as data in all further computations.

Dividing the 42 subjects used to test hypothesis 1 into those compatible with the instructor at both pretest and posttest (21 subjects) and those noncollinear with the instructor at both tests (also 21 subjects) the finding is in the proper direction (t test, satisfies $p < .07$).* Statistics pertinent to this result are shown in Table 6.2.

* All probability figures are two-tailed probabilities.

Although this result would make acceptance of this hypothesis dubious by itself, it will be seen that this result is entirely consistent with the result of the test of hypothesis 2, which reaches traditionally acceptable levels of significance.

Hypothesis 2 stated that the difference in quiz grades predicted by hypothesis 1 will be at least as pronounced when only those students are considered whose pretest and posttest rank orders are compatible.

Table 6.2 Difference between z Scores on Quizzes for Students Compatible and Noncollinear with the Instructor

	N	Mean	Range	S. D.
			z Scores	
Compatible with instructor	21	0.51	−1.16 to 2.77	1.18
Noncollinear with instructor	21	−0.15	−2.56 to 1.74	1.18

In the test of hypothesis 2, 17 subjects were in the group compatible with the instructor and 19 were in the noncollinear group. The t test applied to the quiz scores of these two groups yields a significance level beyond .05. Statistics for this test are shown in Table 6.3.

It should be pointed out that the t test is not entirely appropriate for testing these hypotheses. When noncollinearity is indicated, it can be said according to the theory that the subject could not, from any position

Table 6.3 Difference between z Scores on Quizzes for Students Compatible and Noncollinear with the Instructor, and Who Were Compatible with Themselves from Pretest to Posttest

	N	Mean	Range	S. D.
			z Scores	
Compatible with instructor	17	0.60	−1.16 to 2.77	1.38
Noncollinear with instructor	19	−0.25	−2.56 to 1.74	1.17

on the attribute underlying his response, give a rank order of the stimuli which would unfold with that of the other person. When compatibility is indicated, however, the converse cannot be said. Compatibility indicates only that it *cannot be said*, according to the theory, that the subject's viewpoint is noncollinear with that of the other person. It *may or may not* unfold with his. For this reason, a test of covariation, such as product-moment correlation, χ^2, or the t test demands more of the data than can be predicted.

For the reason that a test like the *t* test treats the data more stringently than the prediction undertakes, the probability of .07 given by the *t* test for hypothesis 1 becomes more acceptable. As was suggested earlier, the result of hypothesis 1, when compared to that for hypothesis 2, argues for the correctness of the theoretical derivations, since it was expected on theoretical grounds that the criteria for the noncollinearity index used in hypothesis 2 would give better results than the less stringent criteria used in hypothesis 1.

Tests of Alternative Hypotheses

The question naturally arises whether the results may not be attributable to other differences between the two groups than noncollinearity, such as similarity of student's preferences to the teachers, the existence of an attitude norm, or differences in scholastic aptitude. These are examined in turn here.

It might be argued that compatible persons are those who agree that certain stimuli are most preferable. If this were the case, it might be argued that the theoretical derivations were unnecessary, and that agreement with the teacher on quiz answers was foreshadowed by agreement with the teacher on the choice of the most preferred among the five attitude statements.

The τ statistic, which measures rank order similarity, was used as a measure of the degree to which a student and his teacher chose the same stimulus statements as best. Since the scatter diagrams suggested that both the τ values and the quiz *z* scores were distributed symmetrically, the product-moment correlation was computed between them. The correlation figure was .23 for 34 degrees of freedom, which is far short of a significant value and which Runkel interpreted as giving no evidence that quiz grades followed a preference for the same stimulus statements preferred by the teacher. It is not agreement with the teacher on which statements are the best that makes the difference in quiz grades; rather it is judging the statements according to the *same underlying attribute*, regardless of whether the student agrees with the teacher about the most desirable point on the attribute.

Another possibility to be examined is that noncollinearity with the particular teacher is not the determining factor, but rather noncollinearity with a *normative* ordering of the stimuli. That is, it might not be the interaction of cognitive fields of teacher and student that accounts for the difference in grade achievement, but rather the sensitivity of the student to a more general "cultural" frame of reference, which is merely mediated by the teacher. If this were the case, the data should show a tendency for mutual compatibility among the responses of the teachers. That this is not the case is shown in Table 6.4, which demonstrates that whereas teachers 1 and 2 are compatible, and teachers 3 and 4 are compatible, neither 1 nor 2 is compatible with either 3 or 4. This indicates that at least two noncollinear viewpoints exist among the five teachers.

In any investigation of symbolic responses, the possibility can always be entertained that the performance of the subjects may be related to performance on some measure of symbolic skill such as a test of intelligence, scholastic aptitude, or scholastic achievement. If a relation was

Table 6.4 Noncollinearity of Viewpoint between Pairs of Teachers

2	3	4	5	
Compatible	Noncollinear	Noncollinear	Compatible	1
	Noncollinear	Noncollinear	Compatible	2
		Compatible	Noncollinear	3
			Compatible	4

found between such an ability and the quiz z score, the novelty of the present findings would be weakened to the extent that noncollinearity with the instructor was related to the symbolic skill.

The American Council on Education test of scholastic aptitude seemed an appropriate measure with which to examine this possible relation. ACE scores were available for 100 of the subjects who responded both to pretest and posttest, including 26 of the 36 subjects used in testing hypothesis 2.

A t test was carried out to see whether the noncollinearity index somehow selected groups which differed in ACE scores. No significant difference was obtained between the group compatible with the teacher and the group noncollinear with the teacher in regard to mean ACE score.

We conclude from this result that members of the compatible group were drawn from the same level of ACE scores as members of the noncollinear group. The difference in z scores between the two groups can be attributed to the noncollinearity condition and not to any difference in scholastic aptitude. To check whether scholastic aptitude could in any case have differentiated among quiz grades, Runkel correlated the ACE scores for the 100 available cases with quiz grades, and a positive correlation of .42 was found, which is significant beyond the .05 level. The nonsignificant result of the t test of the 26 cases in the compatibility groups nevertheless argues that the noncollinearity effect on quiz grades was not due to differential selection of scholastic ability.

In brief, it seems clear that the noncollinearity index predicts a difference among quiz grades which is not attributable to the relation between ACE scores and quiz grades, to response to an attitude norm, or to a preference for the stimulus statements preferred by the teacher.

In summary, this study is concerned with the proposition that similarity of structure between two cognitive fields increases the efficacy of communication between them. If the responses of two individuals cannot be interpreted as mediated by the same underlying attribute, the responses are termed "noncollinear"; otherwise, they are termed "compatible." Computation of the index rests on the unfolding technique.

In these terms similarity of cognitive structure is identified with the noncollinearity index, and the following proposition is tested: Where changes in orientations occur as a result of communication, the changes are less pronounced for noncollinear pairs.

This hypothesis was tested by presenting statements to teachers and students concerning the introductory course in psychology in which they interacted for the period of a semester. It was predicted that students noncollinear with the teacher would receive lower grades on quizzes. This prediction was well supported by the results.

The results of this research imply that differences in abilities between communicators and differences in agreement concerning the content of communication must fail to account for certain effects of communication which can be accounted for by the similarity of cognitive structure between the communicators.

An interesting application of Runkel's ideas is reported by Jean-Marie Lemaine (1959) who related preferences of French students among five political parties to their sociometric choices among themselves. A distinction is made between similarity of preferences (correlational) and compatibility of preferences (cognitive similarity). The results suggest that the effect of compatibility of political preferences on sociometric choice is due partly to similarity of political preferences and partly to collinearity.

2. DEMBER-EARL STUDIES OF EXPLORATORY BEHAVIOR

In this series of studies the basic model underlying the unfolding theory is utilized but the unfolding technique itself is not. The problems with which Dember and Earl (1957) are concerned are novelty and complexity as conditions for arousal of the behavior generally labeled exploration, manipulation, or curiosity. These conditions of novelty and complexity are regarded as relations between the individual and his environment which determine what are selected—attended to—as goal stimuli. The key to their idea is the recognition that an important experimental technique for arousing attention is to present an organism with stimulation which is discrepant from the organism's expectation.*

Exploratory behavior is characterized by its variability, as distinct from stereotypy, and it is this variability which is of special interest. They propose that much behavior is a response to change which may be induced by novelty or complexity. Novelty is defined as a discrepancy between percept and expectancy, and complexity is conceptually equivalent to the amount of uncertainty.

These ideas are captured in the language of the theory of data in their conception of the percept as corresponding to the point q_{hij}, the expectancy as c_{hij}, and the discrepancy then as

$$|p_{hij}| = |c_{hij} - q_{hij}|$$

which is taken to be the measure of the novelty of a stimulus. The organism's complexity value corresponds in a generalized sense to his abilities. Just as an individual has at a given time certain abilities, such as arithmetic and spelling, so also he may have an "ability" to appreciate painting, music, and literature.

This complexity value for an individual, however, is conceived of as changing as a result of experience with stimuli which are *slightly* more complex, called *pacer stimuli*. The pacer stimulus has a scale value $c_{hij} + \delta$, where δ is some positive amount. Dember and Earl postulate, then, that an individual will apportion his attention among stimuli in proportion to their similarity to the pacer stimulus, with the modal amount of attention applied to the pacer. As the individual has experience with these pacer stimuli, his complexity value (c_i) increases and hence his pacer stimulus moves ahead of it, changing the attention-arousing property of the stimuli.

Dember, Earl, and Paradise (1957) report an experimental test of these ideas about stimulus complexity. Two experiments are reported on the same apparatus, which consisted of two circular pathways joined to form a figure eight. Both circles were lined with black and white stripes; in one the stripes were vertical and in the other they were horizontal. It was assumed that the latter path would be more monotonous and less complex than the one with vertical stripes.

In the first experiment each rat was allowed about 45 minutes of free exploration in the maze, and a record was kept of his location in the maze. This period was divided into successive 2-minute periods, and for each period it was determined in which of the two paths, "vertical" or "horizontal," the rat spent the most time.

* An excellent elementary account and detailed review of some of the relevant literature is contained in Dember (1960, Chapter 10).

On the first day 13 of the 17 rats showed a preference for the more complex, vertically striped path (for 9 of them the preference was statistically significant) and 4 of them showed a preference for the horizontal striped path (for 2 of them the preference was significant). On the second day, only 1 of the 13 shifted to a preference to the horizontal path whereas all 4 with an initial horizontal preference shifted to a vertical preference. As anticipated, changes in preference were predominantly from the less to the more complex path.

In the second experiment one path was lined with horizontal stripes, as before, and the other was either homogeneously black or white. The striped path was assumed to be more complex. Sixteen naïve animals were run for 60 minutes on each of 5 consecutive days. On the first day 8 of the 16 rats preferred the more complex and all 8 maintained their preference over the succeeding 4 days. Of the other 8, 4 shifted their preference to the more complex path on the second day and the remaining 4 shifted on the third day. No animal regressed to a preference for the less complex path.

Earl (1957) reports experiments with children aged 10–15 in which "complexity" measures for a puzzle-solving task and for dart throwing were related to their preferences for performing them. In the first experiment the subjects constructed block design puzzles and scaled them by one of the cartwheel methods in terms of similarity with respect to "amount of figuring"; their I scale preference ordering was obtained by judging the "amount of fun" involved in working them. In the second experiment the subjects threw darts from three different distances from a target and judged the similarities among these distances in terms of "amount of skill" in one case and "amount of fun" involved in throwing the darts, in the other.

The "amount of figuring" and the "amount of skill" judgments were used to scale the stimuli on an attribute interpreted as "complexity," a J scale. This scale, of course, was different for the different subjects and also changed with time as a subject had experience with the stimuli.

The "amount of fun" judgments yielded an I scale of preference for each subject which was his complexity scale folded. The experimentally naïve subjects responded initially to the simplest stimuli and proceeded through the remaining stimuli in order of increasing complexity. Each subject apportioned his responding among the stimuli (in terms of time or frequency) in inverse proportion to the differences between the complexities of the stimuli and his ideal, or pacer, complexity. Shifts in subjects' preferred complexity were unidirectional toward more complex stimuli.

In summary, this theory of Dember and Earl proposes that a set of alternative stimuli can be ordered on an attribute called complexity and that an individual has an expectancy point on this attribute of complexity analogous to a concept of "ability." Stimuli which are slightly more complex are called "pacer" stimuli. Individuals will prefer and attend to stimuli to a decreasing degree as they depart from the pacer stimulus. The theory further proposes that commerce with the pacer stimulus will cause the expectancy point to move toward the pacer and hence change the attention-arousing value of the stimuli. The theory has led to experiments on both rats and children with very favourable results.

3. COOMBS-PRUITT STUDY OF GAMBLING BEHAVIOR

This study is a direct application of the unfolding theory and technique to the study of variance and probability preferences in gambling. The most popular theories of preferences in gambling propose that individuals maximize some kind of an expectancy such as a subjectively expected utility (see Edwards, 1955). Such theories would appear to be violated if certain kinds of variance or probability preferences were demonstrated to exist. We might think that a way of testing for variance preferences would be to use two-alternative 50/50 bets with the same mathematical expectation, so that they differ only in variance, and see if an individual has preferences among them. We find that he does, but, on the other hand, these are the very preferences used to construct his utility function for money under the assumption that he is maximizing an expected utility.

Although there seems to be no room for the notion of variance preferences in a theory of maximizing an expected utility, there is still something psychologically compelling in the idea, in that an individual's preference for more or less variance would seem to capture the notion of utility for risk. Similarly, the idea of a probability preference, which is also interpretable as a preference for odds, has some of the flavor of a utility for risk in the sense, perhaps, of an optimistic-pessimistic attitude toward nature.

The work of Davidson, Suppes, and Siegel (1957) is concerned with the construction of individual utility functions for money and clearly illustrates how choices that may reflect variance preferences are used to construct utility functions. They assume that an individual maximizes subjectively expected utility when he is offered a pair of gambles as in Fig. 6.1.

Each gamble has two possible outcomes (indicated by lower-case letters with subscripts in the figure) depending on whether an event E does or does not occur. Davidson et al. carefully selected an event such that the subjective probabilities of its occurrence and nonoccurrence

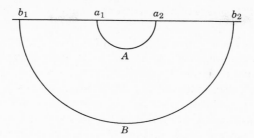

Fig. 6.1 A pair of gambles of the kind used for constructing utility functions for money.

are equal. If an individual prefers gamble A to B (Fig. 6.1), then

$$A \cdot \rangle B \Rightarrow \psi(E)U(a_1) + \psi(\tilde{E})U(a_2) > \psi(E)U(b_1) + \psi(\tilde{E})U(b_2)$$

where $\psi(E)$ signifies the subjective probability of the occurrence of the event E. Since $\psi(E) = \psi(\tilde{E})$,

$$A \cdot \rangle B \Rightarrow U(a_1) + U(a_2) > U(b_1) + U(b_2)$$

or

$$U(a_1) - U(b_1) > U(b_2) - U(a_2)$$

and we see that the difference in the utility of a_1 and b_1 is greater than that between b_2 and a_2. They then manipulate one of the outcomes, for example, increase b_2, until the individual changes his preference to $B \cdot \rangle A$. The point of indifference equates the two utility intervals, and by iterating this procedure a utility function for money which very adequately predicts each individual's preferences on new gambles can be constructed . (See also Coombs and Komorita, 1958.) Note that a preference for A over B may also be interpreted as a preference for the lesser variance of gamble A and vice versa.

The study by Coombs and Pruitt (1960, 1961) presents evidence that a concept of nonlinear utility for money is unnecessary because it accommodates not only the behavior that is observed but also a great variety of unobserved possible behaviors; and that, on the other hand, a concept of variance preferences accommodates the behavior that is observed and would not accommodate the behavior that does not occur. The argument is as follows.

It is evident that the Davidson et al. (1957) procedure will permit the construction of a monotonically increasing utility function for money for any preference ordering an individual may have over n bets where, pairwise, one bet envelops the other as bet B does A in Fig. 6.1. For any set of 50/50 bets whose expected dollar value is a constant, and which differ only in their variance, the theory of maximizing expected utility can accommodate the variety of behavior represented by $n!$ different preference orderings.

Alternatively, if we assume that the utility of money is linear and that the preferences among such a set of points are generated by variance preferences, only a subset of the $n!$ preference orderings are admissible. The bets in such a set, differing only in variance, may each be represented by a point on a unidimensional scale of variance. If this scale is a joint scale, with individuals also represented on it by their ideal points corresponding to their preferred amount of variance, then according to the unfolding theory, their preference orderings on the gambles are restricted to the set of orders obtained by folding this J scale of variance.

If this scale is a quantitative J scale, the variety of admissible preference orderings is $\binom{n}{2} + 1$, and if it is a common qualitative J scale the variety is 2^{n-1}. For example, for $n = 6$ there are $6! = 720$ admissible preference orderings under a maximization of expected utility hypothesis, 32 under a qualitative J scale of variance preferences, and 16 under a quantitative J scale of variance preferences.

The relevance of the distinction between a quantitative and a qualitative J scale, here, lies in whether the index of dispersion of the gambles is sufficiently similar for all individuals to yield a common ordered metric J scale or whether they are sufficiently dissimilar to yield only a common ordinal J scale. The term "variance" is used here only in a generic sense; the term "dispersion" or "spread" would perhaps be better.

The comparative figures on admissible preference orderings under a maximization of expected utility hypothesis and a variance preference hypothesis for $n = 6$ reveals the vulnerability of the latter relative to the former, and an experimental test should yield information as to whether the variance preference hypothesis should be rejected. In the study by Coombs and Pruitt six gambles, which were 50/50 bets with outcomes of ± 35 cents, ± 55 cents, $\pm \$1.00$, $\pm \$2.25$, $\pm \$5.00$, $\pm \$10.00$, were presented pairwise, embedded among many others. The 15 pairs were embedded in a total of 65 pairs presented in random order and replicated a total of 8 times over 3 successive evenings. The stimuli were presented in dittoed booklets with the subjects instructed to indicate their preference in each pair. They were told that at the end of the last session some of the items would be picked and played with no exchange of money so that "you can see how you would have come out if we had played for keeps." Subjects were also instructed that afterwards they would be given an opportunity actually to play two of the bets for real money.

A total of 99 subjects were used, all University of Michigan undergraduates. With 8 replications on each pair of stimuli, a "dominant" preference ordering was constructed for each individual if his estimated pairwise probabilities satisfied weak stochastic transitivity. The preferences of 91 of the subjects satisfied this condition, so a maximum likelihood I scale could be constructed for them. Of these, the dominant quantitative J scale satisfied 89, the qualitative J scale clearly satisfied 90 of the 91,

Table 6.5   The Dominant Quantitative J Scale for Variance Preferences on 50/50 Bets

I Scale Numbers	Simply Ordered I Scales	Number of Cases	Weakly Ordered I Scales*	Number of Cases
1	$A\ B\ C\ D\ E\ F$	17		
2	$B\ A\ C\ D\ E\ F$	2		
3	$B\ C\ A\ D\ E\ F$	1	$(B\ C)A\ D\ E\ F$	2
4	$C\ B\ A\ D\ E\ F$	5		
5				
6	$C\ D\ B\ A\ E\ F$	3	$(C\ D)B(A\ E)F$	1
7	$D\ C\ B\ A\ E\ F$	4	$D\ C\ B(A\ E)F$	1
8	$D\ C\ B\ E\ A\ F$	1	$(C\ D)B\ E\ A\ F$	1
9			$D(C\ E)B\ A\ F$	2
10	$D\ E\ C\ B\ A\ F$	1		
11	$E\ D\ C\ B\ A\ F$	7		
12	$E\ D\ C\ B\ F\ A$	1	$E\ D\ C(B\ F)A$	1
13	$E\ D\ C\ F\ B\ A$	1	$E\ D(C\ F)B\ A$	1
14			$E\ D(C\ F)(B\ A)$	1
15			$(E\ F)D\ C\ B\ A$	3
16	$F\ E\ D\ C\ B\ A$	33		
Total		76		13

* Parentheses about a pair of elements indicates a 4/4 split in the individual's 8 judgments on that pair of bets.

and 1 subject had a transitive I scale that did not fold the J scale. This individual had the rank order $F\ D\ E\ C\ A\ B$, in which the ordered pairs DE and AB violate unfolding; he preferred D over E 5 times out of 8 and A over B 6 times out of 8. The remaining 8 subjects were too inconsistent in their preference for us to determine from the number of judgments they made what their preferences were.

The cases that satisfied the dominant quantitative J scale are presented in Table 6.5. Note that 50 cases are at the two extremes, preferring

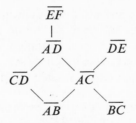

Fig. 6.2   Metric relations on variance preferences.

minimum variance or a maximum amount. These two variance preferences would correspond to decreasing and increasing marginal utility
for money, respectively, under a maximization of utility interpretation.
The remaining cases fold the J scale and correspond to utility functions
that have inflection points.

The metric information in this incomplete set of I scales is meager and
is presented in Fig. 6.2.

This metric, as far as it goes, is compatible with the actual metric on
the variances themselves. This should not be interpreted, however, as
very strong support for true variance preferences as against merely a
qualitative J scale, because unfortunately the stimuli chosen had variances
so distributed on the J scale that almost any kind of a measure of dispersion
would yield the same metric relations. The variances of the six gambles
from A to F were respectively 0.12, 0.30, 1.00, 5.00, 25.00, 100.00 so the
five intervals were successively 0.18, 0.70, 4.00, 20.00, and 75.00. An
experimental design more suited to distinguishing between the existence
of a common qualitative J scale and that of a quantitative J scale would
have stimuli more nearly equally spaced on some objective metric like
variance.

There are more data in this experiment than are reported here but they
are available in the publications cited. The incomplete report here has
only the purpose of illustrating the use of the unfolding theory and technique in another context.

REFERENCES

Coombs, C. H., and S. S. Komorita, 1958, Measuring utility of money through decisions,
    Amer. J. Psychol., **71**, 383–89.
Coombs, C. H., and D. Pruitt, 1960, Components of risk in decision making: proba-
    bility and variance preferences, *J. exp. Psychol.*, **60**, 265–77.
Coombs, C. H., and D. Pruitt, 1961, Some characteristics of choice behavior in risky
    situations, *Ann. New York Acad. Sci.*, **89**, 784–94.
Davidson, D., P. Suppes, and S. Siegel, 1957, *Decision making: an experimental
    approach*, Stanford University Press, Stanford.

Dember, W. N., 1960, *The psychology of perception*, Holt, Rinehart and Winston, New York.

Dember, W. N., and R. W. Earl, 1957, Analysis of exploratory, manipulatory, and curiosity behavior, *Psychol. Rev.*, **64**, 91–96.

Dember, W. N., R. W. Earl, and N. Paradise, 1957, Response by rats to differential stimulus complexity, *J. comp. physiol. Psychol.*, **50**, 514–18.

Earl, R. W., 1957, Problem solving and motor skill behaviors under conditions of free choice, unpublished Ph.D. dissertation, University of Michigan.

Edwards, W., 1955, The prediction of decisions among bets, *J. exp. Psychol.*, **50**, 201–14.

Lemaine, J.-M., 1959, Similitude cognitive et relations interpersonnelles, *Psychol. Française*, **4**, 102–16.

Runkel, P. J., 1956a, Cognitive facilitation of communication effects, unpublished Ph.D. dissertation, University of Michigan.

Runkel, P. J., 1956b, Cognitive similarity in facilitating communication, *Sociometry*, **19**, 178–91.

CHAPTER 7

Multidimensional Unfolding

In this chapter the extension of the unfolding technique to analysis of multidimensional preferences is considered. Parts of the chapter are taken almost without change from the publications of Joseph F. Bennett and William L. Hays. Bennett solved the problem of determining dimensionality and Hays the problem of determining configuration. Their work is published in Bennett and Hays (1960) and in Hays and Bennett (1961).

A reader coming into contact with multidimensional unfolding for the first time could easily feel so deluged with mathematical detail that he loses sight of the central ideas and main results. For this reason we open the chapter with a general overview of multidimensional unfolding that will suffice for most readers. The remaining sections of the chapter provide the mathematical foundations and the procedural details for those who desire them.

The problem with which multidimensional unfolding is concerned may be described as follows. Suppose that the I scales representing the preference orderings of a number of individuals do not satisfy the necessary conditions for unfolding in one dimension. We naturally think, then, of the possibility that the individuals arrive at their preferences among the stimuli in terms of more than one attribute. Bennett and Hays use the following example.

The subject is asked to rank [his preference among] a group of items, for example, the names of hobbies. The model states that each hobby can be characterized by its position on each of several underlying attributes (e.g., scientific-artistic, solitary-gregarious, skilled-unskilled, etc.). The model states further that every subject can be characterized by his own maximum preferences on each of these attributes, and that he will rank the hobbies according to their increasing distances from the ideal hobby defined by his own maximum pref- erence on each attribute; e.g., the scientific, gregarious, skilled subject will probably give model-airplane racing a high rank, photography a middling rank, and finger painting a low rank.*

The unfolding model in a joint space assumes (1) that the individuals and the stimuli are mapped into points in a common space, (2) that an individual's preference ordering between any two stimuli reflects which stimulus point is nearer his ideal point, and (3) that distance in the space is Euclidean. On a plane, for example, an individuals's preference ordering would correspond to the ordering of the stimuli obtained by picking up the plane as if it were a handkerchief at the ideal point, and compressing the handkerchief into a line. The successive order of the stimulus points on this line corresponds to their successive order in "distance from the ideal point" in the plane.

This natural extension of the idea of unidimensional unfolding theory generalizes to spaces of higher dimensionality. In general, then, the theory conceives of the stimuli as having a fixed configuration in a space of r dimensions and states that each individual's preference ordering reflects the order of increasing distance of the stimulus points from his ideal point.

It will be recalled that in one dimension the midpoints between pairs of stimuli played a very important role. They do so again in multidimensional unfolding, but the concept of a midpoint takes a more generalized form. Our concern here is the locus of points which are equidistant from a given pair of points. In one dimension this locus of equidistance is the midpoint between the two points, say A and B. Any arbitrary point in this one-dimensional space is either nearer A or nearer B or coincides with their midpoint.

If this pair of points A and B lie on a plane, the locus of equidistance is a line which also lies in the plane and is the perpendicular bisector of the line joining A and B. This line, of course, passes through the midpoint of the line joining A and B. All subjects with ideal points on one side of this line, the side containing stimulus A, will report $A \cdot \rangle B$; all those on the opposite side will report $B \cdot \rangle A$; only those with an ideal point exactly on the line will report no preference.

If the pair of points A and B should lie in a three-dimensional space, the locus of all points equidistant from A and B is a plane. The line joining A and B is perpendicular to this plane and is bisected by it.

We note that in the case of the one-dimensional J scale the locus of equidistance is a point, which is itself a space of zero dimensionality. In the

* 1960, pp. 27–28.

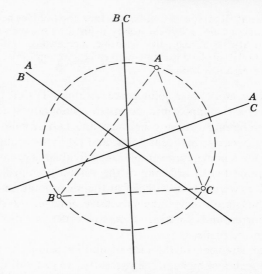

Fig. 7.1 Boundary hyperplanes generated by three points in two dimensions.

case of a space of two dimensions, the locus of equidistance is a line, that is, a space of one dimension. In the case of a three-dimensional J space, the locus of equidistance is a plane, that is, a space of two dimensions.

This relation between the dimensionality of the space and the dimensionality of the locus of equidistance from a pair of points generalizes to a space of any dimensionality. In an r-dimensional space the locus of equidistance from any pair of points is an $r - 1$ dimensional hyperplane orthogonal to and bisecting the line joining the two points. Such a hyperplane is called a boundary hyperplane and is designated by $H(AB)$ where A and B indicate the stimuli for which $H(AB)$ is the boundary hyperplane. In the accompanying figures the J spaces are two-dimensional and the boundary hyperplanes are lines, so they are more simply labeled by the pair of stimuli to indicate the two sides of the boundary hyperplane, as in Fig. 7.1.

Now suppose there are three stimuli A, B, and C in a plane, that is, not collinear (see Fig. 7.1). For each pair there is a corresponding boundary hyperplane. Three noncollinear points always lie on a circle, and as the center of that circle is equidistant from the three stimuli, their three boundary hyperplanes must intersect at the center. Such a center is a locus of equidistance from the three points and the notation for boundary hyperplanes may be generalized to indicate a locus of equidistance from three points, that is, $H(ABC)$.

A boundary hyperplane between two points, like $H(AB)$, divides the whole space into two regions. All the ideal points in one of these regions are nearer A than B and hence form the isotonic (same-ordered) region AB (meaning $A \cdot \rangle B$). Similarly, the other region forms the isotonic region BA.

In a similar manner, $H(BC)$ and $H(AC)$ each divide the space into two regions; each passes through the isotonic regions created by the other two hyperplanes. In doing so, six elemental regions are generated, to each of which there correspond three pair comparisons. Therefore each of these six elemental regions is an isotonic region which uniquely corresponds to a rank order of the stimulus points from any ideal point in that region.

Such a division of a two-dimensional space by three stimuli is illustrated in Fig. 7.2, in which each elemental region is indicated by its corresponding rank order. This rank order is the preference ordering (I scale) characterizing the individuals whose ideals lie in that region.

The total variety of possible preference orderings is $3! = 6$, and we note that this total variety appears in Fig. 7.2. Thus, if for three stimuli all possible varieties of preference orderings have occurred, the geometrical configuration that accommodates them is that of three noncollinear points in a plane.

Nothing can be learned (inferred) from such a configuration because it is a mathematical necessity. In general, inferences can only be drawn when the variety of behavior that is observed is less than the variety that was possible by the method of collecting the data. *When things which were permitted to happen do not happen, "nature" has constrained the behavior and hence has revealed itself; then significant inferences may be drawn.*

In the most obvious case of all, consider the case of just two stimuli, A

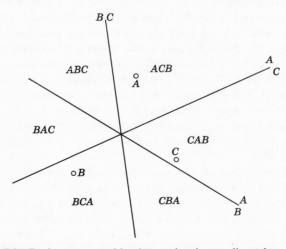

Fig. 7.2   Regions generated by three points in two dimensions.

and B. Some individuals prefer A to B and some prefer B to A. We can accommodate the data by placing A and B on a line divided by their midpoint into two regions. With one region we associate the individuals who prefer A to B and with the other region we associate those who prefer B to A. We have unfolded the data and our progress is nil because we can always unfold them.

Now consider the case of four stimuli. Four stimulus points can always be located in three dimensions because four points define a sphere. All boundary hyperplanes intersect in the center of the sphere and generate $4! = 24$ elemental isotonic regions to each of which corresponds one of the twenty-four possible permutations of the four stimuli.

In general, the total variety of possible preference orderings for n stimuli can always be represented by n points on the surface of an $(n - 1)$-dimensional hypersphere, and there is nothing to be learned by the unfolding analysis of such data. Only when the number and variety of preference orderings are constrained in certain ways can anything be learned by an unfolding analysis.

The "number" and the "variety" of I scales that can be unfolded in a given number of dimensions constitute the "cardinality" criterion and the "groups" criterion, respectively, for determining the dimensionality. These criteria were developed by Bennett (1956) and are presented in later sections.

We continue with this heuristic and introductory discussion of multidimensional unfolding by proceeding with the problem of arriving at the configuration, a geometrical representation, for a set of I scales. We consider a special case first, that of n points on a circle in two dimensions.

If n points are on a circle, their boundary hyperplanes all intersect at the center of the circle. In Fig. 7.3 we have an example with four stimuli. We note that there are twelve I scales in this instance composed of six mirror image pairs. Every pair of vertically opposed regions are joined at the center of the circle. Crossing this point from one region to another crosses every hyperplane simultaneously and generates the mirror image I scale.

For four stimuli in one dimension there are seven I scales which have only one mirror image pair. Bending such a J scale around to form a circle generates the mirror image of each of the remaining five I scales, producing the twelve in all.

In general, with n stimuli on a circle there will be $n(n - 1)$ I scales in the set and all possible mirror image pairs will be present in the set. We may note also that in going around the circle clockwise the order of midpoints is indicated by the sequence of adjacent pairs of stimuli that are reversed in I scale regions abutting each other. We have in Fig. 7.3, for example, the sequence of I scale regions $BCAD$, $BCDA$, and $CBDA$, indicating that the

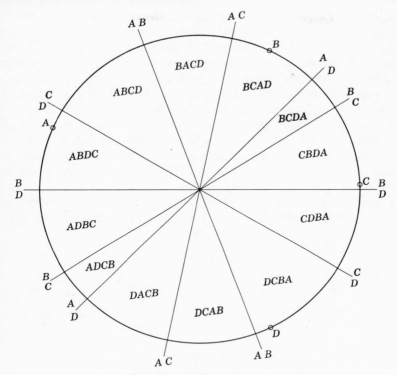

Fig. 7.3 Example of four stimuli on a circle.

boundary hyperplane *AD* precedes *BC*, read clockwise. This sequence of midpoints has the same metric implications it has in one-dimensional unfolding. That is, the chord or line joining *A* and *B* is greater than that joining *C* and *D*.

In the case of a circle there is additional metric information. The sequence of midpoints *DC*, *AB* implies that $\overline{AD}$ is greater than $\overline{BC}$. With more than four stimuli on a circle there would be increased metric information.

Four stimuli on a circle would probably be rarely met with in real data, but a limited finite variety of geometrical configurations are distinguishable for four stimuli in two dimensions. These have been enumerated by McElwain and Keats (1961); their contribution is presented in a later section.

The general case is concerned with the problem of *n* stimuli in $r < n - 1$ dimensions for which procedures have been developed by Hays. The routine is logical but complicated and is presented in detail in Hays and

Bennett's 1961 paper. The paper is summarized in a later section; here we merely try to provide some insights into the logical basis.

In Fig. 7.2 it will be noted that *all* the isotonic regions are "open" regions, in that they are not bounded on *all* sides. This would also be the case for four stimuli in three dimensions, and, in general, for n stimuli in $n - 1$ dimensions. With n stimuli in less than $n - 1$ dimensions, however, some regions are "closed" regions, as may be seen in Fig. 7.4.

This distinction between open and closed regions is critical in multi-dimensional unfolding. Fortunately, it is readily made. Open regions are associated with I scales which are members of mirror image pairs, and closed regions are associated with I scales whose mirror images do not occur in the data.

Consider, for example, Fig. 7.4. Take any open region, for example, the one associated with the rank order I scale $A\ B\ D\ C$. On the other side of

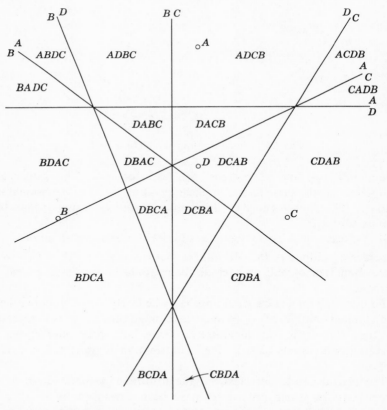

Fig. 7.4 An example of regions generated by four stimuli in two dimensions.

the space there is another open region defined by the rank order I scale $C\ D\ B\ A$, a mirror image of the other. To pass from one of these regions to the other, and thereby reverse the I scale order, we must cross every boundary hyperplane.

Such mirror image pairs exist for all open regions and only for open regions. For none of the closed regions, such as that associated with $D\ C\ B\ A$, will we find a region associated with its mirror image I scale, $A\ B\ C\ D$. The latter I scale does not occur.

The importance of the open regions resides in the fact that they yield an exhaustive solution to the data; the existence of a pair of mirror image I scales implies the existence of a line in the space on which the stimulus points project in the corresponding order. For example, the presence of the mirror image I scales $A\ B\ D\ C$ and $C\ D\ B\ A$ in Fig. 7.4 implies the existence of a line (axis) in the space on which the stimulus points project in the order $A\ B\ D\ C$ (or the reverse).

The mirror image pairs of I scales, however, yield an over-abundance of solutions, and the problem is to select a combination of such axes as a reference frame for the configuration. This, of course, may be done in a variety of ways depending on the criteria we adopt for defining a preferred solution.

Hays has offered a multiple criterion involving analogies with the least squares solution of the principal components method of factor analysis, the simple-structure criterion of Thurstone, and the orthogonality of the several dimensions.

The analogy with least squares involves passing a line through the longest "axis" of the space. To find such a line we take advantage of the fact that $r + 1$ points in an r-dimensional space define a hypersphere about the center of which is a set of regions whose corresponding rank order I scales contain all permutations of the $r + 1$ points defining that hypersphere.

For example, in Fig. 7.4 the center of the circle ($r = 2$) through the three ($r + 1$) points A, B, and C is found in about the center of the figure. The six regions radiating about this point are defined by I scales in which all permutations of A, B, and C occur.

We note that the stimulus D occurs *first* in each of the I scales constituting this "central set" of I scales. This signifies that the stimulus point for D is *inside* this circle. No other set of six I scales will have all the permutations of the stimuli A, B, and C *and* at the same time have stimulus D *last* in each permutation.

Now imagine the circle in Fig. 7.4 defined by the stimuli B, C, and D. The central set for this circle will be seen to have stimulus A *last* in all its I scales, signifying that the stimulus A is *outside* the circle.

Examining all such sets of $r + 1$ stimuli, we seek a pair of stimuli that are on the surface of one or more hyperspheres having no other stimulus outside that hypersphere. At least one such pair will always exist, and Hays provides instructions for finding it. Such a pair provides the end points of an axis through the "length" of the configuration. If more than one such pair are present, procedures are provided for choosing among them.

The analogy with Thurstone's simple structure criterion enters into the next step of determining the rank order of the projections of the rest of the stimulus points between the two end points. Besides fitting the longest axis of the space we want a solution that is in some sense parsimonious or simple. Thurstone's simple structure criterion seeks to maximize zero loadings and minimize the number of high loadings for each variable.

A nonmetric model like multidimensional unfolding has no concept of zero loadings but instead is concerned with *differences* among points. Accordingly, Hays introduced a concept of *quasi-simple structure* which holds that each axis should have a maximum number of zero differences among projections on it and the several axes should describe different sorts of differences.

To achieve this we examine the mirror image I scales that have the two stimuli defining the longest axis of the space at opposite extremes of the I scales. The order on each of these I scales is an "estimate" of the order of the projections of the stimuli, but from opposite ends of the axis. When these I scales agree, they determine the order. If the end point I scales do not agree on the order of projection for some pair of stimuli, the pair remains partially ordered, to be resolved by the rest of the data. We may speak of this process as "merging" I scales to form a common partial order.

The criterion of orthogonality is invoked in the iteration of this procedure to arrive at successive dimensions. To construct the second dimension the open regions giving the exhaustive solution to the data are again examined. This time, however, we consider only those mirror image pairs in which the two stimuli defining the first axis are adjacent in the I scales. This ensures that the second axis will be located so that the extreme points on the first axis will project next to each other on the second axis, thus introducing an approximation to orthogonality.

The procedure, then, for arriving at extreme points and the rank order of projections between them is carried out as in constructing the first axis.

This procedure is repeated as often as necessary.

I call this model a jointly compensatory model because each individual and stimulus pair jointly determine the compensatory function among the primitive attributes. This is in contrast with the personal compensatory model (see Chapter 9), the individual compensatory model, and the stimulus compensatory model (see Chapter 12).

In closing this introductory section I shall mention a conjecture I made which in spite of its "obvious reasonableness" turns out to be wrong.* It also illustrates the difficulty of visualizing spaces of more than three dimensions.

The reader will recall that boundary hyperplanes are of dimensionality $r - 1$ and their intersections are of dimensionality $r - 2$. If we have a set of stimuli in five dimensions, then for any three stimuli the intersection of their three boundary hyperplanes will be a space of three dimensions.

We might "reasonably" suspect that a three-dimensional intersection would be a finite volume of space and be apt to contain the ideal points of a finite portion of the population. This would be a group of individuals for whom the three stimulus points would be equally distant. We might conclude, then, that when $r \geq 5$, inconsistency of choices, latency of decision, and the number of intransitivities would all substantially increase.

That this conjecture is wrong is evident when we note that a boundary hyperplane, under a suitable rotation and translation of the space, may be defined by a fixed point on one dimension and all other dimensions may take on all values. The probability, then, of an ideal point being in the neighborhood of that particular value for the hyperplane on that one dimension is not increased just because its other coordinates are free.

In other words, 3-space is as "flat" in 4-space as a plane is in 3-space and a line is in 2-space. We cannot anticipate that at $r = 5$ there will be a substantial change in preference behavior, at least for such reasons as were incorrectly conjectured here.

The remaining sections of the chapter present the mathematical foundations and the procedural details on which this introduction was based.

1. ISOTONIC REGIONS

The division of a 2-space by three stimuli is illustrated in Fig. 7.2. It is evident that every isotonic (same-ordered) region, being bounded by hyperplanes, is everywhere convex; that is, any two points within the region can be connected by a straight line which does not pass outside it. The poset (partially ordered set) designating a region is the preference-ordering I scale characterizing the individuals whose ideals lie in the region. Let the *elemental regions* of the space be those for which the defining poset is a simple ordering of all the stimuli. All other regions are constructed from the union of elemental regions. Thus the union of the elemental regions ABC and ACB generates a region characterized by both orders.

Here we introduce some additional notation. *Double* parentheses

---

* This was pointed out to me by Robyn Dawes.

enclosing a set of points in a partial order signify the set of all permutations (in the order) of the enclosed set of points. Thus the partial order characterizing the region generated by the union of *ABC* and *ACB* will be designated *A((BC))*. The notation *((ABC))DE* would be read as signifying the set of all six permutations of *A*, *B*, and *C*, followed by *D* and then *E*. *Single* parentheses enclosing a set of points in a partial order always denote equality among all the points in the set. Thus, *(ABC)DE* is read as *A*, *B*, and *C* tied in the first rank followed by *D* and then *E*.

Any region will wholly contain any other region whose defining poset wholly satisfies the poset of the first, with the addition of some further refinement; thus the region *AB* must contain the region *ABC* if the latter exists, and, in fact, the region *A((BC))* if it exists. On the other hand, two regions cannot intersect, that is, have some subregions in common, if the poset of one contains a relation which is the complement of a relation in the other. Thus the region *A((BC))* cannot intersect the region *BA* because no point in the space could simultaneously satisfy the contradictory conditions of being nearer *A* than *B* and vice versa.

When *r* + 2 stimuli (or more) occur in an *r*-space, then certain of the (*r* + 2)! possible elemental regions will disappear. For example, in Fig. 7.5, which represents three stimuli in one-space, there is no region *ACB* and no region *CAB*, that is, the region *((AC))B* present in Fig. 7.2 has disappeared.

It is not an accident that these two particular elemental regions are missing. Their absence was dictated by the dimension of the space and the configuration of the stimuli. This dependence is the analytic tool which makes it possible to reconstruct dimension and configuration from experimentally obtained rankings.

The first problem to be considered is that of finding *r*, the dimension of the space, given the rankings produced by the subjects. The three methods to be presented here, determining dimensionality by mutual boundary, by cardinality, and by transposition groups, provide successively more powerful criteria, that is, more sensitive lower bounds to the dimensionality.

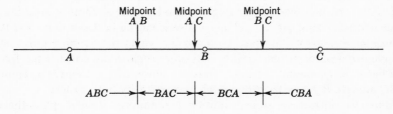

Fig. 7.5 Regions generated by three stimuli in one dimension.

2. DIMENSION BY MUTUAL BOUNDARY

The definition of an isotonic region as the set of all points satisfying a given set of distance relations relative to the stimuli makes the origin of the term boundary hyperplane clear. Every isotonic region is bounded by segments of boundary hyperplanes, that is, by $(r - 1)$-dimensional cells. In Fig. 7.5, for example, the region BAC is bounded by the hyperplanes $H(AB)$ and $H(AC)$ which are zero-dimensional points. In Fig. 7.2 region $A((BC))$ is bounded by segments of the hyperplanes $H(AB)$ and $H(AC)$. Note that it is not bounded by the hyperplane $H(BC)$. This is because the poset defining the region $A((BC))$ specifies no distance relation between B and C, so that a moving point inside $A((BC))$ may reverse its distance relations with B and C, that is, it may pass through the boundary hyperplane $H(BC)$, without leaving the region $A((BC))$.

Of necessity, every hyperplane bounding a given region is represented by a pair of stimuli that are adjacent in the defining poset for the region. (Two elements of a poset are said to be adjacent if one precedes the other in rank and if there is no other element in the poset ranked between them.) The converse, however, that every hyperplane defined by a pair of stimuli adjacent in the poset actually bounds the region, is not always true. For example, in Fig. 7.5 region ABC has B and C adjacent but the hyperplane $H(BC)$ does not bound the region. In all such cases, any remaining hyperplane defined by an adjacent pair, like BC in Fig. 7.5, constitutes the boundary of a larger region containing that region.

Since all isotonic regions are everywhere convex, two isotonic regions can bound only on a single hyperplane or on entirely coincident hyperplanes. Hence two isotonic regions must abut, granted they both exist, if the defining poset of one can be transformed into the poset of the other by the reversal of a single adjacent pair of stimuli; this adjacent pair represents the hyperplane that separates them.

The possibility of coincident hyperplanes does not permit us to conclude that isotonic regions abut only if such a single-pair transposition of their defining posets is possible. If hyperplane coincidence occurs, passing from one region into the other would mean simultaneous passage through two (or several) hyperplanes, and consequently the simultaneous reversal of two (or several) adjacent pairs. However, the existence of coincident hyperplanes could be readily detected in the total set of rank orders returned by the subjects by a complete mutual implication of the defining posets of their isotonic regions. Thus in Fig. 7.5 region ABC abuts the three regions BAC, $B((AC))$, and BA.

The value of the concept of boundary lies in its potential application as an initial dimension criterion to indicate whether the space is of one, two, or more dimensions. In a space of one dimension it is not possible for more than two regions to abut one another, and no more than four isotonic regions may all abut one another in 2-space. The 2-space limit is illustrated in Fig. 7.6, where four regions all abut one another along cells of hyperplanes. The reader may convince himself that it is impossible to add a fifth region which will abut all of the existing four.

A hypothetical example may help to clarify the criterion of mutual boundary. Imagine the following I scales have been obtained on four stimuli:

$A\ B\ C\ D$	$A\ C\ B\ D$	$A\ D\ B\ C$	$B\ C\ A\ D$	$C\ D\ A\ B$
$A\ B\ D\ C$	$A\ C\ D\ B$	$A\ D\ C\ B$	$C\ B\ A\ D$	$C\ D\ B\ A$
$B\ A\ C\ D$	$C\ A\ B\ D$	$D\ A\ B\ C$	$C\ B\ D\ A$	$D\ C\ A\ B$
	$C\ A\ D\ B$	$D\ A\ C\ B$		$D\ C\ B\ A$

The occurrence of $A\ B\ C\ D$ and $B\ A\ C\ D$ in these data is evidence, for example, that $A((BCD))$ abuts $B((ACD))$. Note that in four cases sets of three regions all mutually abut. These are $C((DA))B$, $D((CA))B$, $A((DC))B$; $C((AB))D$, $C((AD))B$, $C((BD))A$; $A((CD))B$, $A((BD))C$, $A((BC))D$; and $A((BC))D$, $B((AC))D$, $C((AB))D$. The occurrence of any one of these excludes at once the possibility that the solution is unidimensional. On the other hand, a two-dimensional solution is not excluded, since in no instance do five or more regions mutually abut. In several instances sets of four regions do mutually abut; for example, $((AB))((CD))$, $((CB))((AD))$, DB, and $((CA))BD$ all abut one another.

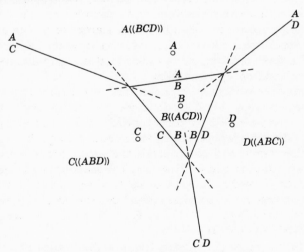

Fig. 7.6 Four mutually bounding regions in 2-space.

It has not so far proved possible to extend the mutual boundary approach into spaces of dimension higher than two. Fortunately the existence of more powerful methods renders this unnecessary. The method may continue to serve as a quick check of the possibility of a solution in one or two dimensions, and as a first outline of the configuration of stimuli in the space.

3. DIMENSION BY CARDINALITY

This method imposes a lower bound on the dimensionality of the space by a comparison of the total number of different rankings returned by the subjects with $C(n, r)$, the maximum possible number of elemental isotonic regions that can be generated for n objects in r dimensions.

It is evident from the previous chapter that in 1-space there will be one more elemental region than there will be boundary hyperplanes (that is, midpoints). Since there are $\binom{n}{2}$ boundary hyperplanes for n stimuli, the maximum cardinality for n stimuli in 1-space is

$$C(n,1) = \binom{n}{2} + 1$$

Special circumstances such as the coincidence of boundary hyperplanes can serve only to lower the number of regions in the space.

K. B. Leisenring of The University of Michigan pointed out in a personal communication to J. F. Bennett that when the stimulus points are in general position, that is, not all lying in a subspace of the r-space, every boundary hyperplane is divided into cells in the same fashion as a complete space of one fewer dimensions and with one fewer stimuli. In Fig. 7.2, for example, there are three stimuli in two dimensions. Note that each boundary hyperplane is divided into two cells as would be the case for two stimuli in one dimension. Figure 7.4 is an example of the regions that are generated by a particular configuration of four stimuli in two dimensions. Note that in this case each boundary hyperplane is divided into four cells as would be the case for three stimuli in one dimension.

A recursive expression* for $C(n, r)$ may be arrived at in the following way. $C(2, 1) = 2$, and adding a dimension does not change the cardinality, so $C(2, 2) = 2$ also. Consider the effect of adding a third stimulus. This adds two new hyperplanes, one with each of the stimuli already in the space. Each new hyperplane adds as many regions as it transects because every region it passes through it divides in two. Every time it passes from one region to another it is itself transected because it passes through a boundary

---

* An elementary discussion of a very similar but more general problem may be found in Polya (1954, pp. 43–52).

hyperplane. This coincidence means that it adds as many new regions as it itself is divided into. According to Leisenring's observation, however, a hyperplane is divided into as many cells as there are regions in a space of one fewer dimensions and one fewer stimuli. Consequently, $C(3, 2) = C(2, 2) + 2C(2, 1) = 2 + 2(2) = 6$. Or, in general,

$$C(n, r) = C(n - 1, r) + (n - 1)C(n - 1, r - 1) \qquad (7.1)$$

No satisfactory nonrecursive expression for $C(n, r)$ has been found. R. M. Thrall of The University of Michigan has pointed out in a personal communication, however, the identity of the values obtained from it with sums of absolute values of Stirling numbers of the first kind (Jordan, 1947), for which again no general expression is known. The relation may be written

$$C(n, r) = \sum_{m=n-4}^{n} |S_n{}^m| \qquad (7.2)$$

where $S_n{}^m$ is a Stirling number.

Some values of $C(n, r)$ are given in Table 7.1. Note that $C(n, r) = n!$ for $r \geq n - 1$. That is, a space of dimension $n - 1$ can always account for all possible orderings of n stimuli. Generally such solutions would be of no interest. To be of psychological significance and interest the solution should accomplish some economy of description by accommodating all or nearly all the data in a comparatively few dimensions. If the method of collecting the data permits $n!$ different orderings to occur and "nature" constrains the variety that does occur, then the data are of scientific interest beyond mere description.

There is an obvious similarity between this cardinality criterion of Bennett's and the one he proposes* (Bennett, 1956) for the dimensionality of rank orders of subjects given by tests, within the general model of factor analysis. Bennett's 1956 paper is restricted exclusively to the case in which the rank orders given by the tests are monotone functions of the dimensions, as is in accord with the factor analysis model. As shown in the discussion of this model in Chapter 12, this restricts the possible isotonic regions strictly to open regions.

On the other hand, no such monotonicity assumption is made in the unfolding theory of preferential choice, because, unlike test performance, an individual's preferences are thought of as nonmonotone functions of the attributes or axes of the space. Thus the possibility of both open and closed regions is allowed. In consequence, other things being equal, the maximum cardinality numbers given in Table 7.1 are always greater than or equal to those given in Table 12.9, which is taken from Bennett.

* See Chapter 12.

Table 7.1   Maximum Number $C(n, r)$ of Rank Orders Generated by n Objects in r Dimensions

n	1	2	3	4	5
1	1	1	1	1	1
2	2	2	2	2	2
3	4	6	6	6	6
4	7	18	24	24	24
5	11	46	96	120	120
6	16	101	326	600	720
7	22	197	932	2.556×10^3	4.320×10^3
8	29	351	2.311×10^3	9.080×10^3	2.221×10^4
9	37	583	5.119×10^3	2.757×10^4	9.485×10^4
10	46	916	1.037×10^4	7.364×10^4	3.430×10^5

Table 12.9 can be used, however, to ascertain the maximum number of open regions which may occur in the unfolding model. This number may be used to supplement the cardinality criterion because there is a way of knowing from the data how many open regions are represented. Each open region in a space must have a mirror image, another region which has the exact reverse of its rank order, and only open regions show such mirror images. Hence the cardinality criterion may be supplemented in the following way. Count the number of mirror image pairs of rankings existing in the data, and compare this number with one-half the number of regions listed in Bennett's Table 12.9 for the appropriate n and a given r. If this number is exceeded, the dimensionality is greater than r.

In the hypothetical example given previously there are eighteen distinct preference orderings. Table 7.1 shows this to be the maximum allowable number for four stimuli in two dimensions. To apply the supplementary criterion based on the number of open regions, we note in the hypothetical example that there are 6 mirror image pairs of I scales: $A\,B\,C\,D$ and $D\,C\,B\,A$, $A\,B\,D\,C$ and $C\,D\,B\,A$, $B\,A\,C\,D$ and $D\,C\,A\,B$, $A\,D\,B\,C$ and $C\,B\,D\,A$, $D\,A\,B\,C$ and $C\,B\,A\,D$, $D\,A\,C\,B$ and $B\,C\,A\,D$. Turning to Table 12.9 we find for $n = 4$ stimuli that $\frac{12}{2} = 6$ open regions are admissible in $r = 2$ dimensions. Hence there is no reason as yet to believe that the space has more than two dimensions.

The criterion of cardinality has the peculiar feature that it does not consider what rankings are returned. This gives it a great advantage in simplicity and ease of application but of course makes it a very insensitive test, likely to give an optimistically low estimate of dimension when applied to a chaotic set of rankings. Furthermore, Table 7.1 indicates that in successively higher dimensions the number of different possible rankings goes up very rapidly with the number of items, and in most practical instances is likely to exceed the whole size of a sample of judges which an experimenter might use. This means that the criterion of cardinality can be applied directly only to data in which the number of experimentally independent rankings (for example, the number of subjects) is large, preferably much exceeding the factorial of the number of stimuli ranked. In most other circumstances we cannot expect to have enough experimentally independent rankings to exhaust the number of permissible rankings indicated in Table 7.1.

4. DIMENSION BY GROUPS

A space of r dimensions contains every possible ranking of any $r + 1$ stimuli in general position, or, expressed another way, contains the complete permutation group of simple orders of these stimuli. This observation is independent of the presence of additional objects in the space. On the other hand, a space of dimension r cannot contain the complete permutation group of $r + 2$ stimuli or more.

These ideas may be summarized in the following proposition. *A set of r stimulus points $A, B, \ldots, Q, R$ will require at least $r - 1$ dimensions for embedding if and only if a set of $r!$ regions exists, characterized by all $r!$ permutations in order, of the stimulus set.* A proof of the necessary condition can be carried out by induction on r, the number of stimuli, and $r - 1$, the number of dimensions. This is trivial for $r - 1 = 1$, since two points may always be put on a line with their midpoint halfway between them, generating two regions showing the two permutations.

Now assume the proposition to be true for any $r - 1$ stimuli in $r - 2$ dimensions. Consider the set of r stimuli $A, B, \ldots, Q, R$ for which by hypothesis all $(r - 1)!$ permutations in order of the set of $r - 1$ points $\{A, B, \ldots, Q\}$ must also exist as regions, and this set of $r - 1$ points is embedded in no less than $r - 2$ dimensions. Now suppose that stimulus point R is also embedded in the same subspace of $r - 2$ dimensions so that all $r!$ permutations correspond to regions in $(r - 2)$-space. This would contradict the cardinality rule, which shows that the maximum number of regions for r stimuli in $r - 2$ dimensions is always less than $r!$; the maximum number is $(r - 1)(r - 1)!$, as a matter of fact. Hence, the dimensionality would always be greater than $r - 2$, and the set of r points may all be embedded in a space of no fewer than $r - 1$ dimensions.

For the sufficient condition, a proof may once again be outlined using an induction argument on r and $r - 1$. The case of $r = 2$ is trivial. Now assume the sufficient condition true for $r - 1$ points in $r - 2$ dimensions.

By hypothesis the set of r points $\{A, B, \ldots, Q, R\}$ requires $r - 1$ dimensions. Thus, some subset of $r - 1$ points from this set, say $\{A, B, \ldots, Q\}$, requires $r - 2$ dimensions, so that by assumption all permutations in order for this set must exist as regions in the $r - 2$ space. The locus $H(AB \cdots Q)$ will exist as a point in the $r - 2$ space, because the expression $r - n + 1$ is the dimensionality of the locus of equidistance from n points in general position in r dimensions. By the same expression, when the set of $r - 1$ points is embedded in an $r - 1$ space, the locus of equidistance would be a line L bounding all $(r - 1)!$ regions showing the permutations in order for the set.

Since the addition of stimulus point R to the space requires, by hypothe-

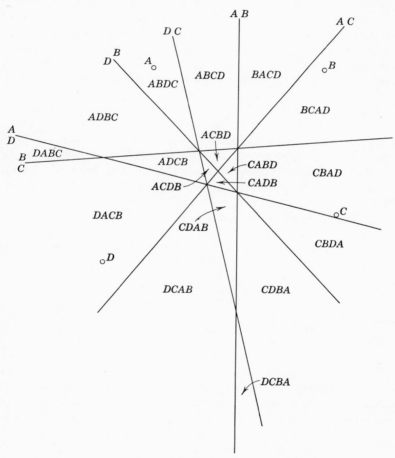

Fig. 7.7 A configuration of four points in two dimensions.

sis, dimensionality $r - 1$ (R may not be embedded in the $r - 2$ space), the intersection of $H(AR)$, for example, and $H(AB \cdots Q)$ must exist—otherwise the required dimensionality would be $r - 2$. Furthermore, by the transitivity of the equality relation, this point of intersection must also be the point of intersection of $H(AB \cdots Q)$ with all the remaining loci $H(BR)$, $H(CR)$, . . . , $H(QR)$, so that by definition the intersection is the locus $H(AB \cdots QR)$. Now any region showing a permutation in order of $\{A, B, \ldots, Q\}$ such as $ABC \cdots Q$ must be bounded by the line L. The intersection of L with $H(AR)$ creates two new regions, such as $RABC \cdots Q$ and $ARBC \cdots Q;$ the intersection of $H(BR)$ with L another two regions, such as $ARBC \cdots Q$, $ABRC \cdots Q$, and so on. Since the intersections of a basic region showing a particular permutation of A through Q with the $r - 1$ hyperplanes of the form $H(AR)$ must generate r distinct new regions, each showing the same permutation of A through Q but a different position of R, and since there were originally $(r - 1)!$ basic regions showing permutations of the set of $r - 1$ stimulus points, exactly $r(r - 1)!$ or $r!$ regions must be generated showing all permutations in order of $A, B, \ldots, QR$.

This fact can be made the final (and perhaps the most useful) criterion of dimension. We may be certain that *the minimum dimension of the space in which a complete solution may be realized must be one less than the number of elements in the largest permutation group present in the experimental data.*

Returning again to the hypothetical data, the complete group over all 4 stimuli is not present, since such a group would have 24 elements and only 18 are present. Searching for groups over subsets of 3 elements, we find, for example, every permutation of A, B, and C:

Region	Represented by
$A\,B\,C$	$D\,A\,B\,C,\ A\,D\,B\,C,\ A\,B\,D\,C,$ and $A\,B\,C\,D$
$B\,A\,C$	$B\,A\,C\,D$ alone
$B\,C\,A$	$B\,C\,A\,D$ alone
$C\,B\,A$	$D\,C\,B\,A,\ C\,D\,B\,A,\ C\,B\,D\,A,$ and $C\,B\,A\,D$
$C\,A\,B$	$D\,C\,A\,B,\ C\,D\,A\,B,\ C\,A\,D\,B,$ and $C\,A\,B\,D$
$A\,C\,B$	$D\,A\,C\,B,\ A\,D\,C\,B,\ A\,C\,D\,B,$ and $A\,C\,B\,D$

The same is true of each of the other subsets of three stimuli, as may be discovered on examination. Since there is considerable evidence that the solution is two-dimensional, we may attempt a geometric realization of the space, as shown in Fig. 7.7. Using this construction we may reexamine the previous examples and relate them to the properties of the figure.

Of these three criteria for dimensionality, the group criterion is the most practical and, to a large extent, the most sensitive for use with preference data. Obviously, with a large number of stimulus items, say 10, it is seldom possible to accumulate enough data to establish the lower limit of the dimensionality at 9, since this would require some 10! distinct rankings.

It is possible, however, to make a good lower-bound estimate from more limited data using a modification of this criterion. Given n stimuli $A, B, \ldots, Q, R$, the required dimensionality is $n - 1$ if there are *two* complete sets of $(n - 1)!$ permutations in order for some subset of $n - 1$ stimuli, say $A, B, \ldots, Q$, such that the remaining stimulus R *precedes* all the remaining stimuli in each permutation in the first set, and *follows* all the remaining stimuli in each permutation of the second set. This is seen to be true if it is recalled that the locus of equidistance from $r - 1$ points in $r - 2$ dimensions is a point, so that there may be only one set of "permuting" regions bounding such a point. If there are two distinct sets of this kind, the locus in question must be at least a line and the dimensionality must be at least $r - 1$. This modification requires only $2(r - 1)!$ rank orders to establish a lower-bound dimensionality of $r - 1$, rather than the complete $r!$.

Finally a very stringent criterion is obtained by a combination of the principles utilized in the cardinality and the groups criteria. It will be recalled that the locus of equidistance between two points in r dimensions is a space of dimensionality $r - 1$. Each and every pair of regions with rank orders differing only by a reversal in order of one pair of stimuli must be separated only by the locus. Furthermore, for n points in r dimensions, the number of such pairs of regions differing only by a reversal in the same stimulus pair (the same hyperplane must then bound each pair of such regions) corresponds to the cardinality of $n - 1$ points in $r - 1$ dimensions. Thus, if a set of such pairs is found, and the number of such pairs exceeds the maximum cardinality of $n - 1$ points in $r - 1$ dimensions, the dimensionality must be at least $r + 1$.

For instance, in Fig. 7.7 there are exactly four pairs of regions differing only in the order of A and B: $ABCD$-$BACD$, $CBAD$-$CABD$, $CDAB$-$CDBA$, and $DCBA$-$DCAB$. Thus the cardinality of these pairs of regions agrees exactly with the cardinality for three stimuli in one dimension—there is no evidence from these orders that the dimensionality exceeds two. Had a fifth pair such as $DBAC$-$DABC$ existed, however, then the dimensionality required would be three.

This last criterion is the most sensitive one discussed, particularly with small numbers of stimuli. Actually, it may be too sensitive for use with fallible data such as would reasonably be obtained, since the estimated dimensionality depends somewhat more on single occurrences among the rank orders than we would expect with the groups criterion alone. Thus in practice the application of the groups criterion is perhaps the method of choice for a "manageably low" dimensionality estimate.

Incidentally, the method for constructing a configuration for such data is also based principally on the incidence of such permutation groups among the rank orders, so that once a preliminary estimate has been made for the required dimensionality there are continual checks on the estimate in the remainder of the procedure.

5. A GENERAL UNFOLDING THEOREM

The one-dimensional unfolding technique relies on the fact that if the rank orders emanate from a one-dimensional joint space it is always possible to construct a unique sequence such that each distinct rank order differs from either neighbor in the sequence by a reversal in order of only one pair of stimuli. The "end" or mirror image rankings then provide the order of the stimuli on the attribute.

This procedure could perfectly well be interpreted as finding a sequence of 2-loci (midpoints) rather than a sequence of isotonic regions, since the reversal in order of a pair of objects for a pair of regions simply fixes such a midpoint. Considering the unfolding technique in this way suggests the principle which allows an extension to the multidimensional case. Since this principle *is* in fact the general statement of the unfolding idea, it seems important and nontrivial enough to state and prove it in the form of a theorem.

Theorem: Given some fixed line L, and three points A, B, and C in general position in an isotonic space of dimensionality r, the line L intersects the 2-loci $H(AB)$, $H(AC)$, and $H(BC)$ in that order (or the reverse, if it does not intersect them simultaneously) if and only if the perpendicular projections of the three points on L are in the order ABC (or the reverse).

PROOF:* The necessary condition will be proved first. Given line L intersecting $H(AB)$, $H(AC)$, and $H(BC)$ in that order, let the intersection of L and $H(AB)$ define the origin $\odot$, and let L be the first coordinate axis in the space; then

$$H(AB) \cap L = \odot = (0, 0, 0, \ldots)$$
$$H(AC) \cap L = (x_1, 0, 0, \ldots)$$
$$H(BC) \cap L = (x_2, 0, 0, \ldots)$$

Let
$$A = (a_1, a_2, \ldots, a_r)$$
$$B = (b_1, b_2, \ldots, b_r)$$
$$C = (c_1, c_2, \ldots, c_r)$$

where a_1, b_1, c_1, their respective first coordinates, are also their respective projections on L.

* This argument was contributed by Robyn Dawes and is slightly simpler than Hays's original proof.

$H(AB)$ is defined as the locus of point $P = (p_1, p_2, \ldots, p_r)$ such that

$$(p_1 - a_1)^2 + (p_2 - a_2)^2 + \cdots + (p_r - a_r)^2$$
$$= (p_1 - b_1)^2 + (p_2 - b_2)^2 + \cdots + (p_r - b_r)^2$$

but since $\odot = (0, 0, 0, \ldots)$ lies on $H(AB)$, we may conclude that

$$a_1^2 + a_2^2 + \cdots + a_r^2 = b_1^2 + b_2^2 + \cdots + b_r^2 \tag{7.3}$$

Since $(x_1, 0, 0, \ldots)$ lies on $H(AC)$ we may conclude

$$(x_1 - a_1)^2 + a_2^2 + a_3^2 + \cdots + a_r^2 = (x_1 - c_1)^2 + c_2^2 + c_3^2 + \cdots + c_r^2$$

or, rearranging terms:

$$2x_1(c_1 - a_1) = (c_1^2 + \cdots + c_r^2) - (a_1^2 + \cdots + a_r^2)$$

or

$$x_1 = \frac{(c_1^2 - a_1^2) + (c_2^2 - a_2^2) + \cdots + (c_r^2 - a_r^2)}{2(c_1 - a_1)}$$

Similarly,

$$x_2 = \frac{(c_1^2 - b_1^2) + (c_2^2 - b_2^2) + \cdots + (c_r^2 - b_r^2)}{2(c_1 - b_1)}$$

Since $x_2 > x_1$, we have

$$\frac{(c_1^2 - b_1^2) + \cdots + (c_r^2 - b_r^2)}{2(c_1 - b_1)} > \frac{(c_1^2 - a_1^2) + \cdots + (c_r^2 - a_r^2)}{2(c_1 - a_1)}$$

From equation 7.3, however, it follows that the numerators of these fractions are equal, thus

$$c_1 - a_1 > c_1 - b_1$$

But since a_1, b_1, and c_1 are respectively the projections of A, B, and C on L, we may conclude that the projection of B on L is closer to C than is the projection of A; hence the order is ABC or the reverse.

The sufficient condition is proved simply by reversing the steps of the necessary condition argument.

The unfolding technique for one dimension is simply a special case of this more general principle for finding projections on lines by constructing sequences of regions. In isotonic space of any dimensionality the existence of $\binom{n}{2} + 1$ regions which fit the unfolding qualifications for one dimension is sufficient for the inference of the order of projections which the points have relative to some line. As an illustration of this principle, consider the following sequence of seven regions drawn from the example of Fig. 7.7: $DACB$, $DCAB$, $CDAB$, $CDBA$, $CBDA$, $CBAD$, $BCAD$. In this sequence $H(CD)$ lies between $DCAB$ and $CDAB$, $H(AC)$ falls between $DACB$ and $DCAB$, and $H(AD)$ lies between $CBDA$ and $CBAD$; the order of these three 2-loci is thus $H(AC) H(CD) H(AD)$ (or the reverse), so that on a line extending through these seven regions, the order of projections of the three stimulus points A, C, and D must be CAD (or the reverse). Likewise, the order of A, B, and C as projected on such a line would be ACB or the reverse, since the order of their 2-loci is $H(AC) H(AB) H(BC)$. An inspection of the 2-loci for all such triples of stimuli establishes that the order of projections on such a line would be $DACB$ or the reverse (obviously, since there is no fixed origin in the isotonic space, the orders of projections on any line may be read in either direction). Any line capable of being located in the space must pass through such a sequence of $\binom{n}{2} + 1$ regions, and any complete "unfolding sequence" of $\binom{n}{2} + 1$ regions occurring in the space must represent at least one possible line in the space.

An important feature of the unidimensional unfolded solution is the recovery of "metric relations" among the stimulus points, yielding an ordered metric scale of the stimuli. This metric information is inferred from the sequence of 2-loci, as is the simple order of the stimuli themselves. Unfortunately, it can be shown that the ability to obtain metric information in this way is restricted to the unidimensional case. Although the theorem given is a complete generalization of the method for obtaining the order (or the order of projections) of the stimulus points in other than the one-dimensional case, the method for inferring metric information does not work for the *projections* of the points on axes in the space.

An important corollary follows directly from the theorem just given.

Corollary: In any isotonic space of n stimuli in r dimensions, two regions may have characteristic orders which are "mirror images" if and only if there is the possibility of a line in the space such that the order of projections of the stimuli on the line is the same as the characteristic order of either of the regions (or the reverse, of course).

6. AN EXHAUSTIVE SOLUTION FOR "COMPLETE DATA"

The practical implication of this corollary is that *any pair of mirror image I scales existing in the data affords a potential solution*, in that there must be the possibility of an axis showing such an order of projections. Even more important is the fact that *any potential solution must be represented by such a mirror image pair of regions in the data, when the data are complete*. In this light the question of a solution for complete data becomes rather trivial. First, in the present context, let "complete data" be understood to mean sets of rank orders such that each and every isotonic region in the stimulus space has its characteristic order represented at least once in the data. Thus, when complete data are at hand, all possible configurational solutions may be recovered from the data simply by finding mirror image pairs of rankings. Each mirror image pair located is one potential axis for describing the configuration; for this reason the solution from complete data may be called "exhaustive."

In the simple example of Fig. 7.7 the mirror image pairs of regions are *DACB-BCAD*, *DABC-CBAD*, *ADBC-CBDA*, *ABDC-CDBA*, *ABCD-DCBA*, *BACD-DCAB*. Thus six possible simple orders may represent axes or "solutions" to the configuration: *DACB*, *DABC*, *ADBC*, *ABDC*, *ABCD*, and *BACD* (or their reverses). These constitute the exhaustive solution for this configuration.

The number of such potential axes varies, of course, with the number of stimuli and the dimensionality. Actually, it is possible to calculate the maximum number of distinct potential axes (that is, distinct mirror image pairs of regions). These maximum numbers have been tabulated in another context by Bennett (see Chapter 12, Table 12.9) in the form of the maximum number of "open" isotonic regions which may exist for given numbers of stimuli and dimensionalities; in order to convert this table into maximum number of rank order axes, we simply divide the entries by two.

Thus, for example, there are 36 different rank orders of projections possible for 5 stimuli in 3 dimensions, 105 different possible rank order axes for 15 stimuli in 2 dimensions, and just over a billion possible rank orders of projections for 30 stimuli in 5 dimensions.

Obviously, such exhaustive solutions leave something to be desired in the way of parsimony of description. Moreover, seldom would we be interested in *all* solutions anyway, even if there were fairly restricted numbers of such possibilities. Rather, under the influence of factor analytic methods, we have grown accustomed to describing *r*-dimensional data in terms of a set of *r* axes chosen in some way from among all the possible ways of describing a particular configuration.

Thus, even for complete data there still remains the problem of choosing from among all possible solutions that set of axes which will in some sense palatably fit the data. In order to do this we must settle on some criteria for choosing among all possible solutions. This problem is considered next.

The Idea of a Central Envelope

One requirement for a solution might be that each successive axis account for a maximum amount of the differences or distances between points in the sense that the projections of points on the axis be most widely spread. That is, the first axis should describe the longest axis or "length" of the configuration, the second axis should describe the "length" of the configuration of projections of points on a space of one less dimension, and so on. Thus, axes may be sought which will be roughly analogous to "principle axes" in the usual factor analysis model.

In order to find such a solution within the isotonic space, the idea of a "central envelope" of a configuration may be introduced. First of all, recall that in any r-dimensional space, the locus of equidistance from any $r + 1$ points in general position is a *point*. This point is the center of a hypersphere of dimensionality r. Thus, the locus of equidistance from three points in two dimensions is the center of a circle (2-sphere); the locus of equidistance from four points in three dimensions is the center of a sphere (3-sphere); the locus of equidistance from five points in four dimensions is the center of a hypersphere of four dimensions (4-sphere); and so on.

Any hypersphere of whatever dimensionality must bear one of three possible relations to any point in the space: the point in question must be either *interior to* the hypersphere (fall within its surface), *exterior to* the hypersphere (fall beyond the space enclosed by its surface), or *conjoint* with the hypersphere (fall on its surface, and thus be at a distance from its center equal to that of any other point on the surface). Furthermore, if a stimulus point X is exterior to an r-sphere, the order of distances which is characteristic of its center must show the point X more distant from the center than any point on the surface. On the other hand, if the point X is interior to the r-sphere, the order associated with the center must show X less distant from the center than any point on the surface. Finally, if the point X is conjoint with the hypersphere, the order associated with the center must show the X equally distant with any point on the surface.

Among n stimulus points in general position in r dimensions, any given stimulus point must be conjoint with $\binom{n-1}{r}$ distinct r-spheres, since there will exist an $(r + 1)$-locus for each set of $r + 1$ points. In addition, any *pair* of points must be conjoint with $\binom{n-2}{r-1}$ r-spheres.

Now for any n points in general position in r dimensions, *there will exist at least one pair of points such that the pair is conjoint with a set of at least one and at most r of the r-spheres, each and every sphere in the set having the property that each and every stimulus point is either conjoint with or interior to it.* The boundary of the convex subspace formed by the intersection of a set of r such r-spheres is referred to as the "central envelope" of the space. The major axis of the central-envelope subspace is the line joining the two points conjoint with each of the set of r-spheres. The minor axes of the subspace must lie in the hyperplane of equidistance (2-locus) defined by these two points.

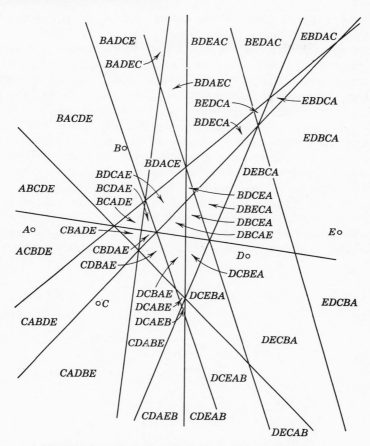

Fig. 7.8 A configuration of five points in two dimensions.

Complicated as this idea may sound, it may be illustrated very simply. Figure 7.8 is an example of a configuration of five points in two dimensions, and Fig. 7.9 shows the circles (2-spheres) defined by their configuration and the central envelope. Note that there are $\binom{5}{3}$ or ten such circles for five points in two dimensions. The main axis of the central envelope is defined by the pair of points A and E, since they are both on the surface of (conjoint with) two circles, each of which either has all the points *inside* the circle or *on* its surface. The central envelope encloses the shaded area, which is the intersection of the two circular areas. Note that it is a convex space such that any line in the configuration falls within the envelope. Note also that the line AE which is the major axis of the envelope does seem to be the line that most nearly passes through the "center" of the space, and about which the points tend to "cluster" most closely.

Since we are dealing strictly with an isotonic space, however, in which the only information available is in the form of rank orders for regions, the problem remains of finding that pair of points defining the axis of a central envelope. This may be done as follows: The center of an r-sphere is, of course, an $(r + 1)$-locus, the point of equidistance from some set of $r + 1$ points. The $(r + 1)$-locus point does not fall into any isotonic region having a simple characteristic order of distances; rather, such an $(r + 1)$-locus must fall on the boundary separating a number of such regions, and consequently have a partial ordering of distances, since it is by definition equally distant from at least $r + 1$ points.

For example, in the configuration of five points in two dimensions, the 3-locus $H(ABC)$ for the three points A, B, and C is the point of intersection of the three 2-loci $H(AB)$, $H(AC)$, and $H(BC)$, thus falling on the boundary lines among six regions. Both D and E are exterior to the circle, so that the

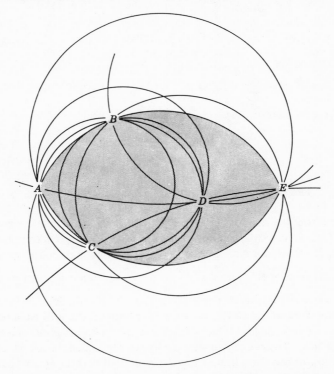

Fig. 7.9 Circles generated by five points in two dimensions showing the central envelope.

order of distances from the center of the circle to the five points is the partial order $(ABC)DE$. (It will be remembered that single parentheses enclosing a set of points in a partial order always denotes a tie in rank among the points in the set.)

Note that the six regions immediately surrounding the center of this circle are all alike in order, except that each shows a different one of the six permutations $((ABC))DE$, the positions of D and E remaining fixed. Such a set of "permuting" regions would also be utilized in the "groups" criterion for dimensionality mentioned earlier.

The general principle such sets of regions exhibit is: If there exists a set of $(r + 1)!$ regions showing exactly the same characteristic orders except for a permutation of some set of $r + 1$ stimulus points, then there exists an r-sphere to which those $r + 1$ stimuli are conjoint. The partial order of distances characteristic of the center of the r-sphere is the same as that of any of the set of "permuting regions," except that all the points of the set of conjoint stimuli are equally distant from the center point, thus giving it a partial order of distances. In other words, the "groups" of permutations occurring in the data tell not only about the dimensionality, but also tell of the existence of r-spheres in the space. An inspection of the five-point example shows this to be the case. Each one of the ten circles is accompanied by a set of six permuting regions, and each set of permuting regions surrounds the center of a circle. No set of 4! permuting regions may be found, however, since the dimensionality is two.

Furthermore, these sets of permuting regions also give information about the positions of all the points relative to each of the circles. It has already been mentioned that the set of $n + 1$ stimuli which permute among the $(r + 1)!$ rank orders contains those which are "on" the r-sphere. If any stimulus falls in order *below* the permuting stimuli for the region orders, then that stimulus is necessarily *exterior* to the r-sphere. On the other hand, if any stimulus point *precedes* the stimuli which permute in order, then that stimulus point is *interior* to the circle. For instance, the regions $CBADE, CBDAE, CDBAE, CDABE, CADBE, CABDE$ which are members of the set $C((ABD))E$ differ only by a permutation of A, B, and D; thus they must "surround" the center of a circle in the example, with A, B, and D on the perimeter. Since among these regions C always precedes A, B, and D, we know that the circle must have C as an interior point. However, E always follows the three permuting stimuli in all the regions of the set of six, so that we must conclude that the circle will have E exterior to it. This is indeed the case, as may be seen from Fig. 7.9.

Since the positions of the points relative to the r-spheres may be read from the orders characterizing such "permutation groups" in the data, a way emerges for "fixing" the central envelope of a configuration of points.

Recall that the central envelope is the subspace formed by the intersection of r distinct r-spheres such that each point is either conjoint with or interior to each r-sphere. Then *a central envelope may be determined by first finding all the permuting sets of* $(r + 1)!$ *orders that show the property that all stimulus points either are in the permuting set or precede the permuting set in order. The major axis of the central envelope is defined by a pair of stimulus points common to the permuting set for* r *such groups of stimuli.* In the example, these r-spheres are represented by the set of six regions falling into the partial order $CD((ABE))$ and the set of six regions falling into the partial order $BD((ACE))$. The points common to the permuting sets for both groups are A and E; consequently A and E describe the long axis of the central envelope for this configuration.

Moreover, the two points which define the major axis of the central envelope of the space have a property which permits them to be identified simply, without the necessity of inspecting all the sets of $(r + 1)!$ permutation groups of regions. The circumstance that these two points are conjoint with the r-spheres intersecting to form the central envelope makes it true that among the *closed* regions of the space (that is, those having no mirror image), this particular pair of points will appear in the *last two places* in order for the *largest* number of regions. On the other hand, the desired pair *will not* appear either in the first two places nor in the last two places in any *open* region. Thus, the end points of the major axis of the central envelope may be found very easily for complete data by merely counting the number of times pairs of stimulus points appear in the last places for closed regions, and the number of times the pairs appear in an extreme position (at either end of the order) for open regions.

For example, in Fig. 7.8 it can be seen that the pair A and E occurs in last place in nine of the closed regions, and in an extreme position together in none of the open regions. Thus the major axis of the central envelope must terminate in A and E.

To recapitulate, one criterion here proposed for choosing among rank order solutions is that the axes chosen reflect the tendency of the points to cluster along the long axis of the central envelope, so that the axes chosen may reflect the general "shape" of the configuration as closely as possible. This is taken as the first requirement for a choice from among all the available solutions for complete data.

Although the axis of the central envelope will be determinate for most configurations, it is possible to construct configurations in which there will be fewer than r distinct r-spheres, each of which will have the property of including all the points within it or on its surface. In this situation there is only a partial envelope, and there will be ambiguity as to which of the pairs of points best characterizes the major axis of the configuration. For example, if in Fig. 7.8 we ignore stimulus A and concentrate on B, C, D, and E only as four points in two dimensions, we can see that the circle generated by B, C, and E fits the qualification for one of the circles describing a central envelope, but that there is no circle among the remaining three described by B, C, and D; B, E, and D; and C, E, and D which fits this qualification. For this configuration, then, there is no special choice among the pairs B and C, B and E, and C and E as determining the end points of a first axis. In any configuration in any dimensionality r, however, *at least one* r-sphere fitting the qualifications for a central envelope will exist.

A "Quasi-simple Structure" Criterion

It does not seem quite enough, however, to insist that the rank order axes chosen should reflect the "length," "breadth," and "height" of the configuration. It seems desirable to seek solutions which have a certain degree of inherent parsimony of description. In other words, another aspect to a "good" solution should be its "simplicity" in some sense. This is true especially since there seems to be no good analogy to rotation within the isotonic model.

The search for such solutions in factor analysis is indissolubly linked with the name of Thurstone and the concept of "simple structure" (Thurstone, 1947). Although the rules for achieving simple structure seem to be very much bound up with the mechanics of factor analysis, and especially of rotation, one aspect does seem to have a rough analogy in the isotonic model. In describing the characteristics of simple structure, Thurstone emphasized the desirability of maximizing the number of zero loadings which any given factor should show, while at the same time minimizing the number of factors on which a test should show high loadings. In the isotonic model there is, of course, no unique origin in the space, and since the possible solutions are only ordinal in character, the concept of "zero loading" has no special meaning for this model. It does seem, however, that a pertinent part of this requirement for simple structure is not that the loadings for a number of tests are zero, but rather that the differences among a maximal number of points are zero when projected on an axis.

In other words, since reference axes are ways of describing the differences which exist among points anyway, maximum clarity is achieved when the various axes describe *different sorts* of differences among the points of the configuration, so that differences which project large on one axis do not project large on others.

This is emphatically not the only interpretation of the concept of simple structure by any means; it is, however, an aspect for which there is at least a distant analogy within the confines of an isotonic space. Thus, a "quasi-simple structure" requirement may also be imposed in the choice of a solution: *Each axis should be chosen in such a way that the number of zero distances among projections on each of the axes is maximal.*

For n points in r dimensions, there are, in a sense, $\binom{n}{r}$ "ready-made" axes consisting of all the r-loci in the space. Recall that the locus of equidistance from r points in r dimensions is a line, and this line must have projections of all the points on it. Hence, each of the r-loci does have one valuable property in the light of the "quasi-simple structure" notion just introduced. This is that the r points defining the locus must project onto exactly the same point on it; that is, since they are all equally distant from any point on the r-locus, their projections onto the locus must coincide.

For example, note in the five-point example that on the line $H(AB)$ the projections of A and B must coincide, and similarly for each pair of points defining a 2-locus line. Consequently, this quasi-simple structure criterion may be approached by taking the r-loci themselves as the axes. This reduces the choice of the set of r axes to some extent, but there are still $\binom{n}{r}$ such loci from which to choose. How may we determine the order of projections on an r-locus from complete data? The answer is, by finding permutation groups in sets of $r!$ *open* regions.

According to the corollary of the theorem, open regions must describe possible orders of projections, and permuting sets of $r!$ open regions must thus describe the order of projections on the line described by an r-locus. In Fig. 7.8 the line $H(AB)$ has an order of projections $(AB)CDE$, which is reflected by the set of open regions $ABCDE$ and $BACDE$, a permuting set $((AB))CDE$ in A and B, and by their mirror image mates $EDCBA$ and $EDCAB$, which also constitute a permuting set $EDC((AB))$ in A and B. Hence the order of projections on the 2-locus $H(AB)$ is $(AB)CDE$. Similar inspection of open regions permuting in A and E shows $B(AE)DC$ for $H(AE)$, $BA(CD)E$ for $H(CD)$, and so on.

Each of the r-loci axes will have, then, the property of zero distance among projections for at least r stimuli. The choice among these axes can be made by finding the axis that tends to parallel the major axis of the central envelope. One further consideration in choosing a set of axes should be discussed, however, before giving an example.

Orthogonality of Axes

A third desideratum in choosing a solution from among the exhaustive possibilities is that the axes chosen be more or less orthogonal to each other. Obviously, the r-loci will not in general be orthogonal, so if we choose among these for our set of axes only approximate orthogonality can take place at best. However, there is an advantage in choosing the r-loci that will have even this approximate degree of orthogonality, in that we may keep our description of the space as nonredundant as possible as far as the interpretations we place on the axes are concerned.

Just as there is a feature of the space which allows us to approach the "quasi-simple structure" criterion easily, so there are "ready-made" guides to orthogonality as well. If any set of r points in general position defines an r-locus line, the subspace of $r - 1$ dimensions in which the r points are embedded is everywhere orthogonal to the line of the r-locus. In addition, if two points define a line in the space, the 2-locus defines a hyperplane of $r - 1$ dimensions such that any line in the hyperplane is orthogonal to the line between the two points. For example, note in Figs. 7.7 and 7.8 how each 2-locus hyperplane is a perpendicular bisector of, and hence orthogonal to, a line between two stimulus points.

Now suppose that the first axis is chosen to be the r-locus that is approximately parallel to the major axis of the central envelope. The remaining $r - 1$ axes should be approximately parallel to the minor axes of the envelope if they are to be orthogonal to the first; in other words, the remaining axes should be guided by the 2-locus which is orthogonal to the axis of the envelope.

In the example, A and E were, of course, found to define the major axis of the central envelope; thus, the 2-locus $H(AE)$ is orthogonal to this line. By taking the second axis as lying parallel to this 2-locus, we ensure that it will be approximately orthogonal to the first axis: in this instance, the second axis must show A and E projecting on the same point. Actually, in the example, the only possible 2-locus which would then qualify as an axis would be $H(AE)$ with order of projections $B(AE)DC$. With dimensionality higher than two, however, there would be a choice among a number of r-loci showing A and E adjacent in order, where A and E are the end points of the major axis.

The procedure for locating axes beyond the first follows the same general plan. Only r-loci showing the end points of the first axis adjacent are considered. Then, *always omitting one of the stimulus points which served as end points for the first axis*, the two stimulus points are found that serve as principal points for a central envelope enclosing the largest number of points and at the same time project as near each other as possible on the first axis, indicated (hopefully) by projecting next to each other on it. For instance, in the example, if the four points A, B, C, D are considered, A and D form the major axis of a central envelope for those four points. However, A and D are not taken as end points for the second dimension, since both B and C fall between A and D on the first axis. On the other hand, if B, C, D, and E are examined, we find that only the circle generated by B, C, and E has all four stimuli either conjoint or interior to the circle. In such a case, any of the pairs BC, BE, or CE could serve as the major axis for this subset of points. However, D falls between B and E and also between C and E on the first axis, so that only B and C apparently qualify

Table 7.2 Open and Closed Regions for the Five-Point Example

Open Regions		Closed Regions	
A B C D E	E D C B A	B D A C E	B C A D E
A C B D E	E D B C A	B C A D E	B D C A E
B A C D E	E D C A B	B D C E A	B D E A C
B A D C E	E C D A B	B D E C A	B D A E C
B A D E C	C E D A B	B E D C A	B D A E C
B A E D C	C D E A B	D C B A E	D C A B E
B E A D C	C D A E B	C D E B A	C D B E A
B E D A C	C A D E B	D C B E A	D B C A E
E B D A C	C A D B E	D B C E A	D B E C A
E D B A C	C A B D E	D E B C A	D E C B A
		D C E B A	E B D C A
		E C D B A	C E D B A

for end points on the second axis. This is a trivial finding for a two-dimensional example, of course, since only one rank order qualifies in the first place. Nevertheless, the procedure would be the same for higher dimensionalities, always locating successive axes in terms of central envelopes of reduced numbers of points such that there is minimal duplication of previous axes' rank orders.

Illustrative Example

We shall now outline the multidimensional unfolding procedure, using the data from Fig. 7.8 for an example. These hypothetical data are shown in Table 7.2. It is well to remember, however, that the discussion is restricted to the case of complete data. The problem of incomplete data requires some alteration in the overall attack and is discussed later.

(1) Given a set of rank order data, assumed to be "complete," the rank orders are first reduced to a set of nonduplicating orders—that is, only one instance of each distinct rank order is retained in the data.

(2) The dimensionality is determined by a simple application of the cardinality criterion. Call this number r. For the example, 44 orders occur, so that the dimensionality must be at least two.

(3) Now all mirror image pairs of orders in the data are located and tabled as "open regions," while nonpaired orders are tabled as "closed regions." For the data of the example, Table 7.2 shows the division into open and closed regions.

(4) The rank orders given by pairs of mirror image open regions are the "exhaustive solution" to the data.

(5) Among the closed regions, find the pair of stimulus points X and Y that appears *most* often in the last two places of the rank orders and appears least often in *either* the first two or last two places for open regions. For the example these are clearly A and E. Call these two points X and Y, the end points of the first axis.

(6) Now consider only those open region rank orders showing X and Y at opposite extremes of the rank orders. Among these rank orders find sets of permutations of r stimuli such that all other stimuli remain constant in order. In the data at hand there is a set consisting of the orders $ABCDE$ and $ACBDE$ and a set consisting of their reverses. If there is only one such set and its mirror images, then their characteristic partial order is the order of projections on the first axis. In the example, the characteristic partial order for the set is $A((BC))DE$; thus $A(BC)DE$ or the reverse represents the first axis.

(7) If several such r-loci are found in step 6, examine the data to find regions which would be closed if Y were eliminated from the set of stimuli and find the stimulus W that most nearly determines a central envelope for the remaining $n - 1$ points. Next omit X, find new closed regions, and determine another stimulus Z just as stimulus W was determined. Now choose the r-locus from those found in step 6 that shows maximal separation in order for X and W and for Y and Z. Although this step is not necessary for the present example, it may be illustrated. Suppose that we wish to choose among the three r-loci with orders $A(BC)DE$, $(AB)CDE$, and $(AC)BDE$. Omitting stimulus E, we find that a central envelope is described by stimulus A and stimulus D. Omitting stimulus A, we find that the nearest approach to a central envelope is given by the circle described by $H(BCE)$—here B and C fit equally well as defining a central envelope with E. Thus we wish to choose the r-locus that shows A and D maximally separated and also shows B and C maximally (and equally) separated from E. The only r-locus that fits this double qualification is $A(BC)DE$, and so this would be taken as the first axis' partial order.

(8) Now return to the list of rank orders of open regions giving the exhaustive solution to the data, and extract those showing the end points X and Y found in step 5 *adjacent* in rank order. Consider any pair of regions differing only in the order of X and Y. In the example the only open regions that qualify as showing A and E adjacent are $BAEDC$, $BEADC$

[which are collapsed as $B((AE))DC$] and their reverses, $CDEAB$ and $CDAEB$ [or $CD((AE))B$].

(9) Now the rank order for the second axis must come from among these open region orders. For the example there is no problem, as the only possible r-locus must be $H(AE)$ with order $B(AE)DC$—hence the solution is complete for this example.

(10) For dimensionality greater than two there must be more than one choice for the order to represent the second dimension. To permit a choice among these possible orders we first omit the two end point stimuli one at a time, as in step 7, and find the two stimuli X' and Y' that are most nearly axes for central envelopes for the remaining stimuli and show the *fewest* stimuli within their respective envelopes falling between X' and Y' in the order of the first axis. This is rather trivial for two dimensions, once again, but the example may serve to illustrate the general idea for higher dimensionality: From step 7 it has already been found that A and D form a central envelope for the set consisting of A, B, C, and D. Both B and C project, however, between A and D in the order found in steps 6 and 7 for the first axis. Hence they do not qualify as the desired pair. When the set B, C, D, and E was considered, it was found that the pairs B and C, B and E, and C and E all seemed to qualify equally well as defining the central envelope for that set. The pairs C and E and B and E each show D projecting between them on the first axis, however, while B and C are adjacent. Hence the pair that should appear as end points for the second dimension, X' and Y', are taken as B and C. Only the orders found in step 8 that show X' and Y' at the extremes are considered for the second axis: In the example the only order available is, of course, $B(AE)DC$. If there are several such orders, the same procedure, *mutatis mutandis*, as for the first dimension, is carried out.

(11) For higher dimensionality the procedure is repeated, each time refining the set of possible orders available as axes. Thus for the third dimension only those orders showing both X and Y adjacent and X' and Y' adjacent are considered, and sets of stimuli are inspected for use as possible end points of axes only when one of either X or Y *and* one of either X' or Y' are omitted from consideration. Otherwise the steps are simply repeated.

The end results are thus a set of rank orders representing projections on axes that parallel major axes of central envelopes, show the property of quasi-simple structure, and are approximately orthogonal to each other. Obviously it is *not* possible to plot such axes and perform any sort of rotational operations on such a solution. On the other hand, all possible solutions are immediately at hand in these data, and if the solution obtained is unsatisfactory for some reason others may certainly be chosen by abandoning one or all of these criteria. The criteria proposed here do seem, however, to have some recommendation on common-sense grounds as well as by analogy to current practice in factor analysis. On the other hand, only properties of the isotonic space itself are relied on in these criteria for selecting among the possible solutions, and these criteria are presented here as isotonic principles *sui generis*, and not as approximations to results which might be found by metric methods. The analogies drawn to principal axes and simple structure are meant to be only expository and suggestive rather than exact.

The Problem of Incomplete Data

It must certainly have occurred to the reader that the method just outlined has very limited practical utility as long as it is limited to the case of complete data. The number of isotonic regions that may exist even for a moderate number of stimuli in a moderately small dimensionality can be truly astronomical. As is evident from Table 7.1, complete data cannot possibly be obtained except in the most trivial cases. The purpose in limiting this discussion to the case of complete data was, however, simply to make an exceedingly complicated topic somewhat more comprehensible.

The method may be extended to "real data," as there is almost nothing in the criteria and general method developed here which necessarily limits it to the complete case. Nevertheless, some complexities do arise, mainly because we do not necessarily have in the incomplete case the exhaustive solution already implicit in the data when it is complete. Hence other steps must be introduced to supply the information given in the complete case by the mirror image pairs. The procedure for the incomplete case has not yet been worked out in complete detail. The general ideas, both for dimensionality and for a configurational solution, may be applied to either complete or very incomplete data. So the principles enunciated here are the basis of a detailed procedure for the incomplete-data situation.

7. THE McELWAIN-KEATS APPROACH TO MULTIDIMENSIONAL UNFOLDING

McElwain and Keats (1961) have attacked the problem of multi-dimensional unfolding from the point of view of enumerating all possible geometrical configurations which are distinguishable in terms of their corresponding sets of I scales. Then they have constructed a simple method of characterizing a given set of I scales so that the corresponding geometrical configuration is immediately determined. They have done this, however, only for the special case of four stimuli in two dimensions.

Geometrical configurations are classified and data are characterized in terms of the number of times each stimulus is placed last. Thus, a set of I scales in which one stimulus has been placed last four times, each of two others three times, and one stimulus twice, would be characterized (typed) by the n-tuple [4, 3, 3, 2]. This would be a set of twelve distinct I scales.

This notation provides a convenient way of designating each stimulus, simply by the number of times it has occurred last. In this case there is one stimulus designated (4), two designated (3), and one designated (2). Particular I scales or sets of I scales may be readily designated in the same notation. Thus {(3, 4, 3, 2)} refers to two orderings in which stimulus (2) has occurred last and stimulus (4) has occurred second.

The value of this method of characterizing the data resides in the fact that each possible geometrical configuration or solution corresponds uniquely to a data type.

McElwain and Keats provide an extensive table, reproduced here as Table 7.3, which provides the correspondences between data types and geometrical solutions. As an illustration of the method, consider the data contained in Fig. 7.3. We note that the data type is [4, 3, 3, 2] because one stimulus, A, appears last four times, another stimulus, C, appears last twice, and each of the others occurs last three times. Under the second column of Table 7.3 we note for this data type that the two orderings ending in (2) should be {(4, 3, 3, 2)} and the two orders missing which end with (4) are {(3, 3, 2, 4)}. The six orders {(3, 2, 4, 3)}, {(3, 4, 2, 3)}, and {(4, 3, 2, 3)} occur. Examining the data we observe that $ADBC$ and $ABDC$ occur; $BDCA$ and $DBCA$ are missing; and finally the six orders $BCAD$, $DCAB$, $BACD$, $DACB$, $ABCD$, and $ADCB$ occur.

The authors provide an interesting application of the method in an analysis of children's preferences for radio stations in Brisbane, Australia. Table 7.4 contains their data, the preference order I scales of 304 children. The data type is [6, 5, 5, 2], and we note in Table 7.3 that no geometrical configuration is a solution to this data type. However, in testing how well the two-dimensional model does fit, they find that the best fit is achieved by the [6, 6, 4, 2] configuration, with only 2 discrepancies in the 304 cases: $DCBA$ and $DBAC$ both occurred and should not have.

No other geometrical configuration fits as well: The [6, 6, 6, 0] has 3 discrepancies, the [6, 6, 4, 0] has 4, and two alternative [6, 6, 3, 3] solutions have, respectively, 6 and 7 discrepancies. These geometrical configurations, with the four radio stations indicated as points, are presented in Fig. 7.10.

In their own words,

[Solutions (*a*), (*b*), and (*c*) in Fig. 7.10] stress the central position of the most popular station, *A*. [Solutions (*a*), (*d*), and (*e*) in Fig. 7.10] stress the contrast of *B* and *D*, with *A* and *C* contrasted on a different dimension and in a certain

Table 7.3 Solutions of the Four Stimuli Unfolding Problem

Data Type	Sufficient Conditions	Geometrical Properties	Solution
[6, 6, 6, 6]	Nil	Any nondegenerate tetrahedron	
[6, 6, 6, 0]	Nil	The point (0) is inside the triangle (6, 6, 6). This is the only case for which the quadrilateral is concave	
[6, 6, 4, 2]	The 2 orders ending in (2) are {(4, 6, 6, 2)}, and the 2 missing orders ending in (4) are {(6, 6, 2, 4)}	The point (2) lies inside the circle (6, 6, 4) and the parallelogram formed by (6), (6), and (4) with (6, 6) as diagonal, but outside the triangle (6, 6, 4). (4) lies inside the circle (6, 6, 2)	
[6, 6, 3, 3]	The 4 orders {(6, 6, 3, 3)} are missing as are 2 of the 4 orders {(6, 3, 6, 3)} beginning with the same point (6)	Each point (3) lies inside the circle (6, 6, 3) but outside the triangle (6, 6, 3) and the parallelogram formed by (6), (6), and (3). (3) and (3) are on opposite sides of (6) and (6). The line (3, 3) is closer to the point (6) which begins the 2 missing orders {(6, 3, 6, 3)}	
[6, 6, 4, 0]	The 2 orders {(6, 6, 0, 4)} are missing as well as all orders ending in (0)	The points (6), (0), (6), are collinear in that order. The point (4) is not in that line or its extension	
[6, 6, 2, 2]	The 4 orders {(2, 6, 6, 2)} occur, but no others ending in (2)	Parallelogram with (6), (6) as major diagonal	
[6, 6, 3, 2]	The 4 orders {(2, 6, 6, 3)} and {(3, 6, 6, 2)} occur with 1 order {(6, 2, 6, 3)}	Trapezium, with the shorter diagonal (2), (3) further from the point (6) appearing first in the order {(6, 2, 6, 3)} that does occur	

(Continued)

Table 7.3 (*continued*)

Data Type	Sufficient Conditions	Geometrical Properties	Solution
[4, 3, 3, 2]	The 2 orders ending in (2) and the 2 orders missing from (4) are {(3, 3, 2, 4)}. The 6 orders {(3, 2, 4, 3)}, {(3, 4, 2, 3)}, and {(4, 3, 2, 3)} occur	Cyclic quadrilateral with diagonals (4, 2) and (3, 3). (2) is inside the parallelogram defined by (3), (4), and (3)	
[3, 3, 2, 2]	With the lettering in the diagram the orders *DABC*, *ADBC*, *BACD*, and *BCAD* and their opposites occur	The line (2, 2) and the line (3, 3) form the shorter and longer parallel sides of a cyclic trapezium. Points (2) and (3) which never occur together at the beginning or ending of an order form diagonals	
[2, 2, 2, 2]	With the lettering of the diagram the 8 orders are *ABDC*, *ADBC*, *BACD*, and *BCAD*, with their opposites	Rectangle or square. Diagonal points never appear together at the beginning or ending of orders	
[4, 3, 0, 0]	1 order {(4, 0, 0, 3)} and its opposite with consequent 5 orders	Straight line in the order 4, 0, 0, 3 with segment (4, 0) greater than segment (0, 3)	
[3, 3, 0, 0]	The 2 orders {(3, 0, 0, 3)} with consequent 5 orders	Straight line in the order 3, 0, 0, 3 with segment (3, 0) equal to segment (0, 3)	

Table 7.4   Children's Preferences for Four Radio Stations

A B C D	112	A B D C	25	A C D B	12	B C D A	—
A C B D	59	A D B C	13	A D C B	8	B D C A	—
C A B D	10	D A B C	4	C A D B	5	C B D A	2
B A C D	25	B A D C	6	D A C B	4	D B C A	—
C B A D	7	D B A C	1	C D A B	—	C D B A	—
B C A D	3	B D A C	—	D C A B	7	D C B A	1

sense closer to each other. Both of these characteristics are shown in [solution (*a*)], with neither being unduly emphasized; this gives the best fit (less than one percent of cases deviating). It is worth noting that D is the government radio station which is free from advertising whereas A, B, and C are commercial stations with B concentrating a considerable amount of its time on short advertisements. Station A has a large number of imported serials in its children's session, and these appeal to the children of the age group studied. (1961, pp. 329–30.)

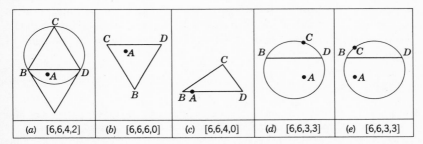

| (*a*) [6,6,4,2] | (*b*) [6,6,6,0] | (*c*) [6,6,4,0] | (*d*) [6,6,3,3] | (*e*) [6,6,3,3] |

Fig. 7.10 Alternative solutions to preferences for radio stations. (*a*) 2 discrepancies, (*b*) 3 discrepancies, (*c*) 4 discrepancies, (*d*) 6 discrepancies, (*e*) 7 discrepancies.

The approach of McElwain and Keats leads to a direct determination of the configuration, unlike that of Hays and Bennett, which leads first to the order of projections on a reference frame. Of course, they are not incompatible and may usefully supplement each other. It is not yet clear, however, that the approach of McElwain and Keats is feasible when generalized to more stimuli and more dimensions.

8. SUMMARY

The very fine work of Bennett and Hays presented in this chapter provides the basic principles for multidimensional unfolding in a Euclidean space with a Euclidean distance function. The lengthy introduction to the chapter is a descriptive account of the total process involved in multidimensional unfolding with an intuitive discussion of the basic concepts.

Sections 1-7 reiterate what is in the introductory section but provide the formal foundations of the theory for the two main phases: the determination of the dimensionality of the space and the determination of the configuration.

The procedures for analyzing a complete set of data are presented in detail and illustrated. The result of such an analysis is r simple orders of stimuli corresponding to the order of the projections of the stimuli on r reasonably orthogonal axes in the space. The method is sensitive to the fine structure of the data and needs further development for incomplete data and for 'pick k' and 'order k' data in which $k < n - 1$.

A different approach to the problem of multidimensional unfolding is contained in the work of McElwain and Keats, discussed in Section 7. They have dealt only with the case of four stimuli in two dimensions. For this case, they have a simple method of "characterizing" a set of I scales for $n = 4$. Each such characterization corresponds to one of the possible geometrical solutions. The process of literally unfolding is avoided completely. The solution is in the form of a geometrical configuration in contrast to the order of the projections on axes as in the Hays-Bennett method. Hopefully, the method will be generalized to larger numbers of stimuli and more dimensions.

REFERENCES

Bennett, J. F., 1956, Determination of the number of independent parameters of a score matrix from the examination of rank orders, *Psychometrika*, **21**, 383–93.
Bennett, J. F., and W. L. Hays, 1960, Multidimensional unfolding: determining the dimensionality of ranked preference data, *Psychometrika*, **25**, 27–43.
Hays, W. L., and J. F. Bennett, 1961, Multidimensional unfolding: determining configuration from complete rank order preference data, *Psychometrika*, **26**, 221–38.
Jordan, K., 1947, *The calculus of finite differences*, Chelsea Publishing Co., New York.
McElwain, D. W., and J. A. Keats, 1961, Multidimensional unfolding: some geometrical solutions, *Psychometrika*, **26**, 325–32.
Polya, G., 1954, *Induction and analogy in mathematics*, Princeton University Press, Princeton.
Thurstone, L. L., 1947, *Multiple factor analysis*, University of Chicago Press, Chicago.

CHAPTER 8

Factor Analysis of Preferences

The work of Bennett and Hays presented in Chapter 7 permits the multidimensional unfolding of preference orderings to recover a joint space as a product space of simple orders. Their methods, like unidimensional unfolding, are sensitive to the fine structure of the data, and it is of interest to consider how a robust procedure like multiple factor analysis may be applied. Given the preference orderings of individuals over a set of stimuli, we might intercorrelate individuals' preference orderings and factor analyze the resulting correlation matrix. What relation would this solution, obtained by factor analysis, bear to a solution obtained by multidimensional unfolding? An answer to this question is proposed by Coombs and Kao (1960) and studied by simple experimental sampling of hypothetical data.

1. THE PROPOSITION

Consider the simple case of a one-dimensional latent attribute generating the preferences of individuals over a set of alternatives. The ideal points of the individuals and the points for the alternatives are all points on a line, a joint scale. To reduce sampling fluctuations, assume that the points are reasonably numerous and, in terms of the space to be uncovered, reasonably uniformly spaced.

Consider the I scale of an individual A at the extreme left end of the scale and that of another individual very close to him. Clearly, their preference orderings will be almost identical and will correlate close to $+1$. Individual A's I scale will correlate progressively less with the I scales of other individuals as they are farther removed from him on the joint scale. In fact, the correlation will be zero between individual A and the median individual in the distribution, and will ultimately be −1 between him and the individual at the extreme opposite end of the scale. The median individual will have correlations ranging from close to +1 with those individuals near him on either side, to zero with the individuals at either end.

Clearly, if each individual is represented by a unit vector from a common origin and the correlation between individuals is the cosine of the angle between the corresponding vectors, the configuration corresponding to the correlation matrix will be a semicircle with the individuals corresponding to a fan of vectors such that the vector of the median individual projects vertically upward and orthogonal to the vectors of the two extreme individuals, which form an angle of 180°. The order of the termini of the vectors on the arc would correspond exactly to the order of the corresponding points on the original line.

If we factor analyze the correlation matrix for such a configuration by the method of principal components, the space obtained will be two-dimensional, and under rotation one dimension will be the original line that generated the preferential choices and the second dimension will be the vector of the median individual on the line. This second dimension, on which the projections of individual points are in reverse order to how close each is to all the others on the line, has a certain similarity to the concept of social utility discussed in Chapter 18. The idea of a social utility is to find a single ordering of stimuli which in some sense best represents the variety of individual orderings found in a society. The social utility discussed in Chapter 18 orders the stimuli from the one that has the least average distance from all the individuals to the one that has the largest average distance. Equating increasing distance with increasing dissatisfaction leads to identifying this as a social utility function.

The relevance of this notion of social utility to the extra dimension found in the factor analysis of preferences is that the higher the projection of an individual's point on this extra dimension the more central the individual in the configuration of individuals. Hence the nearer he is to the others on the average and the better he represents them.

Consider the case of a two-dimensional latent attribute space generating the preferential choices in which there are now two superimposed bivariate distributions, one for individuals and one for stimuli. It seems reasonable that the correlation of the I scale of an individual on the rim of this space with other individuals will progressively decrease through zero to −1 as we approach an individual across the space from him and that the median individual on the plane will correlate nonnegatively with everyone. The configuration generated by the set of unit vectors is now a hemisphere in three dimensions with the median individual represented by a unit vector perpendicular to the plane in which lie the vectors of all individuals on the rim of the plane.

If such were the case, a factor analysis would yield three dimensions, and under rotation one dimension would correspond to a social utility and the other two dimensions would represent the original space which generated the preferential choices.

Although not as intuitively obvious, this proposition may be generalized to a space of r dimensions in which we would expect the configuration corresponding to the correlation matrix to be a semihypersphere in $r + 1$ dimensions, where the $(r + 1)$th principal component would be a social utility and r dimensions would correspond to the original space. It is convenient to refer to the space obtained by unfolding as the *genotypic space* and the space obtained by factor analysis as the *factor space*.

Any attempt to realize the idealized version of the proposition necessarily leads to some distortion, the matching of the two being sensitive to the density of stimulus points and the joint distribution of stimulus points and individual points and to the measure used for the correlation between two individuals' I scales.

2. EMBEDDING OF GENOTYPIC SPACE INTO FACTOR SPACE

In order to test the plausibility of this proposition under rather general and varying conditions, several experimental sampling problems were constructed and run, of which two related ones in three dimensions play the major role. These will be presented first.

Table 8.1   Coordinates of Individuals' Points in E^3

	a	b	c
01	−0.47883	−0.12812	0.30109
02	−0.20438	−0.40540	0.26483
03	−0.49558	0.23608	−0.18766
04	0.41039	−0.42816	−0.29035
05	−0.45173	0.54625	0.41746
06	0.08085	0.29372	−0.04339
07	−0.26920	−0.34540	0.07160
08	0.27289	0.32257	−0.36360
09	0.05593	−0.13210	−0.33086
10	0.15816	0.00408	−0.34882
11	0.40540	−0.27578	−0.23506
12	−0.46175	−0.39914	0.01397
13	0.25472	0.54289	−0.32123
14	0.30705	−0.05145	0.48096
15	0.41614	0.22003	0.49106

Table 8.2   Coordinates of Random Stimulus Points in E^3

	a	b	c
01	0.03991	−0.40188	0.28193
02	−0.38555	−0.34144	0.32886
03	0.17546	0.10461	0.39510
04	−0.32643	−0.52861	0.27699
05	−0.24122	−0.30231	−0.10274
06	0.30532	0.21704	−0.35075
07	−0.03788	0.42402	0.56623
08	0.48228	−0.07405	−0.36409
09	−0.32960	0.53845	0.57620
10	−0.19322	−0.57260	0.07399
11	−0.11220	−0.47744	−0.14454
12	0.31751	−0.48893	0.07481
13	−0.30934	0.16993	0.27499
14	0.22888	0.33049	−0.35902
15	−0.41849	−0.08337	−0.46850
16	−0.46352	0.36898	0.14013
17	−0.11087	−0.48297	0.56303
18	−0.52701	−0.19019	0.39904
19	0.57275	0.32486	0.45134
20	−0.20857	0.01889	0.37239
21	0.15633	0.07629	−0.18637
22	−0.38688	0.43625	−0.05327
23	0.25163	−0.11692	0.43253
24	0.36815	0.25624	−0.53342
25	−0.04515	0.06345	−0.13574
26	0.14387	−0.00008	−0.29593
27	0.51321	0.55306	−0.44989
28	0.05466	0.18711	0.52162
29	−0.39528	−0.16120	0.04737
30	−0.07586	−0.04235	0.16894

Three sets of 15 uniform random numbers are taken to represent the coordinates of 15 individuals in E^3, and another 3 sets of 30 uniform random numbers, those of 30 stimuli in the same space (Tables 8.1 and 8.2).* All numbers are restricted to decimal fractions, positive or negative, and hence the joint space for both individuals and stimuli is, by definition, a cube in E^3 with length of its sides equal to 2 and center at the origin, called the basic *cube*. A third set of points is taken to represent a second set of stimulus points, these being the 64 lattice points of a "grid" contained in the

* See RAND (1955). All numbers were first taken to be seven-place decimal fractions and computations were carried out in this form; they were rounded off to five places after the completion of the study.

basic cube. On each dimension the points take on one of the four values
−0.6, −0.2, 0.2, 0.6, yielding $4^3 = 64$ points. For simplicity, the two sets
of stimulus points are distinguished by calling them *random stimuli* and
lattice stimuli respectively. We took the latter (1) to see if an increase in the
number of stimuli used would yield a "better fit" to the idealized situation,
and (2) to test if the model could be borne out with quite arbitrary selection
of stimulus points, random as well as nonrandom.

The Euclidean distances of each individual from all the stimuli (random
or lattice) are computed, and these measures provide an I scale for the
individual which is a ratio scale rather than an ordinal scale. The product
moment correlations are then computed between each pair of individuals' I
scales, yielding two correlation matrices, one for the random stimuli M_r,
(Table 8.3) and one for the lattice stimuli M_l (Table 8.4).

These correlation matrices with unity in the diagonal are then factored
by the method of principal components.* The characteristic values λ_i for
the two correlation matrices are given in Table 8.5. It can be seen that a
sharp drop in the magnitude of the characteristic value occurs after the
fourth value. Hence the first four columns of the factor matrices (Tables 8.6
and 8.7) are taken as the factor loadings or coordinates of the fifteen
individuals in four dimensions.†

Two crucial questions arise. First, how are the original coordinates of
the individuals' points in three dimensions related to their factor loadings
in four dimensions? Second, what is the significance of the "extra"
dimension obtained?

According to the proposition, the configuration corresponding to the
correlation matrix is a set of unit vectors in E^4 whose projections in a subspace E^3, orthogonal to the vector of the median individual, will faithfully
reproduce the configuration of the individuals' points in the original
genotypic space. Hence the first question can be settled if it can be shown
that Table 8.1 can be "embedded" into Table 8.6 and into Table 8.7.

We shall use Tucker's method of congruence (Tucker, 1951) in which his
coefficient of congruence, Q_r, is similar to a product-moment correlation
between the coordinates on a dimension in the original space and the
loadings on a "most-matching" factor r in the factor space. The value of Q_r
for each of the three original dimensions as recovered by the two factor

---

* Two different subroutines (IBM 704 and RAND JOHNIAC) were used independently
to duplicate all computations. The numbers from these two sources agree to seven
decimal places except for signs, that is, a characteristic vector from one subroutine may
be the reflection of another from the other subroutine.

† The appropriate statistical theory for characteristic roots of a sample correlation
matrix has yet to be worked out (see Anderson, 1958, p. 330). This investigation lends
some convincing evidence that such a theory can be developed.

Table 8.3   Correlation Between

	01	02	03	04	05	06	07
01	1.00000						
02	0.81806	1.00000					
03	0.40572	0.10542	1.00000				
04	−0.36616	0.11950	−0.20383	1.00000			
05	0.53181	0.02277	0.52189	−0.78366	1.00000		
06	−0.33222	−0.46428	0.40337	0.20512	0.18277	1.00000	
07	0.76629	0.94362	0.32694	0.22961	−0.01799	−0.32655	1.00000
08	−0.73815	−0.67589	0.08695	0.46280	−0.33930	0.78433	−0.51320
09	−0.26828	0.02011	0.30207	0.83379	−0.50498	0.51645	0.25743
10	−0.51575	−0.29706	0.19885	0.76176	−0.48119	0.69258	−0.08422
11	−0.46329	−0.02397	−0.19668	0.98148	−0.73770	0.36014	0.08807
12	0.78772	0.90365	0.41895	0.13480	0.03176	−0.36574	0.98322
13	−0.75154	−0.79191	0.11925	0.25679	−0.16748	0.81675	−0.64825
14	0.26843	0.34916	−0.37285	0.02601	0.17020	0.05328	0.13859
15	0.05611	−0.12378	−0.38483	−0.14621	0.27643	0.30513	−0.31281

Table 8.4   Correlation Between

	01	02	03	04	05	06	07
01	1.00000						
02	0.80180	1.00000					
03	0.45996	0.09669	1.00000				
04	−0.34670	0.18399	−0.35755	1.00000			
05	0.61419	0.09619	0.59587	−0.70245	1.00000		
06	−0.00221	−0.16857	0.44345	0.05399	0.45912	1.00000	
07	0.76486	0.93343	0.34352	0.23930	0.07586	−0.08260	1.00000
08	−0.50001	−0.48321	0.20553	0.36304	−0.06191	0.80035	−0.32676
09	−0.13477	0.16287	0.28975	0.75084	−0.35724	0.40084	0.39914
10	−0.33440	−0.10284	0.22977	0.70250	−0.30290	0.60162	0.10993
11	−0.37094	0.12037	−0.32828	0.97985	−0.61672	0.22331	0.16919
12	0.76137	0.84042	0.46245	0.09010	0.09797	−0.18764	0.95990
13	−0.45148	−0.58134	0.27127	0.09957	0.14840	0.84892	−0.45322
14	0.26537	0.42697	−0.38849	0.20445	0.17099	0.28854	0.17630
15	0.05755	0.06988	−0.33573	0.04294	0.29987	0.49538	−0.15479

Table 8.5   Characteristic

		01	02	03	04	05	06
λ_i	random stimuli	6.39715	4.01020	2.35246	1.99655	0.39150	0.10905
	lattice stimuli	5.21363	3.94788	3.44330	2.49448	0.12577	0.07310

analyses is given in Table 8.8, and it is evident that a good fit of the original configuration of individuals' points in a three-dimensional subspace of the factor space is possible.

I Scales for Random Stimuli M_r

08	09	10	11	12	13	14	15

1.00000							
0.63858	1.00000						
0.86011	0.93347	1.00000					
0.59572	0.84772	0.83680	1.00000				
−0.53188	0.22048	−0.12251	−0.01156	1.00000			
0.96836	0.46858	0.73384	0.41059	−0.65380	1.00000		
−0.30203	−0.23865	−0.25308	0.04607	−0.00194	−0.29391	1.00000	
−0.02364	−0.32576	−0.18135	−0.04866	−0.43069	0.06526	0.85786	1.00000

I Scales for Lattice Stimuli M_l

08	09	10	11	12	13	14	15

1.00000							
0.60457	1.00000						
0.83923	0.93606	1.00000					
0.50019	0.76455	0.77163	1.00000				
−0.39451	0.33566	0.02720	−0.00270	1.00000			
0.95522	0.38240	0.65884	0.22527	−0.49730	1.00000		
−0.03695	−0.10708	−0.05619	0.28848	−0.06571	−0.04201	1.00000	
0.19408	−0.19580	−0.02219	0.17765	−0.37016	0.26100	0.90801	1.00000

Values for M_r and M_l

07	08	09	10	11	12	13	14	15
0.06822	0.03352	0.02680	0.01196	0.00999	0.00183	0.00075	0.00034	
0.03068	0.02790	0.02052	0.01096	0.00515	0.00385	0.00161	0.00104	0.00014

3. THE EXTRA DIMENSION IN THE FACTOR SPACE

According to the proposition the genotypic space can be embedded in the factor space, the factor space will have an additional dimension, and the projection of a point on this extra dimension will be related to how close each point is to all the other points in the genotypic space. The first two parts of the proposition have been sustained by the results reported, and it remains for us now to test the last part.

The projection of each vector on the extra dimension of the factor space is readily given from the length of the vector in the factor space of four dimensions and its reduced length in the three-dimensional subspace that corresponds to the original genotypic space.

The average distance of any individual's point from all the others in the original genotypic space is readily obtained from Table 8.1. The smaller the average distance of a point from all the others the nearer the point lies to the median of the population and hence the higher should be its projection on the extra dimension of the factor space. The Spearman rank order correlations between average distances in the genotypic space (ordered from smallest to largest) and projections on the extra dimension (ordered from largest to smallest) are .723 and .896 for random and lattice stimuli respectively, significant at the .005 level.

It is apparent, then, that the last part of the proposition has been sustained: Projection on the extra dimension inversely corresponds to how near an individual point is to all the others—the more "central" an individual point in the space the higher its projection on the extra dimension.

These results also provide some evidence for answering in the affirmative both questions which led to including the second set of stimulus points in the three-dimensional problem—more stimulus points more uniformly distributed yield a better fit to the idealized situation.

Table 8.6 Principal Components Factor Loadings for Random Stimuli

	01	02	03	04
01	0.85262	0.27021	−0.22809	0.33375
02	0.69980	0.62881	0.17248	0.26119
03	0.08652	0.25101	−0.92805	0.20117
04	−0.57057	0.70975	0.38252	0.06207
05	0.47920	−0.48049	−0.56888	0.39698
06	−0.68648	−0.08115	−0.41818	0.54391
07	0.55962	0.78716	−0.04066	0.21914
08	−0.96190	0.00826	−0.20677	0.03215
09	−0.63852	0.73509	−0.16018	0.13697
10	−0.85590	0.46673	−0.15916	0.12525
11	−0.69323	0.60280	0.34346	0.12922
12	0.59545	0.76164	−0.16490	0.11234
13	−0.92659	−0.28631	−0.18912	0.26799
14	0.25163	−0.14168	0.57725	0.74380
15	−0.10412	−0.56050	0.39376	0.76243
Σ of squares:	6.39715	4.01020	2.35246	1.99655

Table 8.7 Principal Components Factor Loadings for Lattice Stimuli

	01	02	03	04
01	0.72719	0.46805	−0.45787	0.14273
02	0.53410	0.78105	−0.01001	0.29306
03	0.10687	0.26099	−0.76577	−0.54484
04	−0.59226	0.60106	0.48881	0.15722
05	0.37333	−0.17152	−0.87300	0.12318
06	−0.58528	0.09476	−0.77412	0.19804
07	0.41858	0.89902	−0.09576	0.00533
08	−0.92210	0.02215	−0.35550	−0.07667
09	−0.61730	0.73370	−0.02764	−0.25316
10	−0.83504	0.50160	−0.12971	−0.16607
11	−0.69580	0.55692	0.36150	0.23753
12	0.51236	0.81177	−0.10147	−0.22775
13	−0.81839	−0.18864	−0.51428	−0.05858
14	0.00093	0.18049	−0.10485	0.97188
15	−0.18760	−0.12257	−0.27787	0.92650
Σ of squares:	5.21363	3.94788	3.44330	2.49448

Table 8.8 Congruence of Original Dimensions with Factor Space

		r_1	r_2	r_3
Q_r	random stimuli	0.99492	0.97699	0.98790
	lattice stimuli	0.99154	0.98254	0.99687

Two more problems were run to test the proposition in the genotypic space with one or two dimensions. For this purpose only one set of stimulus points was retained by pairing off the first column in Table 8.1 against that in Table 8.2, or the first two columns in Table 8.1 against those in Table 8.2. Euclidean distances between individuals and random stimuli in one and two dimensions were first computed, then the correlation matrices of individuals over stimuli, which were then factored by the method of principal components. Only a summary of the results are presented here. The first five (and largest) characteristic values for the one- and two-dimensional cases are presented in Table 8.9.

It can be seen that a sharp drop in the magnitude of the characteristic value occurs after the second value for the one-dimensional case and after the third value for the two-dimensional case, indicating that the factor space for preferences has one additional dimension beyond the genotypic space which generated the preferences.

Table 8.9   Characteristic Values for the One- and Two-Dimensional Genotypic Spaces

	1	2	3	4	5
One dimension	12.02233	2.70781	0.13125	0.10578	0.01797
Two dimensions	7.38998	4.80759	2.36532	0.24135	0.07356

Again Tucker's method was used for maximal congruence, the Q_r for the one-dimensional case is 0.976, and the Q_r's for the two-dimensional case are 0.989 and 0.986 for the first and second dimensions respectively.

Spearman rank order correlations between average distance of an individual's point from all the others in the genotypic space and the projection of the individual on the extra dimension were .761 and .669, significant at the .005 level, for the one- and two-dimensional cases respectively.

4. SOME PRACTICAL CONSIDERATIONS

In any practical application there are two sources of error or distortion, one of which is present in this study. The first is that the basic data normally consist of rank order preference scales rather than the actual distances to stimulus points. This means that the product moment correlation can only be approximated.* The second is that the distribution of stimulus points relative to that for the individuals can distort the factor space. This is most obvious in the one-dimensional case in which the stimuli that lie between two individuals tend to produce negative correlation between their preference orderings, and the stimuli that lie outside them tend to produce positive correlation. Clearly, if the density of the stimulus points between two individuals is unusually high or low, the correlation between their preferences will be biased toward negative or positive correlation and they will appear farther apart or nearer together in the factor space than in the genotypic space.

Another consideration is that in any practical application we arrive first at the factor space and seek the genotypic space. This requires determining the extra dimension in the factor space, with no prior knowledge of the genotypic space, and then rotating it out in order to work with just the genotypic space that remains. The following argument suggests how this may be done.

* We used product moment correlations between actual distances in this study because we were concerned with a purely mathematical relation between two systems of analyzing data.

The problem is to locate the median individual in the space. In the case of a one-dimensional J scale he is easily located by means of weak stochastic transitivity. As discussed in Chapter 18, majority decision always yields a transitive ordering under single-peaked preferences. So for each pair of stimuli we would obtain the majority decision, combine the pairwise choices into a rank order, and the resulting I scale is that of the median individual(s). The social utility dimension is then passed through this individual and rotated out to leave the genotypic space.

The multidimensional case is little different. Arrow (see Chapter 18) has shown that under certain conditions, which in unfolding theory correspond to a multidimensional J space, majority decision will not necessarily be transitive. We may in such a case represent the majority decision by a weak ordering in which intransitive cycles are treated as ties. Then we take all individuals whose rank order I scales satisfy this weak ordering and let the social utility dimension pass through their centroid. It may then be rotated out to leave the genotypic space.

Another method for locating the median individual in the space has been suggested by Robyn Dawes in a personal communication. The correlations between individuals' preferences may be converted to interpoint distances by equation 24.5, and hence the average distance of each individual from each of the others may be computed. The vector of the individual with the least average distance may be taken to define the social utility dimension and rotated out to leave the J space that would be obtained by unfolding.

A test of the adequacy of the solution for the social utility dimension is the rank order correlation between the average distance of each individual from all the others with his projection on the social utility dimension. If the social utility dimension is accurately located, this correlation should be high and negative. I suggest rank order correlation rather than product moment correlation here because of nonlinearity.

5. SUMMARY

The proposition is offered that the factor analysis of the correlation matrix between individuals' preference scales will yield a space of one more dimension than that of the genotypic space obtained by unfolding the preference scales, that the genotypic space is embedded in the factor space, and that the extra dimension in the factor space is a "social utility" dimension on which individuals have projections inversely related to their average distance from all the other individuals in the genotypic space.

The problem was studied by simple experimental sampling. Three sets of 15 random numbers were taken as the coordinates of 15 individuals in E^3 and three sets of 30 random numbers, those of 30 stimuli in the same space.

A second set of stimuli points was taken as the 64 lattice points of a cube 2 units on a side with center at the origin. Given this genotypic space, preference scales of individuals were computed for the random and lattice stimuli, and correlation matrices between individuals' preferences were obtained and factored by the method of principal components. This procedure was carried out for both sets of stimuli with $r = 3$ and with only the random stimuli with $r = 1$ and $r = 2$.

Tucker's method was used to test for congruence of the genotypic and factorial spaces. All three propositions were confirmed for both random and lattice stimuli with some slight superiority in favor of the lattice stimuli. This superiority could be due to the larger number of lattice stimuli, the regularity of their distribution, or both.

The social utility dimension in the factor space was discussed, as were possible methods for isolating it in practical applications.

The most general practical consequence of this development is that the methods of multiple factor analysis are revealed as a substitute for multi-dimensional unfolding for the discovery of the latent attribute variables underlying preferences with the qualification that there will be some sensitivity to the density and the distribution of stimulus points in the space. Factor analysis is particularly useful whenever we wish to avoid the labor of multidimensional unfolding and the additional assumptions are not objectionable, and whenever the data are too sparse for multidimensional unfolding to yield a determinate solution.

REFERENCES

Anderson, T. W., 1958, *An introduction to multivariance statistical analysis*, John Wiley and Sons, New York.

Coombs, C. H., and R. C. Kao, 1960, On a connection between factor analysis and multidimensional unfolding, *Psychometrika*, **25**, 219–31.

RAND Corporation, 1955, *A million random digits with 100,000 normal deviates*, The Free Press, Glencoe, Ill.

Tucker, L. R., 1951, *A method for synthesis of factor analysis studies*, No. 984, Educational Testing Service, Princeton.

CHAPTER 9

Some Alternative Theories of Preferential Choice and Further Problems

In Section 1 of this chapter we introduce an alternative formulation of the theory of preferential choice behavior, and the discussion is confined to the one-dimensional J scale. In Section 2 we discuss some alternative multi-dimensional models. Section 3 emphasizes a limitation on the kind of preferential choice behavior with which these theories are concerned.

1. ALTERNATIVE SINGLE-PEAKED PREFERENCE FUNCTIONS

We may examine unfolding theory in terms of *single-peaked* preference functions on the J scale.* The term single-peaked preference function (SPF) was first introduced by Black (1948) to describe the relation between an individual's degree of preference or utility for stimuli and some uni-dimensional ordering of them. The entire content of unfolding theory and technique may be discussed in terms of such SPF's. The discussion is worthwhile because it suggests new interpretations and generalizations.

The statement in unfolding theory that an individual prefers the nearer of two stimuli may be restated in equivalent SPF terms. Preferring the nearer of two stimuli corresponds to an SPF which has a maximum at the ideal and falls off in each direction strictly monotonically and symmetrically from this ideal. Three individuals (identified as 1, 2, and 3) with such SPF's are shown in Fig. 9.1.

Individual 2 has a linearly descending and symmetric SPF. This function corresponds to the observational equation

$$|p_{hij}| - |p_{hik}| \leq 0 \Leftrightarrow j \cdot \rangle k \qquad (9.1)$$

in which

$$p_{hij} = c_{hij} - q_{hij} \qquad (9.2)$$

_____
* This has been pointed out by Luce and Raiffa (1957, p. 356).

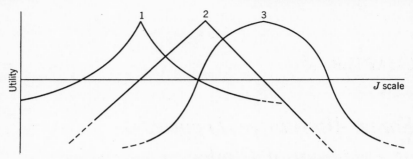

Fig. 9.1 Three strictly monotonic and symmetric SPF's.

The term *I* scale has been used to refer to an individual's preference ordering. It now becomes desirable to make a qualifying distinction. Let us refer to a preference ordering as an *ordinal I scale*. It is not difficult to imagine that by some method we may be able to obtain what we shall call *cardinal I scales*, that is, *I* scales in which there are numbers associated with the stimuli which are measures on an interval or ratio scale. We could also consider, of course, the possibility of obtaining ordered metric *I* scales, but our present purposes do not require it.

The cardinal *I* scales that are obtained according to equations 9.1 and 9.2 correspond literally to folding the *J* scale at the ideal points. The corresponding SPF's fall off linearly and symmetrically. The slope at which an SPF linearly descends reflects an individual's unit of measurement. If two individuals have the same ideal point and the slopes of their SPF's differ, their cardinal *I* scales will differ but their ordinal *I* scales will be identical. The unfolding technique for the analysis of ordinal *I* scales is unable, then, to detect any differences in slopes among linear SPF's.

Indeed, a much stronger statement than this can be made. *The unfolding analysis of ordinal I scales is unable to detect any differences among strictly monotonic and symmetric SPF's even if they are not all of the same shape.*

The argument is as follows. Imagine that the shape of individual 2's SPF is changed to the shape of the SPF of individual 3. It is evident that nothing at all will happen to individual 2's ordinal *I* scale, even though the cardinal *I* scale will certainly change; the preference ordering would be unchanged. It is obvious that for any unilateral pair of stimuli the property of strict monotonicity will preserve their preference ordering. It is equally obvious that for any bilateral pair of stimuli the property of symmetry will preserve their preference ordering. Hence the ordinal *I* scale of an individual will remain invariant over transformations of the *J* scale by SPF's symmetric about the ideal point. *If an ordered metric J scale is obtained by the unfolding analysis of preference orderings, the inference of SPF's which are strictly monotone and symmetric but not necessarily alike is supported.*

This is both a strength and a weakness. The generality of the unfolding method which results from this insensitivity is a strength. The valid application and interpretation of the unfolding analysis requires merely that the SPF's be strictly monotonic and symmetric and not that they meet the stricter requirement of equation 9.2. So, as far as unfolding analysis is concerned, any of the functions in Fig. 9.1 and any other symmetric and strictly monotonic SPF's are all equivalent. This insensitivity to different shapes of the SPF's is, of course, a weakness when the shapes themselves are of interest.

SPF's of a more general form include those that can be classed as weakly monotonically descending from a maximal point at the ideal and not necessarily symmetric. If the preference orderings are from such a class, their analysis by the unfolding technique will normally reveal only a *qualitative* J scale to be common to all individuals. An example of a mixture of SPF's that will yield only a common qualitative J scale is illustrated in Fig. 9.2. In exceptional circumstances involving particular coincidences of ideals, stimuli, and SPF's, preference orderings from such a class of SPF's can satisfy a common quantitative J scale.

In summary, then, the existence of strictly monotone and symmetric SPF's will result in a common quantitative J scale at the level of an ordered metric scale from the unfolding analysis of the preference orderings. The violation of either condition, strict monotonicity or symmetry, will generally yield only a common qualitative J scale on analysis of the preference orderings.

A great deal of experimental work has been related to the existence of SPF's; for example, see Young and Falk (1956) and Hovland, Harvey, and Sherif (1957). The study by Young and Falk is on rats' preferences for salt solutions. They draw the following conclusion:

When rats are free from thirst and tested with the brief-exposure preference method, they show an optimal concentration of sodium chloride within the range of 0.75 to 1.5 percent. When concentrations are below this optimal range,

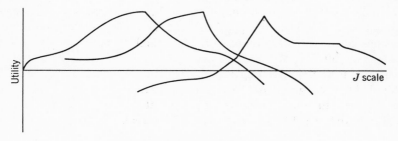

Fig. 9.2   Three asymmetric SPF's.

rats prefer the higher concentrations; when above this optimal range they prefer the lower concentrations. Within this range there are individual differences of preference and indiscriminate patterns · · · .

All things considered, therefore, we conclude that it is possible to locate salt solutions within one of two ranges. There is a *range of acceptance* [italics in original] within which acceptability increases with rising concentration. There is a *range of rejection* [italics in original] within which the level of acceptability falls as concentration increases. An optimal peak of acceptability can be conceived as a point determined by the interaction of a gradient of acceptance and a gradient of rejection. Shifts in the optimal concentration reflect changes in the conditions that determine acceptance and rejection.*

This is a clear statement of SPF's. Similar terms (*latitudes of acceptance and rejection*) are used by Hovland et al. (1957) in a study of the effect on an individual's attitude of a communication advocating some other attitude position. By a *latitude of rejection* they refer to the regions of the *J* scale so far removed from an individual's ideal that he rejects all items falling in such regions. In their Table 4 (1957, p. 250), they present hypothetical latitudes of acceptance and rejection for individuals holding positions along the *J* scale. In this table the latitude of acceptance cells form the parallelogram pattern of "pick" data discussed in Chapter 4, and the latitude of rejection cells form the offdiagonal corners of the data matrix as with "reject" data. They report: "When sufficient numbers of *S*'s are available for a given stand, the empirical distributions of responses show a close correspondence to these hypothetical patterns." (1957, p. 250). This parallelogram pattern derives from an SPF which they phrase in this manner: "Reaction to a communication will decrease in favorableness as the distance between *S*'s own stand and the position advocated in the communication increases." The percentage of favorable evaluations of a communication sustained this hypothesis.

Although the context of the discussion up to this point has been that of preferential choice, these ideas might also be tested for applicability to such processes as generalization and transfer. A paper by Guttman and Kalish (1956) illustrates this applicability. With pigeons as subjects, they utilized aperiodic reinforcement to condition the key-pecking response to color stimuli and examined the generalization gradient. Four groups of 6 pigeons each were conditioned to lights of high apparent purity at wave lengths of 530, 550, 580, and 600 mμ.

The generalization testing was carried out under extinction with 11 stimuli for each group distributed over a range of ± 70 mμ about the conditioned stimulus. Each stimulus presentation was 30 seconds long and was followed by a 10-second stimulus-off interval.

* Young and Falk (1956, pp. 574–75).

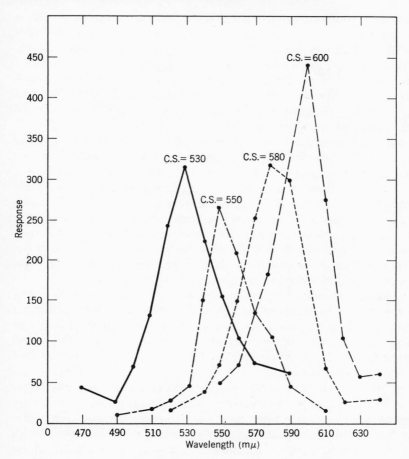

Fig. 9.3 Mean generalization gradients. Here C.S. = conditioned stimulus.

The mean generalization gradients obtained are shown in Fig. 9.3. For each conditioned stimulus group (530, 550, 580, and 600 mμ), the gradient was obtained by plotting the mean total number of responses for each test stimulus against wave length in arithmetic units.

Conditioning a pigeon to a stimulus might be interpreted as equipping it with an ideal on the relevant attribute(s), and we might expect it to respond with the conditioned response to other stimuli in a monotonically diminishing degree as the other stimuli depart from the conditioned one. In this experiment an SPF appears to be indicated.

A second generalization test identical to the first was carried out with highly similar results. Guttman and Kalish also present a number of the individual generalization gradients from the first and second tests. These gradients are almost without exception orderly SPF's, and the gradient for each subject from the second test is almost a replica of that obtained in the first test. The individual curves are described as being bilaterally convex for some subjects, concave for some others, and concave on one side and convex on the other for the rest. Guttman and Kalish suggest that the relative linearity of the average curves, as shown in Fig. 9.3, may reflect a random distribution of concave and convex gradients.

I shall close this discussion of alternative SPF's by looking at the issue from another perspective. The question of the form of a utility function on an attribute is intimately bound up with the question of scaling the stimuli on the *J* scale. For example, a logarithmic transform of a *J* scale would change the form of the generalization gradient. A more fundamental issue, then, is, *which is prior, the scale values or the gradient*? We may choose a gradient and obtain the consequent scale values, or we may choose a scaling method that will yield the scale values and obtain the consequent form of the gradient. This is a decision about which is to be the dependent and which the independent variable.

The choice is dictated by the comparative invariance properties combined usually with some esthetic and historical influences. We might seek a scaling technique for the stimuli that would yield an important degree of invariance of the form of the functions, or, alternatively, we might insist that the function has a certain simple form and then look for invariance of the scale values of the stimuli.

The problem is still more complicated because there are several behavioral processes to be represented by appropriate functions. So far only the behavioral processes of preferential choice and of stimulus generalization have been mentioned. Additional behavioral processes such as discrimination, detectability, and the judgment of similarity are also subject to independent experimental observation. These processes may also be related to suitable functions on the stimulus attributes. So all these processes and their several response measures* must ultimately be related in a unified theory. These are fundamental problems in psychological measurement and behavior theory.

This discussion clarifies the point made in Chapter 1, that psychological measurement and scaling models are theories about behavior and to measure something already requires a theory about it. The unfolding technique, for example, is a model or theory of the judgment process. An experiment like the Amsterdam experiment reported in Chapter 5 is a test of the theory.

* See the discussion of alternative response measures in Chapter 24.

2. ALTERNATIVE MULTIDIMENSIONAL MODELS

The concern of the previous section was behavioral processes on a one-dimensional joint scale. We turn next to some alternative multidimensional models.

The problem may be described in the following terms. Individuals may be observed to have preference orderings on stimuli, and these orderings are generally not the same. How may such different behaviors be accounted for? Let us recapitulate and recall, first, the intuitively reasonable idea that the stimuli have certain basic characteristics and that the individuals differ in their preferred amount of these characteristics, as in the idea of a joint space. Next, we might think that somehow the ideal preferred point of the individual has something to do with his preference ordering on the stimuli and that different ideal points account for the observed individual differences in preference orderings. This idea underlies the unfolding concept. To take the data then and attempt to discover what the basic characteristics of the stimuli are requires a model. The purpose of the model is to specify how an individual arrives at an ordering of the stimulus points. In the Hays-Bennett model this ordering is assumed to be generated by the Euclidean distances between stimulus points and ideal points. Here some other possibilities that have been seriously considered are described. One of these is called the personal compensatory model.

The Personal Compensatory Model

This model can be described as follows: Individuals and stimuli are identified with points in a joint space. Each individual's ideal point and the origin define a line on which all the stimulus points are projected. The individual's preference ordering is generated by folding this line at his ideal. The formal definition of the personal compensatory model is

$$|p_{hij}| = \left| |c_{hij}| - \text{proj.}_{c_{hij}} q_{hij} \right| \tag{9.3}$$

where $|c_{hij}|$ is the norm or length of the vector from the origin to the ideal and $\text{proj.}_{c_{hij}} q_{hij}$ is the projection of the stimulus vector in the direction of the individual's vector.

An illustrative example in two dimensions is presented in Fig. 9.4.

The individual's ideal point, represented by the cross in the figure, defines a line through the origin which represents a one-dimensional attribute constructed by the individual in a compensatory manner out of the two primitive attributes d_1 and d_2. His preference ordering according to this

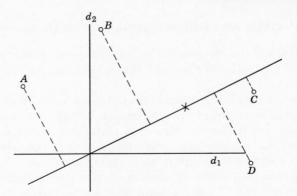

Fig. 9.4 Illustrating the personal compensatory model.

model would be $D\,B\,C\,A$, because D projects on the line nearer to the ideal than any other stimulus, B's projection is next nearest, and A's projection is furthest from the ideal. For the same configuration, the Euclidean distance function, which is a jointly compensatory model developed by Hays and Bennett, would generate the preference ordering $C\,D\,B\,A$.

The psychological idea behind this personal compensatory model is that the primitive attributes interact in such a way that they compensate for each other at some rate that characterizes the individual. For example, he may have a preferred amount of exercise and not care in which of several ways he takes it, separately or in combination. The model is one in which the ideal represents a weighted sum, and the individual is indifferent to the ratio or relative weights of the components.

Although this model has perhaps a certain intuitive appeal, nothing has been done to develop the general case. Tucker (1960) has developed a vector model for analysis of preferences which may be viewed as a special case of this personal compensatory model. He regards the stimuli and individuals as vectors and defines the vector product of a stimulus vector with the individual's vector to be the scale value, the utility, of the stimulus for that individual. This is to say that an individual's utility or preference for any object increases monotonically with the object's loading on any attribute. The further out on the individual's line a stimulus projects the more it is preferred. The result is that an individual's preference ordering on the stimuli is from the one that projects farthest out in his direction on down necessarily in order.

From the point of view of the personal compensatory model this is the ordering for an individual whose ideal point is farther from the origin than the projection of any of the stimuli on his vector. Hence Tucker's model is a way of analyzing a subset of the data we would obtain under the general personal compensatory model—the subset consisting of those individuals whose ideals are on the perimeter of the space, say the surface of a hypersphere which contains all the stimulus points within it or on the surface.

The psychological idea in Tucker's model is that, whatever the primitive attributes may be, an increase in any one of them increases the desirability of the stimulus. This assumption is justified, for example, if we are choosing among applicants for a job in which the relevant attributes are intelligence and physical strength and they compensated for each other, that is, an intelligent but weak individual would be as good (or poor) a candidate as an unintelligent but strong individual.

Another model that deserves consideration as a theory to account for individual differences in preference orderings is the lexicographic model. This old idea in mathematics has not yet been explored or developed for the analysis of preferential choice data.

The Lexicographic Model

The basic idea of a lexicographic model is that an ordering or hierarchy of importance exists on the primitive attributes. Of two alternatives an individual prefers the alternative that is higher on the most important attribute irrespective of the relative positions of the alternatives on the other dimensions. Only if the alternatives are tied on the highest attribute does he turn to the second most important attribute, and so on. For example, we may imagine that a dieter ordering a meal in a restaurant will look at items first in terms of calories. Only among items low in calories will he then consider other attributes in terms of which he will choose. Or perhaps, to be realistic, he will just find the things he likes and then select on the basis of number of calories. As a second example, a student choosing an elective may prefer *any* of the available courses in one department before choosing from those of another. For example, he may prefer an elective in mathematics, but of two equally advanced courses in calculus, he may prefer the one oriented toward theory to the one oriented toward applications.

In a political election a voter may prefer a member of his party to any other candidate and then within that group choose on the basis of other attributes. (This example suggests the possibility of a mixture of models in which the decision process is phased, with the first phase involving one model and a later phase a different model. I am not aware of any work on such complicated phased decision processes, although they are certainly realistic.)

The lexicographic model is untenable in its general form because no two things are ever equal. If we introduce the notion that small differences are disregarded, however, or if the stimuli are partitioned into equivalence classes on each continuum, the model is workable.

An experimental study on food preferences of rats provides a possible illustration of what might be the lexicographic model in operation. P. J. Hutt (1954) used Skinner boxes with different cups containing 3, 12, or 50 mg of a reinforcing substance which was either (1) a basic substance (a homogeneous semiliquid mixture of flour, milk, and water); (2) a citric substance (the basic formula with citric acid solution added until it was barely acceptable); or (3) a saccharin substance (the basic formula with soluble saccharin added to a degree optimally preferred). After extensive pretraining on the medium-sized cup with the basic mixture, the animals were divided into 9 groups of 9 animals each and given 5 successive daily half-hour sessions of periodic reinforcement for bar pressing. During all 5 sessions each group received 1 of the 9 possible combinations of size and food with 30 reinforcements in each half-hour session. The mean cumulative periodic reinforcement curves for day 5 are presented in Fig. 9.5.

The results suggest the possibility of a lexicographic ordering with the greedy rats preferring quantity first and quality second. There is one inversion in this order; the small saccharin cup is responded to more frequently than is the medium citric cup.

These results could equally well be accounted for in terms of Tucker's vector model version of the personal compensatory model, if the stimuli have been selected so they just happen to project in the proper order on a line in the space. It is intuitively plausible to assume that quantity and sweetness might be compensatory. Rather careful experimental work would be required to determine which of the two models is better.

A study by Young and Greene (1953), however, reveals an SPF for acceptability of different concentrations of saccharin solutions. Hutt's sweetest substance was optimal; if still sweeter substances were also used, the general personal compensatory model would be a possible alternative to the lexicographic model. This hypothesis could be tested with Tucker's model, as the analysis should yield one dimension for size and another dimension for the saccharin concentration continuum folded at the optimum concentration.

Landahl's City-Block Model

The second axiom of the theory of data postulates the existence of a distance function such that for every pair of points there is a distance between them. Any particular model designed to recover the space from

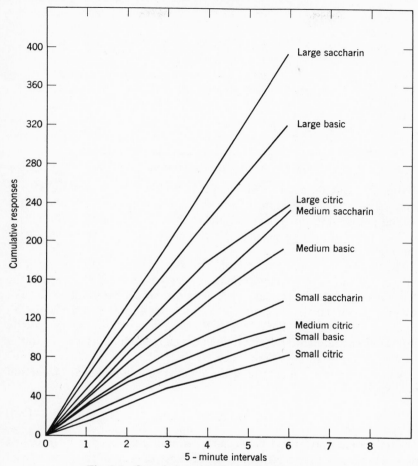

Fig. 9.5 Cumulative periodic reinforcement curves.

data needs to specify more. The Hays-Bennett development of multi-dimensional unfolding assumes that the distance function is Euclidian, which means that the distance between any pair of points x_1 and x_2 is the square root of $\sum_{d=1}^{r}(x_1{}^{(d)} - x_2{}^{(d)})^2$ if the dimensions d are orthogonal. The Euclidean distance function is used almost universally in multidimensional scaling theory.

There are alternative distance functions, however, at least as far as the mathematics are concerned, but not many have been seriously considered in the context of psychological theory. One, which was proposed by Landahl (Householder and Landahl, 1945; Landahl, 1945), is a consequence of a hypothesized neural mechanism designed to mediate judgments

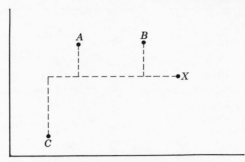

Fig. 9.6 The Landahl distance function.

of similarity and difference. The model is described by Attneave (1950) in these terms: "We must think of the shortest distance between two points (stimuli) as passing along lines parallel to the axes; metaphorically speaking, we must always go around the corner to get from one stimulus to another."

The distance between two stimuli is the simple arithmetic sum of their differences on the individual dimensions, so Torgerson (1958) calls it the "city-block model." Attneave proposed the model for similarities data (QIVa). In similarities data there is only one set of points in the space, all identified with stimuli—but of course the basic idea of the model is equally applicable to preferential choice data in which individuals as well as stimuli are mapped into points in the space.

According to this model the distance between an individual's ideal and the stimulus is

$$|p_{hij}| = \sum_d |c_{hij}^{(d)} - q_{hij}^{(d)}| \tag{9.4}$$

The individual's preference between two stimuli is assumed to be mediated by a comparison of two distances, the distance of each of the stimuli from the individual's ideal.

An analogue of the unfolding technique has not been developed for the analysis of preferential choice data generated by the Landahl distance function, but a preliminary exploration reveals some peculiar characteristics of the model. The basic ideas are most clearly perceived in the simple two-dimensional case. The distance function is illustrated in Fig. 9.6 with one individual (X) and three stimuli. The length of the dotted line from X to each stimulus is its distance from the ideal.

Consider now the bounding hyperplanes in this model that divide the space into isotonic regions such that all individuals in the same region have the same preference ordering. The three stimuli of Fig. 9.6 have been located to illustrate the three varieties of bounding hyperplanes that occur in this model (see Fig. 9.7). (1) Note that A and B have been placed on a line parallel to an axis. (2) B and C are equally distant on each axis, that is, the difference between B and C on each axis is the same, so they may be spoken of as being located at diagonally opposite corners of a square which has each side parallel to an axis. (3) Finally, A and C are at diagonally opposite corners of a nonsquare rectangle, indicated by a dashed outline in Fig. 9.7. The horizontal and vertical axes have been omitted in the figure for clarity.

Each bounding hyperplane is labeled with a pair of letters to indicate the stimuli for which it is the locus of equidistance. Within each region the rank order of preference associated with it is indicated.

In the first instance, for two stimuli on a line parallel to an axis, the bounding hyperplane is a straight line perpendicular to it, as may be noted in the case of stimuli A and B (Fig. 9.7). In the second instance, for two stimuli defining a square, as do B and C, the bounding hyperplane is a diagonal through the square, perpendicular to the diagonal joining the stimuli, and which at each of the corners of the square becomes two perpendicular lines parallel to the two axes, thereby bounding an open region

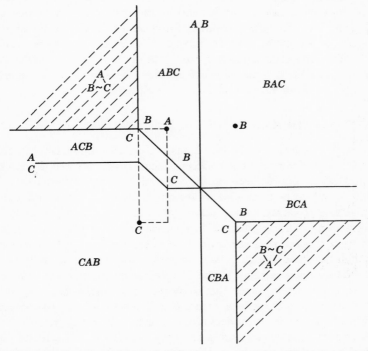

Fig. 9.7 Regions generated by three points in two dimensions (axes not shown).

of indifference to the two alternatives. These two open regions are indicated in Fig. 9.7 by dashed hatching.

The third instance, two stimuli located at diagonally opposite corners of a rectangle which is not a square, as exemplified by stimuli A and C in Fig. 9.7, is perhaps the case to be commonly expected. Note here that the bounding hyperplane is a straight line parallel to an axis but refracted as it passes through the rectangle like a ray of light through a prism.

Figure 9.7 shows how this model looks when it is applied to a Euclidean space in which the shortest distance between two points is the Euclidean distance function. It seems to point up some of the differences between this model and the Euclidean model (see Fig. 7.2). The bounding hyperplane in this city-block model is made up of lines parallel to axes and lines at $45°$ angles to the axes, nothing else. Furthermore, we note that two stimulus points which form diagonally opposite corners of a square, that is, have a constant difference on the several dimensions, generate a region of indifference.

The development of an algorithm for this model is much to be desired. The fact that a neurological mechanism is first postulated and then leads to this model is enough to justify very serious consideration of this distance function. I am not aware of any neurological or biophysical considerations which require a Euclidean distance function for psychological processes. In addition, one of the most desirable consequences of developing alternative models and their algorithms for data analysis is that *their existence destroys any naïve complacency with any one model and leads to a search for ways of testing and comparing alternative theories.*

3. SECOND CHOICES

Everything considered in Part 2 has had to do with what we might call first-choice preferences. Each successive choice is presumed to represent a first choice in the absence of the previously chosen alternatives. This condition would be contradicted, for example, by the preferential choices of graduate students among fields of psychology for their preliminary examinations. Suppose ten fields are available at a given university and each student is required (or permitted) to choose four for his preliminary. We might wish to use such data to seek a joint space to find out what graduate students perceive as the dimensions of the fields of psychology. We might suspect, however, that some students would survey the ten fields with the view of seeking balance and breadth, and the successive choices of such students would not reflect alternative first choices.

A student's choice of learning as a major and mathematical and physiological psychology as minors does not necessarily mean that if learning were not available to him he would pick one of the others as his first choice. He might regard mathematical and physiological psychology as two scientific languages or levels of description in psychology and prefer to substitute motivation or perception as a major. Other examples readily come to mind as in preferences for investment stocks when an investor seeks a balanced portfolio. It is not unreasonable to consider that preferences among gambles may sometimes reflect this same kind of successive dependency, as when a gambler "covers" his bets.

The unfolding theory and technique, as well as all the alternative theories considered here or elsewhere, are applicable to preferential choice data in which all preferences are "first choices." As yet there appears to be neither theory nor experimental work in this interesting area of "second choices."

4. SUMMARY

Section 1 interprets the unfolding theory in terms of preference or utility functions on a latent attribute, in particular, as single-peaked preference functions, SPF's. The relation of the shape of the SPF's to the distinction between qualitative and quantitative J scales is discussed. The existence of symmetric and strictly monotonic SPF's ensures a common quantitative J scale, while SPF's of any form ensure a common qualitative J scale. Some experimental data relevant to the hypothesis of SPF's are presented, and the relevance of the problem to the psychological processes of discrimination, generalization, and transfer, in addition to preferential choice, is suggested.

When the multidimensional case is considered the further problem of a distance function, or, using the more general term, composition function arises. How shall an individual be presumed to make a decision between two candidates when, to his taste, one of them wants too much government regulation of business and also is too aggressive in his international policy, and the other does not want enough government regulation of business and is appeasing? Here we imagine a joint space of two dimensions with the two candidates' points differing from the ideal point on both dimensions. The individual is able to decide which he prefers; the problem is how the model shall provide for this.

In Chapter 7 the distance function is the Euclidean distance from the ideal to the stimulus point. This is an instance of a *jointly compensatory* model; the individual and the stimulus together determine the rate of exchange between the dimensions. In this chapter some alternative composition models are suggested: the personal compensatory model of which Tucker's vector model is a special case, the lexicographic model, and finally Landahl's city-block distance function.

I would not be surprised if each of these models were appropriate for some individuals for some stimuli, and I would be very surprised if one of them were "the" model. It would be foolish to apply a single model uncritically to the analysis of all preferential choice data.

Finally, the interesting psychological area of second choices is introduced. An individual's preference between a pair of alternatives may differ depending on whether or not he has "realized" an earlier preference. Consider preferences among a set of paintings. If an individual received his first choice, his preferences among the remaining alternatives might be quite different than if they were all alternative first choices. No work has been done on second-choice preferences. *All models for preferential choice data consider the preferences to be alternative first-choice preferences.*

REFERENCES

Attneave, F., 1950, Dimensions of similarity, *Amer. J. Psychol.*, **63**, 516–56.

Black, D., 1948, On the rationale of group decision making, *J. pol. Econ.*, **56**, 23–34.

Guttman, N., and H. I. Kalish, 1956, Discriminability and stimulus generalization, *J. exp. Psychol.*, **51**, 79–88.

Householder, A. S., and H. D. Landahl, 1945, *Mathematical biophysics of the central nervous system*, Principia Press, Bloomington, Ind.

Hovland, C. I., O. J. Harvey, and M. Sherif, 1957, Assimilation and contrast effects in reactions to communication and attitude change, *J. abnorm. soc. Psychol.*, **55**, 244–52.

Hutt, P. J., 1954, Rate of bar pressing as a function of quality and quantity of food reward, *J. comp. physiol. Psychol.*, **47**, 235–39.

Landahl, H. D., 1945, Neural mechanisms for the concepts of difference and similarity, *Bull. math. Biophys.*, **7**, 83–88.

Luce, R. D., and H. Raiffa, 1957, *Games and decisions*, John Wiley and Sons, New York.

Torgerson, W. S., 1958, *Theory and methods of scaling*, John Wiley and Sons, New York.

Tucker, L. R., 1960, "Intra-individual and inter-individual multidimensionality," in *Psychological scaling: Theory and application*, edited by H. Gulliksen and S. Messick, John Wiley and Sons, New York.

Young, P. T., and J. L. Falk, 1956, The relative acceptability of sodium chloride solutions as a function of concentration and water need, *J. comp. physiol. Psychol.*, **49**, 569–75.

Young, P. T., and J. T. Greene, 1953, Relative acceptability of saccharine solutions as revealed by different methods, *J. comp. physiol. Psychol.*, **46**, 295–98.

PART 3

SINGLE STIMULUS DATA

The first three chapters in this part, Chapters 10–12, are concerned with QIIa data and their analysis. The first is an introduction and the next two deal with models for unidimensional and multidimensional analysis respectively.

Chapter 13 is a speculative interpretation which I enjoyed writing; Chapters 14 and 15 are concerned with QIIb data and their analysis. In the last chapter we take a look at cognition from the point of view and language of data theory; in addition, we discuss evaluative rating scale procedures.

CHAPTER 10

Introduction to QIIa

1. PREVALENCE OF QII DATA

The data of QII are relations on pairs of elements representing distinct sets. The relation may be one of order (dominance), in which case the data are QIIa; or the relation may be one of proximity (consonance), in which case the data are QIIb. Chapters 10–13 are concerned with the nature and analysis of QIIa data; Chapters 14–16 with the nature and analysis of QIIb data.

If either the variety of content areas in which data are collected or the variety of models for analysis is an indication, the data of QII are the most prevalent in psychology. Observations involving the comparison of an individual and a stimulus are a major source of such data and observations involving the comparison of a stimulus and a response category constitute the source of most of the remainder. Procedures for collecting such data are familiarly known to psychologists as the method of single stimuli and the method of absolute judgment. At the level of data theory there is no distinction between these methods—they both result in behavioral observations which are mapped into relations on pairs of points representing distinct sets.

A word might be said about the reasons for the prevalence of such data and the abundance of appropriate models. One reason is that in some real world contexts we are constrained from making observations appropriate for other kinds of data. For example, in making a survey of housewives' perferences for brands of coffee it would not be reasonable to ask them to go through pair comparisons, much less 'order 2/3.' Collecting such data is much more expensive, and with a few assumptions we can use single stimulus data instead. Furthermore, the purposes for which some investigations are undertaken are satisfied by single stimulus data. When we are concerned with determining the most popular style or color of a product, everyone's first choice is perhaps more relevant than the complete rank order of the preferences of fewer people. But these reasons for the popularity of single stimulus data are essentially practical ones which with suitable incentive could be overcome. There are, however, other reasons for the popularity of single stimulus data.

In the area of mental testing, for example, we seem to be limited to single stimulus data for measuring ability. Asking an individual which of two arithmetic problems he prefers to work hardly seems a good way to find out what his ability is.

Much of real life observation is single stimulus data, of necessity. We may observe which movie a student goes to, which woman a man marries, what kind of car he buys. In each instance it is a 'pick $1/n$' observation. We do not know what his successive choices might have been if the first choice had not been available. Because our ultimate intent is an understanding of real life behavior, it is imperative that models be built for single stimulus observations.

A final reason I shall mention for the prevalence of single stimulus data is the ubiquitous availability of rating scales. No matter what it is, we may still appear to measure it with a rating scale. Since there is no cheaper, quicker, or more certain way to associate numbers with objects, the method is very attractive and is widely used. For such reasons as these, then, we are not surprised to find the data of QII being obtained from all areas of psychology.

2. PHASE 2: MAPPING BEHAVIOR INTO DATA

In this chapter and in Chapters 11–12 we confine ourselves to QIIa data. We begin by illustrating in detail the process of mapping observations into the data of QIIa. Examples will be drawn from mental testing, psychophysics, and the questionnaire inventory approach; these examples will also illustrate some of the ways in which QIIa data vary.

Consider first the response of an individual to a mental test item, like an arithmetic problem, which is then scored as pass or fail. To map this into QIIa data we may conceive of the individual as a point c_{hij}, the stimulus as a point q_{hij}, and the observation, pass or fail, as an order relation on this pair of points. The two points are in a space D' of relevant dimensions. If there is just one dimension, the two points are on a line, and the meaning of an order relation is clear. If the space D' has two or more dimensions, however, there is no "natural" order on pairs of points and a model must define a composition function which induces such an order. Alternative ways of defining one lead to alternative multidimensional models corresponding to alternative theories about behavior.

I find it useful to deal with order and proximity relations in terms of a common language, that is, to translate them both into information about distances between pairs of points.*

In the simple case of one dimension the difference (a "signed distance") between an individual's point and a stimulus point is

$$p_{hij} = c_{hij} - q_{hij} \qquad (10.1)$$

If $c_{hij} \geq q_{hij}$, the difference p_{hij} is ≥ 0 and the individual point dominates the stimulus point. So we say

$$p_{hij} \geq 0 \Leftrightarrow \text{yes, pass, and so on, for items positively directed} \qquad (10.2)$$

In the general case of more than one dimension we may write

$$p_{hij} = c_{hij} \ominus q_{hij} \qquad (10.3)$$

in place of equation 10.1. Here the operation $\ominus$ is to be defined in the model and yields the difference (in r-space) between a pair of points. In verbal terms, we may think of QIIa data as information about the *algebraic* difference between a pair of points, that is, whether the algebraic difference is less than zero or not, where the pair of points represent elements of distinct sets.

A second example of this same kind of data may be found in the kinds of observations made to measure an individual's sensory threshold. Essentially, a subject responds in a way that indicates whether or not he detected an increment in some form of energy. The stimulus increment may be mapped into a point, and detection is interpreted to mean that the stimulus increment exceeded the individual's threshold. All the things said in the previous example about an individual and an arithmetic item, now apply, *mutatis mutandis*, to the individual detecting a stimulus increment.

Although we maintain here that these two kinds of observations may be mapped into the same kind of data, there are still real differences, at least potentially, between what we might call mental test data and such psychophysical data. The difference is quantitative rather than qualitative; psychophysical observations may be experimentally independently replicated on the same individual-stimulus pair, whereas mental test

* That psychological measurement is distance measurement is an old idea in psychology. In this regard see the note by Bentley (1950).

observations on the same individual-item pair cannot. Thus it is possible to estimate directly the probability of detection but not the probability of passing an item.

Responses to some inventories and questionnaires serve as a third example of behavior that may be mapped into QIIa data. Consider the following item from a questionnaire used during World War II: "Do your officers look out for the welfare of their enlisted men?" It is typical of the items used to scale attitudes toward officers. Usually several alternative responses are available from which the respondent chooses one and then the experimenter dichotomizes the alternatives into a favorable and unfavorable class. For our immediate purposes we consider the alternatives to be a simple dichotomy of "yes" or "no."

We may interpret the responses to such items in terms of a J scale representing a latent attribute of attitude toward officers extending from favorable to unfavorable. Each such item and each individual is mapped into a point on this scale and the individual's response is interpreted as an order relation on these points. But how does such an item become mapped into a point? The item would seem to represent an entire continuum and not just a point on it. This is so, but the individual has to choose between answering "yes" or answering "no," and somewhere on this continuum is a point such that the individual possessing that amount of the attribute or more would say "yes" but possessing less would say "no." This point corresponds to the scale value of the item.

Additional examples include the following: An individual is asked to answer "yes" or "no" to such questions as "Are you shy?" "Do you like algebra?" "Do you read lots of books?" In each case we may conceive of the individual corresponding to a point c_{hij} on an attribute and the item being represented by another point q_{hij}, which corresponds to *how much of the attribute is needed to say "yes."* The response, then, may be interpreted as an order relation on this pair of points.

Equation 10.2 indicates a correspondence between the real world observation on the one hand and a distance between a pair of points on the other. An expression of this type may be called an *observational equation*. On the right-hand side of the expression the phrase "for items positively directed" occurs, and perhaps we should make sure that this does not cause confusion. The only reason the possibility of confusion arises is that some items may be written from a positive or negative point of view. For example, the item, "Would you change to some other army job if given a chance?" is not positively directed toward satisfaction because the answer "yes" here indicates low satisfaction with job rather than high satisfaction. Such an item needs to be reversed in orientation in order for "yes" to be interpreted as implied by equations 10.1 and 10.2. This issue is not as trivial as it may seem, for in the multidimensional case serious questions may arise as to the "positive direction" of an item (see Chapter 12).

These illustrations of mapping behavior into the data of QIIa are drawn from mental testing, psychophysics, and the inventory questionnaire approach, yet they are seen to be qualitatively the same on a fundamental abstract level, that is, order relations on pairs of points from distinct sets. There are differences, however, among these three sources of such data. One difference between the psychometric and pyschophysical source has already been mentioned, that of the presumed replicability of the individual-stimulus pair in psychophysics but not the individual-item pair in psychometrics. But these two sources are alike in the *relative* stability of the point associated with a particular stimulus (or item) as different individuals respond to it.

The *difficulty* (q_{hij}) of an increment of energy or the difficulty of an arithmetic problem is presumed constant over individuals, and certainly an experimenter makes every effort to see that it is—by using warning signals and writing unambiguous items, for example—but he has little control over this aspect of a questionnaire item. He can try to write unambiguous items, but he cannot ensure that all individuals agree on how shy you need to be to say "yes." Each individual must decide for himself just how "difficult" the question is. The analogous procedure in mental testing would be to have a pool of items from which an individual drew those he chose to attempt and the number he got right was his score on that test. Perhaps scores on such inventories are "fakeable" because each individual decides for himself just how difficult each item is (that is, just what its q_{hij} value is).

These examples of mapping behavior into QIIa data reveal not only the range of behavioral areas from which these data are obtained but also that there are still real differences in the data from such sources. It is not surprising, then, that quite a variety of models have been constructed for analysis of QIIa data. A recognition of the fundamental similarity of the data to which they apply, however, permits us to overcome their parochial nature and leads to generalizability and transferability not only of models, but of the entire experimental lore.

3. THE ALTERNATIVES AND q-VALUES OF ITEMS

Before we can go on with the various models available for analysis of QIIa data, we must first come to a clear conception of the relation between the alternatives to an item and the attribute continuum. Consider the

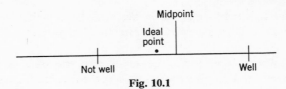

Fig. 10.1

following item and its two alternatives:

How are you?

(a) Well
(b) Not well

The item may be taken to imply the existence of a continuum representing possible measures of the state of one's health and each of the two alternatives may be taken to correspond to points on this continuum. That is, there is a point corresponding to a measure of how one's health is when he is *well* and another point corresponding to a measure of one's health when he is *not well*. An individual is conceived of as having an ideal point corresponding to how he is (or how he perceives his health to be or wishes it to appear), and he makes a choice between the two alternatives available to him. He presumably chooses the alternative which provides the better description and this will be the one whose point is nearer his ideal point.

The case of an individual who is "not too well" is illustrated in Fig. 10.1. As is evident from the figure, an individual's choice between the two alternatives may be interpreted as an order relation between his ideal point and a division point between the two alternatives. This division point is the q-value of the item and is the point that is scaled when such items are scaled. This division point is always between two *adjacent* alternatives, and in the simplest model we assume that it is the *midpoint* between them.

Suppose we decide to use the following pair of alternatives instead:

How are you?

(a) Well
(b) Sick

By exactly the same reasoning this item has a q-value which is the midpoint between the q-values of the two alternatives, as illustrated in Fig. 10.2. We are not surprised to find that more people appear to be well when the second item is used than when the first is. Even our hypothetical individual who just said he was "not well" is now more "well" than "sick."

In summary, any item with two alternatives has one scale value which is the midpoint between the scale values of the alternatives. Although there is a one-to-one correspondence between the two segments of the continuum, separated by the midpoint, and the two alternatives, there is

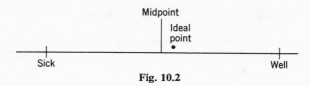

Fig. 10.2

not a unique correspondence between a segment of the continuum and an alternative, because the particular segment corresponding to an alternative depends in part on the two adjacent alternatives.

Although the argument and analysis presented here seems reasonably acceptable for these illustrations, the question of arithmetic problems and psychophysical thresholds naturally arises. I suggest that the argument holds in these cases also and in every detail. Consider the case of the arithmetic problem. The individual works the problem and provides an answer. The instructor decides whether the answer is right or wrong. The instructor decides, for example, what constitutes the right answer— how many decimal places, whether the work need be shown, whether the problem should be worked in a certain manner, and so on. These considerations determine the scale values of "correct" and "wrong" and hence their midpoint. These decisions of the instructor are formally equivalent to the item writer's selection of the alternatives to his item.

The psychophysical threshold procedure may be seen as another example. The individual may be asked to report whether a stimulus increment occurred or not. Instructions of the experimenter always convey, at least implicitly, a cost and utility for the various hits and errors. These in turn determine the scale values, the subjective intensities, of the two alternatives of reporting occurrence or nonoccurrence, and their division point is the individual's threshold.* Thus what appears to be an individual's threshold is within certain limits manipulated by the experimenter.

A final and very important point is illustrated by all three of these examples. Although we may, in theory, conceive of the alternatives to an item as having scale values, it is not these values which are obtained in any QIIa scaling procedure, but rather the midpoint between them. It is, then, the scale value of the item. If we ask why the scale values of the alternatives are not obtained, the answer is that QIIa data do not contain enough information to scale the alternatives. The validity of this answer is evident from the fact that two items may have the same scale value

---

* Part of the basic idea of the Tanner and Swets theory of signal detection (1954) is the manipulation of the observer's apparent threshhold by manipulation of the subjective importance of saying "yes" or "no" via a priori probabilities and a payoff matrix.

because the midpoints between their respective alternatives coincide, without the alternatives themselves coinciding.

This detailed discussion of the scale value of two alternative items has set the stage for the general case—the item with many alternatives.

4. THE SCALE VALUES OF ITEMS WITH MANY ALTERNATIVES

Consider the following item from a questionnaire used during World War II (Stouffer, Guttman, Suchman, Lazarsfeld, Star, and Clausen, 1950, vol. 4, p. 281).

How many of your officers take a personal interest in their men?

    (a) All of them do
    (b) Most of them do
    (c) About half of them do
    (d) Few of them do
    (e) None of them do

Each individual soldier reads the item and picks one of the alternatives as best representing how he feels. The model of the joint space which was used so extensively for QIa data is now equally applicable here. To each item there corresponds a psychological space which is a joint space in that each alternative corresponds to a point in this space and each individual has an ideal point in this space. The individual, presented with n alternatives, picks the one nearest.

Almost invariably the intent of these questionnaires is to construct a unidimensional variable, so our discussion for the present is in terms of a J scale. The extension of these ideas to multidimensional spaces is reserved for a later chapter.

It was pointed out in Chapter 4 that the parallelogram method of analyzing 'pick k/n' data is ineffective when $k = 1$ because the data matrix is maximally decomposable. For n alternatives there are $n!$ distinct arrangements of the matrix in each of which the x's form a diagonal parallelogram. This means that 'pick $1/n$' data cannot be used to scale the n stimuli without something being added. Usually this "something added" is an a priori ordering of the alternatives which is universally accepted, as in the case of the item we have given.

In contrast to such an item consider the following:

When you speak of profits, are you thinking of profit on:

    (a) Amount of sales
    (b) Amount of money invested in the business
    (c) Year end inventory
    (d) Other
    (e) Don't know

Which of these things is important to you in buying a new hat?

(a) Style
(b) Material
(c) Good looks
(d) Appearance
(e) Workmanship

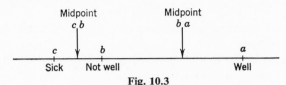

Fig. 10.3

In each of these questions we have no prior idea of the order or the location of the alternatives. If scaling the alternatives is one of the objectives, 'pick $1/n$' should not be used to make the observations. If the interest of the experimenter is in studying the joint psychological space in which these alternatives lie, they should be used as stimuli and QIa methods should be used.*

The alternatives to the item at the beginning of this section obviously lie on a single dimension. Yet even here, if we are interested in scaling the five alternatives to this item, they constitute $n = 5$ stimuli and any method of QIa may be used other than 'pick $1/n$.' If the observations consist of 'pick $1/n$,' then the working midpoints (those between alternatives adjacent in their rank order on the J scale) are $n - 1$ in number. The scale values of these $n - 1$ midpoints are the scale values of the item.

Suppose, for example, we imagine the following item:

How are you?

(a) Well
(b) Not well
(c) Sick

This item might correspond to a J scale, as in Fig. 10.3. The two working midpoints are the one between alternatives a and b and the one between alternatives b and c. This item, with three alternatives, has two scale values. Each alternative corresponds to a segment of the continuum, and the boundaries of each segment are dependent on the location of the adjacent alternatives. It is perhaps worth noting that the scale values of the alternatives need not be in the middle of their respective segments; see, for example, the scale value of the alternative "not well."

As another example, consider the following item, which comes from Stouffer et al. (1950, p. 281).

* This, incidentally, suggests a way of studying experimentally what should be done with those who answer "don't know" or "undecided," for example, use 'pick 2.'

How many of your company officers are the kind who are willing to go through anything they ask their men to go through?

(a) All of them are
(b) Most of them are
(c) About half of them are
(d) Few of them are
(e) Nbne of them are

Such an item would have four scale values, the midpoints between the adjacent alternatives. The number of soldiers who respond by choosing the alternative c, *about half of them are*, may be manipulated by changing the wording of alternatives b or d.

In the method of category judgment, an individual sorts stimuli into some predetermined number of ordered categories. Such data are formally identical to individuals' answering a questionnaire item, in that an item may be thought of as sorting the individuals into piles.

In each case there are elements of two distinct sets (individuals and alternatives; stimuli and categories), and the method of collecting the data is 'pick $1/n$.' The data in either case may be interpreted as order relations between pairs of points from distinct sets. One set contains either the individuals or the stimuli, the other set contains the midpoints between adjacent alternatives or between adjacent categories. Hence, a theory like Torgerson's categorical judgment model (1958), designed for the analysis of data collected by the corresponding method, is immediately a potential model for the analysis of questionnaire data. There could be a serious question of inter-item comparability of category boundaries just as there might be a similar question of inter-individual comparability of category boundaries when individuals are sorting stimuli.

The parallel here between categorical judgment and answering questionnaire items makes us wonder why we tend to use as many as 9 or 11 piles for categorical judgment, in which an individual is sorting stimuli, but rarely more than 5 alternatives to a questionnaire item, in which an individual is sorting himself. The thoughts suggested are that individuals are better at rating others than themselves or that we may have been misled by poor statistics.

5. WHAT IS THE STIMULUS?

In Chapter 1, and again in this chapter, the question of the definition of the stimulus has arisen, and perhaps some further discussion of the issue is in order. On the one hand psychology seems greatly preoccupied with what constitutes the stimulus (Gibson, 1960), and on the other hand data theory, which is so greatly preoccupied with psychology, regards the issue as outside its domain. There is no conflict here. Data theory is concerned with the *mathematics* of what is done with the things psychologists call stimuli. It says that there must always be things which are stimuli, but as far as data theory is concerned, these may be anything the psychologist wants.

Data theory views stimuli as associated with points in a psychological space. Depending on what the psychologist identifies as a stimulus, the corresponding point may be relatively stable and fixed for the same individual at different times and for different individuals, or it may not. In addition, depending on the method of collecting the data, the information about the locus of a point may be different. In some methods the point itself may be localizable; in other methods only boundaries between certain pairs of points are determinable. These are all essentially mathematical matters with which it behooves an experimenter to be thoroughly familiar. Although these methodological considerations do not answer the question of what the stimulus is, they are critically relevant to how the question is to be answered.

There are three classes of things with which psychologists are concerned: stimuli, individuals, and responses. Most discussions about what the stimulus is ignore the possibility that the individual and the response may not be defined, identifiable, and invariant. The question "what is the stimulus" always has a preamble which is usually omitted and forgotten, namely, "knowing the response of the individual . . . ." All the issues raised in respect to what constitutes the stimulus are equally relevant to the question of what constitutes the response.

Consider phase 1 of Fig. 1.1. We pick a fragment of what is observable and call that the response. Well, just as the stimulus is a concatenation of events impinging on a receptor system, so also is the response a conjunction of events. The question of what changes in the stimulus pattern are admissible for an invariant response may be turned around into the question of what changes in a response pattern are associated with an invariant stimulus.

In a psychological experiment there is usually something the experimenter specifies and manipulates called the stimulus. A stimulus, so specified, is some proper subset of all that impinges on the subject. There is also something called the response in which the experimenter is interested and which he has selected out of some larger set. The stimuli and the responses are observable—the individual is a black box between them. The relations between the observables lead us to infer the existence of processes in the black box.

A stimulus may be held constant or varied in certain respects, and the response is studied and observed to be constant or variable. When the response is observed to be variable for what is presumed to be constant stimulation, the response variability is attributed to new variables, for example, motivation, emotion, attention, and set. Our need for conative processes may be said to arise from the fact that responses to a constant stimulus may be variable. We may at one time approach a cheese sandwich and at another avoid it. We conceive of transient and fluctuating states to account for the variable behavior.

When a response is observed to be constant, rather than variable, this gives rise to what we have called cognitive processes. Here we have reflexes, abilities, attitudes, and so on—prevailing, pervasive, relatively stable influences. If the stimuli are constant for the observed constant response, we conceive of abilities and attitudes. If the stimuli are variable with response constant, we conceive of perception.

This highly simplified version neglects such matters as the role of individual differences, but it provides the nucleus for a systematic view of the content of psychology from the point of view of data theory. The issues involved in what constitutes the stimulus or the response become issues in experimental control and alternative levels of description, and, it seems to me, need not be matters of controversy.

6. SUMMARY

The intent of this chapter is to introduce some of the basic concepts of QII data, especially QIIa data. Abstractly they are relations between pairs of points which represent elements of distinct sets. The elements which are compared are typically an individual and a stimulus or a stimulus and a response category. The relation on the pair of elements is either one of dominance or one of consonance, and these relations correspond respectively to the data of QIIa and QIIb. Such data are very prevalent and are collected by such widely used methods as mental testing, psychophysical threshold measurement, questionnaire inventory techniques, diagnostic labeling, rating scale techniques, and magnitude estimation. These techniques are well known as the methods of single stimuli and of absolute judgment. Much of the character of QII data can be captured by describing them as either self-rating or the rating of other objects, where the term rating is used in the broad sense of description and not necessarily as implying a scale. Some possible reasons for the prevalence of such data are offered.

The mapping of behavior into data, phase 2, is discussed in detail and illustrated with three examples: achievement testing, sensory threshold measurement, and questionnaire methods. These examples are also used to suggest some of the ways in which the same kind of data (QIIa in this case) may differ in quantitative ways and hence lead to or require different models for analysis. At the same time the common abstract terminology suggests identifications between different areas and contexts which lead to new insights and to the ability to generalize and transfer models and experimental lore.

The general problem of what constitutes the stimulus in single stimulus data is then discussed from the point of view of scaling theory. We find that there are three possible answers. The first is the real world element of the arithmetic problem, the stimulus increment, the item in the questionnaire, and so on. These, and the environment in which they are embedded, are perhaps the first thought we have as to what is the stimulus. But these are not what are measured or scaled.

The second thought is that the *alternatives* to the items are the stimuli, in the sense that these have scale values and it is from among these that the individual chooses the one which is nearest the ideal point. Again, however, it is not the alternatives which are scaled when such data are analyzed. So finally we come to the third notion of what constitutes the stimulus in single stimulus data. If the definition of the stimulus is that about which the data contain information, then the stimuli are the *midpoints* between successive alternatives. Any item, then, with n alternatives has $n - 1$ scale values. Those items with only two alternatives have exactly one scale value, which then tends to be associated with the item. The scale value is the midpoint between the scale values of the two response alternatives.

These concepts become important in the following chapters on the analysis of QIIa data.

REFERENCES

Bentley, M., 1950, Early and late metric uses of the term "distance," *Amer. J. Psychol.*, **63**, 619.

Gibson, J. J., 1960, The concept of the stimulus in psychology, *Amer. Psychologist*, **15**, 694–703.

Stouffer, S. A., L. Guttman, E. A. Suchman, P. F. Lazarsfeld, S. A. Star, and J. A. Clausen, 1950, *Measurement and prediction; studies in social psychology in World War II*, vol. 4, Princeton University Press, Princeton.

Tanner, W. P., Jr. and J. A. Swets, 1954, A decision-making theory of visual detection, *Psychol. Rev.*, **61**, 401–09.

Torgerson, W. S., 1958, *Theory and methods of scaling*, John Wiley and Sons, New York.

CHAPTER 11

Unidimensional Models, QIIa

With this chapter we undertake the study of unidimensional models for the analysis of QIIa data. The generic description of the behavior that gets mapped into such data is as follows. The individual is presented with a stimulus and chooses a response alternative. The stimulus may be a change in energy and he is to say whether he detects it or not, or he may have to say whether he detects it clearly, barely, or not at all. The stimulus may be an arithmetic problem which he answers, and the answer may be graded pass or fail or may be graded high pass, pass, or fail. The stimulus may be a question about how he feels toward something, and he answers positively or negatively or selects an answer from a longer series of ordered response categories. Finally, the instructions may define or describe some attribute with some seven or nine graded response categories and the individual is asked to select the one category that best describes some object.

We have seen in Chapter 10 how scale values may be associated with the midpoints between adjacent response alternatives. These midpoints divide the presumed attribute continuum into segments which have a one-to-one correspondence with the response alternatives. The selection of a response alternative may be interpreted as an order relation between a point bounding that segment of the continuum and a point corresponding to the individual or the stimulus being evaluated.

The analysis of QIIa data has three major aspects which provide a basis for classifying and organizing the remainder of the chapter. The three aspects have to do with the stimuli, the data, and the models. Each of these will be discussed in turn.

The stimulus, typically an item, may have two alternatives or it may have more. If it has exactly two alternatives, the item has exactly one scale value which can be identified with the item as a whole; as, for example, the difficulty of an arithmetic item graded only as pass-fail, or the difficulty of detection of a stimulus increment based on number of detections. If an item has more than two alternatives, it has more than one scale value and each midpoint between adjacent alternatives needs to be scaled. It has been customary in the case of a two-alternative item to list the alternatives in separate columns of a data matrix. We shall see that this demands a special and additional condition, called orderly interlocking, in order for us to arrive at a unidimensional scale by conventional methods of scale analysis. This condition is independent of, and irrelevant to, whether a unidimensional scale will satisfy the data. We shall provide a procedure for transforming the data matrix that permits testing for unidimensionality without also requiring orderly interlocking.

The second major aspect of the problem of the unidimensional analysis of QIIa data has to do with the data, in particular, just what goes into the cells of the matrix. If an individual responds once to each item, as in mental testing or questionnaire methods, the cells contain a 1 or a 0 depending on whether the individual of that row responded positively to the item or alternative of that column. If there are experimentally independent replications of individual-stimulus pairs, as in psychophysical experiments, the cell entries are frequencies or probabilities rather than just 0 or 1. Similarly, if the data matrix represents the sorting of stimuli into categories by a number of individuals, the data matrix has stimuli as rows and categories as columns; a cell entry is the proportion of individuals who chose that column-category for that row-stimulus.

This aspect of the data matrices is relevant because there are models designed to analyze (1,0) data matrices and models designed to analyze probabilistic data matrices. It is not too binding, however, because procedures have been suggested for converting either kind of matrix into the other, and, if appropriate and feasible, they permit a choice of models. A probabilistic data matrix may be converted into a (1,0) data matrix by mapping probabilities less than .50 into 0 and all others into 1. A procedure for converting a (1,0) matrix into a probabilistic matrix has been suggested by Tucker (1952) in which homogeneous subgroups of subjects are formed on the basis of total score (row sum). The rows of the members of a subgroup are then collapsed into a single row, and the proportion of 1's in a cell is taken as an estimate of the probability that individuals of like degree would respond positively to a given item.

Finally, the third basis of classification is in terms of whether the models are deterministic or probabilistic; that is, whether in the model itself provision is made for a random variable component or whether inconsistency is not recognized as such. Among the best known and most widely used models, then, we may classify Guttman's scalogram model (1950) as a deterministic model for (1,0) data matrices, Lazarsfeld's latent distance model (1959) as a probabilistic model for (1,0) data matrices, and Torgerson's model for categorical judgment (1958) as a probabilistic model for probabilistic data matrices. Both Guttman's and Lazarsfeld's models are formulated in terms of dichotomous items, but there is a natural extension to items with more than two alternatives.* Torgerson's model is formulated in terms of any number of categories of judgment.

The organization of the rest of the chapter is as follows. After a brief section on a mathematical interpretation of the problem of analyzing QIIa data, Guttman's scalogram analysis is discussed, first for dichotomous and then for multicategory items. The probabilistic models of Lazarsfeld and Torgerson are then discussed.

1. A MATHEMATICAL INTERPRETATION

We may describe the mathematical problem with which the models of this chapter are concerned in the following terms.

We have a number of simultaneous inequalities of the form

$$p_{hij} \geq 0 \qquad (11.1)$$

where

$$p_{hij} = c_{hij} - q_{hij} \qquad (11.2)$$

and the problem is to "solve" these inequalities for the c's and q's.

In Guttman's model these expressions take the forms

$$p_{ij} \geq 0 \quad \text{and} \quad p_{ij} = c_i - q_j$$

and if certain conditions are satisfied the solution is a joint rank order of the q_j's and of the c_i's.

The same expressions may be said to hold for Lazarsfeld's model, but the solution is in terms of a joint rank order of the q_j's and of classes of c_i's with a probability distribution for each c_i over the classes.

In Torgerson's model, expressions 11.1 and 11.2 take the form

$$\text{prob. } p_{ij} \geq 0 \text{ is given} \quad \text{and} \quad p_{ij} = c_{ij} - q_{ij}$$

---

* In any application, however, more than mathematical considerations are involved in deciding whether to use a dichotomous response measure or a longer series of ordered responses, as Cronbach and Gleser (1961) have pointed out.

and the solution is a set of scale values for $c_i.$ and $q_{.j}$ on an interval scale, where $c_i.$ is the average c_{ij} taken over j and $q_{.j}$ is the average q_{ij} taken over i.

In Guttman's and Lazarsfeld's models the c_i are individuals' ideal points and the q_j are the scale values of dichotomous items. In Torgerson's model the $c_i.$ are the scale values of stimuli and the $q_{.j}$ are the scale values of category boundaries.

2. SCALOGRAM ANALYSIS

We first summarize the analysis of dichotomous items in order to provide the background for the discussion of the analysis of the multicategory item.

Dichotomous Items

The kind of behavior that might be mapped into data suitable for scalogram analysis may arise from a variety of observations. One source might be the responses of individuals to mental test items graded pass-fail, that is, 1 or 0, as in an arithmetic test. Another source is questionnaire items with many alternatives in which the alternatives are dichotomized by the experimenter and scored 1 or 0. This is a common procedure for such items. A third source might be the transformation of a probabilistic data matrix into a (1,0) matrix on the basis of simply classifying the probabilities as less than .50 (0), or not (1). This procedure throws away information but it might be irrelevant information for the purpose in hand.

The data matrix has each item as a column because there are only two alternatives and hence one scale value for each item. The individual has responded to each item by selecting one of the alternatives. These alternatives are ordered by the experimenter so that the positive direction is defined. In the case of two alternatives, then, one of them is defined to indicate that the individual dominates or, in some sense, exceeds the stimulus. Usually responses of the form pass, yes, and so on, for items positively directed indicate that $c_{hij} \geq q_{hij}$. The cells of the matrix contain a 1 or a 0 according to whether the individual dominates the stimulus or vice versa.

The data matrix is analyzed by a process of permuting rows and permuting columns, to seek a matrix called a scalogram, with the 1's and the 0's on opposite sides of a diagonal. It is usually sufficient to work with the reduced data matrix in which individuals with identical response patterns are treated as a single row of the matrix, and stimuli with the same response patterns over individuals are treated as a single column.

Table 11.1 Triangular Pattern of Perfect Scalogram

Response Patterns	Items 1	2	3	4	5
1	0	0	0	0	0
2	1	0	0	0	0
3	1	1	0	0	0
4	1	1	1	0	0
5	1	1	1	1	0
6	1	1	1	1	1

An illustration of the scalogram sought is presented in Table 11.1 for a reduced data matrix with $n = 5$. When such a pattern is obtained, the order of the columns is the order of the items on the *J* scale and the rows correspond to the rank order of the individuals.

To bring out pictorially the data theory view of scalogram analysis, Fig. 11.1 presents a hypothetical case of five items, each with two alternatives. The figure shows the two alternatives to each item (labeled 1*a*, 1*b*, 2*a*, 2*b*, and so on), their midpoint (that is, the scale value of the item, labeled with the item number), and the response patterns identified with the six segments of the continuum.

The item scale values have segmented the continuum. An individual has an ideal point, *c* value, in one of these segments and will respond positively to all items whose scale values are below him (to the left), and negatively to all those above.

This basic idea of Guttman's scalogram analysis leads to a triangular scalogram pattern and should be distinguished from parallelogram analysis described in Chapter 4 for QIa data. They are, of course, closely related, but it is more important to keep them differentiated and identify each of them with their respective families. This is particularly urgent because sometimes an *extended scalogram matrix* is used for processing the data, as described by Green (1954) and Torgerson (1958). In this form

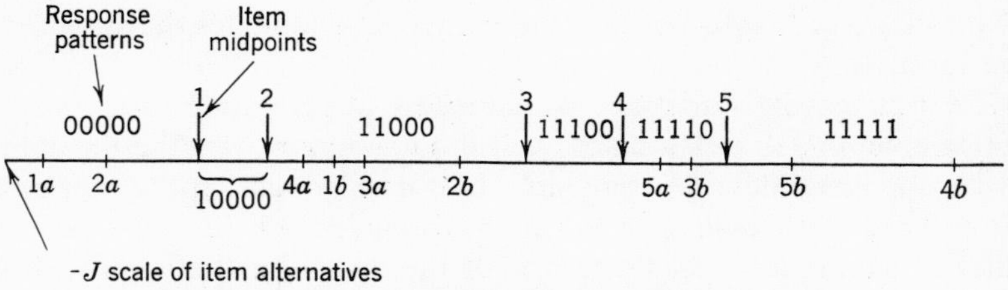

Fig. 11.1 The *J* scale with five dichotomous items.

each alternative of each item has its own column in the data matrix. The scalogram analysis of such a matrix seeks a parallelogram, as illustrated in Table 11.2 for $n = 4$.

The right half of the matrix in Table 11.2 is completely redundant to the first half but there is no harm in this except the wasted effort. The danger arises when the method is applied to items with more than two alternatives. With each item alternative allocated a separate column in the data matrix the process of scalogram analysis consists of seeking a parallelogram pattern, as is illustrated by Torgerson (1958, p. 308). The source of the danger and the way to avoid it is discussed in detail shortly, and a method of analysis is provided in which a triangular pattern is

Table 11.2   Extended Scalogram for Four Dichotomous Items

Response Patterns	Item Alternatives							
	4a	3a	2a	1a	4b	3b	2b	1b
1	1	1	1	1	0	0	0	0
2	0	1	1	1	1	0	0	0
3	0	0	1	1	1	1	0	0
4	0	0	0	1	1	1	1	0
5	0	0	0	0	1	1	1	1

always sought, regardless of the number of alternatives. Consequently the term triangular analysis is used to describe the scalogram technique for the unidimensional scaling of QIIa data and parallelogram analysis for the unidimensional scaling of certain QIa data.

In applying scalogram analysis the perfect triangular pattern is almost never achieved. The problem of measuring goodness of fit by some form of a coefficient of reproducibility is alive in the literature. Besides Torgerson and Green, see also Milholland (1955), White and Saltz (1957), and L. Goodman (1959).

Multicategory Items

The conventional procedure for the scalogram analysis of multicategory items will be illustrated here to show how the procedure depends on satisfying a special condition irrelevant to the purpose in hand, that is, testing the hypothesis of scalability. Then a revised procedure will be presented which requires no new assumptions but eliminates the need for satisfying this special condition.

Consider the following three items, used in essentially this form in a study of attitudes of enlisted men toward their officers during World War II.

(1) How many of your present officers are the kind that always try to look out for the welfare of enlisted men?

(a) All
(b) Most
(c) About half
(d) Few
(e) None

(2) In general, how good would you say your officers were?

(a) Very good
(b) Fairly good
(c) About average
(d) Pretty poor
(e) Very poor

(3) How do you feel about the privileges officers get compared to those enlisted men get?

(a) Officers have far too few privileges
(b) Officers have too few privileges
(c) Officers have about the right number of privileges
(d) Officers have a few too many privileges
(e) Officers have far too many privileges

The alternatives have all been labeled from (a) to (e) to be positively directed on a continuum from pro to con or favorable to unfavorable attitude toward officers. Each soldier selected one alternative under each item as best representing how he felt in answer to the question posed by the item. Each item may be thought of as presenting $n = 5$ stimuli, the five alternatives, and the individuals "pick $1/n$." The midpoints working are those between adjacent stimuli. The data on an item, then, do not permit the scaling of the alternatives, as was seen in the discussion of parallelogram analysis in Chapter 4. However, the universal cultural acceptance of the a priori ordering of the alternatives leads to a corresponding ordering of the subjects on each item. So *the problem becomes one of testing whether the continuum defined by each of the several items is the same one.*

One way of testing this is to dichotomize each set of alternatives and analyze as a (1,0) data matrix of dichotomous items. This procedure throws away information, and there is also a tendency to dichotomize the several sets of alternatives in such a way as to maximize the coefficient of reproducibility. This procedure, although it frankly acknowledges the unreliability of such data, takes advantage of random errors and may

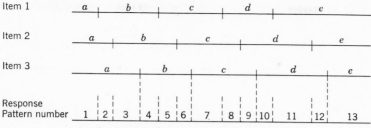

Fig. 11.2 Illustration of orderly interlocking.

give a distorted view. Jane Loevinger's* expression "gerrymander the data" fits this procedure quite well.

If the experimenter does not choose to dichotomize the items, the conventional procedure is to construct a (1,0) data matrix with the individuals as rows and the item alternatives as columns. A cell entry of 1 or 0 indicates that the row-individual selected that column-item alternative or did not. The analytical procedure then consists of permuting rows and permuting columns, preserving the order of alternatives within an item, to seek a parallelogram of 1's in the matrix.

How this comes about in an ideal case is illustrated in Fig. 11.2 and Table 11.3. In Fig. 11.2 the continuum associated with each item is cut into as many segments as there are alternatives and ordered a priori. In the figure the segment of each continuum and the alternative with which it is associated are indicated. If these three item continua are the same, they may be superimposed and will jointly generate thirteen distinct response patterns as indicated at the bottom of Fig. 11.2. The reduced data matrix given in Table 11.3 shows the thirteen response patterns and the perfect parallelogram that may be obtained.

If a table like Table 11.3 is obtained, there is no further problem, as in most idealized instances. The trouble arises when a near parallelogram is obtained and we want an index, like a coefficient of reproducibility, to represent just how near.

The difficulty lies in the fact that to achieve this perfect parallelogram a special condition, called *orderly interlocking*, is required over and above the basic and important condition that the items are all segmenting the same continuum. Note in Fig. 11.2 that the continua of every pair of items may be superimposed in such a way that the joint ordering of midpoints alternates between the two items. For example, if the continua of items 1 and 2 are superimposed, the first midpoint is $1ab$, the next is $2ab$, then $1bc$, $2bc$, $1cd$, $2cd$, $1de$, $2de$. The midpoints of every pair of items must mesh like the teeth in gears. When each item has only two alternatives,

* Personal communication.

Table 11.3 Parallelogram Pattern with Orderly Interlocking*

Item Alternatives

Response Patterns	1a	2a	3a	1b	2b	3b	1c	2c	3c	1d	2d	3d	1e	2e	3e
1	1	1	1												
2		1	1	1											
3			1	1	1										
4				1	1	1									
5					1	1	1								
6						1	1	1							
7							1	1	1						
8								1	1	1					
9									1	1	1				
10										1	1	1			
11											1	1	1		
12												1	1	1	
13													1	1	1

* All omitted entries are 0's.

this condition is automatically achieved because each gear has only one tooth, provided the scale value for each item is relatively constant over the individuals.

If items have more than two alternatives, however, the condition of orderly interlocking cannot be achieved unless all items have the same number of alternatives. Even then it would be a somewhat remarkable occurrence if the condition were met. Recognizing that each alternative corresponds, in theory, to a point on the item continuum, we see that the segment corresponding to an alternative is bounded by the midpoints between an alternative point and its adjacent alternative points. Hence the segment of a continuum associated with an alternative is dependent on the adjacent alternatives. For example, in item 2, the (b) alternative is "fairly good" and the (d) alternative is "pretty poor." If either of these were changed to "pretty good" or "fairly poor," respectively, the segment of the continuum associated with alternative 2c, "about average," would probably have different boundaries. It would be surprising if the condition of orderly interlocking of this item with all others would survive such relatively innocent changes.

If the condition of orderly interlocking is not satisfied, a perfect parallelogram cannot be achieved. For example, if the same three items should happen to segment their respective continua as illustrated in Fig. 11.3, the near parallelogram shown in Table 11.4 would result. In this instance three items are all mutually homogeneous, that is, all measuring the same

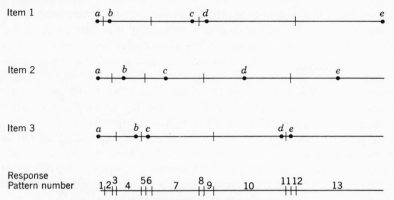

Fig. 11.3 Illustrating disorderly interlocking.

attribute; the data are perfectly reliable, but reproducibility is less than perfect.

The reason for the difficulty is that in listing each item alternative as a column we imply that each *alternative* is to be scaled, so these 3 items, each with 5 alternatives, would have a total of 15 scale values. But we have previously seen that each item with n alternatives has only $n - 1$ scale values. So these 3 items each have 4, or 12 in all. The problem then is to use a technique which will permit scaling these 12 midpoints rather than the 15 alternatives.

Table 11.4 Parallelogram Pattern with Disorderly Interlocking*

Response Patterns	Item Alternatives														
	1a	2a	3a	1b	2b	3b	3c	2c	1c	1d	2d	3d	3e	2e	1e
1	1	1	1												
2		1	1	1											
3			1	1	1										
4				1	1	1									
5				1	1	0	1								
6				1	0	0	1	1							
7							1	1	1						
8							1	1	0	1					
9							1	0	0	1	1				
10										1	1	1			
11										1	1	0	1		
12										1	0	0	1	1	
13													1	1	1

* All omitted entries are 0's.

This is very easily accomplished by converting each item with n alternatives into $n - 1$ dichotomous items. Instead of just dichotomizing each multicategory item once, it is dichotomized at each of the $n - 1$ midpoints between adjacent alternatives. The dichotomous items thereby constructed are then analyzed by triangular analysis, preserving the order of the dichotomous items which are made up from the same multicategory item. This procedure enables us to bypass the orderly interlocking condition and obtain an unbiased picture of the reproducibility.

The procedure is very simple, being that of constructing all the admissible dichotomizations for each item. For example, an item with 5 alternatives may be dichotomized 4 different ways: $a|bcde$; $ab|cde$; $abc|de$; $abcd|e$. Each of these dichotomizations is at a midpoint between two adjacent alternatives; the first is at the ab midpoint, the second at the bc, then the cd, and the last the de. If this were item 3, for example, we would label these four dichotomous items as $3ab$, $3bc$, $3cd$, and $3de$. This order must then be preserved in the scale analysis.

Now suppose an individual responds to item 3 by choosing alternative (c). We adopt a suitable sign convention such as the following: If an individual is to the right of a midpoint he may be regarded as having responded positively to the corresponding dichotomous item. Thus, an individual who chose alternative $3c$ is recorded as responding positively to item $3ab$. Similarly, he may be said to have responded positively to $3bc$, but negatively to $3cd$ and to $3de$. So his response pattern within these four items is 1100.

Each item is dichotomized at each midpoint between adjacent alternatives, and each individual's response is converted into $n - 1$ responses to the $n - 1$ dichotomous items so constructed. The data matrix has individuals as rows and the dichotomous items as columns. The new data matrix, then, for the three items in Fig. 11.3 could be permuted to yield the triangular scalogram pattern observed in Table 11.5. Note that the order of midpoints within any item is preserved in the ordering of the columns, that is, the order of the midpoints of item 1, as embedded in the composite ordering, is $1ab$, $1bc$, $1cd$, $1de$.

This procedure could also be used, of course, with multicategory items which are orderly interlocked and in such a case would yield the same result as parallelogram analysis.

Another way of looking at triangular analysis is as follows. It will be recalled that each item alternative corresponds to a segment of the continuum. Every such segment has, in principle, two parameters, a beginning point and a terminal point. If the rank order of the beginning points of all item alternatives is identical with the rank order of their terminal points, we have orderly interlocking and parallelogram analysis

Table 11.5   Triangular Analysis of Items with Disorderly Interlocking

Item Alternative Midpoints

	1ab	2ab	3ab	3bc	2bc	1bc	1cd	2cd	3cd	3de	2de	1de
1	0	0	0	0	0	0	0	0	0	0	0	0
2	1	0	0	0	0	0	0	0	0	0	0	0
3	1	1	0	0	0	0	0	0	0	0	0	0
4	1	1	1	0	0	0	0	0	0	0	0	0
5	1	1	1	1	0	0	0	0	0	0	0	0
6	1	1	1	1	1	0	0	0	0	0	0	0
7	1	1	1	1	1	1	0	0	0	0	0	0
8	1	1	1	1	1	1	1	0	0	0	0	0
9	1	1	1	1	1	1	1	1	0	0	0	0
10	1	1	1	1	1	1	1	1	1	0	0	0
11	1	1	1	1	1	1	1	1	1	1	0	0
12	1	1	1	1	1	1	1	1	1	1	1	0
13	1	1	1	1	1	1	1	1	1	1	1	1

will yield the same result as triangular analysis. Essentially, the condition of orderly interlocking is that one parameter is sufficient for each alternative. Disorderly interlocking is the condition that the two parameters of each item alternative segment are not perfectly correlated so the scaling procedure must permit independent scaling of the two parameters. Triangular analysis does this; extended scalogram analysis does not.

Interestingly enough, one of the byproducts of triangular analysis, if the items are sufficiently homogeneous, is metric information about the comparative lengths of some of the segments. The order of the columns in the perfect scalogram as in Table 11.5 is the order of the termini of the segments. The midpoints $3ab$ and $3bc$ obviously bound the segment of the continuum associated with the alternative $3b$. Since these two midpoints are bracketed (in Table 11.5) by the midpoints $2ab$ and $2bc$, which bound the segment corresponding to alternative $2b$, it follows that $\overline{2b} > \overline{3b}$, where the bar signifies the width of the segment associated with that alternative. In this same manner the following metric relations may be deduced from the midpoint order given by Table 11.5:

$$\overline{1b} > \overline{2b} > \overline{3b}, \qquad \overline{3c} > \overline{2c} > \overline{1c}, \qquad \overline{1d} > \overline{2d} > \overline{3d}$$

Two weaknesses of this method of triangular analysis of multicategory items lead to cautions in the use of the method. In the first place the method is much more sensitive to unreliability than are items which are single dichotomies. The more alternatives, the more a continuum is broken up into segments, so the widths of the segments tend to be smaller.

Hence if an individual's ideal varies over items or if there are individual differences in the scale values of alternatives so that midpoints vary across individuals, this variability will be more apparent with more alternatives per item, and highly reproducible triangular scalogram patterns are less apt to be obtained.

In spite of this reduced reproducibility, it seems better to me to use all possible dichotomies rather than just one. If each item is dichotomized just once, in a random manner, we have just thrown away information; and if this single dichotomizing is done to obtain the best scale, we are just deluding ourselves.

The second major caution in the use of this method is concerned with the interpretation of the coefficient of reproducibility for the final scalogram matrix. The coefficient will tend to be higher than it would be for the same sized matrix based on independently dichotomized items because of the perfect scalability built in within items. No work has been done, as yet, on the implications this has for the comparability of coefficients of reproducibility. Abelson has suggested (in a personal communication) using Goodman's e' as the appropriate coefficient of reproducibility for this multicategory case. It counts pattern inversions considering only adjacent items, and Goodman provides both significance and confidence limit procedures. Abelson suggests modifying this index by omitting from the count adjacent columns that apply to the same item.

Finally, one further advantage of this method should also be pointed out, and this is its independence of the number of alternatives to items. A necessary condition for orderly interlocking is that the number of alternatives to each item be a constant. Hence parallelogram analysis requires that the experimenter write the same number of alternatives to each item. If the responses are going to be converted to permit triangular analysis and disorderly interlocking, each item may be written with whatever number of alternatives the experimenter deems desirable.

3. PROBABILISTIC MODELS

The scalogram model, like any deterministic model, has a low tolerance for error or inconsistency. It is not surprising, then, that models which have higher tolerance have been constructed. In these models probabilities play an explicit role in the theoretical formulation. Because these models are so comprehensively discussed elsewhere (Torgerson, 1958) they are only briefly described here in order to point out the kinds of data for which they are appropriate and how they are related to each other.

We first discuss probabilistic models for the (1, 0) data matrix and then for the probabilistic data matrix.

The Analysis of the (1, 0) Data Matrix

The first model to be mentioned is Lazarsfeld's latent distance model. This model is a particular one in a very general system of possible models, called latent structure analysis, which Lazarsfeld has contributed. The latent distance model may be thought of as an immediate generalization of Guttman scalogram analysis.

In brief, the general latent distance model assumes that each item is characterized by three parameters: a scale value q_j, a probability α_j that individuals for whom $c_i < q_j$ will respond positively, and a probability β_j that individuals for whom $c_i \geq q_j$ will respond positively. Each item may be said to be represented by a trace line or operating characteristic, as shown in Fig. 11.4. Clearly the deterministic scalogram model is the case in which $\alpha_j = 0$ and $\beta_j = 1$. A restricted form of the general model calls for only two parameters for each item by setting $\alpha_j = 1 - \beta_j$.

The accounting equations and the procedures for estimating parameters are given by Torgerson (1958, Chapter 13), who presents the Hays-Borgatta (1954) computing scheme. In their original article Hays and Borgatta present an empirical comparison of the general and restricted model applied to 15 sets of empirical data. They find, of course, that the general model with 3 parameters for each item fits better than the restricted model ($\alpha_j = 1 - \beta_j$) with 2 parameters for each item. In terms of the relative amounts of the data used to determine the parameters, however, they estimate how *much* better the general model ought to fit and find that it does just about that much better.

The latent distance model could be easily adapted to the multicategory item by postulating a probability for each category and an x value for each midpoint. The model would correspond to a staircase-like trace line with as many steps as categories. Such a process, however, multiplies parameters to an excessive degree. What has tended to happen, instead, is that we still regard each item as a dichotomous item, but postulate some

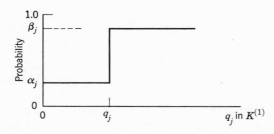

Fig. 11.4   Trace line in latent distance model.

continuous function as the item's trace line. Any monotonically increasing function could serve as a trace line for QIIa data, and would correspond to a theory about the mediation of such behavior. The latent distance model is only one of numerous possibilities; in another model an exponential is postulated with one error parameter, a decay constant, partially explored by Duncan McRae, Jr. (1956). Three other functions, however, have been given most of the attention in the literature—a linear trace line, a normal ogive trace line, and the logistic.

The accounting equations and estimation procedures have been developed for the model with linear trace lines. These are presented in some detail by Lazarsfeld (1959, pp. 506–28). His discussion is an excellent account of the general theory of latent structure analysis.

A model with normal ogive trace lines is of long standing in the area of mental test theory, but the problem of the formal solution to the accounting equations has only recently been attacked with any success. Lord (1953) gives the maximum-likelihood solution, but it does not lead to a feasible or practical procedure. Tucker (1952), working on the normal ogive model, has provided an approximate least squares procedure that involves an iterative process which is not too prolonged. Tucker's approach, however, is for a probabilistic data matrix rather than a (1, 0) matrix. It is mentioned here because in the context of mental testing, where the raw data matrix is a (1, 0) matrix, he suggests a procedure for transforming the data matrix into a probabilistic data matrix. The procedure consists of forming homogeneous subgroups of subjects on the basis of total scores, and then for each subgroup estimating the probability of passing each item.

The logistic has recently come to be used by A. Birnbaum (1957a, 1957b, 1957c) and George Rasch (1960). The latter's work is a major contribution and a new approach in psychometrics which is worthy of very serious study.

This concludes the variety of models available for the analysis of (1, 0) data matrices for dichotomous items and QIIa data, and we turn next to the analysis of probabilistic data matrices for QIIa data.

The Analysis of Probabilistic Data Matrices

These data matrices usually arise when each of a number of individuals sorts a number of stimuli into categories or piles ordered with respect to some attribute. The individuals are presumed to represent random experimentally independent replications of each other. The data are originally recorded in a matrix with categories as columns and stimuli as rows, and a cell contains the proportion of individuals who assigned that row-stimulus to that column-category. This matrix is then converted into a data matrix with category boundaries as columns and in which each cell entry is the accumulated proportion in that row up to the category boundary of that column.

Such a matrix might also easily arise in psychophysical experiments in which stimulus increments are repeatedly presented and individuals report whether they detected the increments. Here each row is an individual and each column is initially a stimulus increment, and a cell contains the proportion of detections. Such a matrix could then be processed as above.

A general theory for this data matrix is Torgerson's model for categorical judgment. It is described by him as follows:

The "law of categorical judgment" is a set of equations relating parameters of stimuli and category boundaries to a set of cumulative proportions derived from the proportion of times each stimulus is judged to be in each category of a set of categories which are ordered with respect to a given attribute.*

The theory and technique are presented in full detail in his Chapter 10, so we primarily concern ourselves with pointing out some ways in which Torgerson's model is related to Thurstone's comparative judgment model and to Lazarsfeld's latent structure models.

The complete form of the observational equation in the model for categorical judgment is

$$t_g - s_j = X_{jg}(\sigma_j^2 + \sigma_g^2 - 2r_{jg}\sigma_j\sigma_g)^{1/2} \qquad (11.3)$$

where t_g = mean scale location of the gth category boundary

σ_g = dispersion of the gth category boundary

s_j = mean scale location of the jth stimulus

σ_j = dispersion of the jth stimulus

r_{jg} = correlation between momentary scale positions of stimulus j and category boundary g

X_{jg} = unit normal deviate corresponding to the proportion of times stimulus j is sorted below boundary g

Even a casual comparison of equation 11.3 with Thurstone's comparative judgment equation 17.3 reveals their close relation. As a matter of fact, Torgerson's model is an adaptation of Thurstone's for a data matrix which is only part of a Thurstone data matrix, and a special kind of part.

Thurstone's comparative judgment model is for the analysis of a probabilistic data matrix on the order relations between pairs of points from the same set. The data are contained in an $n \times n$ matrix, with stimuli as both rows and columns, and a cell contains the proportion of judgments that the row-stimulus was greater than the column-stimulus. If, now, we were to partition the n elements into two disjoint subsets, that submatrix of the

* Torgerson (1958, p. 205).

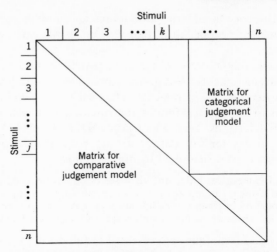

Fig. 11.5 Relation between data matrices of the comparative judgment model and the categorical judgment model.

$n \times n$ matrix which is bordered by one of these subsets as rows and the other as columns we shall call an offdiagonal submatrix; see Fig. 11.5. *Torgerson's categorical judgment model, then, is the analogue of Thurstone's for this submatrix.* The reason for this is that the stimuli designating the columns and the stimuli designating the rows are two distinct sets of elements and all pairs are made up of an element from each set. So as far as the data matrix is concerned, the columns can be stimuli or category boundaries and the rows can be individuals or stimuli. The model does not know the difference.

Of course, various real world considerations lead to various classes and conditions which may be imposed on Torgerson's model much as in the special cases for Thurstone's comparative judgment model.

With m categories and n stimuli there are mn equations. There are $2m$ parameters for categories, $2n$ for stimuli, and mn correlation coefficients, which total more than the number of equations—even though two parameters may be arbitrarily assigned to establish an origin and unit. Consequently, various simplifying restrictions may be placed on the parameters to render the equations solvable. Torgerson labels certain sets of these restrictions as "conditions A, B, C, and D."

Condition A is the restriction that the covariance term $r_{jg} \sigma_j \sigma_g$ in equation 11.3 is a constant, which is effectively equivalent to assuming $r_{jg} = 0$ if the variances may differ. Although the equations are solvable in principle there is little theoretical interest in it, and no practical analytical procedures exist.

Condition B is the restriction that the entire term in the parentheses in equation 11.3 is a constant for a fixed j. This is equivalent to assuming that $r_{jg} = 0$ and $\sigma_g^2 = c$ for all g, where c is a constant. If we let $a_j^2 = \sigma_j^2 + c$, then equation 11.3 becomes

$$t_g - s_j = X_{jg}a_j \qquad (11.4)$$

This is the model known as the method of successive intervals [see, for example, Saffir (1937), Mosier (1940), and Diederich, Messick, and Tucker (1957)]. This method is usually presented as assuming that the category boundaries are fixed, which is equivalent to assuming that $c = 0$ and that $a_j^2 = \sigma_j^2$. We see that only the quantity a_j has empirical identity, so c can be any arbitrary constant not greater than the smallest a_j. Hence, the method of successive intervals assumes not that the category boundaries are necessarily fixed with zero dispersion, but that they all have the same amount of dispersion.

Condition C is a dual of condition B in that the stimuli are assumed to have equal dispersion instead of the category boundaries. The analytical procedure differs only in that the matrix under condition C reverses the roles of stimuli and categories and hence is like the transpose of the matrix under condition B.

Condition D imposes the restriction that the entire term in the parentheses in equation 11.3, the standard deviation of the differences, is a constant for all pairs (j, g). This is equivalent to assuming that the stimulus dispersions are all equal, that the dispersions of the category boundaries are all equal, and that the correlation is a constant for all pairs (j, g). This condition for the categorical judgment model for the offdiagonal submatrix corresponds to case V of Thurstone's comparative judgment model for the intact matrix.

For condition D, equation 11.3 becomes

$$t_g - s_j = X_{jg}c \qquad (11.5)$$

This is formally the model variously known as
    (1) Attneave's method of graded dichotomies (1949),
    (2) Garner and Hake's equidiscriminability procedure (1951),
    (3) Edwards's special case of the method of successive intervals (1952).
We see, then, that Torgerson's categorical judgment model is a general formulation which links together a variety of models.

Finally, I would like to point out one way in which it is related to Lazarsfeld's models, in which, it will be recalled, an item has a trace line and the individual is regarded as a point on the latent attribute. In the categorical judgment model a further step is taken; the individuals and the category boundaries are *both* presumed to have trace lines, in particular, normal ogives in shape.

As a consequence, I consider Lazarsfeld's latent structure analysis with monotone trace lines and Torgerson's categorical judgment model as two interrelated models for the unidimensional analysis of QIIa data. These two general models with their various special cases encompass the analysis of both (1, 0) data matrices and probabilistic data matrices. Such general formulations as Lazarsfeld's and Torgerson's lead not only to an understanding of the interrelations among various models but also to a more precise statement of the actual assumptions implicit in the special cases.

4. SUMMARY

The beginning of this chapter gives a generic description of the behavior which gets mapped into QIIa data using examples from mental testing, psychophysics, questionnaire inventories, and the evaluation of stimuli by an ordered series of categories. All these kinds of behavior may be interpreted as data consisting of order relations on pairs of points from distinct sets.

There are three aspects to the problem of analyzing such data. The first has to do with whether the response categories are dichotomous or multicategorized. The second has to do with what goes into the cells of the data matrix—whether just a dichotomy like (1, 0) for (yes, no) or for (pass, fail) or whether the data are the relative frequencies of such responses. The third has to do with whether the models themselves are deterministic or probabilistic.

These three aspects serve as organizing principles for the rest of the chapter after a brief section which gives a mathematical interpretation to the problem of analyzing QIIa data. The analysis of (1, 0) data matrices by Guttman's scalogram technique is presented as a deterministic model for items with only two response categories. The method is here called triangular analysis to distinguish it from parallelogram analysis, discussed in Chapter 4 for QIa data. The distinction is important for the adaptation of Guttman scalogram analysis to multicategory items. The usual analytical procedures in that case seek a parallelogram pattern. The usual procedure for analyzing multicategory items, however, by seeking such a parallelogram, requires a condition called orderly interlocking between all pairs of items over and above perfect homogeneity of the data. Hence, a revised procedure is offered which avoids this extra condition and converts the analytical procedure into triangular analysis.

Probabilistic models for the analysis of the (1, 0) data matrix are discussed next. These include Lazarsfeld's latent distance model or the use of any other monotone trace lines within the general framework of latent structure analysis. These models are appropriate for probability data matrices. The only cases on which much work has been done are those in which the trace lines are assumed to be the normal ogive, the logistic, or linear.

The categorical judgment model of Torgerson is discussed and related to Thurstone's model for comparative judgment. Torgerson's is seen as an adaptation for the analysis of a special kind of subset of the data for which Thurstone's model is designed—a subset that can be described as an offdiagonal submatrix.

Special cases of Torgerson's model are presented which correspond to various well-known procedures already extant but whose interrelations were not clearly evident.

These models of Lazarsfeld and Torgerson provide the salient features of a simple framework for classifying and relating the current models for the unidimensional analysis of QIIa data.

REFERENCES

Attneave, F., 1949, A method of graded dichotomies for the scaling of judgments, *Psychol. Rev.*, **56**, 334–40.

Birnbaum, A., 1957a, *Probability and statistics in item analysis and classification problems. On the estimation of mental ability*, Ser. Rep. No. 58-15, USAF School of Aviation Medicine, Randolph AFB, Texas.

Birnbaum, A., 1957b, *Probability and statistics in item analysis and classification problems. Efficient design and use of tests of mental ability for various decision-making problems*, Ser. Rep. No. 58-16, USAF School of Aviation Medicine, Randolph AFB, Texas.

Birnbaum, A., 1957c, *Probability and statistics in item analysis and classification problems. Further considerations of efficiency in tests of mental ability*, Ser. Rep. No. 58-17, USAF School of Aviation Medicine, Randolph AFB, Texas.

Cronbach, L. J., and G. C. Gleser, 1961, Quantal and graded analysis of dosage-effect relations, *Science*, **133**, 1924–25.

Diederich, G. W., S. J. Messick, and L. R. Tucker, 1957, A general least squares solution for successive intervals, *Psychometrika*, **22**, 159–73.

Edwards, A. L., 1952, The scaling of stimuli by the method of successive intervals, *J. appl. Psychol.*, **36**, 118–22.

Garner, W. R., and H. W. Hake, 1951, The amount of information in absolute judgments, *Psychol. Rev.*, **58**, 446–59.

Goodman, L. A., 1959, Simple statistical methods for scalogram analysis, *Psychometrika*, **24**, 29–43.

Green, B. F., Jr., 1954, "Attitude measurement," Chapter 9 in *Handbook of social psychology*, I, *Theory and method*, edited by G. Lindzey, Addison-Wesley Publishing Co., Reading, Mass.

Guttman, L., 1950, Chapters 2, 3, 6, 8, and 9 in *Measurement and prediction*, edited by Stouffer et al., Princeton University Press, Princeton.

Hays, D. G., and E. F. Borgatta, 1954, An empirical comparison of restricted and general latent distance analysis, *Psychometrika*, **19**, 271–79.

Lazarsfeld, P. F., 1959, "Latent structure analysis," a chapter in *Psychology: a study of a science*, vol. 3, edited by S. Koch, McGraw-Hill Book Co., New York.

Lord, F. M., 1953, An application of confidence intervals and of maximum likelihood to the estimation of an examinee's ability, *Psychometrika*, **18**, 57–77.

McRae, D., Jr., 1956, An exponential model for assessing four-fold tables, *Sociometry*, **19**, 84–93.

Milholland, J. E., 1955, Four kinds of reproducibility in scale analysis, *Educ. psychol. Measmt.*, **15**, 478–82.

Mosier, C. I., 1940, A modification of the method of successive intervals, *Psychometrika*, **5**, 101–107

Rasch, G., 1960, *Probabilistic models for some intelligence and attainment tests*, Danish Institute for Educational Research, Copenhagen.

Saffir, M., 1937, A comparative study of scales constructed by three psychophysical methods, *Psychometrika*, **2**, 179–98.

Torgerson, W. S., 1958, *Theory and methods of scaling*, John Wiley and Sons, New York.

Tucker, L. R., 1952, A level of proficiency scale for a undimensional skill, *Amer. Psychologist*, **7**, 408 (abstract).

White, B. W., and E. Saltz, 1957, Measurement of reproducibility, *Psychol. Bull.*, **54**, 81–99.

CHAPTER 12

QIIa Multidimensional Models— Nonmetric Factor Analysis

Consider a QIIa data matrix which does not satisfy a Guttman scalogram. Several alternative "next steps" are open to the experimenter. He may "purify" the data by eliminating offending subjects and offending stimuli. He may retain all the data and apply a model which introduces a probability concept as does Lazarsfeld's latent distance model, thus achieving a unidimensional solution. Or he can seek a multidimensional solution. This chapter is concerned with some of the alternative multidimensional models available in the latter case.

The data in QIIa, of course, are order relations on pairs of points from distinct sets, and the usual context in which such data arise is the observation of dominance relations on individual-stimulus pairs. The original data matrix may be the $(1, 0)$ data matrix or may be a probabilistic data matrix transformed into a $(1, 0)$ matrix by a mapping such as that described in Chapter 11. Not having obtained a unidimensional scalogram by triangular analysis, we now conceive of the individuals and stimuli as being represented by points in a joint space of dimensionality greater than one. The behavior is interpreted as inducing an order relation on certain pairs of points in that space, and the problem is to construct a calculus which will yield the joint space.

The crux of the problem resides in the choice of what is called a *composition axiom*. A point in a space of r dimensions may be thought of as a vector or an r-tuple, the r-tuple being the set of r ordered numbers representing the coordinates of the point in the r corresponding dimensions. The interpretation of the behavior has induced an order relation on two such points, two r-tuples. How, in the model, shall it be decided which r-tuple is to dominate another? The model must make such a decision for every pair of points, because any individual may take any item and will either pass or fail. Now if all the elements of one r-tuple are at least as great as the corresponding elements of another r-tuple, an order relation on them is intuitively acceptable. If there are two r-tuples such that each exceeds the other on at least one dimension, however, there is no intuitively compelling order relation on them. Nevertheless, one must be defined, and the model must contain a "composition axiom" to do this.

Because we can conceive of alternative composition axioms, alternative multidimensional models may be constructed. For example, we might postulate that an individual will pass an item in a mental test only if his ability on *each* relevant attribute is at least as great as the difficulty level of the item on the corresponding attributes. That is, successful performance on a task requires a certain minimum on each of the several relevant dimensions. This psychological idea is captured in what is called the conjunctive model. An apt illustration used by J. F. Bennett* is that of an individual taking a history test in French. He has to know enough French to be able to understand the questions, but no matter how much more French he knows, it will not help answer the questions; and he has to know enough history to answer the questions, but no matter how much history he knows, it will not compensate for not knowing enough French to understand the questions.

This model is in the background of a statement like: You cannot be a good teacher without being a good scholar. It is also the model underlying the notion that so-called aptitude tests are really inaptitude tests in that they are more capable of eliminating people who would fail than of picking those who would succeed; that is, a test measuring one component of a complex attribute can eliminate individuals who do not possess that component to an adequate degree. Having enough of that component, however, will not insure a high performance on the complex attribute. Under the conjunctive model, if an individual has too little in any one component, he lacks the complex aptitude, but having more than enough of one component is not a sufficient condition for possession of the complex aptitude.

An example of the conjunctive model has been provided by E. E. Cureton,† who cites the problem of selecting seamen who could carry a heavy shell from an elevator to a gun and who at the same time were less than 5 feet, 6 inches tall, a condition made necessary by an overhead pipe they had to pass under while carrying the shell. The conjunctive model calls for multiple cutting scores.

---

* Personal communication.
† Personal communication.

In contrast to the psychological idea behind the conjunctive model is the idea behind another model based on the disjunctive composition axiom. Disjunctive composition is that in which successful performance on a task requires a certain minimum on *any one* of the relevant dimensions. For example, an individual may be faced with a problem he can solve by prolonged trial and error or by reasoning. Enough effort in the one direction or enough capability in the other is sufficient for success; he does not need both. To oversimplify professional baseball, we might say that an individual's success is dependent on being able to hit or to pitch. *This disjunctive composition model, although psychologically quite distinct from the conjunctive, is mathematically isomorphic with it* (as will be shown), and hence the two models will be treated together.

With either of these two models (conjunctive or disjunctive), the fact that two pairs of items, say *A* and *B* on the one hand and *A* and *C* on the other, each satisfies the conditions for a Guttman scale, does not imply that the pair *B* and *C* will also. Tetrachoric correlation coefficients between items, computed from fourfold tables, could be $+1$ between items *A* and *C* and between items *B* and *C*, but less than $+1$ between items *A* and *B*, because these models, in general, yield a partial order, and those pairs of stimuli which are not comparable would be correlated less than $+1$. An instance is provided by the three items labeled *A*, *B*, and *C* in Fig. 12.2. All the individuals who pass *A* pass *C* and all those who pass *B* pass *C*, but there are individuals who pass *A* and fail *B* and vice versa.

Both these models were first introduced in psychological literature by H. M. Johnson (1935), who spoke of the logical product and the logical sum, which correspond, respectively, to the conjunctive and disjunctive models described here. The examples he used to illustrate the principles require what we would call "mixed" models, in that both the conjunctive and disjunctive models are involved. This paper by Johnson has been completely neglected in subsequent literature, perhaps because the models were only suggested and not constructed rather than because there was fundamental disagreement on principle. The two models, the conjunctive and the disjunctive, are shown to be isomorphic to each other *mathematically* and are treated as one in the next section.

The rest of the chapter is taken up with discussion of the compensatory model. The psychological idea here is that an individual with a shortage in one attribute may compensate with an excess of another relevant attribute. For this reason this type of composition model is called "compensatory." It is the model that seems to come most naturally to mind, judging from its relative frequency of use. Special cases of this model underlie multiple regression theory and analysis of variance as well as multiple factor analysis.

Examples of compensatory models are numerous. In the area of constructing indices, for example, Cronbach and Gleser (1953), analyzing the problem of measuring the similarity of profiles, constructed an index which is a weighted composite of shape and elevation. The sociologist W. Lloyd Warner (1949) constructed a measure of social status called an Index of Status Characteristics, which is a weighted combination of occupation, source of income, house type, and dwelling area.

In the area of theory construction there is C. L. Hull's use of the compensatory model in constructing "excitatory strength" out of the two dimensions "drive" and "habit strength" (1943). Whether these are additive or multiplicative is not the issue; in either case they would be compensatory. The most popular theory of decision making under risk is that of maximizing some kind of an expectation which is a compensatory product of probabilities and utilities. Examples could be multiplied indefinitely.

In the construction of the compensatory model here several distinctions giving rise to variations of the model will be noted. For example, the question immediately arises whether the weighting function on the primitive attributes is determined by the stimulus, by the individual, or jointly. An arithmetic problem may involve a weighted combination of verbal reasoning and numerical ability, and if the weighted combination exceeds some minimum value, the individual will pass. In such a case the individual may have nothing to say about the weighting function, and this would be an illustration of the *stimulus compensatory* model. On the other hand, an individual going on a camping trip has a number of possible items to take with him which vary in utility and weight. Therefore, the individual in this case may construct the weighting function against which the stimuli are judged as accepted or rejected, and this would be an illustration of the *individual compensatory* model.

Although they are psychologically quite distinct it is to be expected that formally these two models are isomorphic. Clearly, if we have a data matrix, then our theory of the behavior, whether individual compensatory or stimulus compensatory, will lead to certain differences in the analytical procedure. In the stimulus compensatory model, the same weighting function would be applied to all individuals, so that a column of the data matrix, with the responses of all the individuals to a given stimulus, would be quite meaningful. A row of such a matrix may be comparatively meaningless. On the other hand, if the individual compensatory model mediated the data matrix, then the exact reverse would be true—the response patterns of individuals to stimuli, the rows of the matrix, would be meaningful, but not the columns of response patterns.

Any model which presumes to make a multidimensional analysis of a data matrix is by its very nature a theory about how these components are put together to generate the behavior. Any theory about a composition function is a theory about behavior. This, it seems to me, is what makes the subject interesting and important. The components in and of themselves are static, inert, and just descriptive, until a composition model imbues them with life. Perhaps most of psychological theory can be described in the context of a search for composition models.

A learning theory, for example, is concerned with changes in performance with experience and attempts to relate these changes to characteristics of the stimulus situation and characteristics of the individual. These "characteristics" are the components out of which the complex "change in performance with experience" is constructed. In the area of group dynamics, research may be directed toward the problem of predicting the behavior or characteristics of groups from the properties of the members and the milieu and their interrelations. For example, the Lorge-Solomon (1955) model for group problem solving is a disjunctive model in that a group will perform successfully if any member of it can. Any number of such examples may be found in psychology from sensory processes and perception to social and clinical theory.

There have been some direct experimental attacks on the problem of the composition model for a dependent variable as a function of two or more independent variables. In these experiments the independent variables have always been manifest rather than latent. Although the discovery of latent variables is the primary concern of this book, I shall summarize three of these experiments here because they will serve to broaden the setting in which we view the problem of composition functions.

Joseph Miller (1939), in a study of eyelid conditioning to shock, used as conditioning stimuli (a) a sound of changing pitch, (b) movement of a black pointer on a white background, and (c) both together. He used 10 subjects in each of the 3 classes of conditioning stimuli, and the proportion of conditioned responses during the course of 50 paired stimulations was: a, 45%; b, 23%; c, 81%. Miller says that it was Pavlov's hypothesis that one of the stimuli of the compound "overshadows" the other and yields as much conditioning as both together. Miller's experiment provides evidence against Pavlov's hypothesis and evidence that each of the components of the complex stimulus contributes to the total effect. (Pavlov's hypothesis represents the disjunctive composition model, and Miller's experiment suggests that a compensatory composition model was operative.)

Whereas Miller's experiment is concerned with the effect of two channels of stimulation (modalities) on the rate of conditioning, the study by M. U. Eninger (1952) involves the effect of these same two channels of stimulation on discrimination learning. Eninger had rats learning a single-unit T-maze under 23 hours of food deprivation and with 10 trials per day. The correct pathway for group a (4 rats) required a visual discrimination (black-versus-white pathway); for group b (5 rats) there was an auditory discrimination (2300-cycle tone); and for group c (5 rats) both the a and b stimulus cues were available. The mean number of trials to reach a criterion of 90% correct choices in a block of 20 trials was: group a, 148 trials; group b, 234 trials; group c, 55 trials. Here again, the components of the stimulus situation appear to be mutually contributing to the total effect.

An experiment by J. M. Warren (1953) was concerned with the mutual effects, if any, of different cues *within* a single modality. He presented monkeys with pairs of geometrical figures which could differ in color, form, size, or in any combinations of these qualities. He found that pairs of figures involving color differences were discriminable significantly better than figures involving only form and size, and the addition of form and size differences seemed to have no effect. He found that, color being constant, a combination of form and size differences was significantly more discriminable than either alone. It is not clear from this experiment what model might mediate the interrelations of color with form and size, but the experiment does suggest that form and size are mutually contributing to the total effect in accordance with a compensatory composition model.*

In these three experiments we have rats, monkeys, and humans; conditioning and discrimination learning; and stimulus components from within and from between modalities. Clearly, these are only suggestive. Although there are other relevant experiments, only the barest beginning has been made on the mutual effects of stimulus components.

In a different content area is a study by Robert F. Powloski (1953) on the joint effects of hunger and thirst motives. He used a Y-shaped discrimination box, black-versus-white discrimination, 8 groups of 10 rats each, and ran them to 2 successive errorless days of 10 trials each day. His 8 groups of rats differed in their combinations of 6 hours of food deprivation (H6), 23 hours of food deprivation (H23), 6 hours of water deprivation (T6), and 23 hours of water deprivation (T23) (see Table 12.1). We note that group 3 is not better than group 1 or 2; group 6 not better than 4 or 5; group 7 not better than group 5 or 1; and group 8 not better than group 4 or 2.

The results of this experiment suggest that simultaneous involvement of motives does not result in a mutual contribution to a total effect, but, as

---

* This is possibly an example of what will here be called a "mixed" model. The attribute of color, if it dominates differences in the other attributes, is being utilized lexicographically, and if color is not a relevant dimension, the other two attributes are mediated by compensatory composition.

quoted by Powloski from K. F. Muenzinger and M. Fletcher (1936): "It is quite possible that this is a fundamental principle of activity, namely that the combination of motivating factors results not in a summation of their effects but in an effect equal to that of the stronger factor." And at another point, this is likened to figure and ground: ". . . one motive stands out as the dominant one at any time while the others form the relatively neutral ground."

These experiments are described here solely for the purpose of enlarging the context within which composition models are viewed. The point is

Table 12.1   Results in Powloski's Experiment

Group	Mean No. of Reinforcements	Mean No. of Errors
1. H6	105	36.0
2. T6	134	41.7
3. H6 and T6	121	39.5
4. H23	78	29.9
5. T23	73	29.6
6. H23 and T23	79	27.6
7. H6 and T23	86	29.6
8. H23 and T6	83	29.2

that there is not necessarily just one composition model to which all behavior conforms but rather that alternative models correspond to alternative theories. Bringing these experiments into juxtaposition with each other and with the formal development of alternative models will, it is hoped, bring this larger context to light.

In Section 1 the conjunctive and disjunctive models are developed, and then the compensatory model is treated; a discussion of further problems, relations among models, and a summary follow.

1. THE CONJUNCTIVE-DISJUNCTIVE MODELS

The material presented here is taken from Coombs and Kao (1955). That monograph contains the technical development of these models in complete detail, so the main effort here is directed toward the communication of the principal results.

Relations between the Two Models

We first direct our attention to two isomorphisms that exist between the conjunctive and the disjunctive models. Their existence is important because, as a consequence, only one of these models needs to be developed mathematically; the results obtained by analyzing data according to one of the models may then be immediately transformed into the results that would have been obtained if the other model had been applied to an appropriate transformation of the data. The composition axioms that define the conjunctive and the disjunctive models are:

(1) *Conjunctive Composition*

$$c_{ij} \geq q_{ij} \Leftrightarrow p_{ij} = 1 \Leftrightarrow c_{ij} \underset{d}{>} q_{ij} \quad \text{for all } d \text{ in } D'$$

where $\underset{d}{>}$ is a relation on $K^{(d)}$ which is a simple order.

(2) *Disjunctive Composition*

$$c_{ij} \geq q_{ij} \Leftrightarrow p_{ij} = 1 \Leftrightarrow c_{ij} \underset{d}{>} q_{ij} \quad \text{for at least one } d \text{ in } D'$$

As a notational convenience let us designate the $(1, 0)$ data matrix generated by either of these models as $\pi = \{p_{ij} \mid p_{ij} = 0, 1\}$. That is, the data matrix has either a 1 or a 0 in each cell corresponding to whether the individual of that row responded positively or negatively (in a suitable sense) to the stimulus of that column. Corresponding to each matrix π is a matrix $\pi^* = \{p_{ij}^* \mid p_{ij} + p_{ij}^* = 1\}$. The matrix π^* is called the complementary matrix to π because to the 1 or 0 in any cell of π there is a 0 or a 1, respectively, in the correspondingly cell of π^*.

Finally, let us form another matrix from π by turning it over its main diagonal. This new matrix, $\pi' = \{p_{ij}' \mid p_{ij}' = p_{ji}\}$, is called the transpose of π because rows have become columns and vice versa. In the transposed matrix stimuli are identified with rows and individuals with columns.

We see then that there are two transformations we might make of the matrix π—complement it and/or transpose it.

When the matrix π says that a row-individual has passed a column-stimulus, the matrix π^* says he failed it and the matrix π' says the stimulus passed him. Each of these transformed matrices, π^* and π', perfectly *misrepresents* the behavior, so each contains all the information in the original matrix. In fact, any four different matrices may be analyzed, π, π^*, π', and $\pi^{*'}$ $(= \pi'^*)$, and each may be analyzed by either the conjunctive or the disjunctive model. The relations among these several analyses is expressed in a double duality.

Perhaps the most immediate way to grasp the implications of these transformations is by means of Fig. 12.1. The figure is restricted for reasons of clarity to the two-dimensional case and to transformations of a π matrix generated by the conjunctive model. An individual under the conjunctive model will respond positively only to stimuli to the southwest of him, for example, see the upper left corner of Fig. 12.1. Or we could

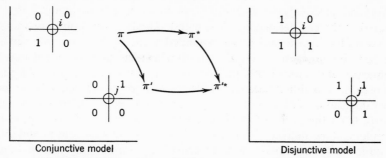

Conjunctive model   Disjunctive model

Fig. 12.1   Illustrating transformations on a conjunctive matrix.

look at a stimulus (lower left corner of Fig. 12.1), and see that a stimulus receives a positive response only from individuals to the northeast of it. This is the interpretation of the information in the π matrix.

Suppose, now, we were to reverse the order relations on each of the dimensions of the conjunctive model. Clearly, the effect would be to make an individual look like a stimulus and vice versa. To reverse the roles of individuals and stimuli is to transpose the matrix π, that is, individuals become columns and stimuli become rows. If we look at the right-hand side of Fig. 12.1, for the disjunctive model, we see that the same thing is true. To reverse the order relations on the dimensions is to reverse the roles of stimuli and individuals in the π matrix, that is, to transpose it into π'. The effect, then, of applying one of these two models to the matrix π' instead of the matrix π is to reverse the order relations on the several dimensions.

Now consider the effect of complementing the matrix π, converting it into π^*, that is, if an individual responded positively we record 0 and if he responded negatively we record 1. If the original matrix π is generated by the conjunctive model, we see from Fig. 12.1 that the response pattern of the individual in the π^* matrix corresponds to that of an individual whose behavior is generated by the disjunctive model with the order relations on each dimension reversed. This is evident from comparing the individual in the upper left corner of Fig. 12.1 with the individual in the upper right corner. It is also evident that if the original matrix π were generated by the disjunctive model, the effect of complementation would be to construct a new matrix π^*, which is generated by the conjunctive model and with order relations reversed on the several dimensions. The effect, then, of complementing a matrix generated under one of these two models is to complement the "junctiveness" and reverse the order on each dimension.

The product of these two transformations, transposition and complementation, in either order, is as follows. Suppose an individual has responded positively to a stimulus by the conjunctive model and 1 is entered in the cell defined by the row-individual and the column-stimulus. This signifies that the individual responded positively by virtue of exceeding the stimulus on each of the relevant dimensions. Such an event may be identically and equivalently interpreted as the stimulus responding negatively to the individual because it failed to exceed the individual on at least one dimension. The latter interpretation is to look at the complementary matrix from the point of view of the stimulus, that is, to transpose the complementary matrix. The effect of this is to change the model from conjunctive to disjunctive and to reverse the order relations on each dimension twice, hence to leave them unchanged. The same argument, *mutatis mutandis*, applies if the response of the individual had been generated by the disjunctive model—the transformation $\pi \to \pi^{*\prime}$ has the effect only of changing the model to conjunctive.

The consequences of the double duality of these transformations are practical ones. Only one of the two models needs to be mathematically developed, and only one calculus needs to be constructed for analysis of data by either model. For every theorem in one of the models there corresponds, isomorphically, a theorem in the other model. *The analysis of a matrix by one model may be transformed into an analysis of the complementary matrix by the other model by simply reversing order relations on the dimensions.* And finally, *we may choose, at will, to analyze the row patterns or the column patterns, and this merely has the effect of reversing order relations on the dimensions.* For these reasons the analytical procedure for only one of the two models needs to be developed, and the conjunctive model for the responses of individuals to stimuli has been arbitrarily chosen.

Theory of the Conjunctive Model

The $(1, 0)$ data matrix we wish to analyze is presumed to have been generated by the responses of individuals to stimuli according to the conjunctive model. As the triangular pattern for a Guttman scale cannot be obtained, the behavior is presumed to be generated in a multidimensional space of common relevant dimensions, and the intent is to construct this space.

The critical idea on which the analysis of the conjunctive matrix depends, due to J. F. Bennett,* is simply this: If the conjunctive model is the operative one and the stimuli and individuals are all in a common space, then, *in any individual's response pattern, an item failed must be higher on at*

---

* Personal communication.

least one dimension than an item passed. To pass an item conjunctively an individual must exceed it on all relevant dimensions. If he fails an item, the item exceeds him on at least one and so must exceed any item he passes on at least one dimension.

To analyze a data matrix a useful but not necessary preliminary step is to obtain a lower bound on the dimensionality. A criterion for this is given by Milholland (1953). The procedure is based on the number of different response patterns with the same number of items wrong (that is, zero entries). Suppose we have a reduced data matrix with, say, ten stimuli, and a row for each distinct response pattern. We may give each row a "score" equal to the number of zero entries in the row. The number of rows with the same score is limited by the number of dimensions. In one dimension, for example, only one row is admissable for each score. This comes about because when the conditions for a perfect triangular scalogram are met there is only one way to get a given number of items wrong. For example, if only one item is missed, it must be the most difficult one. If exactly two items are missed, they must be the two most difficult, and so on.

In more than one dimension, the number of ways to reach the same score is increased. In two dimensions we may get exactly one item wrong in at most two different ways: We may miss the item highest on either dimension. We may get exactly two items wrong in two dimensions in any of three different ways: by missing the two highest items on either dimension or by missing the highest item on each dimension. The general expression given by Milholland for $\eta(r, e)$, the number of distinct response patterns with a given number of errors (zero entries), e, in r dimensions is

$$\eta(r, e) = \binom{r + e - 1}{r - 1} \tag{12.1}$$

Some values of this expression are given in Table 12.2.

To apply this table we count the number of response patterns η_e with exactly e errors, $e = 1, 2, \ldots, n - 1$, and select the minimum r of Table 12.2 for which $\eta(r, e) \geq \eta_e$ for all observed values of e. This value of r is a lower bound to the dimensionality. The power of this criterion is largely lost if the data are incomplete or there are ties in the rank order of an item on different dimensions. In either of these cases the observed number will be less than the maximum allowed by Milholland's criterion.

A special application of Milholland's criterion for $e = 1$, which is useful with incomplete data, is to look for the largest subset of stimuli for which response patterns exist with exactly one of the items wrong. Since having only one item wrong requires that that item be highest on some

Table 12.2 Upper Bound for Number of Distinct Response Patterns with Exactly e Zero Entries in r Dimensions*

	e						
	0	1	2	3	4	5	6
1	1	1	1	1	1	1	1
2	1	2	3	4	5	6	7
r 3	1	3	6	10	15	21	28
4	1	4	10	20	35	56	84
5	1	5	15	35	70	126	210
6	1	6	21	56	126	252	462

* Note the Pascal triangle property of this table.

dimension, having r distinct response patterns in which only one item is failed requires r dimensions.

With this theory we are now in a position to analyze a data matrix.

Analytical Procedure for the Conjunctive Model

In Fig. 12.2 a configuration of $n = 6$ stimuli in two dimensions is presented. The cells numbered from 1 to 18 in the figure are the regions to which there correspond distinct response patterns. Assuming the responses are generated by the conjunctive model, we find the data matrix

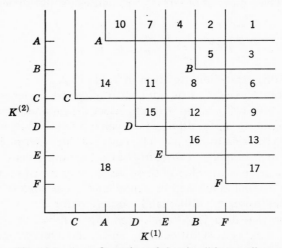

Fig. 12.2 A configuration of six stimuli in two dimensions.

arising from the configuration of Fig. 12.2 in Table 12.3. The rows of the table are numbered to identify the response patterns with their corresponding regions in the figure. The column of Table 12.3 labeled e is the number of zero entries in a row, and the column labeled η_e is the number of distinct response patterns with e zeros. The stimulus columns of the matrix may be in any arbitrary order, but it is convenient to order the rows in order of increasing e as has been done in Table 12.3.

The column labeled η_e may then be compared with the rows of Table 12.2 to determine the minimum r for which $\eta(r, e) \geq \eta_e$, for all e. Thus the column η_e is the sequence of numbers [1, 2, 3, 3, 4, 4, 1], and the second row of Table 12.2 is the sequence [1, 2, 3, 4, 5, 6, 7]. We find that this row, $r = 2$, is the minimum value of r for which every entry is at least as large as the observed number. Consequently we take $r = 2$ as our first estimate of the dimensionality of the matrix in Table 12.3.

The problem of data analysis is to process the data matrix to arrive at the configuration. By means of Bennett's observation this may be done in a reasonably direct manner if there are no empty regions in the configuration. The successive steps in the analysis are shown on the right-hand side of Table 12.3 under the column labeled "inferences."

Table 12.3 Data Matrix Generated by the Conjunctive Model and the Configuration of Fig. 12.2

	A	B	C	D	E	F	e	η_e	Inferences
1	1	1	1	1	1	1	0	1	None
2	1	1	1	1	1	0	1	2	F
3	0	1	1	1	1	1	1		A
4	1	0	1	1	1	0	2	3	F B
5	0	1	1	1	1	0	2		
6	0	0	1	1	1	1	2		A B
7	1	0	1	1	0	0	3	3	F B E
8	0	0	1	1	1	0	3		
9	0	0	0	1	1	1	3		A B C
10	1	0	1	0	0	0	4	4	F B E D
11	0	0	1	1	0	0	4		
12	0	0	0	1	1	0	4		
13	0	0	0	0	1	1	4		A B C D
14	0	0	1	0	0	0	5	4	
15	0	0	0	1	0	0	5		
16	0	0	0	0	1	0	5		
17	0	0	0	0	0	1	5		A B C D E F
18	0	0	0	0	0	0	6	1	

The first row, in which $e = 0$, contains no information about the configuration, i.e., the individuals who pass every item make no discriminations, and so they tell us nothing. From rows 2 and 3 we see that stimuli F and A, respectively, are the single items failed. From this we infer that F and A are each highest on some dimension. Response pattern 4 shows both F and B to be failed, which *suggests* that B is next to but below F. Response pattern 5 with both A and F failed contains no new information; in fact this pattern is predicted from the inferences that A and F are highest on their respective dimensions. Hence the occurrence of pattern 5 is confirming evidence. Confirmation occurs repeatedly, for we see that patterns 8, 11, 12, 14, 15, and 16 all provide confirming evidence for earlier inferences.

Taking another example, we see in pattern 6 that A and B are failed. This suggests that B is next to but below A on A's dimension. An individual could not have failed B by being below it on F's dimension without failing F also. As the individuals represented by row 6 passed F but failed B, they must be below B on some other dimension, in this case A's.

Proceeding in this manner down the matrix we find that two dimensions can completely accommodate the data. Having reached pattern 17, the stimuli are found to project on one of the dimensions in order from high to low: $A\ B\ C\ D\ E\ F$; and on the other dimension $F\ B\ E\ D\ (A\ C)$, in which A and C are as yet unordered. It is sometimes possible to order all the elements by considering each of the alternative orders and testing for the occurrence of the corresponding response patterns. Thus, if the order is $F\ B\ E\ D\ C\ A$, there ought to be a response pattern with only A passed. If the order is $F\ B\ E\ D\ A\ C$, there should be a response pattern with only C passed. We see that the latter is the case so we have two simple orders representing the two dimensions and the configuration of Fig. 12.2 may be constructed.

A simple order of the individuals on these dimensions cannot be arrived at. From Fig. 12.2 we see that individuals with response patterns 1, 3, 6, 9, 13, 17, and 18 cannot be ordered on $K^{(1)}$. The best that can be done is to construct a partial order for each dimension, as is shown in Fig. 12.3, where response 18 is omitted as it is incomparable to all others.

We could obtain these partial orders on individuals by analyzing the transpose of the data matrix presented in Table 12.3. If there were more stimuli than people, the transpose would be the more convenient matrix to analyze.

In summary, we have obtained a simple order on the stimuli and a partial order on the individuals. Here, however, we have used only a few stimuli and many individuals, so it is, perhaps, not surprising that there is more discrimination among the stimuli than among the individuals. If we are interested in finer discriminations among individuals, many more

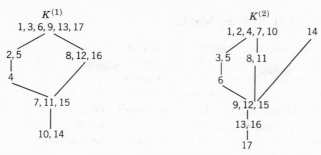

Fig. 12.3   Partial orders of individuals on the two dimensions.

stimuli should be used than individuals, and the transposed matrix, π', would be more conveniently analyzed. The initial solution is simpler in form and easier to construct for the set with fewer elements. In this last example the two simple rank orders for the stimuli are easier to solve for first than are the two partial orders for the individuals. In general, then, it is recommended that the data matrix be oriented so it is longer than it is wide, that is, has more rows than columns.

The conjunctive model was used to analyze the data matrix of Table 12.3. If the disjunctive model had been the operational model for generating the data of Table 12.3, the complementary matrix should be analyzed by the conjunctive model, and the dimensions obtained, reversed in direction, would correspond to the disjunctive analysis of Table 12.3. Hence, to assist us in deciding whether the conjunctive or disjunctive model mediated a data matrix π, we may analyze both π and π^* by the conjunctive model, and whichever solution is more parsimonious and meaningful is generally to be preferred. *If the conjunctive analysis of π^* yields the preferred solution, the disjunctive model for generating π is implied.*

2. THE COMPENSATORY MODEL

In the discussion of the compensatory models two approaches are presented: that of Coombs and Kao (1955) and that of Bennett (1956). Neither of these studies is complete. Coombs and Kao have only solved the case of two dimensions for the (1, 0) data matrix. Bennett has considered the case in which there is more information in the data matrix, in particular, in which each item column contains a rank order of the individuals. For such a matrix he has provided a dimensionality criterion. The problem of configuration has not been solved, but we suspect that it should be closely related to the problem of multidimensional unfolding and should not be insuperable.

Theory of the (1, 0) Data Matrix

The basic idea of the compensatory models is that the response of an individual to a stimulus is mediated by two or more attributes in such a way that they are mutually substitutable—a shortage of one attribute may be compensated for by an excess of another. Two kinds of compensatory models should be distinguished, the stimulus compensatory and the individual compensatory, as discussed in the introductory paragraphs of this chapter. The definition of composition for the stimulus compensatory model is the following:

$$c_i \geq q_j \Leftrightarrow p_{ij} = 1$$

with respect to the function w_j if and only if

$$w_j(c_i) \geq w_j(q_j)$$

The function w_j is associated with the stimulus j, in that the stimulus determines the mutual rates of exchange among the attributes. The definition of the individual compensatory composition simply substitutes a function w_i for the function w_j, in that the individual determines it rather than the stimulus.

A stimulus-determined compensatory function would be found in the performance of a task involving several capabilities where the characteristics of the task determine how these capabilities are to be combined. An example of an individual-determined compensatory function might be found in the judgment of a book publisher deciding whether to accept a manuscript for publication in view of the cost of publication in relation to the potential market.

There is obviously a complete duality between these models in the sense of the interchangeability of the roles of stimulus and individual. A model constructed in terms of a stimulus compensatory model is correspondingly a model for individual compensatory composition if individuals and stimuli are interchanged. Consequently, only the stimulus compensatory model is discussed in the remainder of the chapter.

Potentially a great variety of stimulus compensatory models exists by virtue of various possible definitions of the compensatory function w_j. Here a linear function is assumed, that is, for any pair of attributes there is a constant rate at which one may be interchanged for the other. We might imagine, for example, that success in some academic course of study is a function of hours of study and of intelligence. An individual with less intelligence than another individual may compensate with more hours of study. The linear compensatory function says that each additional hour of study compensates for some fixed number of units of intelligence. This

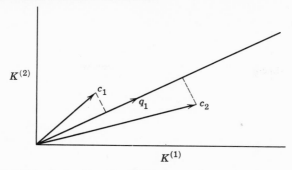

Fig. 12.4 Projection of individuals' vectors on a stimulus vector.

is the familiar composition function we find in multiple regression theory, analysis of variance, and factor analysis.

To capture this idea in the mathematical model we may conceive of the individuals and the stimuli as vectors in the positive sector of a common psychological space. The observation in the real world is that an individual responded positively or negatively to a stimulus. The corresponding feature in the stimulus compensatory model is the projection of the individual's vector on the stimulus vector. If the projection is at least as far in the direction of the stimulus vector as the stimulus vector is itself, we say that this corresponds to the individual having responded positively. These ideas are illustrated in Fig. 12.4 in which the projections of two individual vectors on a stimulus vector are shown. The individual whose vector is c_1 fails or otherwise responds negatively to the stimulus q_1, whereas the individual whose vector is c_2 passes or otherwise responds positively.

In general we may regard each stimulus vector as the normal to a hyperplane of $r - 1$ dimensions such that if the terminus of an individual's vector is on the same side of this hyperplane as the origin, he fails the item; if it is not, he passes it. In Fig. 12.5 an example is given with two stimuli q_1 and q_2. The hyperplane defined by each stimulus in this two-dimensional linear case is a straight line. Each of these hyperplanes divides the space into two regions, one region closed on the side of the origin, the other open away from the origin. Individuals whose vectors terminate on the closed side of the hyperplane (line, in this case) fail the item, otherwise they pass it. The hyperplanes generated by two noncollinear vectors divide the space into four regions, as shown in the figure; to each region there corresponds a unique response pattern. The response patterns corresponding to the four regions are shown in the figure, with the responses to q_1 and q_2 indicated in that order.

A recursive formula for the maximum number τ of response patterns for n stimuli in r dimensions may be constructed following an argument

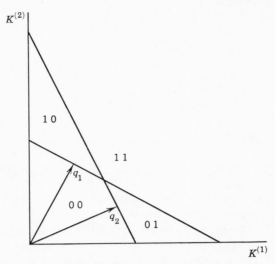

Fig. 12.5 Response patterns to two stimuli.

closely parallel to that in Chapter 7 for the number of I scales for n stimuli in r dimensions. The maximum number of regions that can be introduced by the nth stimulus in r dimensions is

$$\tau(n, r) - \tau(n - 1, r)$$

The number of regions the nth stimulus can introduce, however, is equal to the number of regions the nth hyperplane is itself cut up into by the first $n - 1$ stimuli, which is $\tau(n - 1, r - 1)$. Hence

$$\tau(n, r) - \tau(n - 1, r) = \tau(n - 1, r - 1) \tag{12.2}$$

where
$$\tau(n, 0) = 1 \quad \text{and} \quad \tau(n, 1) = n + 1$$

It is easy to show (see Coombs and Kao, 1955, p. 45) that equation 12.2 is satisfied by the relation

$$\tau(n, r) = \sum_{k=0}^{r} \binom{n}{k} \tag{12.3}$$

Some values of equation 12.3 are given in Table 12.4.

To use the table we count the number of distinct response patterns in the data matrix, which is the number of distinct rows in the reduced data matrix. This number, say τ', is then compared with the numbers in the appropriate row of Table 12.4 for that number of stimuli, to find the minimum r for which $\tau' \leq \tau(n, r)$. For example, if we had $n = 7$ items and found $\tau' = 85$ distinct response patterns, we see from Table 12.4 that in three dimensions with 7 stimuli only 64 distinct response patterns are admissible but that in four dimensions 99 are. Having obtained 85 we know that three dimensions are not enough but that four might be. So $r = 4$ is our lower bound on the dimensionality of that data matrix under a linear compensatory model.

Ideally, what we would like to be able to do would be to take the response patterns as given in a (1, 0) data matrix and construct the order of projections of the stimulus vectors on each dimension assuming the compensatory model. This was accomplished for the conjunctive-disjunctive model but not for the compensatory model. Instead of the rank order of the projections of the stimulus vectors on each dimension, we are able to

Table 12.4 Maximum Number of Admissible Response Patterns for $n \leq 10$ and $r \leq 7$

		r = Number of Dimensions						
		1	2	3	4	5	6	7
n = number of stimuli	1	2						
	2	3	4					
	3	4	7	8				
	4	5	11	15	16			
	5	6	16	26	31	32		
	6	7	22	42	57	63	64	
	7	8	29	64	99	120	127	128
	8	9	37	93	163	219	247	255
	9	10	46	130	256	382	466	502
	10	11	56	176	386	638	848	968

Note: $\tau(n, r) = 2^n$ for all $r \geq n$.

obtain the rank order of the angles made by the stimulus vectors—but only in the case of two dimensions. The merit of this is its relation to the factor loading of the vector on a dimension. Other things being equal, the more nearly collinear a vector is with an axis the greater the factor loading of that vector on that dimension. Hence if one vector makes a smaller angle with an axis than does another vector, that dimension is relatively more important in the task represented by the first vector than it is in the second vector.

This a pretty meager outcome but I do not see how to obtain more from the response patterns in the (1,0) data matrix without making additional assumptions. Whatever virtue this nonmetric approach has lies in the weaker assumptions imposed and the simplicity of the analytical procedure in, at least, the two-dimensional case. Even some of this virtue is lost, however, if modern computer facilities are available for running correlations and factor analyses. These are the reasons for not presenting the mathematical detail on this model, in view of the further fact that the detail is available in Coombs and Kao (1955).

We turn now to the analytical procedure for arriving at the rank order of the relative factor loadings of the stimuli in the case of two dimensions.

Analytical Procedure for the (1, 0) Data Matrix

The procedure presented in the Coombs and Kao (1955) monograph was worked out in detail in the hopes that it would lead to insights which would permit generalization to more than two dimensions. This hope has not been realized. Consequently, a simplified procedure suggested by W. L. Hays* is presented here. This procedure involves examining the response patterns for each subset of three stimuli at a time in order to rank each such triple on each dimension. Then these ordered triples are combined to give the complete orderings.

The key to the method of analysis lies in the fact that *if all hyperplanes intersect, then only two configurations can occur for three stimuli*, given their order on the dimensions. These are illustrated in Figs. 12.6 and 12.7. Only the hyperplane for each stimulus is shown. The regions of the space are numbered and the response pattern associated with each region is shown in the table accompanying each figure. At the bottom of the table the sum of each column is indicated.

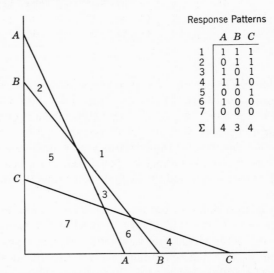

	A	B	C
1	1	1	1
2	0	1	1
3	1	0	1
4	1	1	0
5	0	0	1
6	1	0	0
7	0	0	0
Σ	4	3	4

Fig. 12.6 A configuration of hyperplanes for three stimuli.

* Personal communication.

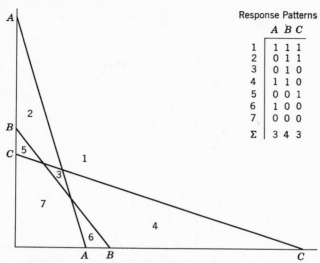

Fig. 12.7   The alternative configuration of hyperplanes for three stimuli.

The difference between the two configurations lies in whether the hyperplane of the middle stimulus (in this case B) passes on one side or the other of the intersection of the other two hyperplanes. In Fig. 12.6, for example, the B hyperplane passes on the side away from the origin, and in Fig. 12.7 it passes on the side toward the origin. In either case, with all hyperplanes intersecting in the positive quadrant of the space, 7 response patterns occur; and the sums of the columns of the accompanying tables immediately reveal which stimulus has the intermediate loading on the two dimensions.

If the configuration is as in Fig. 12.6, the intermediate stimulus is passed in only 3 response patterns, while each of the others is passed in 4. If the configuration is as shown in Fig. 12.7 the intermediate stimulus is passed in 4 response patterns while each of the others is passed in only 3. These two configurations will be identified, respectively, as the 4 3 4 pattern and the 3 4 3 pattern. With this basic key, the analysis of a data matrix is straightforward and is illustrated in the analysis of the data matrix given in Table 12.5.

We note first that there are 16 distinct response patterns to the 5 stimuli; from Table 12.4 we see that the compensatory model can accommodate that many response patterns in two dimensions. We might also note that if we considered analyzing this matrix by the conjunctive-disjunctive model, the fact that there are 4 distinct response patterns with 1 item wrong (patterns 2, 3, 4, and 5) indicates, by reference to Table 12.2, that at least four dimensions would be required.

Table 12.5   A Hypothetical Data Matrix

	A	B	C	D	E
1	1	1	1	1	1
2	1	0	1	1	1
3	1	1	0	1	1
4	0	1	1	1	1
5	1	1	1	0	1
6	1	0	1	1	0
7	1	0	0	1	1
8	1	1	0	1	0
9	0	1	0	1	1
10	0	1	1	0	1
11	1	0	0	1	0
12	0	1	0	1	0
13	0	1	0	0	1
14	0	0	0	1	0
15	0	1	0	0	0
16	0	0	0	0	0

To analyze this matrix by the compensatory model we break it down into 10 submatrices, 1 for each subset of 3 stimuli, showing the 7 distinct response patterns to each subset. Three of these submatrices are shown in Tables 12.6, 12.7, and 12.8, which reveal, respectively, that E falls between B and C, C between A and E, and A between C and D. Thus, these three triples are ordered $B\ E\ C$, $E\ C\ A$, and $C\ A\ D$ on one dimension and the reverse on the other dimension. Hence the complete orderings on the two dimensions are $B\ E\ C\ A\ D$ and the reverse. The information in the rest of the submatrices would confirm this result.

Table 12.6   Submatrix for B, C, and E

	B	C	E
1, 4, 5, 10	1	1	1
2	0	1	1
3, 9, 13	1	0	1
6	0	1	0
7	0	0	1
8, 12, 15	1	0	0
11, 14, 16	0	0	0
Σ	3	3	4

Table 12.7
Submatrix for A, C, and E

	A	C	E
1, 2, 5	1	1	1
3, 7	1	0	1
4, 10	0	1	1
6	1	1	0
8, 11	1	0	0
9, 13	0	0	1
12, 14, 15, 16	0	0	0
Σ	4	3	4

Table 12.8
Submatrix for A, C, and D

	A	C	D
1, 2, 6	1	1	1
3, 7, 8, 11	1	0	1
4	0	1	1
5	1	1	0
9, 12, 14	0	0	1
10	0	1	0
13, 15, 16	0	0	0
Σ	3	4	4

Knowing the ordering on each dimension and noting whether the configuration for each triple is a 4 3 4 pattern or a 3 4 3 pattern, the configuration of the hyperplanes in a two-dimensional space may be drawn. The configuration for the data matrix of Table 12.5 is shown in Fig. 12.8.

With actual data it is to be anticipated that some pairs of hyperplanes will not intersect in the positive quadrant of the space. This procedure will still yield the order in which the hyperplanes intersect the axes, but the relative factor loadings may be only partially ordered in such a case.

The Ranked Data Matrix

The data matrix which has been considered up to this point, the (1, 0) data matrix, is one in which each item or stimulus has dichotomized the individuals in the sense of those who have passed it and those who have failed it. Now we consider a more general case in which the item or stimulus has generated a rank ordering of the individuals. Such would be the case, for example, if we used a mental test as a stimulus and ordered the individuals in terms of the number of items in the test they answered correctly. The usual procedure, of course, is to take such a score matrix, compute correlations between tests, and factor analyze.

The problem considered here is the nonmetric factor analysis of the ranked data matrix—a kind of noncorrelational factor analysis. The work reported in this section was done by Bennett (1956). The problem he solved was the determination of the number of dimensions that would be required to account for the rank orders assuming the linear compensatory model of factor analysis. It was only his untimely death at the age of 29 that

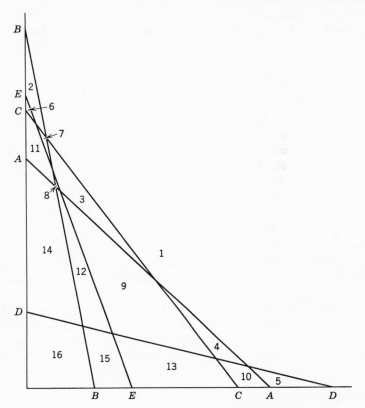

Fig. 12.8 Configuration for the data matrix of Table 12.5.

prevented him from making significant contributions to the problem of configuration.

Suppose that the factor and population matrices are given. Let the factor scores of each subject be taken as the coordinates of a *subject vector* in a *population space*, the axes of which represent a set of orthogonal factors. A subject vector refers specifically to its terminus; the term *subject point* would do as well. For example, the subspace generated by two such vectors will be regarded not as the plane spanned by them including the origin, but as the line connecting their termini and, in general, *not* containing the origin. It is possible to represent a test in such a space as a line through the origin of the space with appropriate direction cosines relative to the axes, such that the orthogonal projections of the subject vectors on a test line are the subjects' scores on that test, up to a linear transformation. The order of those projections on the test line is the order in which that test ranks the subjects. Although a ranking and its exact inverse will not be distinguished in any important way, it is convenient to give the test line an orientation, that is, a direction in which scores are to be called *higher*.

Figure 12.9 represents a two-dimensional population space containing two subject vectors, *A* and *B*. What distinguishes the class of tests which rank *A* over *B* from that of tests which rank *B* over *A*? We construct a hyperplane, in this case a line called *AB*, through the origin and normal to the line connecting *A* and *B*. It is evident that the two subject vectors will have coincident projections on *AB* and distinct projections on any other line through the origin. *AB* divides the space into two halfspaces, labeled I and II in Fig. 12.9, such that any test line whose orientation (positive direction) is from II into I* will yield the ranking $A \geq B$. Such a test line is regarded as "into I." Any test line into II will rank $B \geq A$. (Such hyperplanes are analogous to midpoints.) A test line coincident with *AB* will yield the result $A = B$. In the arguments which follow the convention is adopted that such an assignment of identical scores to two subjects is not a ranking but the simultaneous satisfaction of two rankings, $A \geq B$ and $B \geq A$. The distinction becomes important in referring to the number of distinct rankings.

Every pair of subject vectors generates a hyperplane through the origin and orthogonal to the line connecting their termini. The hyperplanes so formed partition the space into open regions, to each of which corresponds

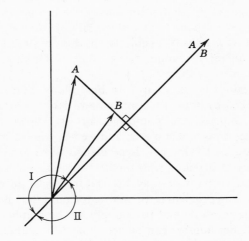

Fig. 12.9 Two subject vectors and their hyperplane.

* The space is not confined to the positive quadrant.

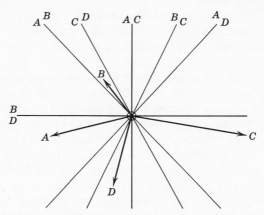

Fig. 12.10   Hyperplanes of four subjects in two dimensions.

a unique ordering of the subjects. The total number of such regions corresponds to the total number of possible rankings a test could impose on the subjects. As an example, consider the 4 subject vectors of Fig. 12.10. There is again 1 line of coincident projection for each pair of subject vectors, or 6 such lines in all. Together they divide the space into 12 regions, each region having the property that any test line in it will rank all the subjects in the same order. This means that when exactly 2 factors are present, there are only 12 different ways in which linear functions of those 2 factors can rank 4 subjects, and 6 of these rankings are exact inverses of the other 6. (Note that regions which lie opposite to each other across the origin correspond to inverse rankings.) Now algebraically there are 24 different ways to rank 4 subjects; in this construction half of them are missing. This raises two questions: Why 12 rankings exactly, rather than 10 or 14, and why these 12?

The first question is essentially: In how many different ways can m subjects be ranked by linear functions of r variables? Briefly, the answer is as follows: Suppose this number is already known for some given number of dimensions and subjects, and we ask what happens when one more subject is added. One new hyperplane will be formed as each subject already present is paired with the new subject. Each of these hyperplanes will create as many new regions as it transects, since it cuts each of them into two. The problem is, therefore, to count the number of regions each hyperplane transects and to multiply by the number of new hyperplanes. The former number can be determined by examining the surface of each hyperplane and noting the cells into which it is divided by its intersections with the other hyperplanes; each such cell will correspond to a region through which it has passed. But how can these cells be counted? Dr. Kenneth Leisenring* pointed out that the division of each *hyperplane* into *cells* by its intersections with other hyperplanes will be identical with the division into *regions* of the complete population space generated by one fewer subjects and one fewer dimensions.

The reason for this identity is that each hyperplane is a legitimate subspace of the population space (that subspace from which all the variance attributable to the axis normal to the hyperplane has been extracted). All lines on its surface created by its intersections with other hyperplanes are where they ought to be if all the other subject vectors were projected normally onto its surface and the hyperplane was treated as a population space in its own right. In this projection the two subject vectors determining the hyperplane will be projected onto a single point, because the hyperplane was originally constructed perpendicular to the line connecting them; hence there is a loss of one subject as well as one dimension.

So it is seen that the number $C_{m,r}$ of regions or rankings created by m subjects in r-space is equal to the number present before the mth subject was added, that is, $C_{m-1,r}$, plus the number of hyperplanes added, $m - 1$, times the number of regions which each transects, $C_{m-1,r-1}$. The result is the recursive expression shown at the top of Table 12.9.

This account of its derivation is rather terse, because the fruit of all this labor proves to have little except theoretical interest since $C_{m,r}$ quickly becomes large for moderate m and r. The number of tests likely to be given is never so large that the limitation on the number of different ways the subjects can be ranked becomes an important constraint on the data. It is usable directly only in the situation in which there are a large number of rankings of a small number of objects, as in psychophysics or in scaling experiments.

The second issue is the constraint on the nature of the permissible rankings imposed by dimension, which arises in the following manner. Suppose that the termini of three subject vectors all lie on a straight line (which does not necessarily pass through the origin) and that on this line they are in the order A, B, C. Such a configuration is illustrated in Fig. 12.11. It is apparent that regardless of the dimensionality of the space in which these vectors occur, there are only three ways in which any linear function of the axes can rank them: A, B, C; C, B, A; and $A = B = C$. In other words, if B is *between* A and C, that is, if B is in the interior of the interval $A-C$, no ranking based on a linear function of the coordinate axes is possible in which the subject B is separated from the set of subjects (A, C).

Consider next the four coplanar subject vectors in Fig. 12.12. Note that the subject vector D is in the interior of the triangle formed by vectors

* Personal communication to J. F. Bennett.

A, *B*, and *C*; consequently, no linear function of the coordinate axes is possible in which subject *D* is separated from the set of subjects (*A*, *B*, *C*). This relation may be generalized formally to an arbitrary number of dimensions in the following way: *If a vector X is in the interior of a simplex formed by a vector set S, no linear function of the coordinate axes is possible in which the subject X is wholly separated from the set S.*

Table 12.9   The Number $C_{m,r}$ of Different Ways in Which *m* Subjects Can Be Ranked by Linear Functions of *r* Factors

$$C_{m,r} = C_{m-1,r} + (m-1)C_{m-1,r-1}$$

m	*r* = 2	*r* = 3	*r* = 4	*r* = 5
1	1	1	1	1
2	2	2	2	2
3	6 = 3!	6	6	6
4	12	24 = 4!	24	24
5	20	72	120 = 5!	120
6	30	172	480	720 = 6!
7	42	352	1,512	3,600
8	56	646	3,976	14,184
9	72	1,094	9,144	45,992
10	90	1,742	18,990	128,288
11	110	2,642	36,410	318,188
12	132	3,852	65,472	718,698
13	156	5,436	111,696	1,504,362
14	182	7,464	182,364	2,956,410
15	210	10,012	286,860	5,509,506
20	380	33,632	1,841,480	69,867,524
25	600	85,102	7,590,600	477,706,092
30	870	180,672	23,843,220	2,245,552,710

This relation, however true, might seem at first to have limited usefulness. What can be done with configurations like that of Fig. 12.10, in which none of the four vectors lies in a triangle formed by the other three? The following device is proposed. Consider the subspace of dimension *d* containing a particular set of *d* + 1 subject vectors in general position, that is, randomly scattered so that no two of them are coincident, no three form a line, no two pairs form parallel lines, and so on. Consider next two such subspaces generated by two distinct subsets of subject vectors. From

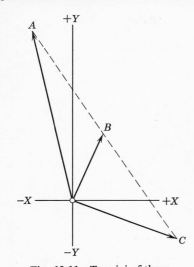

Fig. 12.11 Termini of three vectors on a line.

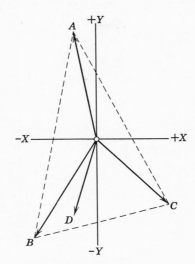

Fig. 12.12 Four coplanar subject vectors.

familiar geometric considerations, *the sum of the dimensions of two inter-secting subspaces is equal to the sum of the dimensions of their union* (the space they span) *and their intersection* (the space that is common). For example, two one-dimensional lines crossing in a plane have the whole two-dimensional plane for their union and intersect in a zero-dimensional point. In that case, $1 + 1 = 2 + 0$.

Now suppose that the total number of subject vectors in the two subsets is equal to $r + 2$, where r is the dimensionality of the population space. One of the subsets, containing m subjects, will generate an $(m - 1)$-dimensional subspace. The other, containing $r + 2 - m$ subjects, will generate an $(r + 1 - m)$-dimensional subspace. The sum of these dimensions is r. On the other hand, the dimension of their union is clearly r also, since any $r + 1$ of them are sufficient to generate the whole population space. It follows that the dimension of the intersection of the subspaces is zero; that is, they must meet in a point.

Such a configuration is illustrated in Fig. 12.13. The two subject vectors A and B generate a line A–B which intersects a second line C–D. In this particular case, the point of intersection is between A and B on the line A–B and between C and D on the line C–D.

It is convenient to consider this point of intersection as a sort of phantom subject, X, who is a part of both subsets of subject vectors and must obey appropriate constraints in each subset. For example, in Fig. 12.13 no linear function of the coordinates could yield the ranking $X\,A\,B$ or

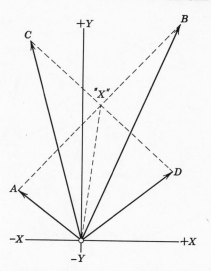

Fig. 12.13 The phantom subject X.

$A\ B\ X$. Only $A\ X\ B$ and $B\ X\ A$ are possible. The same is true of the line $C\text{–}D$. Furthermore, the phantom subject must continue to obey these constraints relative to each subset when the two subsets are combined in any ranking. For example, in Fig. 12.13 the ranking $A\ B\ C\ D$ is impossible, because it would call for the point of intersection X to be between A and B and at the same time to be between C and D, which is impossible. On the other hand, the order $A\ C\ B\ D$ is possible, because it can be written $A\ C\ X\ B\ D$, placing X in the middle of both subsets, AB and CD. The fundamental constraint which is imposed on rankings is that *no ranking is possible in which this phantom subject is called on to be in two places at once.*

There are clearly several different ways in which a given set of $r+2$ subjects can be separated into two subsets. The most important is the way that arises when the point of intersection is in the interior of the simplex in both subspaces. That is, if one of the subspaces is a line, the point of intersection is between the two points which determine the line; if one of the subspaces is a plane, the point of intersection is inside the triangle formed by the three points determining the plane; and so forth. The uniqueness of the separation of the subjects into two sets which accomplishes this leads to the following proposition: *If the population space is of dimension r, then given any set S of $r+2$ subjects, there exists a unique separation of the subjects into two subsets, S* and S − S*, such that no test can rank all the subjects in S* over all the subjects in S − S*.* That is, no ranking can separate the two sets entirely, because then the phantom subject, the point of intersection, could not be inside both of them at once.

The simple cases which have been discussed, for example, that of the vector which lies in the interior of the triangle formed by three other vectors in a plane, are merely special cases of this general proposition in which one of the subsets contains but a single vector.

This result is applicable, with obvious limitations, to the problem of determining the number of independent parameters of the score matrix. The score matrix for subsets of m subjects is examined. If r independent parameters are present, at least some subsets of subjects of size $r + 1$ are separated in rank by the tests in all possible ways; and if there are enough tests, all such subsets will be separated in all possible ways. *But in every subset of $r + 2$ subjects there will be one separation which never occurs in the data, no matter how the elements of each subset are permuted within the subset.* This exclusion indicates that all the rankings can be accounted for by r independent parameters.

To illustrate this exclusion property, we utilize Thurstone's well-known analysis of the box problem (1947, p. 140). Examples will be drawn from the score matrix of that study to illustrate how the number of independent parameters can be determined. The score matrix is reproduced as Table 12.10 on p. 276.

First, consider the scores on tests 1, 2, 4, 7, 10, 13, 14, 18, and 19, which are known to contain only the factors X and Y. Of course, when the scores are ranked the distinction among tests 1, 13, and 18 disappears at once because they are all monotonic, though nonlinear, functions of X. The same is true of tests 2, 14, and 19. It is obvious that there must be more than one parameter present, because in many instances subsets of three boxes (that is, subjects) are separated in all possible ways. For example, boxes 1, 3, and 6 are variously ranked in the order 3, 6, 1 by test 4, and in the order 6, 3, 1 by test 7; no possible way of separating these three boxes into two subsets is absent.

On the other hand, for every set of four boxes there is some separation which no test imposes. For example, boxes 3 and 6 are never ranked apart from boxes 1 and 8. Box 8 is never ranked apart from boxes 1, 11, and 14. Thus two factors are sufficient to account for the score matrix on these tests.

Proceeding to the analysis of all twenty tests together, it will be discovered that some sets of four boxes are separated in all possible ways. For example, boxes 1, 10, 11, and 14 are variously ranked in the order 10, 11, 14, 1 by test 17; 14, 10, 11, 1 by test 8; and 11, 14, 10, 1 by test 7. Every possible way of separating these four boxes into two subsets is represented. But in every set of five boxes a separation is discovered which does *not* occur in the data. For example, boxes 3, 5, and 7 are never separated from boxes 2 and 9. Therefore, three factors are sufficient to account for all the rankings of the boxes generated by these tests.

The determination of configuration from the rankings of subjects by tests clearly has a long way to go as the results discussed in this section

Table 12.10   Score Matrix for the Box Problem

Test

Box	1	2	3	4	5	6	7	8	9	10
	x^2	y^2	z^2	xy	xz	yz	$\sqrt{x^2 + y^2}$	$\sqrt{x^2 + z^2}$	$\sqrt{y^2 + z^2}$	$2x + 2y$
1	9.00	4.00	1.00	6.00	3.00	2.00	3.61	3.16	2.24	10.00
2	9.00	4.00	4.00	6.00	6.00	4.00	3.61	3.61	2.83	10.00
3	9.00	9.00	1.00	9.00	3.00	3.00	4.24	3.16	3.16	12.00
4	9.00	9.00	4.00	9.00	6.00	6.00	4.24	3.61	3.61	12.00
5	9.00	9.00	9.00	9.00	9.00	9.00	4.24	4.24	4.24	12.00
6	16.00	4.00	1.00	8.00	4.00	2.00	4.47	4.12	2.24	12.00
7	16.00	4.00	4.00	8.00	8.00	4.00	4.47	4.47	2.83	12.00
8	16.00	9.00	1.00	12.00	4.00	3.00	5.00	4.12	3.16	14.00
9	16.00	9.00	4.00	12.00	8.00	6.00	5.00	4.47	3.61	14.00
10	16.00	9.00	9.00	12.00	12.00	9.00	5.00	5.00	4.24	14.00
11	16.00	16.00	1.00	16.00	4.00	4.00	5.66	4.12	4.12	16.00
12	16.00	16.00	4.00	16.00	8.00	8.00	5.66	4.47	4.47	16.00
13	16.00	16.00	9.00	16.00	12.00	12.00	5.66	5.00	5.00	16.00
14	25.00	4.00	1.00	10.00	5.00	2.00	5.39	5.10	2.24	14.00
15	25.00	4.00	4.00	10.00	10.00	4.00	5.39	5.39	2.83	14.00
16	25.00	9.00	4.00	15.00	10.00	6.00	5.83	5.39	3.61	16.00
17	25.00	9.00	9.00	15.00	15.00	9.00	5.83	5.83	4.24	16.00
18	25.00	16.00	1.00	20.00	5.00	4.00	6.40	5.10	4.12	18.00
19	25.00	16.00	4.00	20.00	10.00	8.00	6.40	5.39	4.47	18.00
20	25.00	16.00	9.00	20.00	15.00	12.00	6.40	5.83	5.00	18.00

determine dimensions in a painfully literal way. If r dimensions are needed to account for all the rankings, the technique says that there are r dimensions. But, of course, in any real problem there are as many dimensions as there are tests. No factor analysis technique can hope to be useful unless some way is found to restrict the analysis to the *common* factors. In this technique, for example, it might be stipulated that *most* sets of $r + 2$ subjects shall have the exclusion property, or some such approximation, or individual rankings might be broken down into their constituent pair comparisons, with a requirement that *nearly all* these pair comparisons shall fit the model, allowing some deviation.

Second, the determination of the number of dimensions necessary to account for the whole set of tests does not begin to settle the problem of the apportionment of the factors among the tests, that is, the questions of factor loadings and rotation to simple structure. Thus, it is still too early to say whether nonmetric factor analysis of the kind proposed by Thurstone is feasible. It was Bennett's hope that more psychometricians will consider it worthwhile to find out, since the worst that can happen is that

Table 12.10   (Continued)

Test

11	12	13	14	15	16	17	18	19	20
$2x + 2z$	$2y + 2z$	$\log_e x$	$\log_e y$	$\log_e z$	xyz	$\sqrt{x^2 + y^2 + z^2}$	e^x	e^y	e^z
8.00	6.00	1.10	0.69	0.00	6.00	3.74	20.09	7.39	2.72
10.00	8.00	1.10	0.69	0.69	12.00	4.12	20.09	7.39	7.39
8.00	8.00	1.10	1.10	0.00	9.00	4.36	20.09	20.09	2.72
10.00	10.00	1.10	1.10	0.69	18.00	4.69	20.09	20.09	7.39
12.00	12.00	1.10	1.10	1.10	27.00	5.20	20.09	20.09	20.09
10.00	6.00	1.39	0.69	0.00	8.00	4.58	54.60	7.39	2.72
12.00	8.00	1.39	0.69	0.69	16.00	4.90	54.60	7.39	7.39
10.00	8.00	1.39	1.10	0.00	12.00	5.10	54.60	20.09	2.72
12.00	10.00	1.39	1.10	0.69	24.00	5.39	54.60	20.09	7.39
14.00	12.00	1.39	1.10	1.10	36.00	5.83	54.60	20.09	20.09
10.00	10.00	1.39	1.39	0.00	16.00	5.74	54.60	54.60	2.72
12.00	12.00	1.39	1.39	0.69	32.00	6.00	54.60	54.60	7.39
14.00	14.00	1.39	1.39	1.10	48.00	6.40	54.60	54.60	20.09
12.00	6.00	1.61	0.69	0.00	10.00	5.48	148.41	7.39	2.72
14.00	8.00	1.61	0.69	0.69	20.00	5.74	148.41	7.39	7.39
14.00	10.00	1.61	1.10	0.69	30.00	6.61	148.41	20.09	7.39
16.00	12.00	1.61	1.10	1.10	45.00	6.56	148.41	20.09	20.09
12.00	10.00	1.61	1.39	0.00	20.00	6.48	148.41	54.60	2.72
14.00	12.00	1.61	1.39	0.69	40.00	6.71	148.41	54.60	7.39
16.00	14.00	1.61	1.39	1.10	60.00	7.07	148.41	54.60	20.09

more will be learned about the underlying logic of the factor analytic method.

3. FURTHER ISSUES AND PROBLEMS

These studies of the conjunctive-disjunctive model and the compensatory model provide the basic machinery for determining dimensionality and a nonmetric configuration, but much more remains to be done.

The conjunctive-disjunctive model has been more completely developed than the compensatory, and a complete analysis of a data matrix is feasible. In fact, the analytical procedure is ready for programming on a computer. The model as constructed here, however, is designed for the analysis of the

(1, 0) data matrix, in which responses are characterized only on a dichoto-mized scale—positive and negative. An obvious extension is to data in which the responses are measured on a multicategory scale. This extension will not be difficult.

More serious problems remain. The models constructed here are completely deterministic; there is no concept of error and fluctuation which would permit neglecting some responses and only "fitting" a portion of the data. It is certainly true that the data will contain error and fluctuations, and some sort of stochastic generalizations will have to be constructed to make these models useful in such a domain as mental testing. On the other hand, in some domains, such as psychophysics, it is sometimes possible to get *experimentally* independent replications of an individual's response to a stimulus, and hence the stochastically dominant response may be determined and these models applied to relatively error-free data.

A problem related to that of error and fluctuations in data is the problem of incomplete data. It is obvious from such figures as 12.2 and 12.8 that the relative compactness of subject points in the space may lead to vacant regions, and this is particularly likely for the smaller regions. In addition, in the case of the compensatory model for the (1, 0) data matrix, some pairs of hyperplanes may not intersect in the positive quadrant of the space. Milholland (1953) found that the consequence of incomplete data is that the solution is not unique, a simple ordering on every one of the several dimensions is not obtained. Resolving such partial orderings is somewhat analogous to the rotational problem of multiple factor analysis.

A question of considerable interest is how to choose between models. In principle, any one of these models can be applied mechanically to a given data matrix and a solution obtained in some number of dimensions. I have generated hypothetical data matrices by applying one of these models and then analyzing them by the same and the alternative model. My experience has been that the incorrect model requires more dimensions, yields a solution which is not unique, and generates more empty regions. This is offered as an empirical rule-of-thumb in the absence of anything better.

I would like to suggest that there may be further varieties of composition models not conceived of here, other than mixtures of these models. Every composition model is of fundamental interest to psychological theory, as well as for analysis of data, since it provides another potential model for constructing theories of behavior.

Finally, I would like to discuss a special problem which arises in the application of any multidimensional model in QIIa, and that is the apparently small matter of specifying the direction of an order relation between a pair of points. We somehow have no trouble in specifying the direction of an order relation between an individual point and a stimulus point when the individual passes or fails an arithmetic item. But this problem of specifying a positive direction is not always so simple. Suppose, for example, we wished to interpret the verdict of a Supreme Court judge on a case as an order relation between his point and a point corresponding to the case at issue. It is not at all obvious what verdicts correspond to 1 and 0. We could, as Schubert (1962) does, identify 1 and 0 with verdicts that are with the majority and against the majority, respectively, in each case. It is not clear, however, how this insures that the 1, 0 orientations of different cases are the same. Aside from its merits in this instance, it is certainly no general solution applicable to all kinds of instances.

There is, however, a way in which a uniform orientation for all items may be ensured under certain circumstances, which was pointed out to me by Robyn Dawes.* In any instance of multidimensional behavior for which these models are appropriate, there will always exist, in principle, a pair of response patterns which will be complete mirror images of each other and which properly define the pattern "1, 1, . . . , 1" and the pattern "0, 0, . . . , 0." Which is which is unimportant for analytical purposes because one assignment versus the other corresponds to complementing the matrix, the effect of which has been discussed.

The trouble is that there may exist more than one mirror image pairs of response patterns, as we may note, for example, in Table 12.3 where response patterns 1 and 18 constitute one mirror image pair and patterns 2 and 17 constitute a second. Patterns 1 and 18 are the proper ones to define the positive direction in this case but how do we determine that given only the data matrix? The cue is given by the fact that response patterns 2 and 17 invoke failing and passing, respectively, only stimulus F, and this is possible because F is first on one dimension and last on the other.

In fact, to every stimulus which appears first on one dimension and last on another there will correspond a mirror image pair of response patterns. Indeed, if the stimuli which are first and second on one dimension are last and next to last, respectively, on another, there will be two additional mirror image pairs of response patterns. Additional mirror image pairs may be generated in a similar manner.

The only way I know at this writing to choose which of these pairs properly defines the positive direction is to try the various ones out. The proper pair will give the fewest dimensions and will most adequately fit the data—also, the solution will indicate how the other mirror image pairs of response patterns occurred. Hopefully, with a reasonable number of

* Personal communication.

stimuli in reasonably few dimensions, there would rarely be many mirror image pairs.

The problem with the Supreme Court example would not arise if we were to interpret a judge's verdict as a *proximity* relation on the pair of points. This would make QIIb data out of the behavior instead of QIIa, and an analysis by such models would lead to a different result than an analysis by QIIa models. This is just one more example of the creative step in mapping behavior into data, phase 2.

4. RELATIONS AMONG QIIa MODELS

Sometimes it is helpful to see the relations among various models in different ways. The organization of the last two chapters, of course, has been based on such relations, and we may now put them together in a single picture.

The models may be compared in terms of whether they have a low or high tolerance for inconsistency and in terms of whether they are designed to yield a one-dimensional or multidimensional joint space. A classification of QIIa models on this basis is shown in Table 12.11. The first row

Table 12.11 A Classification of QIIa Models

Tolerance for Inconsistency

	low	high
Unidimensional	Guttman's scalogram analysis	Lazarsfeld's latent distance model Lazarsfeld's latent structure analysis with monotone trace lines Torgerson's model for categorical judgment
Multidimensional	Conjunctive-disjunctive model of Coombs and Kao Compensatory models of Coombs and Kao and of J. F. Bennett	Multiple factor analysis

of the fourfold table lists principle models discussed in Chapter 11, and the second row on multidimensional models lists the models with which this chapter is concerned, except that no attempt is made to discuss factor analysis. There is, later, some discussion of factor analysis in Chapter 15 in relation to Lazarsfeld's general system of latent structure analysis.

5. SUMMARY

In this chapter multidimensional generalizations of Guttman's scalogram analysis were presented. The heart of any such model is referred to as the composition axiom, the construction of a simple order relation on a pair of points in a multidimensional space. In QIIa data an individual, at a minimal primitive level, responds either positively or negatively to a stimulus and this behavior is interpreted as an order relation on a corresponding pair of points. As any individual in the sample may be observed to respond in such a way to any stimulus in the set, the model must generate the corresponding relation between their respective points. Three such composition functions are considered; a conjunctive, a disjunctive, and a compensatory one.

According to the conjunctive model, an individual will respond positively to a stimulus if and only if he has a certain minimum on each one of the components of a complex attribute. The conjunctive model is implicit in any multiple cut-off criterion. The disjunctive requires a minimum on any one of the components. The conjunctive model is an "and" model, the disjunctive an "either-or." According to the compensatory model, a surplus on one component may be substituted for a shortage on another.

An illuminating comparison of the disjunctive and the compensatory models is seen in college football under unlimited substitution and under limited substitution. Under unlimited substitution a player could be successful with any one of a number of capabilities whereas in limited substitution players must be compared by the coach in terms of an overall capability, requiring a compensatory model. The coach's task is far more difficult in this respect under limited substitution than under unlimited. It is easier to compare the pass-catching ability of two ends than to compare their overall capability when one is a better offensive and the other a better defensive end. Incidentally, even if the success of the player is determined by the disjunctive model, team success is determined by the compensatory model.

The conjunctive and the disjunctive models are seen to be mathematically isomorphic in that a double duality exists. There is an individual-stimulus duality which permits a transposition transformation on a data matrix, and there is a pass-fail duality which permits a complementation transformation on the data matrix. Either transformation reverses the role of individuals and stimuli and reverses the order relations on each component; in addition, the complementation transformation converts a data matrix from one model to the other.

All the models discussed in this chapter are to some degree incomplete. Some of the issues and problems that remain are discussed. The models in this chapter have all been identified as nonmetric factor analysis models, and perhaps a word should be said about this. The data of QIIa are characterized by an assumption of monotonicity between performance and amount of attribute. If a certain amount of ability is useful in performing a task, more of the ability cannot be detrimental. This, to me, is a prime characteristic of factor analysis, though not a necessary one. Whether the conjunctive-disjunctive models, then, are called nonmetric factor analysis is just a matter of whether the term should be confined to the compensatory model, and even more restrictively to the linear compensatory model in particular, which is a prime characteristic of factor analysis. Thus in a sense Bennett's model is the more immediate generalization of factor analysis and the conjunctive-disjunctive models are more removed.

The role that monotonicity plays in this may be seen by comparing Bennett's model with models discussed in Chapter 9 for the analysis of preferential choice data. Bennett's model is cast in terms of a stimulus compensatory model in that a test (stimulus) ranks individuals according to a function determined by the test. Of course, because of the individual-stimulus duality in the mathematics of this model, it applies with equal force to an individual compensatory model in which the stimulus vectors are projected on a line in the space defined by an individual. But we recognize this as identically the model that Tucker proposes for analysis of preferences—a model which says that if an individual likes coffee with sugar in it he will like it more with more sugar. Tucker's model then is the dual of the multiple factor analysis model with the roles of individuals and stimuli reversed. This model, however, we pointed out in Chapter 9 to be a special case of the personal compensatory model for analysis of preferences, in which the individual's preferences are generated by folding the line on which the stimuli are projected. In this latter model there is non-monotonicity of preference strength with degree of attributes. So now we may see Bennett's model as a nonmetric analogue of factor analysis and Tucker's as a dual of factor analysis with roles of individuals and stimuli reversed—and both are QIIa models. This illustrates the confusion that may arise in thinking about these models in real world terms rather than mathematical ones. Tucker talks of his model in terms of preferential choice, but it is a QIIa model, not QIa.

In a final section some of the relations among QIIa models are brought out in terms of their low or high tolerance for inconsistency and in terms of whether they are unidimensional or multidimensional.

REFERENCES

Bennett, J. F., 1956, Determination of the number of independent parameters of a score matrix from the examination of rank orders, *Psychometrika*, **21**, 383–93.
Coombs, C. H., and R. C. Kao, 1955, Nonmetric factor analysis, *Engng. Res. Bull. No.* 38, University of Michigan Press, Ann Arbor.
Cronbach, L. J., and G. C. Gleser, 1953, Assessing similarity between profiles, *Psychol. Bull.*, **50**, 456–73.
Eninger, M. U., 1952, Habit summation in a selective learning problem, *J. comp. physiol. Psychol.*, **45**, 604–08.
Hull, C. L., 1943, *Principles of behavior: an introduction to behavior*, Appleton-Century-Crofts, New York.
Johnson, H. M., 1935, Some neglected principles in aptitude-testing, *Amer. J. Psychol.*, **47**, 159–65.
Lorge, I., and H. Solomon, 1955, Two models of group behavior in the solution of eureka-type problems, *Psychometrika*, **20**, 139–48.
Milholland, J. E., 1953, Dimensionality of response patterns, unpublished Ph.D. dissertation, University of Michigan.
Miller, J., 1939, The rate of conditioning of human subjects to single and multiple conditioned stimuli, *J. gen. Psychol.*, **20**, 399–408.
Muenzinger, K. F., and M. Fletcher, 1936, Motivation in learning. VI. Escape from electric shock compared with hunger-food tension in the visual discrimination habit, *J. comp. Psychol.*, **22**, 79–91.
Powloski, R. F., 1953, The effects of combining hunger and thirst motives in a discrimination habit, *J. comp. physiol. Psychol.*, **46**, 434–37.
Schubert, G., 1962, The 1960 term of the Supreme Court: a psychological analysis, *Amer. pol. Sci. Rev.*, **56**, 90–107.
Thurstone, L. L., 1947, *Multiple factor analysis*, University of Chicago Press, Chicago.
Warner, W. L., M. Meeker, and K. Eells, 1949, *Social class in America*, Science Research Associates, Chicago.
Warren, J. M., 1953, The additivity of cues in visual pattern discrimination by monkeys, *J. comp. physiol. Psychol.*, **46**, 484–86.

CHAPTER 13

Comparing Incomparables: Compression of Partial Orders to Form Decisions

Much of what I have said and written in the past could be taken as a plea for the use of weak measurement models such as partially ordered, ordinal, and ordered metric scales. My position was, and still is, based on an essentially untutored uneasiness about the assumptions we adopt in whatever model we use, and I am less uneasy with fewer assumptions.

All knowledge, every empirical statement about the real world, is an "if . . . , then . . ." proposition; there is no "fact" without "theory." But we buy knowledge with the assumptions we make—the more assumptions made the more knowledge obtained. If, for example, we assumed a distribution was normal, we could convert an ordinal scale into an interval scale. Then we would know magnitudes of differences, which we had not known before, and this knowledge would have been purchased with assumptions as coin.

The usual justifications given for making strong assumptions and using strong models include the following: (1) The analysis of data is easier to carry out, for example, a clerk can do the computing; (2) the results are in a form easier to communicate and to compare with the results of other studies; (3) the results are usually not very different, or at least not in conflict with, the results that would have obtained with a weaker model anyway. These are very persuasive arguments, although they do not dispel my still persistent uneasiness. But there is another argument which can be made to justify the use of strong measurement models in certain instances, an argument which I find more persuasive than the preceding ones. This argument provides justification based on entirely different grounds; it rests on society's needs for decision and action.

The basic idea is that *behavior is intrinsically partially ordered.* Individuals A and B take a mental test and each passes items the other does not. In such a case it is not a clear and valid inference that A is better than B, because if he were he could do all that B can and more; nor can the contrary inference be made. Both have passed some of the same items, but each has also passed some that the other has failed. This example may be multiplied over and over again. One worker has more seniority, another has higher productivity. One professor is a better teacher of graduate students, another is a better teacher of large classes, another is a better-known research man, and another has administrative responsibilities. Whenever the task demands are a function of more than one dimension, the possibility of incomparabilities arises. A can be better than B in one aspect and B better than A in another. The result is a partial order.

Much of the research in psychological measurement is concerned with what we might call the *analytical* problem of decomposing or factoring a partial order into a product of simple orders (for example, see Chapter 12). The object of such research is to discover the latent attributes, the relevant variables, generating the observed complexity of behavioral relations.

There is another problem area, however, that of collapsing or compressing this natural partial order into a simple order. We might call this the problem area of *synthesis* as distinct from *analysis.* This problem is of interest because there is no natural or necessary or unique simple order to be obtained by compressing a partial order, and yet this natural partial order must be compressed if life and society are not to come to a standstill. In other words, choice and decision constitute an *indispensable* condition for existence, but choice and decision may require comparability of *all* pairs; *incomparability is intolerable.*

As an illustration, suppose we have the task of selecting candidates for musical scholarships. We would like to give the scholarships to the most talented. When we compare candidates on various aspects of musical talent, we observe that A is better than B in interpretative performance but B is better in composition. Which has more talent? If the scholarship committee feels it imperative to make such a decision, it thrashes about deciding whether to use a lexicographic model or a compensatory model or something else. The issue with which it is concerned may be phrased in abstract terms as how to collapse a partial order into a simple order, that is, map the points from a multidimensional space into a line.

Promoting foremen requires evaluating both technical know-how and ability to deal with people. If these component traits combine in a conjunctive or disjunctive way, then supervisory ability, perhaps like musical talent, is not a unidimensional trait in a multidimensional space, but the attribute is the entire space. Some individuals may clearly be said to have more talent than others, or more supervisory ability, but other individuals are not comparable. One may be better in face-to-face leadership situations and the other better in executive or administrative leadership.

The need to synthesize a line of decision is a justification for strong models. A good example of this area of research in a significant context is the work of the Information and Education Division of the War Department in constructing a point system to determine priority of discharge (Stouffer et al., 1949, p. 529). After considerable study the Research Branch arrived at the following point scale, which was announced after VE day:

Length of time in the Army	1 point/month
Length of time overseas	1 point/month
Combat	5 points/Campaign Star or combat decoration; including Purple Heart
Parenthood	12 points/child under 18, up to three children

The entire effort of the research was directed toward a weighting of these four factors which would "minimize, not eliminate, feelings of injustice" (Stouffer et al., 1949, p. 527). A compensatory composition model was constructed so that each soldier, a point in a four-dimensional space, would map into a real line which was a line of decision. No single set of compensatory weights would satisfy everyone; they could only seek a set which by some criterion would minimize dissatisfaction.

Society requires that decisions be made, and hence these natural partial orders must be compressed into simple orders. Thus, a trait called musical talent or supervisory ability or eligibility for demobilization is constructed artificially, is made up to serve the requirements of imperative choice. Other such variables probably include morale, socio-economic status, leadership, professional status, and a large part of the socio-psychological variables of interest to behavioral scientists. Although we may all recognize that these are multidimensional variables, the necessary demands of determining salary level, promotions, and so on, require at least an implicit function which converts these natural multidimensional traits into a necessary though "unnatural" line. All this implies a composition model—a decision function—the assumptions of which are not, and cannot be, "valid," and yet *it is both necessary and desirable that social scientists study such variables.* These variables are part of the functional framework of a society even though they may exist only in the minds of some of its members and are evident only in their choices and decisions.

Commonly, the decision function is implicit; in fact, we may even be unaware of the relevant variables. For example, if we could measure an interpersonally comparable utility, it has been suggested that a reasonable social utility function* for society would be to maximize the average value. That is, to each alternative, if adopted, there corresponds a consequent distribution of utility over the members of the society. This decision function says that the choice between two alternatives is to be dictated by the means of the corresponding distributions. This decision function clearly neglects other parameters of these distributions, like variance and skewness, which surely should not be completely irrelevant to a choice.

That variance and skewness of a utility distribution are not completely irrelevant is suggested by the existence of political philosophies which idealize an equal share of utility for all members of the society and others which idealize a *laissez-faire* attitude of everyone for himself. The first neglects some of the prevailing characteristics of human motivation, the second violates our humanitarian principles because some people might be very badly off. The first idealizes very low variance of the distribution of utility in a society, the second idealizes high variance. Both extremes have been compromised to seek an intermediate, presumably optimum variance.

Skewness of the utility distribution in a society is also, perhaps, not an irrelevant parameter. It might be interesting to view the history of civilization in terms of shifts from societies which were skewed to the right (with a small minority very well off) to societies with more symmetric distributions. A positively skewed distribution of utility in a society gives rise to internal pressures which may lead to revolution.

Now and then the decision functions which map partial orders into a line are made explicit, as in the Army's point system for priority of discharge. But more generally the functions are implicit and vague. We need only participate in a college committee's deliberation as to who should be promoted in terms of their teaching capability, research production, and service to the academic and public community to see the vagueness of the composition model itself and to see this vagueness further increased by that of the components themselves.

A decision function is always a value system about the relative merits of attributes and how to combine them. In our society a decision function tends to be a compromise among the value systems of those participating

---

* See Chapter 18 for a discussion of this topic.

in the decision. This is almost inevitable in any society. Value systems are individual and a society's decision function cannot be equally gratifying to all.

The point of this discussion is that *the necessity for mapping partial orders into simple orders is one of the sources of social conflict.* Conflict and pressures for change *are normal states*, and a healthy society is one in which these processes may be undertaken without havoc.

Before concluding this discussion of the effects of incomparability, let me add that not all the consequences are bad. There are real advantages in this incomparability for some purposes. From the point of view of individual mental health, for example, it is probably a good thing that one individual is better than another in something.

We may actively take advantage of the incomparability of behavior, also. When we want to organize a department of psychology with members representing a balanced set of capabilities, we choose an experimental psychologist from among a relatively homogeneous class and a personality developmental psychologist from another. The process resembles that of peeling off the top of each of the several dimensions of a disjunctive space.

Wolfle (1960)* proposes that in the search for talent society has much to gain if it takes advantage of this incomparability. He suggests that society's benefit would be maximized if individuals were not selected just for their own good balance but for their diversity of talent and was allowed to receive the products of extreme talents. The idea is that we should peel the top individuals off the component attributes rather than force a compensatory model which leads to uniformity and well-balanced talents among the individuals selected. If such a procedure were followed by society, stresses and strains would undoubtedly be created, but an important point is that they are already present and inherent in the necessity to make decisions. Old stresses and strains would be replaced by new ones, and the real question is whether society would gain more under Wolfle's proposal than it has under current compensatory or conjunctive selection procedures.

In a *New York Times* magazine article Kemeny (1962) has suggested that well-rounded colleges are more desirable than well-rounded students. What he is proposing is essentially a disjunctive selection procedure for college students, rather than a conjunctive selection procedure.

Robyn Dawes (1964) has made a mathematical study of the comparative effects of these two selection procedures on the distribution of talents in a social group. Under certain simplifying assumptions he shows that, with a conjunctive selection procedure, the distribution on each talent

* See also *Science*, **133**, 71 (1961).

(measured in percentile ranks) is a uniform distribution above the conjunctive cutting point, and no part of the distribution is below that cutting point. The distribution under a disjunctive selection procedure will be uniform with low probability density below the disjunctive cutting point, and uniform with higher probability density above this cutting point.

Furthermore, the disjunctive cutting point on a given talent will be higher than the conjunctive cutting point. Dawes considers the following hypothetical example: A college wishes to accept a third of its applicants whom it evaluates on four independent attributes regarded as equally important. The conjunctive cutting point under these conditions will be the 24th percentile, the disjunctive cutting point will be the 90th percentile. The overlap in the student bodies selected by these procedures would be about 44%, that is, about 56% of the student body selected by each procedure would not have been selected by the other.

These figures, although for a particular example, illustrate the contrast between the two procedures. In general, as the number of attributes used increases, the two procedures increasingly differ. The conjunctive cutting point diminishes, the disjunctive cutting point increases. In other words, as the number of attributes used in conjunctive selection procedures increases, the probability of selecting individuals with extreme talents decreases.

A disjunctive selection procedure guarantees selection of all individuals with an extreme talent; the conjunctive selection procedure guarantees rejection of all individuals with an extremely small talent. Hence, there should be a correspondence, he argues, between a society's utility function over percentiles of talent and its selection procedure. If the utility function is negatively accelerated, a conjunctive selection procedure will result in greater total utility; if the utility function is positively accelerated, a disjunctive selection procedure will maximize total utility.

Behavioral science is concerned with processes of analysis and synthesis. Analysis includes the decomposition of a partial order into component factors of which it is the product. Such an analysis calls for a composition model which is a theory about the behavior. Synthesis includes the construction of another composition model (the decision function), which will map the partial order into a line.

A diagram illustrating the relation between the processes of analysis and synthesis is presented in Fig. 13.1. The diamond in the center represents the natural partial order on the observed behavior. The other parts of the figure reflect three areas of research. These areas are as follows. Multidimensional models, to take this as the first area, seek to decompose this partial order into a product of component attributes, the composition function representing a theory of the behavior in question.

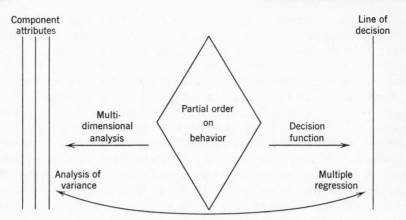

Fig. 13.1   Analysis and synthesis in behavioral science.

In a second area of research, a decision function seeks to compress this partial order into at least a simple order, because action and decision cannot tolerate incomparabilities.   A third area of much research is the direct attempt to synthesize a line of decision out of component attributes, as in multiple regression theory, or to analyze the line of decision into components, as in analysis of variance.

In summary I wish only to reiterate that whereas a partial order on individuals or stimuli is the natural outcome of behavioral observation, such a state of affairs is intolerable to a group faced with decision, choice, or action.   Decisions require at least a weak ordering.   The result of collapsing a partial order is the creation of an attribute which becomes a structural component of the society.   Such attributes can only be studied by strong models, which are necessarily limited in the degree to which they fit the data.   A good example is the IQ, a weighted combination of inherently incomparable abilities.   Nevertheless from this weighting is obtained a single IQ score which has significant though imperfect predictive validity.   But such a variable is important in the functional framework of a society and hence is of significance to the behavioral scientist.

These line-of-decision variables, demanded by society because of the necessity of decision and choice, are one of the sources of social conflict. Compressing a partial order requires compromises between inherently incompatible value systems and the resulting order cannot be equally acceptable to all.   Hence stresses and strains are normal states in a complex and varied society.   The problem is not to eliminate conflict but to resolve it without creating havoc and disruption.

REFERENCES

Dawes, R. M., 1964, Social selection based on multidimensional criteria, *J. abnorm. soc. Psychol.*, **68**, No. 1.

Kemeny, J. G., 1962, Needed: well-rounded colleges, *New York Times Magazine*, March 25.

Stouffer, S. A., A. A. Lumsdaine, Marion H. Lumsdaine, R. M. Williams, Jr., M. B. Smith, I. L. Janis, Shirley A. Star, and L. S. Cottrell, Jr., 1949, *The American soldier: combat and its aftermath*, vol. 2, Princeton University Press, Princeton.

Wolfle, D., 1960, Diversity of talent, *Amer. Psychologist*, **15**, 535–45.

CHAPTER 14

Introduction to QIIb

In the first section of Chapter 10 QII data were introduced with some general remarks that applied equally to both QIIa and QIIb. With that as a preliminary introduction, we continue now with QIIb data in particular. We begin with phase 2, mapping behavioral observations into QIIb data, and illustrate it with a variety of examples drawn from different areas of psychology, including attitude measurement, diagnostic labeling, rating scales, and magnitude estimation. These examples all illustrate proximity relations on pairs of points from distinct sets. There are differences, however, among models for these data, which reflect differences in the characteristics QIIb data may have. In the next section we point out some of the characteristics that differentiate QIIb data.

1. PHASE 2: MAPPING BEHAVIOR INTO DATA

One of the characteristics of QIIb data is whether they are regarded as 'pick $1/n$' data or 'pick any/n' data. These will be discussed in turn.

Pick $1/n$

I shall discuss four examples of mapping behavior into QIIb data of the 'pick $1/n$' variety. As will be evident, these four examples will illustrate still another characteristic of such data.

Consider the act of a clinician diagnosing a patient. We may conceive of a set of points in the clinician's psychological space corresponding to idealized, textbook syndromes. The symptoms of some particular patient as perceived by the clinician correspond to a point in this same space, and the behavior of the clinician may be interpreted as picking one of the label points as nearest the patient point. One may think of the clinician as having been presented with a patient on the one hand and a question on the other, that is, "what is your diagnosis?" followed by several alternative answers (response categories) from which he picks one. The syndrome of the patient corresponds to an r-tuple, and the response categories each correspond to other r-tuples. The response of attaching a label is interpreted as a proximity relation on the corresponding pair of points from distinct sets.

Consider next an individual presented with a statement of opinion like:

Athletic participation should be given the same consideration in awarding scholarships as participation in any other extracurricular activity.

(a) Strongly agree
(b) Agree
(c) Indifferent
(d) Disagree
(e) Strongly disagree

The individual is asked to choose one of the five alternative response categories. We may conceive of a point in the individual's psychological space corresponding to how he feels about athletic scholarships, another point corresponding to the attitude expressed by the statement, and the behavior of the individual being interpreted as picking the response alternative that best matches the "distance" between his ideal point and the item point. These several response categories may be thought of as expressing different degrees of proximity between an ideal point and an item point, and the individual as matching the distance between his ideal and the item point to one of these degrees of proximity. Thus each alternative represents a criterion distance, and the subject matches his distance to the stimulus point with one of these criterion distances. We have a proximity relation on a pair of points from distinct sets.

The examples of clinical diagnosis and of responding to an attitude statement may both be interpreted as instances of picking 1 out of n response alternatives. The two examples are not identical, however, and one difference resides in the fact that the response elements in the case of clinical diagnosis are presumably elements of a nominal scale, whereas the response elements for endorsing the item are presumably elements of at least an ordinal scale.

An example formally equivalent to that of endorsing an attitude statement is that of rating the efficiency of foremen on a scale of five steps labeled appropriately from "inadequate" through "average" to "superior." It is as if the rater were presented with the question "What is the efficiency of this foreman?" and asked to choose one of the five response categories.

Once again we have a set of objects on the one hand and a label set on the other, and the matching behavior is interpreted as a proximity relation on the corresponding pair of points. In this particular instance the elements of the label set are again presumed to be simply ordered as in the previous case of endorsing the item. In the previous case the individual was rating himself on the item, in the latter case he is rating a foreman; very real distinctions in one sense but still the same QIIb data.

In many applications of rating scale technique integers are used as the categories of the rating scale, the integers usually being accompanied by appropriate descriptions. The object being rated corresponds to a point, the response categories correspond to points, and the rating is interpreted as a proximity relation on the corresponding pair of points from distinct sets. The response categories, being numbers, are frequently regarded as elements of an interval scale.

A final example of this direct form of measurement is S. S. Stevens' (1956) method of magnitude estimation. In this method the response categories consist of all nonnegative real numbers, and the instructions to the judge are such as to permit us to presume that the numbers are elements of a ratio scale.

Each of these four examples may be thought of in terms of presenting an individual with a stimulus (for example, a question or an item) and an instruction, accompanied by a set of response alternatives from which he selects one. They differ in the relation presumed to hold among the response alternatives—from assuming that they are elements of only a nominal scale to assuming that they are elements of a ratio scale.

Many psychological data are formally of this latter kind. Counting the drops of saliva in a conditioning experiment, for example, and the number of reinforced trials required to reach a criterion are other examples of such measurement. Most physical measurement, as in measurements obtained by counting or reading a dial or gauge, are examples of QIIb data. In each case an element of one set, an object being measured, is matched against an element of another set, the set of real numbers. *The processes from observation to data to inferential classification in cases like these are immediate and direct, and no model for inferential classification is called for.* The classification has been achieved by the correspondence between the object and a number.

Such data are of little interest to scaling theory in themselves, because the answers are built in, as we saw in the discussion of parallelogram analysis in Chapter 4. 'Pick $1/n$' data are useless for scaling a set of objects unless there is prior knowledge of the relations on one of the sets of elements—and with prior knowledge it is direct measurement; as in physical measurement, there is no scaling problem. Interest in such direct measurement would lie in asking such questions as "Where do the numbers come from?" which is a question to be asked of all responses, not just those which lend themselves to direct measurement.

'Pick Any/n'

A more interesting form of QIIb data may be characterized as 'pick any/n' in contrast to 'pick 1/n.' In the case of 'pick 1/n' each item is looked on as a set of response alternatives with some degree of prior knowledge about relations among the response categories. If each item has just two alternatives, such as yes-no or accept-reject, the entire item may be mapped into a point. The individual's acceptance of some items and rejection of others, then, may be described as 'pick any/n' data.

A study of radio listening by Gibson (Lazarsfeld, 1959, pp. 533–34) provides an excellent illustration. The original technical report was not available to me, but according to Lazarsfeld's account Gibson obtained the listening habits of individuals for a number of evening radio programs. In a survey of 2200 radio listeners he obtained data on which of 13 types of evening programs they listened to.

Each type of radio program may be thought of as a point, an r-tuple, and each listener as a point. The statement that an individual listens to a certain type of radio program may be interpreted as a proximity relation on the corresponding pair of points, an ideal point and a program point. The variety of programs may be looked on as n stimuli from which each individual 'picks any/n.' At the previous level of description of 'pick 1/n,' each program would be conceived of as an item with an ordered set of response alternatives related to how much an individual listened to each program. Dichotomizing this set of response alternatives to a pair (listen, do not listen) leads readily to classifying the data as 'pick any out of the n' alternative radio programs.

In an exactly similar manner the responses of an individual to a set of statements of opinion may be mapped into 'pick any/n' data. By interpreting the response to each statement as an agree-disagree dichotomy, an individual's responses to a set of n items may be regarded as 'pick any out of the n' alternative items.*

The other characteristic of QIIb data, prior knowledge of relations among the alternatives, also applies to 'pick any/n' data. The radio programs may or may not be scaled, and similarly the statements of

---

* Only 'pick 1/n' is an explicit instance of the searchingness structure as it was constructed in Chapter 2. I did not introduce the idea of a 'pick any/n' method at that point because of the detailed explanation that would be required and because it would contribute little to the formal development of the searchingness structure system.

opinion may or may not be scaled. If there is no prior knowledge, the model for analysis will seek to locate both sets of points in a joint space; if there is prior knowledge of one of them, the model only seeks to locate the remaining set.

The 'pick any/n' data of QIIb may be described in terms of the common language of distances between points—the terms in which we have chosen to describe all varieties of data. An individual is presented with a number of statements of opinion and asked to indicate which he endorses. Intuitively we would imagine that if a statement of opinion reflected how the individual felt, he would endorse it, otherwise not. We may observe, though, that an individual will commonly endorse more than one item and yet at the same time agree that the items are not identical in the attitude expressed—it is just that they are "close enough" to the individual's attitude to be acceptable. These ideas are readily formulated in terms of distance relations as follows.

The general expression we use for the vector displacement from point c_{hij} to point q_{hij} is

$$p_{hij} = c_{hij} \ominus q_{hij} \tag{14.1}$$

In the case of QIIb data, the interpretation that has been given to the data refers to the magnitude of the absolute distance between such a pair of points

$$|p_{hij}| = |c_{hij} \ominus q_{hij}| \tag{14.2}$$

which in the simple unidimensional case is

$$|p_{hij}| = |c_{hij} - q_{hij}| \tag{14.3}$$

The interpretation of the observed behavior in the model is

$$|p_{hij}| \leq \epsilon_{hij} \Leftrightarrow \text{yes, agree, endorse, and so on} \tag{14.4}$$

The characterization of 'pick 1/n' data in these terms is that the individual chooses the stimulus associated with minimum ϵ whereas in 'pick any/n' data he responds positively to all stimuli within his criterion distance.

It is interesting to note that QIIa and QIIb, which together constitute all of the instances of the method of single stimuli, involve the comparison of a difference between a pair of points (a vector displacement) with an absolute (abstract) standard. *In the case of QIIa the difference is an algebraic difference compared with the abstract standard of zero*; for example, whether an individual point is "above or below" a stimulus point. *In the case of QIIb, the difference is an absolute difference compared with an abstract finite standard ϵ*; for example, whether an individual point and an item point are "near" together or not.

The organization of the discussion of models for the analysis of QIIb data in the next chapter is in terms of the two characteristics we have discussed: whether they are classified as 'pick $1/n$' or 'pick any/n' and whether there is or is not prior knowledge of the relations among the n alternatives. Before turning to these models, however, some discussion of the relation of alternatives to the J scale and to the I scale will be useful and relevant. This will be followed by a brief discussion of the parameter ϵ.

2. RELATION OF ALTERNATIVES TO J SCALE AND I SCALE

The relation of an item's alternatives to the attribute continuum is different for QIIb than for QIIa. For example, we saw in Chapter 10 that in the one-dimensional case of QIIa there is a one-to-one monotonic relation between the ordered alternatives of an item and the ordered segments *of the J scale*. In the case of QIIb a monotonic relation holds between the ordered alternatives of an item and the ordered segments *of the I scale*; but because the order of the segments of the I scale is generally nonmonotone with the J scale, the ordered alternatives of an item may be nonmonotone with the J scale, and in fact not even one-to-one.

How these relations come about may be readily seen. Consider the following item, which might be used to study peoples' attitudes toward country X.

We should make the loan to X if we are sure they will pay it back.

    (*a*)   Yes   (agree)

    (*b*)   No   (disagree)

Each individual responds by saying either *yes* or *no*. Each such item may be regarded as corresponding to a point on an attitude scale from pro to con in regard to country X. Each individual is also regarded as corresponding to a point on this same J scale, a point representing a measure of his attitude toward country X. The individual's "liking" for an item is a function of the absolute distance between the corresponding pair of points. The nearer the stimulus point to the ideal point the more nearly the item represents how the individual feels.

The alternatives, in this case "yes" and "no," determine for the individual the position of the point representing the item. As Runkel puts it (private communication), they provide a "handle" on the item, and "handles" can be differently placed. If the alternatives were "yes" and "never" the stimulus point could be further away and still be endorsed since "never" moves the midpoint between the alternatives farther away from the individual's ideal and thus widens the region the individual labels "yes."

Fig. 14.1 ϵ as a function of alternatives.

If the alternatives were "strongly agree" and "no" the critical distance would be considerably less. These are illustrated with an example in Fig. 14.1. The top line in the figure is a J scale with the ideal point of a hypothetical individual shown, and then on each side of him on this J scale are the scale values of some possible alternative response categories for an item. (Of course, the scale values shown are just as imaginary as the individual.) Below the J scale are shown the three different latitudes of acceptance* (that is, the ranges of $\pm\epsilon$ about the ideal point) for this individual corresponding to which of three pairs of response categories was used.

This figure illustrates how each alternative to an item is interpreted as a point on each side of the ideal point at some fixed absolute distance from it. So on a unidimensional J scale each alternative has two scale values, one on each side of the ideal and symmetric about it. In Figs. 14.2 and 14.3 we show the folding of the J scale at the ideal point to yield an I scale on which each alternative is scaled and the ϵ corresponds to the midpoint between them. This individual, then, will say "yes" rather than "no" to any item within a distance ϵ of his ideal. If we take his I scale and unfold it as in Fig. 14.4. we see how the response categories are related to the segments of the J scale. Items or stimuli in the immediate neighborhood of the ideal are responded to positively and items further away in *either direction* are responded to negatively. Thus, although the ordered response alternatives are related monotonically to ordered segments of the I scale, when it is unfolded they are seen to be nonmonotonically related to the J scale. *Two disjoint segments of the J scale are associated with the response category "no."*

This is completely compatible with our intuitive conceptions of why individuals respond the way they do to such an item as the one we gave on

---

* I adopt this term from Hovland, Harvey, and Sherif (1957); see also Chapter 9.

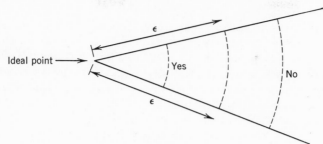

Fig. 14.2   Partially folded *J* scale.

Fig. 14.3   *I* scale with the alternatives yes-no scaled and their corresponding ε.

making a loan to country *X*. Individuals may refuse to endorse the item because they are so favorably inclined toward *X* that they want to make the loan without insisting on being "sure they will pay it back." Others may refuse because they are so unfavorably inclined toward *X* that they do not want to make the loan even with the condition. Consequently these two groups of individuals respond in exactly the same way for very different reasons and are represented in the model by disjoint segments of the *J* scale.

It need hardly be pointed out that there may be instances in which the "no" group is homogeneous and corresponds to a unique segment of the *J* scale. For example, if the individual were relatively extreme on the *J* scale, then the ordered response categories would be monotonic with the ordered segments of the *J* scale. An individual in such a case only has the *J* scale on one side of him, so his *I* scale is the *J* scale unfolded.

3. THE PARAMETER ε

In equation 14.4 the subscripts *h*, *i*, and *j* are associated with the ε. This is simply to indicate that, in principle, the criterion distance an individual utilizes to determine whether to agree or not agree may be different for different individuals or for the same individual at different times or for different stimuli. As seen in the last section, we might accept

Fig. 14.4   Unfolded *I* scale showing relation of response categories to *J* scale.

on intuitive grounds the possibility of controlling an individual's ϵ by manipulating the alternatives to an item, as in Fig. 14.1, to the extent of making it larger or smaller as an element of an ordinal scale. But comparability of ϵ's between individuals is a very different matter. If we have a series of items scaled on an attitude continuum, and one individual endorses more items than another, we are tempted to conclude that his ϵ is larger. This conclusion requires that the intervals between the scale values of the stimuli are the same for the two individuals.

This parameter ϵ is generally disregarded in models for analysis of QIIb data, but it has a potentially significant psychological interpretation which would make its study and measurement worthwhile. It seems to me that the parameter might well be an index of an individual's susceptibility to change, that is, the lability of his ideal. Imagine two individuals with the same ideal point on the same J scale but one with a much larger ϵ than the other. His larger ϵ indicates a willingness to endorse more disparate statements of opinion and could reflect less certainty about his opinion, a more loosely held ideal point. If this were the case, we would also suspect that the magnitude of an ϵ in QIIb would also be related to the individual's degree of inconsistency in QIa data as represented by the information measure, H, as used, for example, in the Coombs-Pruitt study (1960, 1961).

The experimental study of ϵ as inferred from QIIb data is recommended in relation to the degree of inconsistency in QIa data and in relation to the effect of efforts to induce change in an ideal point as in attitude change research.

4. SUMMARY

Formally, the data of QIIb are characterized as proximity relations on pairs of points from distinct sets. The manner in which such data are obtained from behavioral observations is discussed at length. The data so obtained may be characterized in two further ways: whether they may be regarded as 'pick $1/n$' or 'pick any/n' data, and whether the n alternatives are known (or assumed) to be scaled or are not. These distinctions are introduced and illustrated in the discussion of mapping behavior into QIIb data.

'Pick $1/n$' data are discussed first with illustrations of prior knowledge ranging from none, as in clinical diagnosis, through ordinal, interval, and finally a ratio scale level of prior knowledge, as in magnitude estimation and in the direct measurement of behavior—for example, measuring amplitudes of response. 'Pick any/n' data are then discussed and illustrated with prior knowledge ranging from none as in radio listening, to a higher level of prior knowledge as in the endorsement of any out of n attitude statements which may be elements of an interval scale. Moreover, replications of a rating scale or magnitude estimation may also be characterized as 'pick any/n' data because replicating an individual's evaluation of a stimulus may lead to more than one response category being picked. 'Pick any/n' data may also reflect prior knowledge ranging from nominal to ratio scale levels.

The next chapter, which deals with models available for analysis of QIIb data, is organized in terms of these characteristics.

The formal definition of QIIb data is given in terms of distance relations and contrasted with that of QIIa data. In QIIb the data consist of comparisons between an *absolute* distance between a pair of points from distinct sets and some nonnegative quantity ϵ. In QIIa the data consist of comparisons between an *algebraic* difference between a pair of points from distinct sets and the quantity *zero*.

Relations between the response alternatives of an item and the J scale and I scale are discussed and illustrated in detail. Each of the ordered response alternatives to an item, like those from "strongly agree" to "strongly disagree," corresponds to a point on an individual's I scale, and the midpoint between an adjacent pair generates an ϵ. If only two alternatives are used, then choice of one in responding to an item indicates that that item is on the proximal end of the I scale and choice of the other indicates the item is on the distal end.

The magnitude of ϵ can be manipulated to some degree by the experimenter's choice of alternatives, for example, instructions to "endorse only those items you wholeheartedly agree with" will probably invoke a smaller ϵ than "indicate which items you endorse." Incidentally, it is probably easier for a subject to respond if the alternative response category is explicit. Asking an individual "Did you like the movie?" is apt to be more difficult to answer than "Did you like the movie or was it pretty bad?" Furthermore, the first question leaves the subject free to pick the alternative response. Hence he will more likely have a variable ϵ over a series of items. A question like "Did you like the movie?" cannot be answered without elaboration, and the simplest way is to choose between it and an alternative like "or was it pretty bad?" With the alternative not explicit, next time it might be "or was it horrible?" This means a different ϵ and a misinterpretation of what the subject means.

Unfolding the I scale reveals the nonmonotone relation between the alternatives to an item and the segments of the J scale. This is illustrated pictorially.

A possible psychological interpretation of the parameter ϵ is offered by suggesting that it is indicative of the ease with which an individual's ideal can be moved. It is not an individual's attitude, his ideal point, which reflects a resistance to change, but rather, perhaps, how firmly held the position is. The larger ϵ the more lability. It is also suggested that the magnitude of an individual's ϵ in QIIb data might be reflected in a measure of his inconsistency in QIa data. These would be appropriate problems and worth pursuing in attitude change research.

REFERENCES

Coombs, C. H., and D. Pruitt, 1960, Components of risk in decision making: probability and variance preferences, *J. exp. Psychol.*, **60**, 265–77.

Coombs, C. H., and D. Pruitt, 1961, Some characteristics of choice behavior in risky situations, *Ann. New York Acad. Sci.*, **89**, 784–94.

Hovland, C. I., O. J. Harvey, and M. Sherif, 1957, Assimilation and contrast effects in reactions to communication and attitude change, *J. abnorm. soc. Psychol.*, **55**, 244–52.

Lazarsfeld, P. F., 1959, "Latent structure analysis," in *Psychology: a study of a science*, vol. 3, edited by S. Koch, McGraw-Hill Book Co., New York.

Stevens, S. S., 1956, The direct estimate of sensory magnitudes—loudness, *Amer. J. Psychol.*, **69**, 1–25.

CHAPTER 15

QIIb Models

The data that characterize QIIb are proximity relations on pairs of points from distinct sets. Essentially a matching or consonance relation exists between pairs of points each representing elements of distinct sets. Typically one has a set of individuals (or stimuli) and a set of response alternatives, and each individual (or stimulus) is matched to one or more response alternatives. In the previous chapter this kind of data was further distinguished on the basis of whether an individual is matched to exactly one of the response alternatives ('pick $1/n$') or whether he may be matched to more than one ('pick any/n'). It was also characterized by prior knowledge—that is, how much information the experimenter already has about the set of response alternatives—whether they are just labels in the sense of a nominal scale, as in clinical diagnosis or position played on a football team, or whether the response alternatives are scaled on a J scale (by experiment or by assumption) as elements of an ordinal, interval, or ratio scale.

After a brief mathematical interpretation of the problem of analyzing QIIb data, these two dichotomies provide the basis for organizing the discussion of models.

1. A MATHEMATICAL INTERPRETATION

In QIIb the fundamental observation is

$$|p_{hij}| \leq \epsilon_{hij} \tag{15.1}$$

where the quantity $|p_{hij}|$ is the absolute distance between a pair of points representing distinct sets and the quantity ϵ_{hij} is a nonnegative real number.

Almost universally the models assume that the points lie on a line, in which case we have

$$|p_{hij}| = |c_{hij} - q_{hij}| \tag{15.2}$$

The data consist of a set of simultaneous inequalities of the form of 15.1, one for each triple, h, i, j, in which it is known that the expression is greater or less than some nonnegative real number, ϵ_{hij}. What is sought is information about the c's and q's. Of course such a system is generally insoluble without more being assumed, and different assumptions give rise to the different models.

2. 'PICK $1/n$' DATA

No Prior Knowledge

These data consist of the matching of each point in one set to exactly one point in the other set, as in medical diagnosis, in which *no formal relations on the points in either of the sets are known or assumed and there is no replication*. Nothing can be done with such data by means of a model or procedure for inferential classification that would lead to finding out something about the c's and the q's. Parallelogram analysis, for example, is a way of representing and analyzing the data to test for unidimensionality. As pointed out in Chapter 4, however, the resulting matrix is maximally decomposable and nothing can be learned from it without prior knowledge of one of the sets of points.

An illustration of such data would be a matrix with French political parties as columns and individual Frenchmen as rows with a single X in each row indicating party membership. No internal analysis of the data may be made to yield a geometrical representation of the political structure.

More interesting inferential classification systems arise for data which are replications of such observations such that the data may be described as 'pick any/n.'

With Prior Knowledge

These data differ from the preceding in that the elements of one of the two sets of points are simply ordered or correspond to points on an interval or ratio scale which is to serve as a J scale. Where that prior knowledge comes from is irrelevant to our immediate purpose. It may be a result of a previous experiment in which the elements were scaled, it may be a result of convention in the sense of a common ordering on descriptive adjectives, or it may be an assumption.

Data obtained with prior knowledge is direct measurement in the most immediate sense. This is the kind of data we have when individuals are asked how strongly they approve or disapprove an extreme statement of opinion or are simply asked directly where they stand on X, from very favorable to very unfavorable. Another example would be the mapping of a set of objects of judgment into an ordered set of rating categories, in which each object is matched with exactly one response category.

Finally, 'pick $1/n$' with prior knowledge is the kind of data that represents most instances of measurement in the physical sciences, as in using a foot rule or reading a gauge.

The inferential classification of the objects is immediate, and little is usually done with such data except to try to raise the scaling level if the prior knowledge is an ordinal scale. An example might be to assume that the individuals are normally distributed and then, knowing the frequencies of individuals in the several ordered categories, an interval scale may be constructed. This is not recommended; it is merely mentioned as descriptive of the type of analysis to which the data may be subjected.

In general, 'pick $1/n$' data is uninteresting from the point of view of the theory of psychological measurement, that is, from the point of view of the internal productivity of the data. The interest in and value of such measures lie in the relations which such classifications of objects have to other classifications of the same objects, that is, their external productivity.

3. 'PICK ANY/n' DATA

'Pick any/n' data may be represented in a matrix with individuals as rows and the n response alternatives as columns. If a row-individual chooses a column-stimulus, then an X is placed in the corresponding cell. The data matrix may look much like the data matrix of 'pick k/n' (see Table 4.1) except that there is no restriction on the number of X's in any row. If there is replication, the cell entries may be the frequencies or the relative frequencies with which a row-individual chose a column-stimulus.

We first discuss the analysis of such data when there is no prior knowledge. The models discussed in turn are Lazarsfeld's latent class model, parallelogram analysis, and Lazarsfeld's latent structure analysis with nonmonotone trace lines.

No Prior Knowledge

Latent Class Model: The basic idea of the latent class model is that individuals and stimuli may be divided among two or more latent classes. Individuals who are members of the same latent class will, for a given stimulus, have the same probability of endorsing it. The fundamental assumption of local independence is the assumption that the responses to different stimuli of individuals in the same latent class are independent. On this assumption the equations for the item marginals and joint frequencies may be written in terms of the latent parameters.

Formally, the model assumes that the total population of individuals is divided among distinct subsets or latent classes, containing respectively $v_1, v_2, \ldots, v_i, \ldots, v_m$ proportions of the population. To each latent class i there corresponds a unique probability, α_{ij}, that the members of that class will respond positively to item j. Since items are assumed to be independent

**Table 15.1   Joint Frequencies for
Two Items Illustrating Correlation**

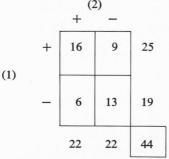

within classes, the proportion of members of a given class who respond positively to the two items j and k is the product $\alpha_{ij}\alpha_{ik}$. The correlation between two items is a consequence of differences in α_i over the latent classes.

As an illustration, consider these two items:

(1) Do you subscribe to _____ magazine?
(2) Do you belong to the _____ club?

For some sample of 44 individuals the fourfold Table 15.1 illustrating a correlation between the two questions might be obtained.

Now suppose the sample is made up of individuals who may be divided into classes that represent distinct subpopulations, called latent classes, for example, liberals and conservatives, high- and low-income groups, or management and labor. Then Table 15.1 may be regarded as a combination of two other fourfold tables, one for each latent class, each of which exhibits independence of the two items. For example, Table 15.1 might be made up of the two fourfold parts of Table 15.2.

Proportionality of arrays reveals the independence between items *within* a latent class or subpopulation. But when these subpopulations are combined, as in Table 15.1, the result is correlation between items due to differences in the item marginals from class to class.

Equations known as accounting equations express the relation between item marginals and joint frequencies on the one hand and the latent parameters on the other. If P_j is the proportion of the sample that responds positively to item j, and P_{jk} the proportion responding positively

Table 15.2 Joint Frequencies for Two Items for Each of Two Latent Classes Separately

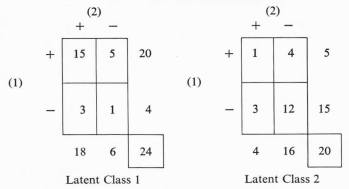

Latent Class 1   Latent Class 2

to *both* items j and k, and so on for higher order joint frequencies, the following observational equations may be written.

$$P_j = \sum_{i=1}^{m} \alpha_{ij} \nu_i$$

$$P_{jk} = \sum_{i=1}^{m} \alpha_{ij} \alpha_{ik} \nu_i \qquad (15.3)$$

$$P_{jk\ldots l} = \sum_{i=1}^{m} \alpha_{ij} \alpha_{ik} \cdots \alpha_{il} \nu_i$$

This discrete class model for a latent typology is described by Lazarsfeld (1959, p. 533) as the most useful case from a practical point of view thus far studied. Joint frequencies only up to the third order are needed to compute all latent parameters. Higher order joint frequencies may then be used to test the goodness of fit of the model.

Methods for estimating the latent parameters are available (Green, 1951) using multiple factor analysis and requiring that the number of latent classes not be greater than the number of items plus 1: that is, that $m \leq n + 1$. The method requires, however, the diagonal elements in the data matrix of joint proportions which cannot be observed and must be estimated. T. W. Anderson (1954) has developed a method involving matrix manipulations only, which avoids this difficulty and is simpler computationally but uses much less of the empirical data and uses it asymmetrically. W. A. Gibson (1955) has extended Anderson's method to make use of more of the empirical data. These methods all involve a certain amount of trial and error in arriving at a satisfactory solution; they also involve rather large errors except for huge samples, and we may obtain estimates outside the interval from 0 to 1. The underlying variable is assumed to have a discrete point distribution, and the results of an analysis lead to classification at the level of nominal scaling.

Table 15.3 Latent Probabilities for Program Preferences in Four Latent Classes and Marginal Manifest Frequencies (P_j) for a Sample of 2200 Radio Listeners

Preferred Program Type	Class				Manifest Marginal
	A	D	E	F	
Comedy	.37	.58	.85	.37	.62
Mystery	.34	.29	.83	.22	.46
Semiclassical music	.08	.92	.41	.09	.37
Classical music	.10	.89	.25	.27	.34
Religion	.04	.32	.55	.61	.21
News	.40	.84	.80	.96	.77
Proportion of people in class	.27	.21	.10	.11	1.00

An interesting example is provided by Gibson's study of radio listening referred to in the previous chapter, which is summarized by Lazarsfeld (1959, pp. 533–34) as follows:

... He has shown that the manifest joint response frequencies can be produced very successfully by assuming six types of listeners. To simplify the presentation we reproduce the latent probabilities for four of the latent classes pertaining to six of the programs. The data of [Table 15.3] suggested to Gibson a rather convincing interpretation.

"The most outstanding single characteristic of Class A is that none of its latent marginals is greater than .40. This class must, therefore, consist principally of people who do not care much for listening to the radio in the evening.

"Class D is also not difficult to identify, for a very high proportion of its members, in contrast to those of other classes, like to listen to semi-classical and classical music. (They are also fairly high on talks on public issues.) These are undoubtedly the sophisticates or 'highbrows.' Characteristically, they have also little interest in mystery programs.

"In contrast with Class A, Class E is characterized primarily by consistently high latent marginals, none of which is lower than .25. (Substantial proportions of this class even like to listen to serials and hillbilly music, which are quite unpopular with all other classes.) It is interesting to note further that the two more serious music programs liked least by this group are the same ones that are liked most (except for news) by the sophisticates. All of these characteristics suggest that this might be the 'low-brow' group.

"Finally we come to Class F, which is distinguished by the highest latent marginal for religious programs (the lowest for popular music), quite low ones for comedy and mystery, and no extremely strong likes other than for news. This combination of a religious component, a lack of interest in what might be regarded as a younger type of program, and a somewhat subdued enjoyment in radio in general, except for news programs, points toward one large group of radio listeners—that of older and/or small town people."

To test his interpretation, Gibson selected respondents who had a high recruitment probability of coming from one of these classes and studied their demographic characteristics and other information available about them. He found indeed a clear educational difference between Classes D and E, many more older people in Class F, and so on. It should be noticed, incidentally, that, correlative to this interpretation of the classes, [Table 15.3] also throws light on the latent appeals of the programs themselves; the rather universally high preference for news programs is here the best example.

No ordering of the classes is derived from the model, but an after-the-fact ordering may be suggested by the content of the items and the latent probabilities, as, e.g., when the items are Thurstone-type attitude statements.

To recover the joint space, we would like to ask where in the latent space an individual and an item can be located. The model assumes that each individual belongs to a particular class. But each individual is identified with a response pattern, however, and, because of the probabilistic nature of the model, a given response pattern may arise from any latent class. This gives rise to the notion of a *recruitment pattern*. Each response pattern has its recruitment pattern, a distribution of probabilities over the latent classes which indicates the probability that an individual with a given response pattern could be recruited from each of the latent classes in turn. There is a corresponding concept for each item. So an individual, identified with a given response pattern, could be located anywhere in the space with known probabilities, and similarly for an item.

We may expect that the behavior of individuals in 'pick any/n' is generated by a multiplicity of factors, as perhaps in radio listening, and only violence would be done by trying to describe the data in terms of a one-dimensional latent attribute. Lazarsfeld's latent class model is beautifully suited for such a case, although, of course, it is also applicable to the case in which one dimension satisfies the data.

In the latter instance, however, a model that permits testing for unidimensionality and that yields a one-dimensional solution would presumably be preferred. Two models are available for this purpose, parallelogram analysis and latent structure analysis.

Table 15.4 A Perfect Parallelogram Structure
for 'Pick Any/n' Data

	A	B	C	D	E	F	G	H
1	X	X						
2	X	X	X					
3			X	X	X	X		
4			X	X				
5			X					
6		X	X	X				
7				X	X	X	X	
8				X	X			
9				X	X	X	X	X
10						X	X	X
11						X		
12							X	X

Parallelogram Analysis: This is the same model as that discussed at length in Chapter 4 for the analysis of 'pick k/n' data, except that the number of X's in a row of the data matrix is not fixed under 'pick any/n.' As a result, even with perfectly reliable and unidimensional data the borders of the diagonal are very irregular and there is no necessary and unique ordering of the rows. Such a pattern is illustrated in Table 15.4, where the stimuli are labeled in order on the J scale and the rows represent distinct response patterns which are not necessarily simply ordered.

The parameter ϵ introduced in 'pick any/n' data may lead to one response pattern being "contained in" another, as 5 is in 2, 3, 4, and 6; in such a case there is no necessary ordering of the patterns. For example, response pattern 5 might be that of an individual who is further to the left on the J scale than is individual 2. How this may come about is shown in Fig. 15.1, in which an individual with response pattern 5 has a sufficiently small ϵ not to reach item B, whereas an individual with response pattern 2 will endorse A, B, and C and may be to the right of 5 if his ϵ is large enough and stimulus D is far enough away.

This example has assumed the data to be perfectly reliable. In any real instance, the best parallelogram that can be formed will generally have gaps in one or more rows which lead to further ambiguities about order relations between rows. An example of what would occur with unreliable data may be illustrated with Table 15.4, if we transpose it and ask the

Fig. 15.1 Showing ambiguity of relation between ideals inferred from relation between response patterns.

question about the order of the stimuli (that is, the columns of Table 15.4). Some of the columns have gaps, and it is not clear from the data what the order of the columns should be.

In general, then, parallelogram analysis of 'pick any/n' data will usually involve permuting columns in order to construct a parallelogram with as few gaps as possible in the rows. This will imply an ordering of the stimuli on the J scale. The rows will generally only be partially ordered. No criteria or methods exist for the evaluation of a solution on the basis of internal analysis of the data, except to maximize an index analogous to the coefficient of reproducibility and based on a count of the number of vacant cells within the rows of the parallelogram. Vacant cells within the columns of the parallelogram are to be expected on the basis of different ϵ's.

This deterministic model is mentioned here only because it provides a simple method of evaluating at least qualitatively the unidimensionality of 'pick any/n' data and arriving at a best unidimensional representation in the sense of maximizing a reproducibility index.

This method may be readily extended to the case in which there is no prior knowledge of the scaling of items on the J scale and the individual has responded to each by selecting a response alternative out of an ordered set from "strongly agree" to "strongly disagree," for example, in five steps numbered successively from 1 to 5. The data correspond to his chopping his I scale into 5 ordered segments; parallelogram analysis may be readily extended to unfolding such I scales. Each boundary on the I scale corresponds to an ϵ which is a midpoint between the two corresponding response alternatives, as was illustrated in Figs. 14.1, 14.2, and 14.3. The data matrix would have individuals as rows and items as columns with an integer in a cell indicating which response alternative that row-individual chose for that column-item.

Analysis of the data matrix would call for seeking a permutation of the columns such that the integers in any row monotonically decrease to 1 and then monotonically increase. This method of analysis is similar to the ordinal analysis of order k/n' data as discussed in Section 5 of Chapter 4, except that in 'pick any/n' data several columns may have the same integer in a row of the matrix. An example of an admissible parallelogram structure in such a case is given in Table 15.5. The number of possible response patterns that would satisfy such a matrix is not predetermined within a very large upper bound. There is no constraint on the order of the integers descending a column as there is in the parallelogram analysis of 'order k/n' data. This lack of constraint makes determination of the order of the individuals somewhat ambiguous. This method would be appropriate for testing for unidimensionality in Q sort data.

Table 15.5   A Perfect Parallelogram Structure for 'Pick Any/n' Data with Ordered Response Alternatives

	A	B	C	D	E	F	G	H
1	1	2	2	3	3	3	4	5
2	1	1	2	3	4	4	5	5
3	2	1	2	3	4	4	5	5
4	2	2	1	2	3	4	5	5
5	4	2	1	1	1	3	5	5
6	4	3	2	1	3	4	5	5
7	5	4	3	1	1	1	2	3
8	5	5	5	4	1	2	3	5
9	5	5	4	3	2	1	2	3
10	5	5	5	4	3	2	1	2

Parallelogram analysis is designed for the analysis of Thurstone-type items, items which may be identified with a point anywhere on the attribute continuum, and not for the analysis of Likert-type items. These are discussed on p. 315 ff.

Latent Structure Analysis: One difficulty with parallelogram analysis is its vulnerability. It is a completely deterministic model and in the presence of error and inconsistency the quality of a solution and the confidence we have in it diminish. Lazarsfeld's latent structure analysis (LSA) is a probabilistic model for the same kind of data. It is also much more than that, however; it is a general theory of the relation between manifest and latent variables for single stimulus data. The general model takes the following form.

Let x be the latent variable. Each item is represented by its operating characteristic (trace line) $f_j(x)$, giving the probability of a positive response to item j at each value of x. The probability density of the population of individuals is $\phi(x)$; that is, in any small interval $(x, x + dx)$, $\phi(x) \, dx$ gives the proportion of the population whose points are contained in that interval. The basic idea of LSA is that the correlation between items is due to the latent variable x, and if this is held constant or partialed out, the probability of responding positively to two or more items is the product of the probabilities of responding positively to each. This is known as the *axiom of local independence* and is at least tacitly assumed in all QII models. This axiom was explicitly invoked in the latent class and the latent distance models which are special instances of this general LSA theory.

We may write the following general equations of LSA. The proportion of individuals in the population who respond positively to a given item j

is P_j and is given by

$$P_j = \int_{-\infty}^{+\infty} f_j(x)\phi(x)\,dx$$

The proportion of the population who respond positively to both items j and k is P_{jk} and is given by

$$P_{jk} = \int_{-\infty}^{+\infty} f_j(x)f_k(x)\,\phi(x)\,dx$$

Clearly corresponding equations may be written for all response patterns over any subset of items, yielding 2^n equations for n dichotomous items.

Nothing of interest can be done with the model without making further assumptions, for example, the shape of the trace lines $f_j(x)$ and the population distribution $\phi(x)$. These assumptions lead to such special cases as the latent distance model, the linear model, the normal ogive, and the logistic model for QIIa data, and the latent class model for QIIb data. Just as assumptions of particular monotone trace lines lead to special cases of LSA for QIIa data, assumptions of particular nonmonotone trace lines lead to special cases of LSA for QIIb data. Each form assumed for trace lines gives rise to its own mathematical difficulties and problems that can be formidable, especially if we want to consider mixtures of trace lines.

A general model for the probability of endorsing items on a latent attribute might consider parabolic trace lines, for example, or any of the functions illustrated in Fig. 9.1, 9.2, and 9.3 as examples of SPF's. In fact, nothing in principle prevents us from considering multipeaked preference functions.

Lazarsfeld has been considering the use of polynomials of any degree for both $\phi(x)$ and $f_j(x)$ but he says (1959, p. 533) "quite a number of combinations have been tried, but none turned out very successfully. So far this is the point where the least progress has been made."

The beauty of LSA is that it is the model of almost all models for QII data. It makes explicit assumptions which are commonly left implicit, and leads naturally to special cases, generalizations, and extensions not always otherwise obvious. The relation of LSA to multiple factor analysis is a case in point which has been brought out by Green (1952) and by Gibson (1959). A very generalized form of the trace line of LSA could be taken to be a polynomial in several underlying variables, called a trace surface in multidimensional space. If these functions are linear, we have the basic assumption of multiple factor analysis. There are further differences, however. The data processed by factor analysis consist of the zero-order correlations among the manifest variables which correspond to the second-order joint frequencies in LSA. In the theory of LSA, we find that nonlinear trace lines require the computation of higher-order joint frequencies. This suggests that extending the range of factor analysis to nonlinear functions will require the computation of higher order covariances. Lazarsfeld remarks that "in a rather crude generalization one can say that the number of coefficients in the trace lines determines the level of manifest joint frequencies which enter the accounting equations." (1959, p. 540.)

Many mathematical problems still need to be solved for the continuous multidimensional cases of LSA and nonlinear multiple factor analysis. However, Green points out that the latent class model is appropriate to such cases, the algebra of which has been solved, but it yields a solution only at the level of a nominal scale.

Such a solution, however, might be adequate in many instances. An illustration might be the use of the latent class model to study classes of behavioral responses. Instead of individuals to be classified we might classify responses. Let each row of the data matrix represent a response—a physiological indicator, overt behavior, verbal judgment, what have you. Let each column represent a stimulus. A cell entry may then represent the proportion of individuals who associate that row-response with that column-stimulus. The matrix may then be converted into and analyzed as a (1, 0) data matrix by latent class analysis. Most of the research effort of psychologists is directed toward studying the characteristics of individuals or of stimuli with the response form held constant. A study of the former kind might be useful in building "response" theory.

With Prior Knowledge

Prior knowledge, as I have used the term, refers to the existence of ordinal, interval, or ratio scale measures on the elements of one of the two sets, for example, the set of response alternatives from which a subject picks one each time he responds to a stimulus or item. These levels of measurement represent the most common forms of such information. The source of this information may be convention, assumption, or prior experimentation. Examples are found in the behavior of individuals responding to attitude statements by selecting an alternative from a series ranging from "strongly agree" to "strongly disagree," assigning objects of judgment to a rating scale consisting of an ordered series of adjectives, or of numbers in a closed interval (category scaling), or to numbers in a semiclosed interval (magnitude estimation).

A single response, in these cases, is 'pick $1/n$' data with prior knowledge and has previously been discussed. Replication of such observations leads to 'pick any/n' data, and the problem that exists is only that of amalgamation to arrive at a single unique assignment to each of the objects of judgment. The three levels of prior knowledge have given rise to their respective procedures for arriving at a descriptive statistic. We shall discuss them in turn.

The so-called Likert-type items are self-rating scales on an attitude continuum. The attitude statements are either extreme statements or are questions which essentially ask the individual where he stands on the J scale. Examples of both kinds, taken from Likert (1932), are given here.

All men who have the opportunity should enlist in the Citizen's Military Training Camps.
   (1) Strongly approve
   (2) Approve
   (3) Undecided
   (4) Disapprove
   (5) Strongly disapprove

The United States should have the largest military and naval air fleets in the world.
   (1) Strongly approve
   (2) Approve
   (3) Undecided
   (4) Disapprove
   (5) Strongly disapprove

Our country should never declare war under any circumstances.
   (5) Strongly approve
   (4) Approve
   (3) Undecided
   (3) Disapprove
   (1) Strongly disapprove

Do you favor the early entrance of the United States into the League of Nations?
   Yes_____   No_____

Is it an idle dream to expect to abolish war?
   Yes_____   No_____

Are you in sympathy with the movement for the outlawing of war?
   Yes_____   No_____

How much military training should we have?
   (1) We need universal compulsory military training
   (2) We need CMTC and ROTC but not universal military training
   (3) We need some facilities for training reserve officers but not as much as at present
   (4) We need only such military training as is required to maintain our regular army
   (5) All military training should be abolished

In any particular attitude context, a series of such items is presented, on each of which the individual rates himself, and the problem is to amalgamate the ratings in order to scale the individuals. It is evident from the point of view of data theory that this is identically the same problem as amalgamating the ratings of a foreman made by a number of supervisors when the rating categories are simply ordered. It is also evident that both kinds of data are formally the same as the kind collected by the method of categorical judgment. In all these instances we have proximity relations on pairs of points from distinct sets with the addition of an order relation on the elements of one of the sets.

A procedure for processing such data to arrive at an interval scale for both sets of elements is described in Guilford (1954). It assumes that each element of the unordered set projects a normal distribution on the J scale, so the proportion of times an element has been assigned to a category corresponds to the area under the normal curve and over the segment of the continuum corresponding to that category. The procedure is presumed to lead to scaling the means of the categories and the mean values of the stimuli's distributions. Green (1960) has shown, however, that the theory is invalid.

It is obvious that the same behavior or judgments could, alternatively, be mapped into QIIa data by virtue of the a priori order on the categories of judgment. We may specify that one of the sets of points corresponds to the objects of judgment and the other set of points corresponds to the boundaries between categories. Torgerson's model for categorical judgment would then be applicable.

There are other varieties or versions of these procedures involving more or fewer assumptions, with more or less simplified processing of data. Experimental studies comparing such various procedures seem invariably to show that the results are extremely highly correlated, and this is usually taken to signify that the simplest version is adequate—the simplest being the one with the strongest assumptions and least computational routine. It has always seemed to me that the evidence for such conclusions is weak. The models all lead to computing scale values for the elements of an ordinal scale. Any model that violated this given ordering would be rejected out of hand. But now given the ordering, how much *can* the models disagree in scale values? The product-moment correlation has a minimum value of $1/(n - 1)$ for n points on two monotonically related scales. Yet we can construct examples in which the *differences* between successive points on the one scale compared with those on the other may be perfectly negatively correlated. In other words, two models could disagree with one another as far as the limits allow within the common ordinal solution and appear to be practically equivalent if we correlate scale values. I would recommend, in general, when measurement models are compared, that *interpoint distances* be compared as well as scale values.

The other two levels of prior knowledge, interval and ratio scales, correspond respectively to the well-known method of equal appearing intervals and the method of magnitude estimation, the experimental procedures for which are described in detail in Stevens (1956). Each calls for an averaging process. An arithmetic mean is commonly used in the first case; Stevens (1957) has been using the median or geometric mean in the latter case because of the skewed distribution of the numbers assigned to a stimulus. See also the paper by Jones and Marcus (1961), which is concerned with the problem of pooling such data from different subjects. There is a great deal to be said about the advantages and disadvantages of these methods from the point of view of psychophysics (for example, Stevens, 1961; Garner, 1958; Torgerson, 1960).

One other method of observation should be mentioned here as yielding this same kind of data in its initial processing: S. S. Stevens' method of ratio estimation. In this method a pair of stimuli is presented and a subject is asked to report a number that corresponds to the ratio of their subjective magnitudes for him. We may consider the "ratios of subjective magnitudes" to constitute one set of elements and the real numbers the second set of elements. Then the behavior may be interpreted as a matching relation between an object in one set and an object in the other. Because the number so reported then implies an order relation (and more) on the pair of stimulus objects themselves, I have mapped such behavior into QIIIa, where it may be used to construct one-dimensional stimulus scales.

Since more than one number may be emitted as corresponding to the ratio, the analysis of such behavior as QIIb data would surely involve the problems of amalgamation that go along with 'pick any/n' data. Stevens recommends here, as with magnitude estimation, that the geometric mean or the median be used. In other words, the problem as QIIb data is to determine the number to associate with the ratio. The problem as QIIIa data is to locate the stimuli as points on a line.

4. RELATIONS AMONG QIIb MODELS

Interrelations among the QIIb models can be pointed up, as they were with the QIIa models, in terms of low versus high tolerance for inconsistency and in terms of whether the models are designed for unidimensional or multidimensional analysis. This manner of classification turns out to be not very useful for these models, primarily because of the great mathematical flexibility of LSA. In fact, LSA is not a model at all but a

	No Prior Knowledge	Prior Knowledge
'Pick 1/n'	No models for inferential classification. Observations (nominal labels) are taken as inferred classification	No models for inferential classification. Observations are taken as inferred classification (measurements). Methods of observation are known as (1) rating scales, (2) method of EAI, (3) magnitude estimation
'Pick any/n'	Latent class model Parallelogram analysis Latent structure analysis	Models are methods for arriving at descriptive statistics for replications of any of the above methods of observation

Fig. 15.2   A classification of QIIb models.

system of models, and a particular instance of application leads to a particular instance in the system. For example, instances of LSA may be unidimensional or multidimensional with monotone or nonmonotone trace lines at the choice of the experimenter.

A more useful way to organize and relate the models of QIIb is in terms of whether the data are 'pick 1/n' or 'pick any/n' on the one hand and whether the model requires prior knowledge of the scale values for one of the sets of elements. These bases lead to the fourfold table shown in Fig. 15.2.

As is stated in the figure, there are no models for the analysis of 'pick 1/n' data either with or without prior knowledge. The case of no prior knowledge is the kind of behavior we observe in clinical diagnosis. A label is pinned on each patient; knowing only that, there is no system for processing such observations to arrive at an inferred latent classification. The case of 'pick 1/n' with prior knowledge is the kind of behavior we observe in using such methods as rating scales, method of equal appearing intervals, and magnitude estimation. This occurs in physical measurement, as in reading footrules or gauges, or in much of experimental psychology where we count drops of saliva, changes in skin resistance, number of trials to learn, or reinforcements, or errors, and so on. All these instances involve the mapping of one set into the elements of a second set. The elements of the first set are objects of interest such as individuals, stimuli, or responses, and the elements of the second set are the n labeling categories.

There is no way to *process* such data to arrive at an inferred classification other than the one given in the observations themselves. The issue might be put as follows. The processes with which the theory of data is concerned are those in which a set of behavioral observations leads to a set of data, phase 2, which leads to a set of inferential classifications, phase 3. In the case of 'pick $1/n$' data these three stages constitute an identity: that is, behavioral observations = data = inferential classifications. *The model involved in the inferential process has been pushed back into the observer or other real world system which yields the classification directly.*

The only QIIb models explicitly concerned with inferential classification are parallelogram analysis and Lazarsfeld's latent class and latent structure analysis. These models are designed for the analysis of 'pick any/n' data with no prior knowledge. Essentially, in each of these models we propose an inferential classification and test it against the data. Parallelogram analysis is limited to unidimensional analysis, but the others are not.

Finally we have the models for processing 'pick any/n' data with prior knowledge. Essentially these amount to nothing more than arriving at an efficient description of the central tendency of the measures assigned to an object of judgment. When these measures are ordinal numbers only, as in ordinal rating scales, models exist for inferring a classification on an interval scale. Or, alternatively, we may map ordinal scale observations into QIIa by defining the sets of ordered elements to be the category boundaries rather than the categories. In this case any QIIa unidimensional model is applicable. If we want an interval scale, some version of Torgerson's model for categorical judgment is appropriate.

5. SOME RELATIONS BETWEEN QIIa AND QIIb

No other quadrant is so susceptible to confusion between its octants as QII. The reasons for this are many. One of them lies in the fact that certain QIIb data may be mapped readily into QIIa by virtue of prior knowledge that is added to the QIIb data. An example is the use of ordinal rating scales. The individual maps the elements of one set into the elements of a second set consisting of ordered response categories. Such behavior may be interpreted as proximity relations on pairs of points from two sets, clearly QIIb data. It is also clear, however, that we might consider the boundaries between successive categories rather than the response categories themselves to correspond to the elements of the second set. In which case the behavior may be interpreted as order relations between pairs of points from distinct sets.

The problem of which kind of data to make out of such observations is most seriously at issue when the elements of the second set (whether they are response categories or category boundaries) are ordered *on a J scale*. The problem arises not only when ordinal rating scales are used to collect the observations, but, in another context, when Likert-type items are used, as in attitude scaling. Such items correspond to points so extreme on the *J* scale that successive degrees of endorsement correspond to successively ordered categories on the *J* acale. We may think of each such item or question as sorting individuals into categories on the *J* scale. Examples are the items and questions on p. 315 taken from Likert's early monograph. In this chapter the analysis of such items is discussed as QIIb data. However, additional examples of the same kind of items were given in Section 2 of Chapter 11, where they were interpreted as QIIa data and analyzed by scalogram analysis adapted for disorderly interlocking.

Observations collected by use of Likert-type items are formally the same kind of data as that obtained by use of ordinal rating scales. In the first instance individuals are rating themselves and in the latter instance the individuals are rating a set of stimuli other than themselves. In either case we have two distinct sets of points and a relation between pairs of points, one from each set. Whether the relation is a proximity relation or an order relation is a matter of whether the experimenter decides one of the sets of points corresponds to categories or to category boundaries, yielding proximal or ordinal relations respectively. If the data are identified as QIIa rather than QIIb a considerably wider variety of models are available from which to choose. These include Guttman's scalogram analysis with disorderly interlocking, the latent distance model with a staircase trace line, LSA with linear, ogival, or other monotone trace lines, or one of the special cases of the model for categorical judgment—the latter yielding a solution at the level of an interval scale. As QIIb data, one of the models for amalgamating ordinal ratings is in order, as discussed in Section 3 for 'pick any/n' data with prior knowledge.

We must clearly distinguish between Likert-type items, in which the response alternatives are monotonically related to the *J* scale, and Thurstone-type items. The latter are items whose scale values are not necessarily extreme on the *J* scale relative to the population of individuals, but rather may have scale values greater than those of some individuals and less than those of others. The consequence is that the response categories for such items are nonmonotonically related to the *J* scale because they are monotonically related to the *I* scale, as discussed in Section 2 of Chapter 14. Now, if such items have not been previously scaled, so that there is no prior knowledge, then nonmonotone models are appropriate, such as parallelogram analysis or an LSA model with nonmonotone trace lines. If such items have been previously scaled, however, the appropriate model is one which provides a descriptive statistic for 'pick any/n' data with prior knowledge. In this particular case we typically have numerical scale values for the items, and a measure of central tendency applied to the scale values of the items picked or endorsed is applicable, as in any other numerical rating scale data.

This freedom to identify certain observations as QIIa or QIIb data at will is only one of several reasons for a tendency to blur the distinction between these two kinds of data ànd their respective models. Another reason lies in the mathematical flexibility of the general system of latent structure analysis. Some of its basic assumptions, like that of local independence, are probably universally common, at least implicitly, to all methods for analyzing QII data. When the general system is given a particular structure it can be one for QIIa data, for QIIb data, or for a mixture; and it can be for unidimensional or multidimensional spaces. Because of this neat unified mathematical system, then, we tend to think of the entire quadrant in a unified way.

In Lazarsfeld's system a monotone trace line would provide a probabilistic model for QIIa data and a nonmonotone trace line would provide one for QIIb data. Either is, in principle, generalizable to trace surfaces in a multidimensional space, and finally, the model can accommodate, again in principle, à mixture of QIIa and QIIb data. Thus we might tend to learn Lazarsfeld's system as a general model without reference to the distinction made here between the two octants.

I have maintained the distinction (1) because of the existence of particular models designed for just one of the octants; (2) because, knowing the distinction, we may clearly see what is required to convert the data of one of the octants into data of the other; and (3) because it classifies together models which are alternatives for analyzing *the same data.*

To illustrate this last point, parallelogram analysis and scalogram analysis, although similar in many respects, are each designed for analysis of a different kind of data. They are not mutually interchangeable. If one is appropriate the other is not. An alternative to parallelogram analysis is an LSA model with SPF's, whereas an alternative to scalogram analysis is an LSA model with monotone trace lines.

A major objective of the theory of data is to classify models in terms of their being alternatives *for the same data,* so that it is clear to an experimenter just what choices he has for making inferential classifications from any particular kind of data. For this reason I classified data first and then discussed the special cases of LSA that would be applicable. But this procedure does not do justice to an integrated system of models such as Lazarsfeld's.

The distinction made between monotone and nonmonotone trace lines has been made repeatedly in psychological literature on scaling but usually in a different vocabulary and referring to a typology for scales themselves. These terms include unidirectional versus bipolar, cumulative versus differential, and quantitative versus qualitative. Each of these pairs corresponds respectively to what I have referred to as monotone and nonmonotone data. The term "quantitative" has been used in the sense that more implies less (for example, if an individual has more of an ability he also has all lesser amounts) and the term "qualitative" has been used in the sense that more does not imply less (for example, as an individual becomes more favorable in his attitude toward x he does not continue to be less favorable). I think that all these terms are unfortunate because it is not the scales that need to be typed but the kinds of data. I prefer to classify the data in terms of proximity versus order relations, but a good pragmatic argument could be made for returning to monotone versus nonmonotone trace lines. Torgerson (1958, p. 304) seems to prefer the latter dichotomy.

6. SUMMARY

Analysis of the data of QIIb may be interpreted as a problem in the solution of simultaneous inequalities, as is the case in every octant. The method of solution involves a model which adds information to that in the equations themselves and makes them more uniquely soluble. Part of the information that may be added is prior knowledge, from whatever source, of the scale relations among the elements of one of the sets. This characteristic is used as a basis for the orderly discussion of models, because this is also the basis in terms of which models are most nearly mutually substitutable.

The minimal level of data is 'pick $1/n$' with no prior information, by which we mean that the elements of both sets are elements of only a nominal scale, as, for example, a data matrix indicating to which political party every Frenchman belongs. The level of information here is too low to permit constructing a configuration in a psychological space to reflect such choice behavior.

With some prior knowledge about the elements of one of the sets something can be said about the elements of the other set. By prior knowledge is meant scale relations at the level of an ordinal scale or higher. This is the kind of data we have in the one-time use of a rating scale or single occurrence of a magnitude estimation. These are exemplified by an individual saying, "the concert was great," or "there were 1500 people there." These are "direct measurement." The process from observations to data to inferential classifications, phases 2 and 3, are immediate and direct. The process is hidden and not exposed to the experimenter.

If some form of replication is used so that 'pick any/n' data are obtained, then, with no prior knowledge, Lazarsfeld's latent class model is available for a nominal classification of individuals and stimuli; parallelogram analysis is a deterministic model for an ordinal classification; and Lazarsfeld's LSA with nonmonotone trace lines is a probabilistic model for the same purpose. Only the general theory of LSA is discussed. Detailed procedures for processing data are not considered. LSA has a potential for multidimensional analysis of a psychological space, and in fact the latent classes in the latent class model can be thought of as clouds or regions in the space.

Parallelogram analysis for the one-dimensional case of 'pick any/n' data is discussed and extended to include more than the dichotomous categories of 'pick' and 'not pick.' This is a kind of data that approaches more closely to 'order k/n' data. The individual reports degree of endorsement, for example, on a five-point scale, and this divides his I scale into five ordered segments. 'Pick any/n' divides his I scale into only two segments, those picked and those not picked.

If, finally, we introduce both prior knowledge and replication, we arrive at models concerned with processing the data from replicated rating scales, the method of equal appearing intervals, and the method of magnitude estimation. The processing of ordinal rating scales to arrive at interval scales puts the assumptions of a process into the model, whereas the methods of equal appearing intervals and magnitude estimation hide the process in the individual making the judgments. Stevens' method of ratio estimation yields behavior which may also be mapped initially into QIIb data. The initial analysis involves estimating the ratio of two stimuli from 'pick any/n' data. The method of ratio estimation corresponds to magnitude estimation if the "ratio of the two stimuli" is itself regarded as the stimulus. When we have obtained measures of the ratio from the QIIb data, the stimulus points themselves may be obtained by analyzing the ratios as QIIIa data, as discussed in Chapter 17.

Behavior obtained in using ordinal rating scales is interpretable as either QIIa or QIIb data depending on whether the experimenter tries to scale category boundaries or the categories themselves. Models for either are available, typically adding information by making distribution assumptions in order to arrive at an interval scale.

The classification of these models is summarized in a fourfold table based on the two dichotomies: 'pick $1/n$' or 'pick any/n' and presence or absence of prior knowledge.

A section is devoted to the relations between QIIa and QIIb models because of their unusual intimacy. Certain QIIb data may be mapped at will into QIIa and analyzed by any of a considerable variety of models.

This is not true of all QIIb data, however, but only of data in which there is prior knowledge (order relations) about the response categories. We then have the choice of trying to scale response categories (QIIb data) or category boundaries (QIIa). Such data may be obtained from rating scales (for example, the method of successive intervals) and Likert-type items. The latter must be carefully distinguished from Thurstone-type items. The fact that the alternatives to the items are a series of degrees of endorsement does not distinguish these two types at all.

The important distinction lies in whether the items are extreme items relative to the population of ideals (Likert-type) or whether the scale values of the items might be intermediate on the J scale and fall between the ideals of individuals (Thurstone-type). In the Likert-type there is a one-to-one correspondence between response alternatives and regions of the space, whereas in the Thurstone-type there is a one-many mapping. For example, in a Thurstone-type item two different individuals may reject the same item, one because it is too pro-x, the other because it is not enough pro-x.

There is also a close intimacy between some of the models in QIIa and QIIb. This is well illustrated by Lazarsfeld's system of LSA, which by simply choosing monotone or nonmonotone trace lines is a model for QIIa or QIIb respectively. In spite of these close relations, however, I have adhered to the distinction based on the kind of data, because this is the basis for a classification that relates models in terms of their mutual substitutability for analysis of the same data.

REFERENCES

Anderson, T. W., 1954, On estimation of parameters in latent structure analysis, *Psychometrika*, **19**, 1–10.

Garner, W R., 1958, Advantages of the discriminability criterion for a loudness scale, *J. acoust. Soc. Amer.*, **30**, 1005–12.

Gibson, W. A., 1955, An extension of Anderson's solution for the latent structure equations, *Psychometrika*, **20**, 69–73.

Gibson, W. A., 1959, Three multivariate models: factor analysis, latent structure analysis, and latent profile analysis, *Psychometrika*, **24**, 229–52.

Green, B. F., Jr., 1951, A general solution for the latent class model of latent structure analysis, *Psychometrika*, **16**, 151–66.

Green, B. F., Jr., 1952, Latent structure analysis and its relation to factor analysis, *J. Amer. statist. Ass.*, **47**, 71–76.

Green, B. F., Jr., 1960, "A technical note on the method of successive categories using category means," Chapter 5 in *Psychological scaling: theory and applications*, edited by H. Gulliksen and S. Messick, John Wiley and Sons, New York.

Guilford, J. P., 1954, *Psychometric methods*, second edition, McGraw-Hill Book Co., New York.

Jones, F. N., and Maxine J. Marcus, 1961, The subject effect in judgments of subjective magnitude, *J. exp. Psychol.*, **61**, 40–44.

Lazarsfeld, P. F., 1959, "Latent structure analysis," a chapter in *Psychology: a study of a science*, vol. 3, edited by S. Koch, McGraw-Hill Book Co., New York.

Likert, Rensis, 1932, A technique for the measurement of attitudes, *Arch. Psychol.*, *No.* 140, p. 55.

Stevens, S. S., 1956, The direct estimate of sensory magnitudes—loudness, *Amer. J. Psychol.*, **69**, 1–25.

Stevens, S. S., 1957, On the psychophysical law, *Psychol. Rev.*, **64**, 153–81.

Stevens, S. S., 1961, To honor Fechner and repeal his law, *Science*, **133**, 80–86.

Torgerson, W. S., 1958, *Theory and methods of scaling*, John Wiley and Sons, New York.

Torgerson, W. S., 1960, Distances and ratios in psychological scaling, a paper presented at the XVI° International Congress of Psychologists, Bonn, Germany, August 2, 1960.

CHAPTER 16

Some Interpretations
of QIIb Theory

1. A QIIb MODEL OF PERCEPTION AND COGNITIVE STRUCTURE

The formal model underlying QIIb data suggests a framework for organizing our thinking about the area of perception and the broader area of cognitive structure generally. Our ideas here bear a resemblance to Hayek's (1952) "systems of connexions"; to the "schemata" of Vernon (1955), who got them from Bartlett (1932); to Bruner, Goodnow, and Austin's (1956) use of the term "categorizing"; and to Miller, Galanter, and Pribram's (1960) concept of the "image."*

The basic datum of QIIb consists formally of a point in one set being matched with a point in another set. We may describe the process of perception in the same terms. A stimulus may be thought of as a particular combination of attributes, an r-tuple, which consitutes the input. This input is identified, perceived, when it is mapped into a class. Each such class is an equivalence class of r-tuples, equivalent in that they are all identified with the label of that class. Each such equivalence class has an ideal which is a specification of the properties universal to that class for the individual.

For example, most individuals have an equivalence class with which the name "chair" is associated. Exactly what the r-tuple is that defines the ideal point for any one individual for the class "chair" we hesitate to say, but it may consist of the properties of having legs, a seat, and a back, and certain proportions. Functional properties may also be relevant

---

* But all these are versions of a theory of categorizing on the basis of an ideal viewpoint which may be found in Plato's philosophy, so I'm told.

aspects, and not all properties of the ideal point are equally important. The ideal point c_{hij} corresponds to this r-tuple. Not all objects called a chair will exactly match this ideal, so a certain departure from the ideal is admissible for an object without keeping it from being identified with the class. A particular sensory input, then, is another r-tuple q_{hij}, which will fall at a distance, $|p_{hij}| = |c_{hij} \ominus q_{hij}|$, from the ideal of this nominal class. If this distance $|p_{hij}|$ is less than some admissible prescribed amount on each dimension $\epsilon_{hij}^{(d)}$, the stimulus is identified as a member of the class and tends to become endowed with the ideal properties of that class. The $\epsilon_{hij}^{(d)}$ is a way of emphasizing the importance of a dimension.

Without attempting to cover the vast literature relevant here, a few selections may help to illustrate these concepts. Boring (1953) tells of published drawings of cell nuclei dated both before and after the discovery and description of chromosomes. Chromosomes kept showing up in the later drawings, not in the earlier. When the ideal for the class "cell nuclei" included chromosomes, chromosomes were perceived as part of the r-tuple of the visual input.

A study by Carmichael, Hogan, and Walter (1932) is relevant. Subjects were presented with ambiguous figures such as that shown on the top of Fig. 16.1. Half were told it resembled curtains in a window; the remainder were told that it resembled a diamond in a rectangle. When asked to reproduce the figure from memory, the two groups' reproductions showed a marked influence of the verbal labels, tending to veer toward the figures shown on the bottom of Fig. 16.1. The verbal label provides a class into which the stimulus point is mapped, and the stimulus then tends to take on the ideal properties of that class, that is, the r-tuple associated with the stimulus input may be thought of as migrating toward the ideal point of the class in which it is embedded.

A more recent study showing the same process at work is that of Harold Kelley (1950). In this study a guest lecturer was asked to conduct an hour of class. He was previously described to half the class as a rather "cold" person and to the other half as "warm." At the end of the hour the class rated him on some 15 attributes. The results are shown in Table 16.1.

For the entire set of 15 rated attributes, the "cold" group rated the visitor toward the less socially desirable end of the scale on every one, 5 of them showing differences significant at the 1% level. Kelley's study reveals some of the attributes associated with the ideals of these subjects for a "warm" and a "cold" person.

From this point of view, then, we would expect subject's reports of what is perceived to be modified toward an ideal point and to include other attributes of the ideal. This is what is involved in some studies of redundancy in perception and is the same process, I think, as that of

Stimulus

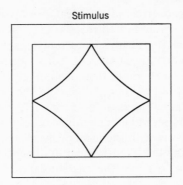

Curtains in a window   Diamond in a rectangle

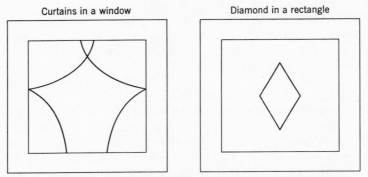

Fig. 16.1 Stimulus figure and effect of language on reproductions.

perceptual constancies and closure. We would, in fact, expect there to be a "perceptual constancy" for every attribute of the ideal point of a class. In fact the three studies mentioned are of the same kind as perceptual constancy from this point of view.

A psychological process like "set" and its relation to latency of response may be thought of in terms of manipulating the psychological space so that a sensory input is closer to the ideal point. This might be accomplished, for example, by reducing the number of relevant dimensions, that is, projecting the ideal point and the stimulus r-tuple into a subspace. The "set" may be considered to have reduced the relevant dimensions.* Thus any noise at the right moment will start off a race, all other attributes of the stimulus being irrelevant.

Although perception may be thought of as the process of mapping into classes, learning may be thought of as the process of creating, partitioning,

---

* This idea suggests a possible model for an important theoretical point receiving much attention these days: that heightened emotion or tension focuses attention (that is, reduces dimensionality); see Easterbrook (1959) and Runkel and Damrin (1961).

and relating these classes, giving rise to a cognitive structure. This cognitive structure then may be viewed in terms of relations on the ideal points of the various classes and of set-theoretic relations on the classes themselves. At any point in time we have a cognitive structure which has arisen out of

Table 16.1   Comparison of "Warm" and "Cold" Observers in Terms of Average Ratings Given Stimulus Persons

Item	Low End of Rating Scale	High End of Rating Scale	Average Rating		Level of Significance of Warm-Cold Difference, %
			Warm $n = 27$	Cold $n = 28$	
1	Knows his stuff	Doesn't know his stuff	3.5	4.6	
2	Considerate of others	Self-centered	6.3	9.6	1
3*	Informal	Formal	6.3	9.6	1
4*	Modest	Proud	9.4	10.6	
5*	Sociable	Unsociable	5.6	10.4	1
6	Self-assured	Uncertain of himself	8.4	9.1	
7	High intelligence	Low intelligence	4.8	5.1	
8	Popular	Unpopular	4.0	7.4	1
9*	Good-natured	Irritable	9.4	12.0	5
10	Generous	Ungenerous	8.2	9.6	
11	Humorous	Humorless	8.3	11.7	1
12	Important	Insignificant	6.5	8.6	
13*	Humane	Ruthless	8.6	11.0	5
14*	Submissive	Dominant	13.2	14.5	
15	Will go far	Will not get ahead	4.2	5.8	

* These scales were reversed when presented to the subjects.

the totality of our experience. I like the description of the process given by Kershner and Wilcox (1950, p. 14).

At some time during a child's life, a moving object, which has four legs and makes a clattering noise, comes down the street. Simultaneously, Mother, who is standing near him, uses the word *horse*. The coincidence of the new object and the new word impresses him, and he assumes the word to refer to the object which he saw and heard. Some time later another object passes. This one is different: the first was white while this one is brown; the first one was running while this one is walking. Yet Mother again uses the word *horse*, and reasonably so, since the two objects do resemble each other.

After this situation has arisen a number of times, the child feels that he knows what qualities are allowed to be different and what must be the same, in order that the word *horse* be applicable. Then comes the happy day when an object comes down the street, and, although he has never seen this particular object before—this one is gray—he points triumphantly at it and says, "*Horsie!*" Mother agrees and beams. At this point *horse*, or its variant *horsie*, is a meaningful word to the child.

Yet no one would argue that *horse* means the same to the child and his mother. A visit to the zoo might prove otherwise: the child might use the word in reference to striped animals which his mother calls *zebras* and not *horses*. Yet gradually, as his experience broadens, the child will find fewer and fewer conflicts between his terminology and that of his mother. Eventually one might say that the child and his mother have "essentially" the same meaning of *horse*.

The process of acquiring a meaning for even such a concrete word as *horse* is elaborate and does not lead to quite the same understanding on the part of all people. Clearly the meaning to any one person depends on the totality of his particular experiences. With abstract terms like *truth*, *beauty*, and so on, the situation is the same, except that meanings differ much more from one individual to another. There is certainly no general agreement on the applicability of the term *beauty* in any particular instance. Indeed, agreement here is so poor that the term is unusable in logical discussions.

What is suggested here is that the occurrence of positive instances has the effect of eliminating those aspects or dimensions on which the instances differ. The occurrence of negative instances affects the ϵ's on dimensions the negative instances have in common with positive instances.

Some remarks by Hayek (1952) and by Klüver in the Preface to Hayek's book are very pertinent. Klüver says (pp. xviii–xix):

In a brief space, it is impossible to outline even the essentials of Dr. Hayek's theory, but from a broad point of view his theory may be said to substantiate Goethe's famous maxim "all that is factual is already theory" for the field of sensory and other psychological phenomena. According to Dr. Hayek, sensory perception must be regarded as an act of classification. What we perceive are never unique properties of individual objects, but always only properties which the objects have in common with other objects. Perception is thus always an interpretation, the placing of something into one or several classes of objects. The characteristic attributes of sensory qualities, or the classes into which different events are placed in the process of perception, are not attributes which are possessed by these events and which are in some manner "communicated" to the mind; they consist entirely in the "differentiating" responses of the organism by which the qualitative classification or order of these events is created; and it is contended that this classification is based on the connexions created in the nervous system by past "linkages." The qualities which we attribute to the experienced objects are, strictly speaking, not properties of objects at all, but a set of relations by which our nervous system classifies them. To put it differently, all we know about the world is of the nature of theories and all "experience" can do is to change these theories. All sensory perception is necessarily "abstract" in that it always selects certain aspects or features of a given situation. Every sensation, even the "purest," must therefore be regarded as an interpretation of an event in the light of the past experience of the individual or the species.

Hayek himself says, "Whenever we study qualitative differences between experiences we are studying mental and not physical events, and much that we believe to know about the external world, is, in fact, knowledge about ourselves." (Pp. 6–7.)

What makes these equivalence classes a cognitive structure is the existence of a "system of connexions." This system may be thought of in neurophysiological terms as Hayek does, or just in formal relational terms. The individual's variegated experience imbues the cognitive structure with a variety of relations among equivalence classes, and the relations among classes require a corresponding variety of formal relational systems to describe them adequately. This variety includes that described in Coombs, Raiffa, and Thrall (1954), which ranges from the level of equivalence classes (a nominal scale) through a partial order and a lattice, to the level of the real numbers.

Which level in this abstract system is appropriate and adequate to describe the relations among some particular classes depends on the nature of the experiences that created the classes and created their relations to each other (see Coombs, 1948). We may conceive of the forces (cultural, educational, biological) being so strong and uniform that the relations between classes and between their ideals can only be fully represented by the real numbers. I think this is an extreme case. It is not so extreme to conceive of these classes being simply ordered as a result of reasonably uniform forces jointly influencing their structure. The formation, however, of cognitive structures which are common to a number of individuals requires not only a reasonably homogeneous set of forces for each individual, but also requires such sets to be homogeneous across individuals. This is a very stringent requirement if social, educational, and cultural factors are part of these forces.

Hence, it seems obvious to me that some cognitive structures may have quantitative aspects which are representable by interval and ratio scales, but it also seems to me that psychologists should be sensitive to relations in a cognitive structure that do not satisfy interval and ratio scales. I think this is especially true of psychologists interested in areas other than sensory phenomena, for example, the area of the cognitive structure of attitudes. It would not seem surprising to me that a partial order should be necessary to describe the attribute "attitude toward the British" for some individuals, whereas a simply ordered scale may completely describe the behavior of other individuals to the same stimuli.

In the area of athletic scholarships, to take another example, the coaches and the athletic director of an American university probably have a highly structured and organized attribute. Almost every conceivable statement has already been thoroughly evaluated and mapped into a point having appropriate distances from other points. The faculty, on the other hand, have given less thought to and have had less experience in the domain. As a result, their cognitive structure of the attribute will correspond either to a relatively weak mathematical system involving uncertainty as to relations among some points, or possibly a very strong but very simple one in the sense of things being "either black or white."

The general idea being discussed here is related to Loevinger's (1957, p. 662) notion of a "characteristic intercorrelation": "For any given trait it seems reasonable to assume that there is an upper limit to the intercorrelation of its manifestations, which might be called its characteristic intercorrelation. For example, two manifestations of numerical ability would be expected to be more closely related than, say, two manifestations of aggressiveness. Two manifestations of verbal facility would be more closely related than two manifestations of introversion."

Areas in which measurement, and inferential classification in general, is in terms of "weaker" relational systems are called "soft" by some psychologists. Its usual use as a term of opprobrium for the area is quite unfair. Work in such areas need not be any less rigorous or scientific; truth statements in such weaker systems would merely tend to be less specific.

I have said that the theory of data is concerned with the theory of inferential classification (Chapter 1). We can now go on to call it a theory of how, from behavioral observation, we arrive at a representation of the cognitive structure for an individual, and a theory of how we arrive at a representation of the class structure, or the power structure, or what have you, for a society. As far as the theory of data is concerned these are the same problem, formally. All that the theory of data does is organize the discussion of structures in terms of the variety of models available for each of the varieties of data. It perhaps goes a little further than this, though, in that it suggests how one kind of data is related to another kind. I shall point this up in the next paragraphs by relating this interpretation of perception as QIIb data to an interpretation of it as QIa data. Such a reinterpretation helps to make clear the role that ϵ plays.

The process of perception has been interpreted as involving relations between pairs of (multidimensional) points from distinct sets. On the one hand there are the ideal points for the equivalence classes in the individual's cognitive structure, and on the other hand there are the points for the stimulus inputs. I have discussed this in terms of the nature of QIIb data, as if the mapping of an input into a class was a matter of the distance between a pair of points being less than some critical threshold value, ϵ. That is, I have been describing the process of perception as if the individual searched his cognitive structure of ideal points, comparing the distance of a stimulus point vis-à-vis each such point until he found one *which satisfied the criterion for matching*—and thereby the stimulus is identified, labeled, and perceived. We might make this process more reasonable by adding that the stimulus somehow controls the space of relevant dimensions in which this search takes place.

I wish now to propose that although the process may look like single stimulus data—and although we may have to use models for inferential classification appropriate to that kind of data—nevertheless the process may in reality be quite different. We might conceive of the process as a stimulus point choosing from among a set of class ideals, as in QIa, preferential choice data. Consider, as an illustration, an individual about to remark on the beauty of a girl's face. A set of adjectives is available, simply or partially ordered, perhaps ranging from comely to gorgeous, each of which corresponds to an ideal point. The stimulus input is another point. The adjective associated with the face is the one *whose point is nearest the stimulus point*.

The reason such perceptual behavior cannot be analyzed as QIa data is that only one alternative has been picked from the set. The situation is 'pick 1/n.' If the adjective chosen, for example, is *attractive*, we do not know what the second choice would be, or whether she is more nearly *lovely* or *good-looking*. This is the kind of information that would be necessary for analysis of the data by a QIa model. But the data remain 'pick 1/n' and the experimenter is unaware even of the set of alternatives available to the "perceiver," so all the experimenter can say is that the distance from the stimulus point to the class ideal is less than some quantity ϵ which is the half-way point to the next alternative, whatever it might be.

As we have seen from the discussion of ϵ in Section 3 of Chapter 14, the magnitude of ϵ is not necessarily a characteristic of a class in itself but is dependent on the associated alternative classes. Thus, when the price of an object is called *expensive* by someone, is *exhorbitant* an available alternative, or does *expensive* include the entire upper end of the continuum? What distinction was he drawing on the other side of the continuum? Is the next lower alternative *fair price* or *cheap*?

I suggest, then, that, according to this model, perception is actually choice behavior in the sense of QIa, but that what we normally observe in the natural case is 'pick 1/n', which must be interpreted as single stimulus data, QIIb. I think there is much to be gained from studying perception by QIa methods instead of QIIb, particularly where cognitive structure and relations on class ideals are of interest.*

* In this regard see Runkel (1958).

2. A DATA THEORY VIEW OF STUDENT RATINGS OF FACULTY

In this section I consider an example of student ratings of faculty (and, in general, any "evaluative" type of rating in which judges may differ in their ideals on an underlying attribute), and analyze it from the point of view of the theory of data. The result, I think, is some insight which provokes more careful interpretation of such data analyses.

The literary college of The University of Michigan, concerned with the improvement of instruction, carried out a study a few years ago which required students in various courses to rate their instructors on a number of attributes. The attributes included the following: approachability, regularity, open-mindedness, thoroughness, general effectiveness, stimulus to thinking, organization of work, clarity of objectives, fairness of examinations, and adequacy of text. An average rating was computed for each instructor over the attributes and for each attribute over the instructors. It may be informative to look at the processes involved here from the point of view of data theory and inquire into what might make high and low ratings.

Suppose that for each of these rated attributes there is an underlying latent attribute, a joint scale of students and instructors, such that the manifest rating reflects a discrepancy between student and instructor points on the J scale. For example, take an attribute like *fairness of examinations*. Every student, of course, wants a fair examination, but a given examination is not equally fair to everyone. We might imagine that there is an underlying scale such as *achievement level** on which each student has an ideal corresponding to how difficult an examination should be to be fair. We might also imagine that each examination corresponds to a point on this same scale as to its general difficulty level. To be fair for a particular student, the examination must demand just the right amount of achievement. The further the examination point departs from the student's ideal point the less fair it is and the lower the rating. From this point of view there would be students who would regard too easy an examination as unfair.

The numerical rating, then, that a student assigns to an instructor is the student's "measure" (inversely) of how great the absolute distance is between this pair of points. That is, a high rating is assigned when the points nearly coincide and the rating diminishes as the distance between the points increases.

---

* There are surely other components of "fairness." We choose this one as illustrative.

Distribution of c_i for students

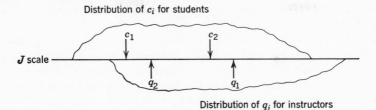

Distribution of q_j for instructors

Fig. 16.2 Joint distribution on latent attribute underlying rating.

The general situation is illustrated in Fig. 16.2. The J scale is a presumed latent attribute underlying a particular rating. On top of the J scale is a hypothetical distribution of students' ideal points, c_i, with the ideal points of two students, c_1 and c_2, indicated. Hanging from the J scale is a distribution of instructors' stimulus points, q_j, with the stimulus points of two instructors, q_1 and q_2, indicated. The rating assigned by a student to an instructor is assumed to be given by an SPF* which for our general purposes will be assumed to be linear, that is, the rating assigned is inversely proportional to $|p_{ij}| = |c_i - q_j|$. Thus if c_i and q_j coincide, the individual assigns a maximum rating, which diminishes as c_i and q_j become more different. In the figure, for example, c_1 will give a lower rating to q_1 than to q_2 whereas c_2 would give a lower rating to q_2 than to q_1.

Let a rating be designated $\pi_{ij} = k_i |p_{ij}| + 1$, where the additive constant, unity, is merely for the convenience of translating a zero distance to correspond to the highest rating, 1, on the rating scale. The k_i is a different matter entirely and is very important. It is a proportionality constant for a rater.

This constant may be thought of as a stretching factor on the student's I scale to match it against the given rating scale. It is also interpretable as a correction factor for his unit of measurement on his I scale to bring it into conformity with that implied by the rating scale. It may be interpreted as a weighting factor on individuals. It is further interpretable as the correction factor necessary to introduce interpersonal comparability of utility. And there's the rub. The numbers on the rating scale are assumed to have the same interpretation for all students. Let us discuss this in more detail.

Consider a student at c_1, which is near the extreme of the q_j distribution. The rating scale, which runs from 1 to 5, say, is to be applied to stimuli q_j, which may be as far away as the range of the q_j distribution. In contrast, a student at c_2, who is near the middle of the q_j distribution, has no

* See Chapter 9, Section 1.

stimuli to rate which are farther away than about half the range of the q_j distribution.

In other words, c_1's I scale will be as long as the range of the q_j distribution, and c_2's I scale will be only about half as long. Each of these students, now, is asked to match his I scale to the rating scale from 1 to 5. Presumably c_1 will match his I scale with the range of numbers from 1 to 5, and perhaps $k_1 = 1$. How about c_2? Will he match his to the rating scale from 1 to 5, in which case $k_2 = 2$, or will he match it to the interval from 1 to 3, in which case $k_2 = 1$ also?

If the common effect of range on absolute judgment applies here, students will stretch their I scales to match the rating scale and $k_2/k_1 \cong 2$. Now, as may be seen from the figure, $c_1 - q_2 = c_2 - q_1$, yet because of the ratio of their proportionality constants, $\pi_{21} > \pi_{12}$. In other words, the student at c_1 will rate the instructor at q_2 much higher (that is, lower numerically) than the student at c_2 will rate the instructor at q_1.

If the students are using the same absolute standards of judgment, usually assumed to be the case in such ratings, then in terms of this model they are using the same k_i and $\pi_{12} = \pi_{21}$. This is equivalent to assuming that they have the same unit of measurement on the J scale, that is, interpersonal comparability of utility, and thus k_i's, all alike, are merely adjusted to the unit of measurement on the rating scale.

Let us assume the latter, that k_i is a constant for all i, that is, that all students have the same standards of absolute judgment in their assignment of values on the rating scale. Each instructor is assigned an average rating

$$\pi_{\cdot j} = \frac{1}{m} \sum_{i=1}^{m} |p_{ij}| + 1$$

on each attribute, which is clearly seen to be essentially nothing more nor less than the mean absolute deviation of the students' ideal points about the instructor's q_j point as an origin.

There is a well-known theorem to the effect that the mean absolute deviation of a distribution of points is a minimum about the median point. For any other point taken as origin the mean absolute deviation can be no less. Furthermore, the mean absolute deviation will be higher the further the origin from the median point if the distribution is symmetric.

All this simply means that the instructor with the highest rating will be he whose q_j is nearest the median student's c_i and his average rating will be less the further from that point his q_j is. We note, again, that this has been calculated under the assumption that k_i is a constant for all i; that is, that the individuals do not stretch their I scales to fit the rating scale.

If the students do not have a common unit of measurement and do stretch their I scales to fit the rating scale, this conclusion will no longer hold in general. The instructor with the lowest mean disutility may be shifted away from the median student. The argument is as follows.

The quantity $|p_{ij}|$ for each student-instructor pair will be multiplied by the student's stretching factor. This stretching factor will be proportional to the individual's distance from the center of the distribution of instructors. A student whose ideal point is at an extreme end of the distribution of instructors will need to stretch his I scale less than an individual whose ideal is near the center. The effect of the stretching factors, then, is to weight individuals unequally in contributing to the average rating of an instructor.

If the two distributions of student ideals and instructor points are not symmetrically opposed but one is displaced relative to the other, the effect is to weight more heavily the students in that part of their distribution which overlaps the instructors' distribution. This effectively skews the distribution of student ideals, and the instructor with the best average rating will be not the one nearest the median student but the one displaced toward the more heavily weighted portion of the students' distribution, that is, more central to the distribution of instructors.

For any given attribute, then, we see that an instructor's average rating will be better the nearer he is to the median student ideal unless the two distributions are displaced; in which case the "best" instructor will be displaced toward the more heavily weighted overlapping portion of the students' distribution.

On each attribute, now, we have a $\pi_{.j}$ for each instructor j which, of course, are not in general the same for all. These may be averaged over all attributes for each instructor, giving him his average rating. The relative weighting of the different attributes in contributing to an instructor's average rating is a direct function of the relative magnitude of the standard deviation of the $\pi_{.j}$ for each attribute. The greater the variance of the $\pi_{.j}$ for one attribute relative to other attributes, the more that attribute contributes to the variance of the totals. But the variance of the $\pi_{.j}$'s, we must now recognize, is exclusively a function of the variance of the instructors' q_j points and is independent of the distribution of c_i's, for if the students all had the same ideal point, instructors would still receive different average ratings, whereas if the instructors were all at the same point they would all receive the same average rating.

So we come finally to the following interpretation. If the students' ratings represent judgments on a common scale in the manner here assumed, then the nearer an instructor's point to the median student's point, the higher his rating will tend to be on that attribute. *To improve his average rating it behooves him to follow this admonition: to match the median student ideal and particularly on those attributes on which instructors are most different.*

In passing I might point out that there is a completely parallel argument, *mutatis mutandis*, for the average rating assigned by a student. The nearer a student's ideal point is to his median instructor the higher will be the average rating he assigns, that is, the happier (?) he will be.

We may pursue the subject one step further and consider what the average rating of an attribute taken over all the instructors might mean. This is more complicated. For each attribute d each instructor has a mean rating $\pi_{\cdot j}^{(d)}$, and we are interested in the

$$\pi_{\cdot\cdot}^{(d)} = \frac{1}{n} \sum_j \pi_{\cdot j}^{(d)}$$

the mean rating on an attribute. Presumably if the faculty has a higher rating on one attribute than another the interpretation is that there need be less concern about the faculty performance in that regard.

Unfortunately, this does not follow. The mean rating on an attribute is a function of the distributions of the q_j and the c_i in relation to each other and of their variances. The situation is this. There are two distributions and the $\pi_{\cdot\cdot}^{(d)}$, the mean attribute rating, is a function of the mean absolute distance of each point in one distribution from each point in the other. Clearly, other things being equal, the smaller the variance of either distribution and the more nearly symmetrically located they are with respect to each other, the higher the mean attribute rating (that is, closer to 1). These conditions might be interpreted as follows. High average rating for an attribute requires uniformity among students in what they regard as desirable, uniformity among the faculty on the attribute, and a close matching between the two. This is not a precise set of conditions but is adequate for our general descriptive purposes. A low average rating (higher numerically) for an attribute, then, may reflect a large variance of students' ideal points, that is, they differ widely in what they regard as desirable.

All in all, I wonder sometimes whether the value of such evaluative ratings for scientific purposes are worth their cost, cheap as they are. They are, of course, eminently practical and can guarantee "results" when nothing else can. The discussion in Chapter 13 would be my grounds for supporting such a procedure, that is, society's need to make decisions compels the comparison of incomparables.

The assumptions I have made in arriving at these interpretations of student ratings of faculty are, I am sure, as unpalatable to the reader as to me. I can only add that the use of rating methods avoids these assumptions only by blindly accepting an unspecified set of alternative assumptions which I am also sure are equally unpalatable. For example, averaging ratings of different individuals assumes interpersonally comparable utility, an assumption of questionable validity.

Of course, I feel that this discussion has to do with much more than student ratings of faculty. This has merely been an interesting context in which to discuss some basic issues relevant to the use of what I have here called "evaluative" rating scales. It should be pointed out that this critique is in the context of rating scales for which it is reasonable to assume that students may differ in their ideals on an underlying latent attribute. This would be the case when ratings are "evaluative" in contrast to ratings that are "substantive," such as, "How often does he call students by name?" or "Does he correct wrong answers?" As Robert Abelson has pointed out (personal communication) my critique here is of the analysis of evaluative rating scales treated as if they were Likert-type items.

3. SUMMARY

The basic datum of QIIb is a matching relation between elements of two distinct sets. Some rather common ideas about perception and cognitive structure are interpreted in these terms. The perceptual process is interpreted as a mapping between a stimulus input and an ideal point for a perceptual category. The perceptual constancies, latency of perception, and the effect of set are interpreted in the model.

Cognitive structure is interpreted in terms of relations among the perceptual categories or their ideal points. It is argued that these relations are the result of a variety of influences in the life history of an organism. Because of the variable homogeneity of these creative influences we might expect a variety of mathematical relations to be necessary to capture and describe the resulting cognitive structures adequately. This is an argument against any universal practice of mapping a cognitive structure into a real line.

The first section is closed by interpreting perceptual behavior as inherently preferential choice behavior which manifests itself as 'pick $1/n$' and so becomes classified as QIIb single stimulus data.

The second section is a discussion of the use of "evaluative" rating scales in which the instance of student ratings of faculty is looked at from the point of view of this theory of data. A student rating of an instructor is interpreted in terms of a distance relation between an ideal point for the student and a stimulus point for the instructor on a latent attribute. The student's I scale for the instructors is "fitted" to the prescribed rating scale numbers.

It is argued that (1) averaging the students' ratings for an instructor on an attribute will yield higher ratings the closer the instructor point is to the median student; (2) averaging the instructors' ratings over attributes will weight the attributes directly with the variability of the instructor points; (3) the average rating of the faculty on an attribute may not necessarily imply the relative merit of the faculty with respect to these attributes, for example, a low average rating on an attribute may reflect variability of the students' ideal points.

This critique of such evaluative ratings does not apply in all its aspects to all uses of rating scales. In particular this critique applies to the use of ratings in which the variable being rated is a nonmonotone function of a latent attribute. The process of averaging ratings, although not condoned for Likert-type items, is subject to serious misinterpretation when Thurstone-type items are used and individuals may differ in their ideal points.

The assumptions leading to these conclusions are strong and unverified, but alternative assumptions which lead to the conventional interpretations given to average ratings, even on Likert-type items, include interpersonal comparability of utility and perhaps other assumptions equally strong.

It seems to me that the use of ratings indicates that feasibility and convenience outweigh the absence of a theoretical foundation.

REFERENCES

Bartlett, F. C., 1932, *Remembering: a study in experimental and social psychology*, The Macmillan Co., New York.
Boring, E. G., 1953, The role of theory in experimental psychology, *Amer. J. Psychol.*, **66**, 169–84.
Bruner, J. S., J. J. Goodnow, and G. A. Austin, 1956, *A study of thinking*, John Wiley and Sons, New York.
Carmichael, L., H. P. Hogan, and A. A. Walter, 1932, An experimental study of the effect of language on the reproduction of visually perceived form, *J. exp. Psychol.*, **15**, 73–86.
Coombs, C. H., 1948, Some hypotheses for the analysis of qualitative variables, *Psychol. Rev.*, **55**, 167–74.
Coombs, C. H., H. Raiffa, and R. M. Thrall, 1954, Some views on mathematical models and measurement theory, *Psychol. Rev.*, **61**, 132–44.
Easterbrook, J. A., 1959, The effect of emotion on cue utilization and the organization of behavior, *Psychol. Rev.*, **66**, 183–201.
Hayek, F. A., 1952, *The sensory order*, University of Chicago Press, Chicago.
Kelley, H., 1950, The warm-cold variable in first impressions of persons, *J. Pers.*, **18**, 431–39.
Kershner, R. B., and L. R. Wilcox, 1950, *The anatomy of mathematics*, Ronald Press Co., New York.
Loevinger, Jane, 1957, Objective tests as instruments of psychological theory, *Psychol. Rep. Monogr. Suppl. No. 9.*

Miller, G. A., E. Galanter, and K. Pribram, 1960, *Plans and the structure of behavior*, Holt, Rinehart and Winston, New York.

Runkel, P. J., 1958, Some consistency effects, *Educ. psychol. Measmt.*, **18**, 527–41.

Runkel, P. J., and D. E. Damrin, 1961, Effects of training and anxiety upon teachers' preferences for information about students, *J. educ. Psychol.*, **52**, 254–61.

Vernon, M. D., 1955, The functions of schemata in perceiving, *Psychol. Rev.*, **62**, 180–92.

PART 4

STIMULI COMPARISON DATA

The previous chapter brought to a close the discussion of joint spaces. Both QI and QII, discussed in Parts 2 and 3 respectively, are concerned with relations between two sets of points. Usually the two sets represent individuals and stimuli, but they may represent stimuli and response categories. The data of those quadrants have been described in terms of a "distance," that is, a vector displacement, between a point in one set and a point in the other set. In QI the data consist of relations on pairs of such distances, and in QII the data consist of the information that an algebraic magnitude is, in some sense, greater or less than zero (QIIa), or an absolute magnitude is greater or less than some critical finite value (QIIb).

With Part 4 we begin the study of stimulus spaces in contrast to the joint spaces of QI and QII. In Parts 4 and 5 we deal with the cases in which there is only one set of objects, called stimuli, which are mapped into points and so only one set of points in the space. Observed behavior will be interpreted as relations among these points. The variety of these relations, few as they are, is enough to characterize a considerable variety of models available for the analysis of such kinds of data. In Part 4 we discuss QIII, stimuli comparison data, in which the relation is on a pair of points.

CHAPTER 17

QIIIa Data and Models

1. THE DATA OF QIIIa

The kind of data with which we are now going to deal, QIIIa data, is the only kind that rivals single stimulus data (QII) in popularity. QIIIa data also appears early in the history of psychology, going back at least as far as Weber's research into the constancy of the so-called Weber ratio (Boring, 1950, p. 280). The most typical example of behavior which is mapped into a datum of the QIIIa type is the judgment of an individual as to which of two stimuli has more of some specified attribute.

Formally, the data consist of order relations on pairs of points all representing elements of the same set. Each stimulus corresponds to a point, and the individual's judgments are interpreted as creating order relations on pairs of points. In formal terms,

$$p_{hi,jk} = q_{hij} - q_{hik} \tag{17.1}$$

and $$p_{hi,jk} \geq 0 \Leftrightarrow j \rangle k$$

where the expression on the right, $j \rangle k$, signifies the judgment that "j has more of . . . than k" or it signifies the observation that "j dominates k."

If the objective of the experimenter is to scale stimuli on some explicit attribute, the data and methods of QIIIa are eminently suitable.

Invariably, in obtaining judgments, the attribute with respect to which the individual is to make his judgment is explicitly specified, and it is always assumed that the attribute can be represented by a unidimensional scale. This is the case whether we are comparing the apparent brightness of lights, the quality of handwriting specimens, or the aesthetic merit of paintings. No matter how many dimensions there may be in the psychological space of the stimuli, the attribute is assumed to be a line on which the stimuli may be mapped or projected and the goal is to determine these projections.

There is another source of QIIIa data which can lead to some confusion with the preceding and must be clearly distinguished. This occurs when pairs of distances are compared as in cartwheel methods. The judgment, for example, that one pair of stimuli are more alike than another pair may be interpreted as an order relation on the corresponding pair of interpoint distances. Here a distance is itself taken as a point, and in order to scale the distances the data are mapped into QIIIa. Having scaled the distances in QIIIa, these measures may be transferred to QIVa and analyzed by methods there which may yield a multidimensional stimulus space (see Chapter 21).

The first models developed in QIIIa were for the more common type of QIIIa data involving order relations on pairs of stimulus points and leading to the scaling of stimuli on an a priori attribute. These models differ among themselves in the level of measurement they seek to achieve, and relevant to this is their dependence on particular methods of collecting the data.

In the next section we discuss methods of collecting data in QIIIa before taking up the particular models available for analysis of such data.

2. METHODS OF COLLECTING DATA

All methods of the searchingness structure except 'pick $1/n$' are available for collecting QIIIa data. In principle, for n stimuli, subsets of p at a time may be presented, and for each subset the subject may be asked to 'pick k' or 'order k' with respect to magnitude on some attribute. The instructions in this case, of course, would be to pick or order the k among the p stimuli in that presentation that had the most or least of some attribute X.

Whenever the methods of the searchingness structure are appropriate, then the balanced incomplete block designs are appropriate also. I might remark, in passing, that there is nothing sacred about incomplete block designs for collecting data being balanced—and an unbalanced or partially balanced incomplete block design might be considered. An unbalanced design could consist of any subset of presentations the experimenter wanted to use. The fact that various stimuli and combinations of stimuli would be presented a different number of times (unbalanced) might even become a virtue if more information is needed on some pairs than others, as indeed is usually the case. The risk is in the possible loss of experimental independence in the replications; if some combinations are presented more frequently, they may come to be recognized, and memory of previous responses may contaminate the independence of new responses, or just out-and-out response bias may be introduced.

The cartwheel methods, a particular set of unbalanced designs, are also applicable for collecting QIIIa data, but only for the particular instance in which the *stimuli being scaled are distances.* Our n "stimuli," then, are used to generate our $n' \left[= \binom{n}{2} \right]$ "stimuli," the absolute distances between pairs of points. I shall use the terms distance stimuli or n' stimuli as synonymous, and the term stimuli by itself always refers to the n stimuli.

In summary, then, the complete methods of the searchingness structure and incomplete block designs are available for collecting QIIIa data on the n stimuli and on the n' stimuli. In addition, the cartwheel methods are also available for the n' stimuli.

3. MODELS FOR ORDINAL AND ORDERED METRIC STIMULUS SCALES

Some General Issues

Generally speaking, there has been less interest in constructing stimulus scales at the level of ordinal and ordered metric scales of measurement than at higher levels of measurement, the reason being that much of the research involving the use of QIIIa data is concerned with the relation between the subjective magnitudes on the stimulus scale and the physical attributes of the stimuli (for example, Stevens, 1957). The lack of interest in these weaker scales is a consequence of the fact that there frequently is a universally accepted ordering monotonic with the relevant physical dimension, as, for example, in the case of the subjective brightness of lights or the felt-heaviness of weights.

There is an increasing interest in such scales, however, for two reasons. One reason is that an experimenter may be interested, not in constructing a common stimulus scale for a population of individuals, but rather in partitioning a population into subgroups, each of which has a common but distinctive stimulus scale. Then the intent is to find the distinguishing characteristics of the subpopulations which are associated with the corresponding distinctions between stimulus scales.

As an illustration of this, I was curious to see how academic people viewed the relative magnitudes of the steps between academic ranks. Everyone knows, of course, the rank order from Teaching Fellow through Instructor to Full Professor, so there is no problem of an ordinal scale on the n stimuli. However, there is nothing in our culture which leads us to common agreement on the relative magnitudes of the intervals between ranks, the "felt-spacings." So it is interesting to test whether the perception of differences between ranks is a function of the rank held.

I ran a small study as a laboratory exercise in a course at Michigan. We used a cartwheel method (case 1: $p = 3$, rims only), and constructed an ordinal scale of distances between ranks for each subject separately using the decomposition model of Chapter 2 (see also Coombs, 1954). The evidence seems to indicate that people at the lower ranks view the lower intervals as the largest psychological steps; whereas people at the higher ranks view the step between Assistant and Associate Professor as the largest psychological step.*

Thus, by constructing an ordered metric stimulus scale for each subject, we were able to partition them into groups which had similar stimulus scales and to examine these groups for relatedness on other variables.

A second reason why an experimenter may be interested in such weaker stimulus scales is that methods now exist in QIa and QIVa for the analysis of ordinal scales of interpoint distances to yield the structure of preference and the structure of appearance, respectively, in multidimensional space. The last example, as a matter of fact, is a particular example of the structure of appearance in a one-dimensional case, and the result was ordered metric scales of the stimuli. In the general case, we seek ordinal scales of interpoint distances which may be analyzed in QIa or QIVa to yield multidimensional spaces.

For example, in the study of preferential choice data we first seek to construct an individual's I scale of preference. Such a scale is nothing more than an ordinal scale of interpoint distances, the relative distances of the stimulus points from an ideal point. These distances, for any one individual, are members of the same set, and so his pair comparisons may be interpreted as QIIIa data to be analyzed to obtain an ordinal scale of the distances of the stimulus points from the ideal point. This gives the I scales, and with these we can study the structure of preference by QIa methods. If one dimension satisfies the data, the methods will yield an ordinal or ordered metric J scale; otherwise the structure of preference is multidimensional.

An experimenter interested in the structure of appearance rather than the structure of preference may first seek an ordinal scale of the distances between the stimulus points. These results may then be transferred to QIVa as similarities data and analyzed to obtain an ordered metric stimulus scale if one dimension satisfies the data, or a multidimensional space.

---

* These results are possibly related to those of Becker and Siegel (1962) in their study of the assertion ". . . the level of aspiration is associated with the goal that bounds the top of the largest distance . . ." (p. 115).

These examples give us some orientation to the kinds of observations we may wish to analyze in QIIIa. We note that the observations may be on stimulus points or on interpoint distances. We should also note that interpoint distances may be QIa data, distances from an ideal, or QIVa data, distances between stimuli. In every instance, when the observations are mapped into QIIIa, we are concerned with arriving at an ordinal scale, either of stimulus points or of interpoint distances. An ordinal scale of the latter, however, may lead to an ordered metric scale of the stimulus points if one dimension suffices to satisfy the data.

We see, then, that in QIIIa we may be concerned with constructing ordinal scales from the observations—either an ordinal scale of stimulus points or an ordinal scale of interpoint distances.

There are basically two models for accomplishing this purpose of constructing ordinal scales. One of these is the use of weak stochastic transitivity, associated with a decomposition model such as that discussed in Chapter 2, and the other is by use of expected matrices. I shall first discuss some of the advantages and disadvantages of these two methods and then, in the two subsections which follow, discuss the details of utilizing triangular analysis (Chapter 11) to obtain an ordinal or partially ordered scale by weak stochastic transitivity. The two subsections are distinguished in terms of whether the data have reference to the stimulus points in themselves or to interpoint distances. In the latter case, with certain methods of collecting the data (cartwheel cases 1, 2, and 3), we shall see that we may obtain only a partially ordered metric.

The simplest case of constructing an ordinal scale occurs in the reduction of a single set (unreplicated) of pair comparisons. In this case all pairs of stimuli (or interpoint distances) are presented and the individual 'picks 1/2.' If a transitive ordering exists, a tally of the number of times each stimulus has been chosen yields the set of n integers from 0 to $n - 1$. That is, the stimulus first in order is chosen in all $n - 1$ pairs in which it occurs. The stimulus next in order is chosen in all the pairs in which it occurs with the exception of that in which it is paired with the first stimulus, so there are $n - 2$ pairs in which it is chosen; and so on.

This is the method used to reduce a set of pair comparison preferences to a rank order I scale, for example. If intransitivities occur, then all the integers from 0 to $n - 1$ do not occur, some are omitted, and others are repeated. This implies that intransitivities exist.

We should note here that the familar axiom concerning independence from other alternatives may be put in the weaker form "not differentially dependent on other alternatives." Consider, for example, the preferences of an individual over a set of stimuli including apple pie, a peanut butter sandwich, and ice cream. The discriminal process for apple pie for an individual may be correlated with that of the alternative stimuli with which it is paired, in the sense of the correlational term in Thurstone's model for comparative judgment. So there may be dependence, but the important thing is that there not be *differential* dependence. Suppose that when apple pie is paired with a peanut butter sandwich the individual's preference reflects a "between-meals snack" preference and when paired with ice cream it reflects a "dessert" preference. That is, pie is preferred over the sandwich and the sandwich over ice cream as a between-meals snack, but ice cream is preferred over pie as a dessert after a full meal. There might well be a differential dependence on other alternatives, then, if the pairing of the stimuli influences the relevant dimensions. Usually the instructions to the subject are designed to avoid these changes in the relevant dimensions.

This simple method of reducing a single set of pair comparisons to a rank order may be regarded as a special case of each of the two otherwise distinct models: the weak stochastic transitivity model and the method of expected matrices. These are both generalizations but in different respects. The set of integers, for example, constitutes the single row of the expected matrix for 'pick 1/2' or, alternatively, the pairwise choices may be thought of as having probability 1 and the ordering is that obtained by weak stochastic transitivity.

The method of expected matrices is merely a generalization to methods in which p stimuli are presented at a time and the individual picks or orders k of them. We then permute the columns of the observed data matrix to obtain a "best" match with the expected matrix, and the ordering of the columns then corresponds to the order of the stimuli.

The decomposition model is also a generalization to methods in which p stimuli are presented at a time and the individual picks or orders k of them, but it yields pairwise probabilities which may be other than 0 or 1, and then requires weak stochastic transitivity to obtain an ordering. For example, in the method of triads, we present all sets of three and the individual ranks them, that is, 'order 2/3.' Then to apply the decomposition model presented in Chapter 2, we take all sets of three in which a particular pair occurs and determine the proportion of times one member of the pair was ranked higher than the other. From the pairwise probabilities, obtained in this manner or any other, an ordering can be constructed of all n stimuli if the condition of weak stochastic transitivity is satisfied.

These two methods do not necessarily yield the same result, because they use the data differently. The column in the expected matrix for any one stimulus has tallies from *all* the presentations in which that column-stimulus occurs. The decomposition model fragments the data differently. It determines the relative order of any pair of stimuli from only those presentations in which that pair occurs. A disadvantage of the method of expected matrices is the lack of a clear criterion and simple algorithm for arriving at a "best" match between the observed data matrix and the expected data matrix.

We see, then, that we have at least these two methods for arriving at ordinal scales in QIIIa and that these two methods are not alike; and so we become interested in how they differ in order that we may more intelligently choose between them. Both methods assume experimental independence between presentations, which we have learned to live with, but, in addition, each also requires some form of the axiom of independence from other alternatives. In the method of expected matrices each stimulus must not be *differentially* dependent on other stimuli or on clusters of stimuli. In the decomposition model it is the pairwise probabilities which must not be *differentially* dependent on other alternatives.

When the stimuli are "felt-spacings" I think the decomposition model may satisfy its form of the axiom whereas the method of expected matrices cannot. This conclusion arises from a consideration of the laterality effect found experimentally in preferential choice data. Preferential choices may be interpreted as judgments about "felt-spacings," that is, distances of stimulus points from an ideal point. In such a case the method of expected matrices cannot satisfy its form of the axiom of independence from other alternatives because the laterality effect is a differential effect for unilateral and bilateral pairs. Although the pairwise probabilities obtained by the decomposition model are also subject to the laterality effect, it is strong and not moderate stochastic transitivity that is violated as a result, and hence moderate (therefore weak) stochastic transitivity is a viable criterion for constructing an ordinal I scale. This is why the two models applied to identically the same data do not necessarily yield the same ordinal scale.

Now if the data are not from preferential choices of individuals but judgments of "felt-spacings" between stimuli, as in cartwheels, the laterality effect should still arise, in theory, because some pairs of distances will have a common terminus (conjoint distances) and some will not (disjoint distances). It is the pairs of conjoint distances which introduce the laterality effect.

In conclusion, then, I think both the method of expected matrices and the decomposition model need intensive study, and the consideration of additional alternatives is desirable. In the meantime, I would suggest that either model may be used to construct an ordinal scale of stimuli except when the stimuli are "felt-spacings," that is, either preferential choice data or similarities data, in which case the method of expected matrices is distinctly *not* recommended.

Aside from these considerations, the method of expected matrices is not useful when the data have been collected by a cartwheel method. The reason for this is that the columns in the expected matrices for such data are more nearly similar, and perturbations in observed data will easily lead to confusion and error in the ordering of columns.

In the following two subsections we discuss methods for constructing ordinal scales by weak stochastic transitivity for complete data matrices and for incomplete data matrices. The latter are particularly an issue when the stimuli are "felt-spacings," as, for example, when certain of the cart-wheel methods (cases 1, 2, and 3) are used to collect the data. Such data, when certain conditions are satisfied, yield ordered metric stimulus scales.

Ordinal Scales for Complete Data Matrices

It is convenient to have some method by means of which pair compari-sons may be tested for transitivity and, if not satisfied, by which intransi-tivities may be readily pinpointed. This may be done very simply by a method that is readily adapted to some special problems in constructing scales of interpoint distances.

If the matrix is probabilistic rather than a $(1, 0)$ data matrix, the method provides a means of testing for weak stochastic transitivity by converting the probabilities to a $(1, 0)$ data matrix, that is,

$$a_{jk} = \begin{cases} 1 & \text{if} \quad p_{jk} > .5 \\ 0 & \text{if} \quad p_{jk} < .5 \end{cases}$$

where p_{jk} is the probability of choosing j over k and is not permitted to equal .5 if equation 17.2 is to be applicable. We enter a dash, "—", in cells with no data, as in diagonal cells.

This matrix may then be processed by triangular analysis. Guttman scalogram analysis is obviously intimately related to this; it differs only in that the row and column elements are distinct as if we had struck out a subset of the rows and the complementary subset of columns of a QIIIa matrix and constructed a QIIa matrix. In a QIIa matrix rows and columns may be independently permuted. In a QIIIa matrix they may not.

If a perfect triangular pattern is not obtained, there are intransitivities among the pairwise orderings. The total number of intransitivities, for complete data omitting diagonals, may be computed by means of a for-mula given by Kendall (1955, p. 148). He calls an intransitivity a circular triad, and the number of them, d, is given by the expression:

$$d = \tfrac{1}{12}n(n - 1)(2n - 1) - \tfrac{1}{2}\sum_j a_j{}^2 \qquad (17.2)$$

where a_j is the sum for row j.

As an example consider the matrix in Table 17.1. A cell entry $a_{jk} = 1$ implies that j dominates k and $a_{jk} = 0$ implies that k dominates j.

From equation 17.2 we have $d = 5$, that is, there are five intransitive triples. From the triangular pattern in Table 17.1 we see that these all involve the pair AG with each of the other five stimuli in turn. This is

Table 17.1   A Hypothetical Data Matrix with Intransitivities

	A	B	C	D	E	F	G	a_j	a_j^2
A	—	1	1	1	1	1	0	5	25
B	0	—	1	1	1	1	1	5	25
C	0	0	—	1	1	1	1	4	16
D	0	0	0	—	1	1	1	3	9
E	0	0	0	0	—	1	1	2	4
F	0	0	0	0	0	—	1	1	1
G	1	0	0	0	0	0	—	1	1
									81

evident if we recognize that the rank order of the columns is the rank order of the stimuli and any entry of 1 below the diagonal violates that rank order and creates an intransitive triple with every stimulus between them.

If we permute the columns and the corresponding rows of this matrix, we will, of course, obtain the same set of integers for the a_j and the number

Table 17.2   A Permutation of Table 17.1

	D	C	F	E	B	A	G	a_j
D	—	0	1	1	0	0	1	3
C	1	—	1	1	0	0	1	4
F	0	0	—	0	0	0	1	1
E	0	0	1	—	0	0	1	2
B	1	1	1	1	—	0	1	5
A	1	1	1	1	1	—	0	5
G	0	0	0	0	0	1	—	1

of intransitivities will be unchanged. Such a permutation of this matrix, however, will not in general pinpoint the intransitivities. For example, the same matrix is presented in Table 17.2 but permuted.

It seems best to permute the matrix so the row sums successively decrease, breaking ties to get the best triangular pattern, as in Table 17.1.

In passing we may also note that the maximum number of intransitivities, as pointed out by Kendall (1955, p. 156), is as follows:

$$\text{for } n \text{ odd}: \quad d_{\max} = \frac{n(n^2 - 1)}{24}$$

$$\tag{17.3}$$

$$\text{for } n \text{ even}: \quad d_{\max} = \frac{n(n^2 - 4)}{24}$$

Ordinal Scales for Incomplete Data Matrices

The case when the stimuli to be ranked are interpoint distances often contains the problem that not all pairs of distances are compared. A particular example is provided by data gathered by methods such as cartwheels, in which only conjoint distances are compared, that is, only distances containing a terminal point in common are compared. As a consequence the triangular pattern has unfilled cells.

Table 17.3   Stimulus *I* Scales

$$A\ B\ C\ D$$
$$B\ A\ D\ C$$
$$C\ A\ D\ B$$
$$D\ B\ A\ C$$

Suppose, for example, we have the stimulus *I* scales, shown in Table 17.3, obtained from cartwheel data or from a conditional proximity matrix (see Chapter 19, Section 3).

It is obvious that these *I* scales cannot unfold in one dimension because they end in more than two different stimuli. Consequently we would like to construct a partial order of the distances in order to analyze the distance relations in QIVa to construct a multidimensional stimulus space.

**Table 17.4   Triangular Analysis of Stimulus *I* Scales
Contained in Table 17.3**

	$\overline{BC}$	$\overline{CD}$	$\overline{AD}$	$\overline{BD}$	$\overline{AC}$	$\overline{AB}$
$\overline{BC}$	—	1	—	1	1	1
$\overline{CD}$		—	1	1	1	—
$\overline{AD}$			—	1	1	1
$\overline{BD}$				—	—	1
$\overline{AC}$					—	1
$\overline{AB}$						—

We may construct the partial order of distances by use of triangular analysis. Here we have an order relation between each pair of conjoint distances. Entering these relations in a matrix of distances and permuting rows and corresponding columns, we arrive at the triangular pattern illustrated in Table 17.4.

We observe from Table 17.4 that the triangular pattern is satisfied and that there are no intransitivities. We should note, however, that the triangular pattern is also satisfied if the order of $\overline{BD}$ and $\overline{AC}$ is reversed.

Such a pattern signifies that while the order relations on distances are all transitive, certain incomparabilities exist and in this case the resulting partial order is

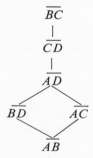

Note that *one distance covers another* (that is, is immediately above it in the partial order) *if and only if they have a common terminus.*

This is a simple example with no complications. Complications may arise, however, with such data, in that the distance relations may not satisfy transitivity. Suppose, for example, we had collected data on four stimuli by case 2 cartwheels to get the pairwise comparisons of conjoint distances. Suppose further that the data are as follows:

(1) with A as hub an I scale $A\ D\ C\ B$ implies: $\overline{AB} > \overline{AC} > \overline{AD}$

(2) with B as hub an I scale $B\ D\ C\ A$ implies: $\overline{AB} > \overline{BC} > \overline{BD}$

(3) with C as hub an I scale $C\ B\ D\ A$ implies: $\overline{AC} > \overline{CD} > \overline{BC}$

(4) with D as hub an I scale $D\ C\ B\ A$ implies: $\overline{AD} > \overline{BD} > \overline{CD}$

We wish to test whether these order relations between distances are transitive. If they are, we want to merge them in a common partial order. If they are not, we would like to detect the intransitivities. Triangular analysis assists us in accomplishing this.

Table 17.5 contains the triangular analysis of these data. A dash in a cell indicates that data were not collected on that pair of distances. We note that certain offdiagonal cells have dashes—those involving pairs of disjoint distances, as in Table 17.4 also.

We observe that the best triangular pattern we can obtain has an error in it. To apply equation 17.2 to this matrix we must count dashes above the diagonal as 1's and below the diagonal as 0's. We find then, that $d = 1$.

Table 17.5   Triangular Analysis of Cartwheel Data

	$\overline{AB}$	$\overline{AC}$	$\overline{AD}$	$\overline{BC}$	$\overline{BD}$	$\overline{CD}$	a_j	a_j^2
$\overline{AB}$	—	1	1	1	1	—	5	25
$\overline{AC}$	0	—	1	1	—	1	4	16
$\overline{AD}$	0	0	—	—	1	1	3	9
$\overline{BC}$	0	0	—	—	1	0	1	1
$\overline{BD}$	0	—	0	0	—	1	1	1
$\overline{CD}$	—	0	0	1	0	—	1	1
								53

The error in the pattern is in the cell $(\overline{BC}, \overline{CD})$. The partial order of the columns and the entry of 1 below the diagonal pinpoint the intransitivity.

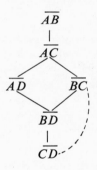

To detect this intransitivity in the original data we would note that:

(1) with B as hub $\overline{BC} > \overline{BD}$
(2) with C as hub $\overline{CD} > \overline{BC}$
(3) but with D as hub $\overline{BD} > \overline{CD}$

Because of this single intransitivity the last three rows and the last three columns of Table 17.5 may be cyclically permuted to yield three different matrices, each of which would reveal exactly one error and would involve the same triple of distances.

One further complication or confusion may arise involving the application of Kendall's equation for the number of intransitivities when we are working with a partial order rather than a chain ordering. Suppose, for example, we have collected data by case 1 cartwheels and tabulated it as in Table 17.6.

Table 17.6   Intransitivities in a Triangular Pattern for a Partial Order

	$\overline{BC}$	$\overline{BE}$	$\overline{CD}$	$\overline{AD}$	$\overline{AB}$	$\overline{AC}$	$\overline{BD}$	$\overline{DE}$	$\overline{CE}$	$\overline{AE}$	a_j	a_j^2
$\overline{BC}$	—	1	1	—	1	1	1	—	1	—	9	81
$\overline{BE}$	0	—	—	—	1	—	1	1	0	1	7	49
$\overline{CD}$	0	—	—	1	—	1	0	1	1	—	6	36
$\overline{AD}$	—	—	0	—	1	1	1	1	—	1	6	36
$\overline{AB}$	0	0	—	0	—	1	1	—	—	1	5	25
$\overline{AC}$	0	—	0	0	0	—	—	—	1	1	4	16
$\overline{BD}$	0	0	1	0	0	—	—	1	—	—	4	16
$\overline{DE}$	—	0	0	0	—	—	0	—	1	1	2	4
$\overline{CE}$	0	1	0	—	—	0	—	0	—	1	2	4
$\overline{AE}$	—	0	—	0	0	0	—	0	0	—	0	0
												267

The number of intransitive triples according to equation 17.2 is 9. If, however, we actually construct the partial order for Table 17.6, we have the following:

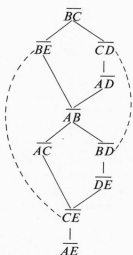

The actual number of intransitive triples of distances embedded in the partial order is six:

(1) between $\overline{CD}$ and $\overline{BD}$ are two, $\overline{AD}$ and $\overline{AB}$, each of which forms an intransitive triple with $\overline{CD}$ and $\overline{BD}$.

(2) between $\overline{BE}$ and $\overline{CE}$ are $\overline{AB}$ and $\overline{AC}$, by one path, each of which forms an intransitive triple with $\overline{BE}$ and $\overline{CE}$.

(3) between $\overline{BE}$ and $\overline{CE}$ are $\overline{BD}$ and $\overline{DE}$, by a second path (and also $\overline{AB}$ but it has already been counted), each of which forms an intransitive triple with $\overline{BE}$ and $\overline{CE}$.

So when we have a partial order, as we may when the matrix is bordered by interpoint distances, the actual number of intransitivities may be less than that given by equation 17.2. The formula gives us the number of intransitivities if the order of rows and columns is taken to be a complete order.

If we did this for Table 17.6, for example, we would have the following for a complete order:

$$\overline{BC}$$
$$\overline{BE}$$
$$\overline{CD}$$
$$\overline{AD}$$
$$\overline{AB}$$
$$\overline{AC}$$
$$\overline{BD}$$
$$\overline{DE}$$
$$\overline{CE}$$
$$\overline{AE}$$

We see here the 9 intransitivities given by the formula: 6 between $\overline{BE}$ and $\overline{CE}$, 3 between $\overline{CD}$ and $\overline{BD}$; whereas the partial order reveals that there are actually only 6 intransitivities.

This is a good place to point out one other limitation of the formula when applied to data matrices with incomplete data, as here. The value given by equation 17.2 is not invariant over permutations of columns (and rows), as is the case with complete data. Hence, to determine the number of intransitivities the formula should only be applied to the "best" triangular pattern, that is, the pattern for which the number of intransitivities is a minimum.

What has been presented here of the method of triangular analysis of QIIIa data reveals that the development of this method has only begun.

Many problems remain, including the relation between the index of reproducibility and the number of intransitive triples. Already, however, the method has proved its usefulness in merging stimulus I scales to arrive at a partial order of distances, as we see in later chapters.

Having pinpointed the intransitivities the next step is to remove them, that is, "correct" the data, if a metric space is to be constructed. The changes made in the data should, in general, be minimal. An example of one criterion used when changes in the data are necessary is contained in Chapter 22, Section 1. Another manner of eliminating intransitivities is described by Vastenhouw (1962, Appendix C).

Having arrived at a perfect triangular pattern by eliminating intransitivities, if they exist, the corresponding partial order of interpoint distances follows immediately as was illustrated for Table 17.4. The next step is to construct a configuration or map for the stimuli which satisfies these metric relations. A general method for doing this is discussed in detail in Part 5 of the book because such data are similarities data. Similarities data may require a multidimensional configuration to describe the structure of appearance, but in certain cases a single dimension may be adequate, yielding an ordered metric stimulus scale (Coombs, 1954). Illustrative examples of both the one-dimensional case and the multidimensional case are presented in Chapter 21.

4. MODELS FOR INTERVAL AND RATIO STIMULUS SCALES

The kind of data with which we are concerned in QIII is stimulus comparison data. The nature of QIIIa data is the observation of an order relation on pairs of stimuli. How such order relations may be processed to arrive at ordinal scales of the stimuli has just been discussed. In order to construct stronger scales for the stimuli, such as interval and ratio scales, a metric needs somehow to be obtained.

There is good reason to believe* that order relations on distances, like those obtained in QI and QIV, impose rather surprising (to me) constraints on the uniqueness of a numerical representation. Having a partial order on the interpoint distances, that is, an ordered metric scale of the stimuli, we may use Frank Goode's method with the constant Δ assumption (see Chapter 5) to obtain an interval scale. A simple example may be provided using a data matrix published by De Soto and Bosley (1962).

In a paired-associates verbal learning task subjects learned to associate "freshman," "sophomore," "junior," and "senior" as labels to 16 men's names, 4 to each label. There were 28 subjects, 7 from each class. The subjects were run individually to a criterion of two successive errorless

* From work by Frank Goode and by Roger Shepard.

trials by the anticipation method, using a deck of cards with a man's name on one side and the correct label on the back.

The data consist of the errors made in the course of learning, summarized in Table 17.7. The table shows the mean number of errors of each kind made in the course of learning the correct label, averaged over subjects and items.

Table 17.7   Mean Number of Errors

Label Given by Subject

Correct Label	Freshman	Sophomore	Junior	Senior	Σ
A Freshman	—	3.48	2.74	1.72	7.94
B Sophomore	2.36	—	4.77	3.29	10.42
C Junior	2.23	3.54	—	3.29	9.06
D Senior	1.78	3.00	4.08	—	8.86
Σ	6.37	10.02	11.59	8.30	

This data matrix may be classified as a conditional proximity matrix (see Chapter 19) involving one set of points, one point for each of the four labels. The assumption may be made that the confusions in a *row* are monotonically related to the distances of the corresponding column points from that row point. Hence we may immediately write down the four stimulus I scales: $A B C D, B C D A, C B D A, D C B A$.

Table 17.8   Triangular Analysis of Stimulus I Scales for Table 17.7

	$\overline{AD}$	$\overline{AC}$	$\overline{AB}$	$\overline{BD}$	$\overline{CD}$	$\overline{BC}$
$\overline{AD}$	—	1	1	1	1	—
$\overline{AC}$		—	1	—	1	1
$\overline{AB}$			—	1	—	1
$\overline{BD}$				—	1	1
$\overline{CD}$					—	1
$\overline{BC}$						—

The triangular analysis of the interpoint distances is given in Table 17.8, and so the rank order of the distances corresponds to the rank order of the columns.

The analysis for the scale values is presented in Table 17.9. In this analysis, Δ_1 is the width of the smallest interval between two stimuli and, under the constant Δ assumption, successive differences in the rank order of distances, when unknown, are assumed to be constant and set equal to 1.

Hence $\overline{CD}$, next in order over $\overline{BC}$, is given the value $\Delta_1 + 1$. The next distance, $\overline{BD}$, equals $\overline{BC} + \overline{CD} = 2\Delta_1 + 1$. The next distance, $\overline{AB}$, is then given the value $2\Delta_1 + 2$. The remaining distances are additive combinations of the preceding.

From these values for the interpoint distances we may immediately obtain expressions for the scale values of the stimuli by setting $A = 0$.

Table 17.9   Computation of Scale Values

Rank Order of Distances	Distances under Constant Δ Assumption	General Expression	Scaled from 0 to 100
$\overline{AD}$	$4\Delta_1 + 3$		
$\overline{AC}$	$3\Delta_1 + 2$	$A = 0$	$A = 0$
$\overline{AB}$	$2\Delta_1 + 2$	$B = 2\Delta_1 + 2$	$B = \dfrac{2\Delta_1 + 2}{4\Delta_1 + 3}(100)$
$\overline{BD}$	$2\Delta_1 + 1$	$C = 3\Delta_1 + 2$	$C = \dfrac{3\Delta_1 + 2}{4\Delta_1 + 3}(100)$
$\overline{CD}$	$\Delta_1 + 1$	$D = 4\Delta_1 + 3$	$D = 100$
$\overline{BC}$	Δ_1		

The expressions for the scale values, on a scale from 0 to 100, are presented in Table 17.9.

The scale values of the stimuli are given in Table 17.10 for four different values of Δ_1 (0, 1, 10, ∞) to indicate the general effect of the magnitude of Δ_1. The smaller the value of Δ_1 that is chosen, the more dramatized or

Table 17.10   Scale Values of the Stimuli for Various Values of Δ_1

	$\Delta_1 = 0$	$\Delta_1 = 1$	$\Delta_1 = 10$	$\Delta_1 = \infty$
A	0	0	0	0
B	66.67	57.14	51.16	50
C	66.67	71.43	74.42	75
D	100	100	100	100

"figural" are the metric relations, that is, the second-order differences. The smallest interval, Δ_1, could, of course, be less than 1, which would dramatize the second-order differences even more. In the limit, as $\Delta_1 \to 0$, the scale values of B and C both approach 66.67, from opposite directions.

As Δ_1 is increased, *differences* in interpoint distances are diminished and any distortions due to the constant Δ assumption are diminished. In

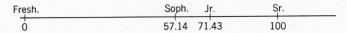

Fresh.   Soph.   Jr.   Sr.

0   57.14 71.43   100

Fig. 17.1 Scale of class labels with $\Delta_1 = 1$.

Fig. 17.1 the scale is portrayed with $\Delta_1 = 1$, which makes the second smallest interval twice the size of the smallest. It is evident from Table 17.10 that the second interval would have to be many times larger to make any substantial change in the scale values. Choosing $\Delta_1 = 1$ seems to yield a reasonably representative and stable scale and at the same time makes clearly visible the differences in metric relations.

Finally, it should be pointed out that this method is applicable to any ordered metric stimulus scale, whatever may have been the source of the data, whether verbal judgments, errors in a learning task, latencies, probabilities, and so on. Another example, based on similarity judgments, is presented in Section 3 of Chapter 21.

In QIIIa data, however, if the pairs of points correspond to stimuli and not to *distances* between stimuli, we have only order relations on stimuli and not an ordered metric scale. The standard practice has been, in such a case, to measure some characteristic of the response and transform these measures into a metric.

Thus, having observed the response of an individual to the effect that one stimulus is greater than another, is there some further characteristic of the response that might be used to obtain a metric? Psychologists answer "yes," and the characteristics that seem intuitively reasonable include amplitude, latency, and frequency (probability): How big is the response, how long did he take to respond, how consistently does he make the same response? Such measurement is derived measurement and not fundamental measurement in Campbell's sense (Campbell, 1920; see also Suppes and Zinnes, 1963) in that something else must first be measured in order to obtain measures of the stimuli.

Only probability has been used widely—Thurstone, Bradley and Terry, and Luce, among others,* have constructed models which transform probabilistic QIIIa data into a metric. Stevens has moved in the direction of increasing the verbal content of the original observation in his method of ratio estimation. In this latter method the subject directly judges the ratio of the subjective magnitude for two stimuli. Ratios greater or less than 1 imply an order relation, but the more refined observation, the actual value of the ratio, is used to construct a metric (ratio) scale. These models and procedures will be discussed in turn.

* For example, see Vastenhouw (1962, Appendices A and D).

Thurstone's Model for Comparative Judgment

Thurstone's model is well known as the law of comparative judgment*
and has been recently very fully discussed by Torgerson (1958, Chapter 9);
hence I shall do no more here than summarize the main aspects of the model.
Each stimulus is presumed to project a distribution of subjective magnitudes on the stimulus scale. When an individual compares two stimuli and
judges which is greater than the other, the model says he selects an element x_k at random out of the distribution of subjective magnitudes for
stimulus k, and another element, x_j, out of the corresponding distribution
for stimulus j. If $x_k - x_j \geq 0$, the individual says $k \rangle j$.

This corresponds to choosing an element at random out of the distribution of algebraic differences between subjective magnitudes. The proportion of times that an individual judges k to be greater than j is an
estimate of the area of this distribution of differences over the region in which
the differences are positive (see Fig. 17.2). We may write the equation

$$S_k - S_j = z_{kj}(\sigma_j{}^2 + \sigma_k{}^2 - 2r_{jk}\sigma_j\sigma_k)^{1/2} \qquad (17.3)$$

which is an observational equation known as the complete law of compara-
tive judgment, where S_j, σ_j and S_k, σ_k are the mean and standard deviation
of the distributions of subjective magnitude for stimuli j and k respectively,
and z_{kj} is the normal deviate corresponding to the observed proportion of
times k is judged greater than j. The second factor on the right of equation
17.3 is the standard deviation of the distribution of differences.

An equation may be written for every unordered pair of the n stimuli,
providing a system of simultaneous equations which, in the complete form
of the model for comparative judgment, is indeterminate because there
are always more unknowns than equations. A number of special cases may
be constructed, characterized by special conditions and simplifying assumptions, which lead to solvable systems of equations (see Torgerson,
1958).

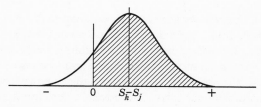

Fig. 17.2 The distribution of subjective differences.

* We will refer to it, however, as his model for comparative judgment.

The most common assumption is that the expression in parentheses in equation 17.3 is a constant for all pairs of stimuli, and hence may be set equal to 1 to provide a unit of measurement. When this assumption is made, the resulting expression, $S_k - S_j = z_{kj}$, is known as case V.

The B.T.L. Model

The other model for transforming probabilities into a metric scale was first developed by Bradley and Terry (1952; see also Terry, Bradley, and Davis, 1952). Luce (1959) independently developed it in axiomatic form and extended it to apply to more than pair comparisons and also more fully explored its ramifications and applications in psychology. I follow Luce's development, but I follow Suppes and Zinnes (1963) in referring to the model as the B.T.L. model.

The data matrix for analysis by Thurstone's model of comparative judgment consists of the pairwise probabilities of choosing each stimulus over each of the others, that is, 'pick 1/2' data. The B.T.L. model is more general in that it applies to data of the 'pick $1/p$' variety where p can be any integer greater than 1 for a given matrix. Luce developed the system from a fundamental postulate about choice behavior. Introducing Luce's notation, we have

T is a finite set of alternatives or stimuli.
$p(x, y) = $ probability that x is chosen over y.
For $S \subset T, p_T(S) = $ probability that the alternative chosen out of T is in S.

His choice axiom is the following:
   i. If $p(x, y) \neq 0, 1$ for all $x, y \in T$, then for $R \subset S \subset T$

$$p_T(R) = p_S(R) \, p_T(S)$$

   ii. If $p(x, y) = 0$ for some $x, y \in T$, then for every $S \subset T$

$$p_T(S) = p_{T-\{X\}} (S - \{x\})$$

That is, if y is invariably chosen over x, we may delete x from T when considering choices from T. The heart of the axiom is part i; it is cumbersome to illustrate, but let us try. The probability that a particular girl will be chosen to be Queen of the Ball at a university function is the probability that she will be chosen out of her class times the probability that the choice will be made from her class. Moreover, it does not matter whether we substitute for "class" her sorority, her age group, her hair color group, or any other group (including those with no "natural" definition) of which she is a member and whose members are students. Part ii of the axiom simply says that any boys in the "class" can be neglected. The example is subject to possible misinterpretation which I would like to caution against. For one thing, the girl, a single element, constitutes the entire membership of the subset R, whereas the axiom is not so confined. For example, we could substitute "blonde" for the particular girl.

It is also important to have in mind that Luce proposes the axiom to apply to *individual* choice behavior, and not necessarily to a group choice, so in the above example the probabilities should be those of some one individual, like the Dean of Men.

It would appear that the axiom is a mere tautology of conditional probability and is part of formal probability theory. Luce is asserting, however, that choice behavior conforms to probability theory. On the real world level the choice situation is different for class, sorority, and age group. The axiom demands independence from *any* partitioning of the university.

With this postulate (and the ordinary probability axioms*) the constant ratio rule, which is sometimes regarded as just another version of the axiom, may be derived. The constant ratio rule is

$$\frac{p(x, y)}{p(y, x)} = \frac{p_S(x)}{p_S(y)} \tag{17.4}$$

for any $S \subset T$ such that $x, y \subset S$.

The proof is short. From the choice axiom and probability axiom 3 we may write

$$p_S(x) = p_{x,y}(x)P_S(x \cup y)$$

and also

$$p_S(y) = p_{x,y}(y)p_S(x \cup y)$$

Dividing one equation by the other yields the constant ratio rule:

$$\frac{p_S(x)}{p_S(y)} = \frac{p_{x,y}(x)}{p_{x,y}(y)} = \frac{p(x, y)}{p(y, x)}$$

That is, the ratio of the probability of choosing x to the probability of choosing y is independent of the set S in which they are embedded. This is the idea of independence from other alternatives which is found in one version or another in so much of choice theory. Some research on the empirical validity of the constant ratio rule has appeared (Clarke, 1957, and perhaps also Bower, 1960) which tends to be confirmatory. It is this

---

* 1. For $S \subset T$, $0 \leq p_T(S) \leq 1$.
  2. $p_T(T) = 1$.
  3. If $R, S \subset T$ and $R \cap S = \varnothing$, then $p_T(R \cup S) = p_T(R) + p_T(S)$.

constant ratio rule which permits the model to be applied to data collected by the 'pick $1/p$' method for any fixed value of p.

Luce goes on to show that if we define a function v on T such that $v(x) = kp_T(x)$ where $k > 0$, then

$$p_S(x) = \frac{v(x)}{\sum\limits_{y \in S} v(y)} \tag{17.5}$$

This is the fundamental equation relating observed probabilities to the stimuli's scale values. The complete statement of the theorem and its proof follow:

Theorem: Given T, $p(x, y) \neq 0,1$ for all $x, y \in T$, and that the choice axiom holds for T and its subsets, then there exists a positive real-valued function v on T which is unique up to multiplication by a positive constant such that for every $S \subset T$

$$p_S(x) = \frac{v(x)}{\sum\limits_{y \in S} v(y)}$$

PROOF: Define $v(x) = kp_T(x)$ where $k > 0$.
From the choice axiom

$$p_S(x) = \frac{p_T(x)}{p_T(S)}$$

From probability axiom 3 we may write

$$p_T(S) = \sum\limits_{y \in S} p_T(y)$$

and substituting in the previous equation we may write

$$p_S(x) = \frac{kp_T(x)}{\sum\limits_{y \in S} kp_T(y)} = \frac{v(x)}{\sum\limits_{y \in S} v(y)}$$

so $k = \sum\limits_{y \in S} v(y)$; and this proves existence.

To show uniqueness, suppose v' is another such function. Then for any $x \in T$

$$v(x) = kp_T(x) = \frac{kv'(x)}{\sum\limits_{y \in T} v'(y)}$$

Let
$$k' = \frac{k}{\sum\limits_{y \in T} v'(y)}$$

Then
$$v(x) = k'v'(x).$$

We see that $v(x)$ is unique up to multiplication by a constant so the v scale is a measure on a ratio scale and is proportional to the probability of x being chosen from the set T.

With just two alternatives, equation 17.5 becomes

$$p(x, y) = \frac{v(x)}{v(x) + v(y)} \qquad (17.6)$$

Bradley and Terry begin their development with this scale definition (equation 17.6), which is logically equivalent, at least for pair comparisons, to Luce's axiom. Abelson (1958) has discussed the relation of these two approaches and pointed out that the Bradley and Terry approach is in the spirit of statistical theory and is not an attempt to construct a model of the judgment process. Luce's approach, in contrast, is a theory about the nature of the reality underlying the psychological process in choice behavior.

Luce's axiom, as has been pointed out by Zinnes (1958), cannot be tested directly in a pair comparison matrix because the axiom requires the presentation of three or more stimuli at a time. The axiom, however, imposes certain constraints on the pair comparisons, which may be shown as follows.

Utilizing the constant ratio rule and the identity

$$\frac{p_T(x)p_T(y)p_T(z)}{p_T(y)p_T(z)p_T(x)} = 1$$

yields

$$\frac{p(x, y)p(y, z)p(z, x)}{p(y, x)p(z, y)p(x, z)} = 1$$

which says that if the pairwise judgments are taken independently, the probability of the two opposite intransitivities is equal. Substituting $1 - p(x, z)$ for $p(z, x)$ and solving, we obtain

$$p(x, z) = \frac{p(x, y)p(y, z)}{p(x, y)p(y, z) + p(z, y)p(y, x)} \qquad (17.7)$$

which says that for every three stimuli x, y, and z in the matrix the probability of x being chosen over z must be predictable from the probability of x being chosen over y and y over z. If this constraint on the probabilities holds throughout the matrix, the matrix can be completely represented by a ratio scale as defined above.

One simple way of computing the scale values of the stimuli, in this case, is to select arbitrarily one stimulus, say s, as a standard and then to compare every other stimulus with this one. For example, if stimulus s is selected as standard, the scale value for j will be equal to the probability that j is preferred to s, divided by the probability that s is preferred to j, that is,

$$\frac{p(j, s)}{p(s, j)} = \frac{v(j)/[v(j) + v(s)]}{v(s)/[v(j) + v(s)]} = \frac{v(j)}{v(s)}$$

We may set $v(s) = 1$ to define the unit of measurement. Then the scale value of any stimulus j is the ratio of its probability of being chosen when paired with the standard over the complementary probability.

If another stimulus, t, had been selected as standard, the existence of this constraint on the probabilities in the matrix guarantees that the new scale would be related to the first by a multiplicative constant. In fact, the multiplicative constant would be the ratio of two probabilities: the probability of s being selected over t and that of t being selected over s,

$$\frac{p(s, t)}{p(t, s)} \quad \text{or} \quad \frac{p(t, s)}{p(s, t)}$$

This result suggests another way of stating Luce's results: If the probabilities in a pair comparison matrix satisfy certain constraints, each stimulus used as standard gives rise to the same ratio scale.

From the point of view of the experimenter there is one obvious difficulty with these conclusions. Any actual data matrix containing experimentally determined probabilities will almost certainly not satisfy the given constraint exactly. Bradley and Terry and later Ford (1957) have discussed maximum likelihood techniques, statistical tests, and so on. Ford's method is very general and has wide applicability. It provides a single-dimensional maximum likelihood fit, by means of an iterative procedure, to the data matrix of pair comparisons. It permits both perfect and imperfect discriminations and it allows certain pairs to be entirely absent from the matrix.

The condition imposed on the matrix by Ford's method is such that in every possible partition of the stimuli into two nonempty subsets some element in the second set has been chosen at least once over some element in the first set. Zinnes (1958) has described this condition in another way, in terms of a directed graph. Each stimulus is represented by a point, and the directed line from stimulus j to k implies that there exists at least one preference of j over k. If there is imperfect discrimination between j and k, then there will be two lines between the two points, one directed from j to k and the other from k to j. Now the condition imposed by the method is, in these terms, that there must be a cycle between every two points in the graph.

Comparison of Thurstone and B.T.L. Models

The comparison of the Thurstone case V and the B.T.L. model is not a simple matter of saying that the former yields an interval scale and the latter a ratio scale,* the reason being that the B.T.L. ratio scale is *not* more powerful than the Thurstone case V interval scale. To demonstrate the point, I shall discuss more specifically what is meant by the Thurstone case V and the B.T.L. model and we shall then see how they differ from each other.

The Thurstone case V equation may be obtained from equation 17.3 by assuming σ_j is a constant for all j and r_{jk} is a constant for all pairs (j, k); then it is convenient to set the standard deviation of the differences, the second factor on the right of equation 17.3, equal to 1 to define the unit of measurement.

Equation 17.3 then becomes

$$S_k - S_j = z_{kj} \tag{17.8}$$

which is known as case V.

If we make an antilog transformation of the stimuli's scale values, then

$$\text{antilog } S_j = e^{S_j} = S_j' \qquad \text{for all } j$$

Substituting $\log S_j'$ for S_j and $\log S_k'$ for S_k in 17.8 we have

$$\log S_k' - \log S_j' = z_{kj}$$

from which it is readily seen that

$$\frac{S_k'}{S_j'} = e^{z_{kj}}$$

and we have what appears to be a ratio scale.

The significant point is this. This ratio scale of S' values is no better, and no worse, insofar as fitting the original data matrix is concerned, than is the original interval scale of S values.

I would call both of these scales Thurstone scales because the essential character common to them is the *normal curve transformation of a probability into a distance* and there is no empirical distinction between them.

Now let us take a look at the B.T.L. model. In an analogous way we may make a logarithmic transformation of the scale values v_j, and we have an alternative representation of the same data matrix which is no better and no worse. We shall now see by means of this transformation

---

* My comparison of these models owes a great deal to discussions with Warren Torgerson and Joseph Zinnes.

that the B.T.L. model utilizes a *logistic transformation of a probability into a distance.*

The general logistic distribution is

$$p = \frac{1}{1 + e^{-(a+bx)}} \tag{17.9}$$

and the logit of p is defined to be

$$\text{logit } p = \log_e \frac{p}{1 - p} \tag{17.10}$$

Then substituting from 17.9 for p we have

$$\text{logit } p = \log_e \frac{1/(1 + e^{-(a+bx)})}{1 - [1/(1 + e^{-(a+bx)})]}$$

which reduces to

$$\text{logit } p = a + bx$$

The general logistic distribution, equation 17.9, expresses a relation between a variable p, a probability, and another variable, x. Luce's equation 17.5 relates the variable p to another variable v, which is a point on a scale. We now show how these are related by pointing out that Luce's transformation of probabilities is a special case of the general logistic transformation in which x in the logistic distribution is a distance in Luce's model.

In Luce's notation and from equation 17.6 we have

$$\text{logit } p(jk) = \log \frac{p(jk)}{1 - p(jk)}$$

$$= \log \frac{v(j)/[v(j) + v(k)]}{1 - \{v(j)/[v(j) + v(k)]\}}$$

$$= \log \frac{v(j)}{v(k)} = \log v(j) - \log v(k)$$

If we let

$$v'(j) = \log v(j) \qquad \text{for all } j$$

then

$$\text{logit } p(jk) = v'(j) - v'(k) \tag{17.11}$$

Equation 17.11 is a special case of the general logistic transformation in which $a = 0$, $b = 1$, and $x = v'(j) - v'(k)$ in equation 17.9. We see, then, that the B.T.L. model is a logistic transformation of a probability into a distance.

The relation of the cumulative normal to the logistic transformation is very close to linear over the range of probabilities customarily used, as Torgerson (1958, p. 202) points out.

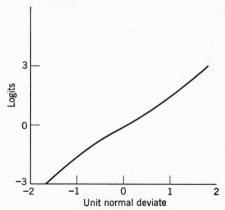

Fig. 17.3 Showing relation between logits and normal deviates. Taken from Torgerson (1958, p. 202).

Figure 17.3, taken from his figure, is presented here to show the relation between the two transformations. It is evident that it would be very difficult with empirical data to distinguish the curve pictured in Fig. 17.3 from a straight line, yet this is the essential distinction between the Thurstone case V and the B.T.L. model.

Stevens' Method of Ratio Estimation

A method completely different from any of these for arriving at a ratio stimulus scale is Stevens' method of ratio estimation (1958).* In this method a pair of stimuli is presented and the subject's behavior consists of reporting a number which is presumed to reflect the ratio of their corresponding subjective magnitudes. This differs from the method of magnitude estimation, discussed as QIIb data in Chapter 15, in which a single stimulus is presented at a time and the subject reports a number presumed to reflect its subjective magnitude. Ratio estimation might also be regarded as QIIb data if the *ratio* of the subjective magnitudes is regarded as an element of the set of objects of judgment and the number system as the set of response alternatives. As the analysis of the data clearly regards the *stimuli* themselves as the points, however, and not their *ratios* of subjective magnitude, I have classified the method as QIIIa data.

* An earlier version of the method of ratio estimation is known as the constant sum method. As originally proposed by Metfessel (1947), the subject is asked to divide, say, 100 points between each pair of stimuli in such a way as to reflect their ratio. Comrey (1950) has proposed a method for analyzing such data to arrive at a subjective scale. His method involves taking averages of ratios, and the method might be improved on if geometric means were used.

The ratios reported may be directly processed to obtain a ratio stimulus scale by assigning an arbitrary scale value to any one stimulus to define a unit of measurement and then applying the reported ratios to compute the scale values of the remaining stimuli. When the observations are replicated some measure of central tendency of the reported ratios or the computed scale values for each stimulus is necessary, such as a median or geometric mean.

Stevens has studied an impressive variety of continua (some two dozen or more) in every sense modality by his methods of magnitude estimation and ratio estimation. He has repeatedly found a power law relating subjective magnitudes to physical magnitudes for a large class of psychological continua which he calls prothetic. Prothetic continua are to be distinguished from metathetic continua:

The prototypes of the two kinds of continua are exemplified by loudness and pitch. Loudness is an aspect of sound that has about it what can best be described as degrees of magnitude or quantity. Pitch does not. Pitch varies from high to low; it has a kind of position, and in a sense it is a qualitative continuum. Loudness may be called a *prothetic* continuum, and pitch a *metathetic* one. The criteria that define these two classes of continua reside wholly in how they behave in psychological experiments, but the names themselves are suggested by the nature of the physiological processes that appear to underlie each of them.

Sensory discrimination may be mediated by two processes: the one additive, and the other substitutive. Additional excitation may be added to an excitation already present, or new excitation may be substituted for excitation that has been removed. An observer can tell, for example, when a light pressure becomes a strong pressure at a given point on the arm, and he can also tell when the stimulus is moved from that point to another location. Different sets of general laws govern these two types of sensory discrimination.

The metathetic, positional, qualitative continua seem to concern *what* and *where* as opposed to *how much*. They include such things as pitch, apparent position, apparent inclination, and apparent proportion. Perhaps they also include visual saturation and visual hue—at least to whatever extent hue may be made to behave as a continuum. All in all, the metathetic continua do not seem to comprise a neat and orderly class of perceptual variables, and as yet they have not been very thoroughly explored.

The prothetic continua, on the other hand, have lately yielded rich rewards for the systematic efforts made to scale their magnitudes. Some two dozen continua have been examined, always with the same outcome: the sensation magnitude ψ grows as a power function of the stimulus magnitude ϕ, i.e.,

$$\psi = k\phi^n \qquad [(17.12)]$$

In this equation, the constant k depends on the units of measurement and is not very interesting; but the value of the exponent n may vary from one sensory continuum to another. (Stevens, 1959, pp. 613–14; see also Stevens, 1957.)

He has also found that subjects may make cross-modality comparisons yielding an equal-sensation function that is also a power function. A cross-modality comparison involves no verbal behavior, that is, no numerical judgments, and yet he finds the slope of the equal sensation function on a log-log plot to be that given by the ratio of the exponents of the power laws for the separate modalities which are obtained by magnitude or ratio estimation.

This impressive array of empirical relations suggests to him the existence of a single, simple, pervasive psychological law, the power law. This has lead Stevens to attack the indirect methods of measurement utilizing intra-subject confusion, like the Thurstone and the B.T.L. models. It seems to me, however, that these different approaches are not necessarily incompatible when viewed in a different light. Stevens' approach does not pretend to be a model or theory about the psychological judgment process but rather is a straightforward means for generating numerical scales (Abelson, 1958). The other methods, in contrast, are theories about the nature of reality, and, in this instance, about the probabilistic nature of the judgment or response process.

The fact that certain methods yield a logarithmic relation between the subjective magnitude and the physical magnitude instead of a power function is an accident of the particular "modes of expression," as John Tukey calls them, which these methods have chosen to express subjective magnitude. The comparison of the Thurstone and the B.T.L. models involved changing their modes of expression in order to reveal more clearly the relation between them. These changes in mode of expression do not affect the empirical validity of the models.

To take an example not yet charged with such controversy, we might be interested in other aspects of the judgment process like amplitude or latency, and a model might seek to relate one of these to subjective magnitude. Such a model might choose one or another mode of expression for subjective magnitude as a matter of mathematical convenience, and then it is merely a mathematical problem to interrelate these several aspects of the judgment process, for example, confusion, amplitude, latency, and magnitude and ratio estimation.

Ever to be able to say that one particular mode of expression is the *right* one or *true* one for subjective magnitude is a problem for the speculative philosopher, not the scientist.

The development of models for processing response characteristics other than probabilities into a subjective metric is much to be desired in its own right. Many kinds of stimuli are so identifiable that no experimentally independent replication is possible, as, for example, attitude statements; so even if the concept of probability is applicable, its estimation empirically may not be possible. We might, of course, replicate over individuals, but the strong assumption that different individuals may be regarded as random replications of each other may be undesirable. If, then, it becomes possible to process the latency of a single choice into a metric equivalent to that obtained from other response measures, much has been gained.

5. SOME REMARKS ON CONTINGENT AND COMPOUND PAIR COMPARISONS: INDIVIDUAL UTILITY SCALES

As far as I know the terms *contingent* and *compound* were first used to refer to certain kinds of pair comparisons by Shuford, Jones, and Bock (1960). The term *contingent* is used to refer to alternatives in a pair comparison which may be lotteries or probability mixtures. For example, one of the alternatives offered an individual may be a lottery or gamble in which he will receive outcome A_1 with probability p and outcome A_2 with probability $q = 1 - p$, that is, $A_1 p A_2 = A$. If an individual were to choose A in preference to some other alternative, it is understood that some random device would determine, according to the probabilities specified, whether in actuality he received A_1 or A_2.

The term *compound* pair comparisons is used to refer to alternatives in a pair comparison which consist of two or more outcomes, all certain. For example, one of the alternatives an individual may be offered may consist of *both* outcomes A_1 and A_2.

These two kinds of pair comparisons have been studied in the past. Paul Horst (1932) proposed a method for obtaining an absolute zero point on a scale of affective value by means of compound pair comparisons. He combined pairs of outcomes one of which was desirable and one of which was undesirable, for example, "go to a good musical comedy" and "hear a beginner practice his violin lesson."

He assumed that the affective value of the compound alternative was the sum of the affective values of the two components. If over half the subjects accepted the compound option, the inference was that the sum of their affective values was greater than zero. He extended Thurstone's model for comparative judgment to apply to such behavior by regarding the judgment to accept or reject such an option as a pair comparison between the affective value of the option and the rational zero point. He then developed a method to solve for this affective zero point.

It is not always convenient or easy to construct compound options consisting of both positive and negative components, so Thurstone and Jones (1957) extended Horst's method to deal with compound options both of whose components were positive. They developed a method for locating a zero point on the scale of subjective value by scaling alternatives separately and as members of compound options. They assumed that the subjective scale value of *both* alternatives A and B is equal to the sum of their separate scale values.

Considerable experimental work on contingent pair comparisons has been done, much of it in studying decision making under risk. The studies of Davidson, Suppes, and Siegel (1957) and of Coombs and Komorita (1958) illustrate the use of contingent pair comparisons to measure utility of money on at least the level of an ordered metric scale. Siegel (1956) used contingent pair comparisons to scale the utility of prizes other than money on an ordered metric scale. Most recent of all is the work of Shuford et al. (1960) on the construction of a rational origin for a utility scale by the use of contingent pair comparisons.

Although the origin of these ideas appears to be in Ramsey (1931, pp. 180–82) they may be more immediately traced to the von Neumann and Morgenstern (1953) conception of utility. The basic idea may be illustrated as follows. In a contingent pair comparison an individual is faced with a choice between, say, options A and B where $A = A_1\,p\,A_2$ and $B = B_1\,p'\,B_2$, where $A = A_1\,p\,A_2$ signifies that the option A is a lottery in which the individual will receive A_1 with probability p and A_2 with probability $1 - p$. The individual is assumed to maximize expected utility, so if we let $U(A_1)$ signify the utility of outcome A_1, and if he prefers option A to option B, then

$$pU(A_1) + (1 - p)U(A_2) > p'U(B_1) + (1 - p')U(B_2)$$

The work of Davidson et al., Siegel, and Coombs and Komorita all involve equating $p = p' = 1 - p = 1 - p'$; Coombs and Komorita used objective probabilities, the others subjective probabilities (degrees of belief). In either case, the inequality may be written as

$$U(A_1) - U(B_1) > U(B_2) - U(A_2)$$

If certain conditions are met by the data, an ordered metric scale may be constructed.

Shuford et al. used objective probabilities and did not restrict them to $p = .5$. The contingent options they used include those of the form A_1 with probability p and "nothing" with probability $1 - p$, the latter being the "status quo" and assumed to be a constant for all subjects. Their method is, then, an extension of Thurstone's model for pair comparisons to yield the average utility of each of the outcomes with the status quo set at the zero point.

I wish now to make some remarks about compound and contingent pair comparisons which are relevant to all these methods. The typical behavior observed in all of them is preferential choice behavior, and the problem with which they are concerned is that of constructing a utility scale, either for an individual or for a group as a whole; that is, the behavior is being mapped into QIIIa and a stimulus scale is constructed at the level of an ordered metric scale or higher.

The models of Horst (1932) and Thurstone and Jones (1957) working with compound pair comparisons equate the sum of the scale values of the components with the scale value of the compound. The models dealing with contingent pair comparisons equate a weighted average of the scale value of the components of an option with the scale value of the option. When these weights are equal, the scale value of the option is the midpoint on the utility scale between the scale values of the components.

The models of Horst and Thurstone and Jones are all concerned with measuring a utility which may be described figuratively as of the following kind. If things may be "good," "better," "best," and "simply wonderful," the kind of utility with which these models are concerned is that in which adding "good" things to "best" things yields something nearer "simply wonderful." I wish now to consider another model concerned with a different kind of utility, one in which adding "good" things to "best" things yields something nearer "better."

In utility measurement we are concerned with preferential choice behavior. Instead of mapping such behavior directly into QIIIa let us consider it first from the point of view of QIa and unfolding theory. To simplify the discussion, suppose an individual's preferences for a particular set of alternatives are generated by an SPF falling off linearly and symmetrically along a J scale. To make the discussion concrete, suppose the alternatives are attitude statements and the individual has an ideal point on the same scale, as in Fig. 17.4.

We assume there is a distance ϵ on both sides of this ideal such that he will endorse all items whose points fall within that distance and he will reject all items outside of that region. According to this theory an individual will be maximally happy with an attitude statement that corresponds to his ideal point and his utility will fall off with statements further away. At a distance ϵ from his ideal point, utility changes from positive to negative; this is his zero point (see the bottom of Fig. 17.4).

Let us first consider compound pair comparisons in this model. Suppose one of the alternatives offered an individual is a combination of two statements with the understanding that such an alternative implies endorsing *both* or preferring *both* to some other alternative. It would be reasonable, in this model, to assume that such a compound option corresponds to a point on his I scale which is the midpoint between the two points *on the I scale* corresponding to the two components of the option. This midpoint, or option point as it is called here, has an interesting interpretation in terms of the unfolded J scale because of laterality effects.

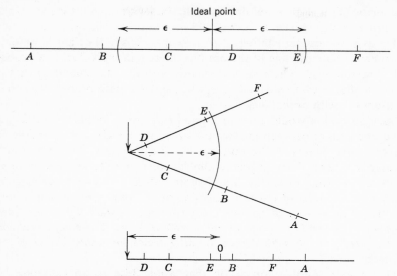

Fig. 17.4 Relation of an individual's utility to a J scale and an I scale.

If the two components of such an option are unilateral on the J scale to the ideal point, their midpoint on the J scale corresponds to the option point on the I scale. The option point may be thought of as just another alternative and may be unfolded along with the single alternatives. This is readily evident from a consideration of the middle part of Fig. 17.4. The compound option (AB) is their midpoint on one arm of the partially folded J scale and would unfold into the midpoint between A and B on the J scale.

In striking contrast is the case of an option made up of two alternatives which are bilateral on the J scale to the individual's ideal point. A bilateral compound would also correspond to a point on the I scale which is the midpoint between the two component alternative points on the I scale. But such a point on an I scale *does not* correspond to a unique point on the J scale. Consider, for example, alternatives B and F and the compound option (BF). The compound option corresponds to the midpoint between B and F on the I scale. But consider any other ideal point on the J scale for which B and F are also bilateral. Such an ideal point, if it is nearer B, is farther from F by an equal amount, with linear and symmetric SPF's. Hence *the midpoint of a compound option is a fixed point for linear SPF's on the I scales of all ideal points for which the components are bilateral.*

This conclusion, incidentally, offers the possibility of testing for some of the characteristics of the shape of the SPF's by the appearance, if any, of systematic shifts in bilateral option midpoints with different ideals. That is another matter, however, and would be a digression here.

Let us now consider contingent pair comparisons in the light of unfolding theory. Suppose one of the options offered an individual is a probability mixture of two attitude statements, with the understanding that if he chose that option he would accept statement X with probability p and statement Y with probability $1 - p$.

Such an option would also correspond to a point on his I scale which would be a point between the two points on the I scale corresponding to the two components of the option. The locus of this "between-point" relative to X and Y would presumably be some monotone function of p; the larger p, the nearer the option point to X. All these conclusions relative to the effect of laterality on compound options would now apply identically to contingent options. *Any contingent option $X p Y$ for a fixed p would correspond to a point on the J scale if X and Y are unilateral and would correspond to a fixed point on all I scales for which X and Y are bilateral.*

One readily testable conclusion that would lead to an experimental distinction between this unfolding kind of utility and the additive kind of utility in the Horst and the Thurstone and Jones theories is the following. In the unfolding theory of utility the point on the I scale corresponding to a compound option, whether unilateral or bilateral, would be the same as the point corresponding to a contingent option with $p = .5$, that is, the midpoint between the component points on the I scale. For additive utility this is not the case. The compound option point is the *sum* of the utilities of the components, and the contingent option with $p = .5$ is their midpoint.

It is likely that in some domains one of these kinds of utilities is a closer approximation to reality and in others the other kind of utility is. With amounts of money as alternatives, for example, there can be no doubt that the compound option of $1 and $5 has higher utility than the contingent option $1 p $5 for *any p*. On the other hand, an individual may be willing to endorse either of two statements but would presumably be less willing to endorse the compound option of both statements than the one of them that he prefers.

Preferential choice behavior, then, if interpreted as reflecting utility, may reflect either of two kinds of utility, an "additive" kind of utility or a "semibounded" kind of utility. It might help to conceptualize the difference between these kinds of utility if we think of the semibounded utility as "disutility." It is necessarily nonnegative. Minimum disutility is zero and corresponds only to a stimulus point that coincides with the ideal point.

The relation between the items on each of the two kinds of utility scales may also provide a way of conceptualizing the difference between the two kinds of utility. The elements on a scale of semibounded utility are essentially incompatible or mutually exclusive in some sense, whereas in additive utility they are not. For example, while we might not ordinarily think of holding two different positions on an attitude scale simultaneously, we would not feel this way about holding two different amounts of money simultaneously. Or consider grades in courses: A grade of B is good, a grade of A is better; but a grade consisting of *both* A and B is not still better. Grades do not add as money does.

To counter an argument that this semibounded utility is not really utility at all but something different I would point out that social utility is usually thought of in terms of amalgamating individual utilities including those generated by SPF's on a *J* scale, which are semibounded utilities.

Either of these two kinds of utilities may be mapped into QIIIa data, but *only the semibounded may be mapped into QIa for analysis by unfolding theory*. By comparing different individuals' utility scales for compound and contingent options we may experimentally distinguish between the two.

6. SUMMARY

The first section of this chapter discusses the nature of QIIIa data; first formally defining them as order relations on pairs of points from the same set and then discussing them at the real world level of behavioral observations. The point is made that QIIIa data are inherently confined to unidimensional representation, and, in fact, every model for the analysis of such data has as its objective the construction of a unidimensional scale. The methods of QIIIa are perhaps the best models that psychology has for that purpose.

If the experimenter is interested in inferring the classification of stimuli on some specified attribute of interest to him, QIIIa data and methods are well suited for the purpose. If an experimenter is interested in inferring the psychological space of perceptual classification of the n stimuli, QIIIa data may be obtained on the distances between the n stimuli. No matter what the dimensionality of this space may be, the distances between points must satisfy a unidimensional scale if the space is a metric space. This chapter, then, is concerned only with QIIIa data and the methods for processing them to arrive at unidimensional scales, whether the points to be scaled are the n stimulus points or the $n' = \binom{n}{2}$ distances between them.

The models available for constructing such scales have been developed with particular methods of collecting the data in mind, and hence a section is devoted to the methods of collecting such data. In general all the methods of the searchingness structure (except 'pick $1/n$' and 'pick any/n') are possible, including incomplete block designs and, if distances are to be scaled, the cartwheel methods.

Models for analyzing such data are discussed in the order of the level of measurement that each model yields. One section takes up the construction of ordinal and ordered metric scales, which are generally of less interest unless distances are being scaled. Methods for arriving at such scales include the method of expected matrices and weak stochastic transitivity. Some of the assumptions underlying these methods are discussed as well as their comparative suitability for scaling stimulus points and for scaling interpoint distances. The method of triangular analysis is then presented as a means of testing for transitivity, detecting intransitivities, and constructing an ordinal or partially ordered scale of either stimuli or their interpoint distances.

The next section takes up the models for arriving at interval and ratio scales. The first method discussed is the application of Frank Goode's method to the conversion of an ordered metric stimulus scale into an interval scale. This method is illustrated using error data in a paired-associate verbal learning task.

The well-known Thurstone model is discussed briefly and then a more recent model, referred to as the Bradley-Terry-Luce (B.T.L.) model, is discussed in more detail. Both of these models process pairwise probabilities, the former being presumed to yield an interval scale, the latter a ratio scale. A comparison is drawn between the two models, however, and it is shown that the essential difference between the models is that the Thurstone model makes a normal ogive transformation of a probability into a distance and the B.T.L. model makes a logistic transformation of the probability into a distance. These two functions are almost linearly related over the range of probabilities customarily processed.

Stevens' method of ratio estimation is briefly discussed as a method of constructing a ratio scale of subjective magnitude on some a priori attribute.

The fact that Stevens' methods and the Thurstone-B.T.L. methods do not yield scales which are always linearly related to each other has given rise to some lively discussion of psychophysical laws.

The position taken here is that Stevens' methods are direct methods for obtaining numerical scales which have led to a psychophysical law of very considerable empirical validity. Other models, like Thurstone's and the B.T.L. model, are concerned with some aspect of judgment, response, or preference behavior and are theories about the nature of such processes. Such theories may lead to a relation between a response measure and a measure of subjective magnitude. The mode of expression for subjective magnitude may be chosen for reasons of mathematical convenience, as in the case of the power law, and the relation between various response measures is then a mathematical problem. Which particular mode of expression for subjective magnitude is the *true* one is a problem in speculative philosophy.

The final section of the chapter discusses the use of compound and contingent pair comparisons to construct utility scales. The methods of Horst and of Thurstone and Jones involve compound pair comparisons and the methods of Davidson et al., Siegel, and Shuford et al. involve the use of contingent pair comparisons. These two kinds of pair comparisons are interpreted in terms of unfolding theory, and a distinction is drawn between two kinds of utility, an "additive" utility and a "semibounded" utility (or disutility). A method of experimentally determining which of the two may obtain in a particular instance is suggested. Either kind may be mapped into QIIIa, but only the semibounded utility may be mapped into QIa for analysis by unfolding.

This discussion of individual utility measurement leads naturally into the problem of amalgamating a variety of such individual utility scales to arrive at a social utility, a problem discussed in the next chapter.

REFERENCES

Abelson, R. P., 1958, Purposes of scaling techniques and the choice among them, a paper delivered at the American Statistical Association meeting, December 1958.

Becker, S. W., and S. Siegel, 1962, Utility and level of aspiration, *Amer. J. Psychol.*, **75**, 115–20.

Boring, E. G., 1950, *A history of experimental psychology*, Appleton-Century-Crofts, New York, second edition.

Bower, G. H., 1960, Response strengths and choice probability: a consideration of two combination rules, Institute for Mathematical Studies in the Social Sciences, *Stanford Univ. Tech. Rep. No. 36*, December 19, 1960.

Bradley, R. A., and M. E. Terry, 1952, Rank analysis of incomplete block designs. I. The method of paired comparisons, *Biometrika*, **39**, 324–45.

Campbell, N., 1920, *Physics: the elements*, Cambridge University Press, London. Also published in paperback under the title *Foundations of science*, by Dover Publishers, New York, S372, 1957.

Clarke, F. R., 1957, Constant-ratio rule for confusion matrices in speech communication, *J. acoust. Soc. Amer.*, **29**, 715–20.

Comrey, A. L., 1950, A proposed method for absolute ratio scaling, *Psychometrika*, **15**, 317–25.

Coombs, C. H., 1954, A method for the study of interstimulus similarity, *Psychometrika*, **19**, 183–94.

Coombs, C. H., and S. S. Komorita, 1958, Measuring utility of money through decisions, *Amer. J. Psychol.*, **71**, 383–89.

Davidson, D., P. Suppes, and S. Siegel, 1957, *Decision making: an experimental approach*, Stanford University Press, Stanford.

De Soto, C. B., and J. J. Bosley, 1962, The cognitive structure of a social structure, *J. abnorm. soc. Psychol.*, **64**, 303–07.

Ford, L. R., Jr., 1957, Solution of a ranking problem from binary comparisons, *Amer. math. Mon.*, **64**, 28–33.

Horst, A. P., 1932, A method for determining the absolute affective value of a series of stimulus situations, *J. educ. Psychol.*, **23**, 418–440.

Kendall, M. G., 1955, *Rank correlation methods*, Hafner Publishing Co., New York, second edition.

Luce, R. D., 1959, *Individual choice behavior*, John Wiley and Sons, New York.

Metfessel, M., 1947, A proposal for quantitative reporting of comparative judgments, *J. Psychol.*, **24**, 229–35.

Ramsey, F. P., 1931, *The foundations of mathematics and other logical essays*, London, Republished in paperback by Littlefield, Adams, and Co., in the International Library of Psychology, Philosophy, and Scientific Method, Series No. 214, 1960.

Shuford, E. H., L. V. Jones, and R. D. Bock, 1960, A rational origin obtained by the method of contingent paired comparisons, *Psychometrika*, **25**, 343–56.

Siegel, S., 1956, A method for obtaining an ordered metric scale, *Psychometrika*, **21**, 207–16.

Stevens, S. S., 1957, On the psychophysical law, *Psychol. Rev.*, **64**, 153–81.

Stevens, S. S., 1958, Problems and methods of psychophysics, *Psychol. Bull.*, **55**, 177–96.

Stevens, S. S., 1959, The quantification of sensation, *Daedalus*, **88**, 606–21.

Suppes, P., and J. Zinnes, 1963, "Basic measurement theory," a chapter in *Handbook of mathematical psychology*, Vol. I, edited by R. D. Luce, R. B. Bush, and E. H. Galanter, John Wiley and Sons, New York.

Terry, M. E., R. A. Bradley, and L. L. Davis, 1952, New designs and techniques for organoleptic testing, *Food Technol.*, **6**, 250–54.

Thurstone, L. L., and L. V. Jones, 1957, The rational origin for measuring subjective values, *J. Amer. statist. Ass.*, **52**, 458–71.

Torgerson, W. S., 1958, *Theory and methods of scaling*, John Wiley and Sons, New York.

Vastenhouw, J., 1962, *Relationships between meanings*, Mouton and Co., The Hague.

von Neumann, J., and O. Morgenstern, 1953, *Theory of games and economic behavior*, Princeton University Press, Princeton.

Zinnes, J. L., 1958, The relationship between two methods for scaling pair comparison data, *Amer. Psychologist*, **13**, 416 (abstract).

CHAPTER 18

On the Problem of Social Utility and Majority Decision

Economists have a great deal of interest in the problem of social welfare functions and have done a lot of work on it. This problem may be briefly described as the problem of how to construct a preference structure (for example, an ordering) on a set of alternatives out of the diverse preference structures contributed by members of a social group, and to do this in such a way as to achieve some kind of social maximum. In this chapter I shall present certain well-known results, especially those of Arrow, and interpret them in the context of psychological scaling theory. The first section is an orientation to the problem, the second section reviews certain results of Arrow, and the last two sections translate the problem into data theory terms and interpret Arrow's results from the point of view of unfolding theory. The chapter closes with a discussion of the Hare system from the point of view of psychological scaling theory and offers an alternative procedure to it which has some advantages and some disadvantages.

The preferences of an individual over a set of alternatives might be taken to reflect the "utility" of the alternatives to him. The term "utility" refers to the amount of preferability or general overall desirability, and we shall identify an individual's preference structure with his utilities for the various alternatives.

Social groups of all kinds are commonly faced with choices between alternatives; a hiking club must decide which of several trips to take next, a legislature must decide how much import tariff to place on coffee. The decisions of the club or the legislature, however they may have been arrived at, reflect, by definition, the *social utility* of the alternatives to the group as a whole. This is the problem we have at an athletic meet such as the Olympic Games or a track meet among several universities (Huntington, 1938). Each event may be thought of as ordering the competing units and the problem is to arrive at a composite ordering. The method conventionally used in these last cases is a version of averaging ranks. We saw in Section 9 of Chapter 5, however, that such a procedure is not "independent from other alternatives." That is, University A may or may not win in the competition over University B depending on whether University C participates or not. This property may be considered by some to be an undesirable property of such a group decision function.

A problem of interest to the economist is that of constructing a social utility out of the individual choices (utilities). The mechanism by which this is done may be called a decision function or a social welfare function in that some kind of a social "good" is intended to be achieved. Mathematicians (see Luce and Raiffa, 1957, Chapter 14) and political scientists (for example, Black, 1948a; Riker, 1958, 1961) have also been interested in the same problem. To the mathematician it is an interesting problem in that a social welfare function might be required to satisfy a number of intuitively reasonable axioms but the axioms are not all mutually compatible (see Milnor, 1954).

To the social scientist the problem is of interest for many reasons. It is, for instance, an example of a significant problem in which important progress has been made by logical analysis. Arrow's monograph (1951) on social choice is one of the best examples of mathematical social science. Another reason for the social scientist's interest in the problem lies in the extensive use society makes of mechanisms for reaching group decisions, as, for example, in juries and legislatures. To capture the essence of each such system in an axiomatic model is a fascinating problem for descriptive social science. Finally, a significant source of interest in the problem lies in the fact that the prevailing democratic mechanism of majority decision is captured, so far, only by axiomatic systems which impose apparently unpalatable constraints. A major objective of this chapter, incidentally, is not to provide a more palatable axiom system but to make the constraints more palatable, at least to the extent of providing a reasonable psychological interpretation of them.

The first and obvious solution for a social welfare function was offered by Jeremy Bentham who proposed to compute the average utility for each alternative and thereby scale the alternatives on a stimulus scale that represents the group as a whole. This procedure requires that a measure of each individual's utility for each alternative be assigned, and that these measures all be elements of the same interval scale, a condition called interpersonal comparability of utility. The objection to Bentham's proposal is that interpersonally comparable utility can only be accepted on faith. Pareto was among the first to abandon interpersonally comparable utility and to seek a solution in terms of combining *ordinal* utility scales corresponding to individuals' preference orderings. This problem has a long history in economics but the story is out of place here. The reader is referred to Arrow (1951) for a condensed summary of the principal issues and a partial listing of contributors.

The problem is clearly one of psychological measurement, and it seems reasonable that psychological measurement models might be relevant. Many are. Every time an experimenter averages ratings he is assuming interpersonal comparability of utility, as in the student ratings of faculty discussed in Chapter 16. Again, whenever Thurstone's model for comparative judgment is used by replicating over individuals a similar assumption is made. Each of these procedures, and many others in psychology, may be considered as social welfare functions when the observations are preferences.

Looked at from this point of view, the assumptions underlying Thurstone's model are no longer assumptions; they are value judgments. A preferential choice probability is converted into a psychological distance between two stimuli by a normal curve transformation. As a social welfare function, this assumption is translated into the value judgments that individuals shall be weighted increasingly with the popularity of their vote. If we wanted to weight both individuals and votes equally, we could use a uniform distribution to transform probabilities into distances. This would not be an assumption about the nature of a reality, then, as it is in Thurstone's model for judgmental behavior, but a deliberate value judgment about the kind of social welfare function that was desired.

It is interesting that to economists none of the psychological measurement models are acceptable when applied as social welfare functions, because they all involve interpersonal comparability of utility as a gratuitous assumption; economists are interested in studying social welfare functions based on conjoining individuals' ordinal utilities. One such function is that of majority decision. In the rest of this chapter I propose to discuss majority decision as a social welfare function, presenting first a significant result of Arrow's and then an interpretation of the problem from the point of view of data theory and unfolding theory.

1. ARROW'S THEOREMS ON SOCIAL WELFARE FUNCTIONS AND MAJORITY RULE

Arrow's little monograph (1951) summarizes the history and main issues of the problem of social choice. The monograph becomes very technical, but a very clear and less technical exposition is contained in

Luce and Raiffa (1957, Chapter 14). My discussion does not depend on a prior knowledge of either of these but is very brief and will not do justice to either the scope of the problem or the technical details.

We are concerned here with two of Arrow's results. The first is his proof of the nonexistence of a social welfare function which satisfies certain general conditions, as modified by Blau (1957), and then the proof that majority decision is a social welfare function which will satisfy these conditions when one of them is restricted in a certain way.

That majority decision can in certain instances yield a transitive social ordering is obvious from the following example. Suppose three individuals have the following preference orderings on three alternatives A, B, and C: $A B C$, $B A C$, $C B A$. Then by majority rule $B > A$, $A > C$, and $B > C$, so we have the social ordering $B A C$.

Majority rule, however, sometimes fails to yield a transitive ordering. For example, suppose our three individuals had had the following orderings: $A B C$, $B C A$, $C A B$. Then by majority rule we have $A > B$, $B > C$, and $C > A$, and no social ordering results.

This possibility has been known for many years as the paradox of voting. Each individual voter may be transitive but the majority rule may not be. With intransitivity, the sequence in which the pairwise decisions are made determines the outcome. Thus if the group should decide between A and B first, A would survive B and B would be eliminated. The remaining vote, then, between C and A yields C as the group's first choice. If, however, the initial choice were between some other pair, the final outcome would be different; in general, the last one to be paired would be the one to survive. This, of course, has been of interest to political scientists. Riker (1958, p. 353) says, "Inasmuch as legislative rules all over the world permit at least three choices [alternatives] to face legislators simultaneously, the possibility of the occurrence of the paradox exists in every legislature."

Arrow's main result is known as his general possibility theorem. He proposes five presumably reasonable, desirable, and intuitively acceptable conditions that a social welfare function should satisfy and proves that they are inconsistent. That is, no welfare function which satisfies all of them can exist.

The first condition specifies that there will be at least two individuals and at least three alternatives to be ordered (otherwise the problem is uninteresting) and requires that the social welfare function be defined for all* sets of individual orderings. By a social welfare function is meant a

---

* This is the modification introduced by Blau. Arrow's original first condition required that there be at least one triple of alternatives for which all conceivable individual orderings occur. Blau disproved the theorem with a counter example. Then by

rule or mechanism which assigns to a set of individual preference orderings a corresponding unique transitive social ordering. The important part of condition 1 is the specification that this rule yield a social ordering regardless of the variety or divergence of individual orderings. To restrict the domain of the function is to say that there are certain preference orderings which individuals in the society are not permitted to hold.

Condition 2 is known as the positive association of social and individual values. This is surely an unobjectionable condition. Essentially it says that the preference ordering of no individual in the group should have a *negative* or *contrary* influence on the social ordering, that is, the social ordering should not be perverse. Of course, the social ordering cannot agree with every individual's preference ordering, but the fact that an individual prefers A to B should not influence the social ordering in the direction of preferring B to A. A way of putting the idea is this: Suppose for a given set of individuals' preference orderings the social welfare ordering ranks A over B. Then if A is raised in the preference orderings of some or all of the individual orderings, but no other change is made, the new social ordering should still rank A over B.

Condition 3 is the familiar condition of independence from other alternatives. As used by Arrow it states that if the preference orderings of individuals are changed for some of the alternatives, the ordering of the remaining alternatives should be unaffected in the revised social ordering. In a simple instance, if an individual changed his preference ordering on A and B, the revised social ordering should not affect the *order* between C and D. This condition says that the social ordering of any pair of alternatives depends only on the preferences of the individuals between the members of that pair. The importance of this condition lies in its being an effective prohibition to strategic misrepresentation by a group of voters in order to influence the social ordering (see Vickery, 1960).

Conditions 4 and 5 are known respectively as the conditions of citizens' sovereignty and of nondictatorship. The condition of citizens' sovereignty says that for each pair of alternatives A and B there must exist at least one set of individual orderings such that society prefers A to B. Otherwise the social ordering of these alternatives would have been imposed, that is, predetermined independently of the constituents' preferences. The condition of nondictatorship says that there is no individual with the power that if he prefers A to B society does likewise regardless of other individuals' orderings.

---

modifying the condition to increase the variety of preference orderings allowed to occur, the inconsistency of the conditions is restored.

Arrow's general possibility theorem states that these five conditions are inconsistent. No social welfare function can exist which satisfies them all. Another way of putting it is that the first three conditions are incompatible with the last two: Any social welfare function which satisfies the first three conditions must be either imposed or dictatorial.

The following sketch of the proof of Arrow's theorem is taken from Luce and Raiffa (1957, pp. 339-40).

The central steps of the proof can be outlined without too much rigorous argument. With respect to a given social welfare function a subset V of individuals is said to be *decisive* for the ordered pair (x, y) if whenever the members of V each prefer x to y society does likewise—regardless of what members not in V have to say about x versus y. In other words, if V is decisive for (x, y), then the coalition V can always enforce x over y by having each member express preference for x over y.

By condition 2, a set V is decisive for (x, y) if and only if society prefers x to y when all of the members of V prefer x to y and all other individuals prefer y to x.

From conditions 1, 2, and 4 it is easy to prove

Pareto optimality: The set of all individuals is *decisive* for every ordered pair (x, y), i.e., if each individual prefers x to y, so does society.

··· i. Suppose V is a minimal decisive set, i.e., it is decisive for some x against some y, whereas no proper subset is decisive for any ordered pair of alternatives. Such a set must exist since, as we mentioned above, the set of all individuals is decisive and the individuals can be removed one at a time until the remaining set is no longer decisive for any pair. This remaining set must contain at least one individual, for, if it were the empty set, its complement, the set of all individuals, would not be decisive for any pair.

ii. Let j be a specific individual in V, W the remaining individuals in V, and U the set of all individuals not in V. Since the society has at least two individuals, U and W may not both be empty. Let z be any third alternative, and consider the following profile of orderings:

$$\begin{array}{ccc} \{j\} & W & U \\ x & z & y \\ y & x & z \\ z & y & x \end{array}$$

iii. Since x is preferred to y for all i in $V = \{j\} \cup W$, and since V is decisive for x against y, society prefers x to y, i.e., xPy.

iv. If society preferred z to y, this would mean that W is decisive for z against y since all members of W prefer z to y whereas all others prefer y to z, which is contrary to the choice of V as a minimal decisive set. Therefore, society does not prefer z to y, i.e., $z\bar{P}y$.

v. By transitivity, xPy and $z\bar{P}y$ imply xPz.

vi. But j is the only individual who prefers x to z, so j is decisive for x against z. Thus, $\{j\}$ cannot be a proper subset of V, so $\{j\} = V$, and by hypothesis $\{j\}$ is decisive for x against y.

vii. Since we now know that j is decisive for x against any z different from x, it is sufficient to show that it is decisive for any w, different from x, against z and for w against x. Suppose $w \neq x$, and consider the profile

$$
\begin{array}{cc}
\{j\} & U \\
w & z \\
x & w \\
z & x
\end{array}
$$

By Pareto optimality, wPx, and, since $\{j\}$ is decisive for x against z, xPz. Thus, by transitivity, wPz, so $\{j\}$ is decisive for w against z. Next, consider the profile

$$
\begin{array}{cc}
\{j\} & U \\
w & z \\
z & x \\
x & w
\end{array}
$$

Since $\{j\}$ is decisive for w against z, wPz, and, by Pareto optimality, zPx. Therefore, by transitivity, wPx, so $\{j\}$ is decisive for w against x, as was to be shown. We have therefore established that $\{j\}$ is decisive for all pairs and so $\{j\}$ is a dictator. But this is impossible, so no function exists which meets the five conditions.

Attempts to avoid this impasse have centered primarily on modifying condition 1 or condition 3.* Our attention will be directed at modifying condition 1, in particular at restricting the admissible preference orderings. It seems reasonable that if we do not demand that a social welfare function be able to process all possible varieties of individual orderings, then perhaps some may exist which satisfy Arrow's other conditions.

It was seen in Part 2 that if individuals' preferences among a set of alternatives are based on evaluations along a relatively few common characteristics, then the variety of admissible preference orderings may be reduced. In particular we found this to be so when preference orderings are a consequence of SPF's on a J scale (see Section 1 of Chapter 9), and we related certain varieties of SPF to what we called quantitative and qualitative J scales.

Arrow (1951, Chapter 7) extended a result of Black's (1948a, b) to show that if preferences are generated by SPF's on a qualitative J scale majority decisions yield transitive orderings.

Insight into Arrow's result is provided by Luce and Raiffa's (1957, pp. 356–57) discussion, which may be abbreviated and paraphrased as follows. With SPF's, if a stimulus lies between two others on a J scale it is impossible for it to be preferred less than both the others by any individual, and, furthermore, any individual's pairwise preferences must be transitive. With those observations in mind it is easy to see that the

* Kemeny (1959), for example, proposes two different ways of arriving at a social utility scale which he calls a consensus ranking. Each of his methods will always yield such a ranking, in spite of Arrow's theorem, and this is because his procedures violate two of Arrow's conditions: that the social ordering be unique (his methods sometimes arrive at multiple orderings) and the condition of being independent from other alternatives (number 3).

first is contradicted by intransitive majority decisions. Take any triple of stimuli, say A, B, and C, in rank order on the J scale. Suppose that a majority (not necessarily the same) prefers A to B, B to C, and C to A. The majority that prefers A to B and the majority that prefers C to A must have one person in common, who would then have the preference ordering $C\ A\ B$, which is incompatible with the assumption of SPF's. Hence, *majority decision based on preferences generated from a qualitative J scale, and with SPF's, must satisfy weak stochastic transitivity, and must itself yield an ordering which is a folded J scale.*

So much for background. I wish now to discuss these problems from the point of view of data theory and psychological measurement models and to place an interpretation on the social utility scale obtained by majority choice in the particular instance in which preferences are generated by a common *quantitative J scale.*

2. PREFERENTIAL CHOICE BEHAVIOR AS STIMULUS COMPARISON DATA

The construction of a social welfare function by aggregating individual preference orderings may be looked at from the point of view of the theory of data as interpreting preferential choice behavior as stimulus comparison data. Part 2 deals with the analysis of QIa data, which I called preferential choice data because, generally speaking, the real world context from which they are obtained is that of preferential choices which individuals make among a set of alternatives. Preferential choice data are made out of such preferential choice behavior by assuming each individual to be mapped into an ideal point, c_i, and each alternative into a stimulus point, q_j; a preferential choice between two stimuli is then interpreted to mean that the preferred stimulus point is nearer the ideal point than is the other's.

The same behavior, however, might be interpreted as stimulus comparison data, QIIIa, rather than QIa. An individual's judgment that he prefers one alternative over another might be interpreted as a comparison of the two alternatives on a common attribute of preferability or utility. In this case individuals are not mapped into points; only the alternatives are. There is, then, a single set of points, and the observations are interpreted as an order relation on pairs of points from this one set—QIIIa data.

We see from these arguments, then, that preferential choice behavior may be interpreted as either QIa or QIIIa data. In the first instance a joint scale* with both the individuals and stimuli on it is obtained by

---

* Throughout the remainder of this chapter, unless the contrary is indicated, preference orderings are assumed to satisfy a common unidimensional J scale.

unfolding analysis; in the second instance a stimulus scale with only the stimuli on it is obtained. It is to be anticipated that these two scales will be related, because the two kinds of data, QIa and QIIIa, have been obtained from the same original preferential choice behavior. The relation between these two scales will be brought out in the next section.

The information in preferential choice data is defined as follows:

$$|p_{hij}| - |p_{hik}| \leq 0 \Leftrightarrow j \cdot \rangle k \qquad (18.1)$$

and the unfolding technique is an algorithm for processing such inequalities to obtain information about the unknown c's and q's (see Chapter 5), where

$$|p_{hij}| = |c_{hij} - q_{hij}| \qquad (18.2)$$

The two sets of points on the J scale are the c's and the q's corresponding to individuals and stimuli respectively. In other words, the quantity $|p_{hij}|$ is an absolute distance between an individual's ideal point and a stimulus point. This distance might be interpreted as a *disutility* in that when the two points coincide the individual is maximally satisfied with the stimulus and the distance between them is zero; as the distance increases the utility diminishes, so we say the disutility increases. For each individual, then, each stimulus has a disutility, and of any two stimuli the individual prefers the one with the smaller disutility.

Let us now interpret the same behavior as QIIIa data. We shall say that only the stimuli are points, not the individuals, and a preference ordering merely reflects which stimulus has less disutility. But we see that this characteristic of the stimulus is its distance from the individual. So the q values for stimuli in this QIIIa interpretation are the $|p|$'s for the stimuli in the case of the QIa interpretation. That is, as QIa data we have the expression of 18.1; as QIIIa data we have

$$q_{hij} - q_{hik} \geq 0 \Leftrightarrow j \rangle k$$

so $\qquad |p_{hij}| = q_{hij} \quad \text{and} \quad |p_{hik}| = q_{hik}$

The import is as follows: If we interpret preferential choice behavior as QIa data we seek to scale the c's and q's of equation 18.2, and if we interpret the same behavior as QIIIa data, we seek to scale the $|p|$'s of equation 18.2. The solution to QIa data is a joint scale from which the individual preferences may be derived. The solution to QIIIa data is a stimulus scale which is an aggregated disutility scale for the stimuli, which we shall call a *group scale*.

The term *group scale* for the results of a QIIIa analysis of preferential choice behavior is almost synonymous with the phrase *social utility scale*, but sometimes the latter phrase hardly seems appropriate; for example, when the alternatives being voted on are individuals or nations. It would

A vs B A vs C A vs D B vs C B vs D C vs D

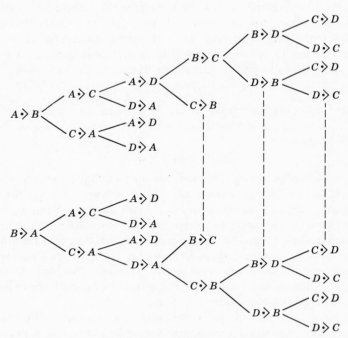

Fig. 18.1   Tree representing preferential behavior for four stimuli.

seem more appropriate to talk about a group scale of preferences for nationalities rather than a social utility scale of nationalities. Another example may be found in Chapter 8 in the discussion of the results of factor analyzing intercorrelations of individuals' preferences. It will be recalled that this procedure introduces an extra dimension which is a group scale in the sense that the order of the projections of individuals on it is the order of their proximity to all the other individuals in the space; again, we would not be inclined to call such a dimension a social utility scale.

There is another way to see the difference between a QIa and a QIIIa interpretation of preferential choice behavior. It is most clearly brought out by a figure. Figure 18.1 shows the total possible variety of pairwise preferential choices for four stimuli laid out in a tree. Starting* at the left of the figure, every individual prefers A to B or B to A; this determines where his path through the tree starts. His path to the second column is

---

* It is, of course, not implied that the sequence of pair comparisons in the tree from left to right necessarily corresponds to the order in which they were presented.

determined by whether he prefers A to C or vice versa. The six columns correspond to the six preferential choices, and each individual's behavior, when he is restricted to pairwise choices and is forced to choose, may be represented by a branch of this tree. The final column has 64 ($= 2^{\binom{n}{2}}$) different terminal points (not all shown in the figure) indicating that preferential choices among four stimuli could distinguish, at most, 64 kinds of people.

To map such behavior into QIa data is to undertake the obligation of "explaining" the variety of branches. The unfolding theory presented in Part 2 is an example of a theory by means of which such an explanation may be sought. The explanation, according to this theory, is in terms of a J scale or J space, as the case may be.

To map such behavior into QIIIa is an entirely different matter. All connections between columns, all branches, are eliminated. Each column is reduced or collapsed into the two distinct preferences, as in the case of the first column on the left. With each preference is associated the number of individuals having the preference in question. Hence the entire tree is reduced to a set of six experimentally independent numbers and the objective of a model such as Thurstone's is to "explain" these numbers. The explanation according to such a theory is in terms of the scale values of the stimuli on a unidimensional stimulus scale. Such a scale, when it is obtained from an aggregation of individual orderings, I have, for convenience, called a group scale.

It should be obvious that each of these two different approaches to the same behavior is completely legitimate and proper, in its appropriate circumstances. If, for example, the four stimuli are weights and the subject is responding by saying which of each pair is heavier, the Thurstone model assumes that different individuals are merely replications of each other and a branch has no significance. In such a case, to map the behavior into QIa data and try to "explain" the paths is futile. On the other hand, if individuals do not differ from each other randomly, as I presume they do not in the case of preferences, the explanation of their different branches is a legitimate endeavor. Nevertheless, this by no means implies that a QIIIa analysis may not be of interest, even for preferential choice behavior.

One way of putting the distinction between a QIa and a QIIIa analysis of preferential choice behavior is that the unfolding technique deals with patterns of individual preferences and the analysis of the fine structure of the data. A QIIIa analysis treats individuals as replications of each other and collapses the data into certain major features. It is much like the difference between latent structure analysis, which is concerned with patterns of responses to items, and test theory, which is concerned with the distribution of total scores.

Considering individual preferential choice behavior as QIIIa data and regarding different individuals as replications lead to a pairwise probability for the group as a whole on each pair. Hence Thurstone's and the B.T.L. model are possibilities for social welfare functions because of their formal structure. Thurstone explicitly considered estimating pairwise probabilities by replicating over individuals and called it case II of his model for comparative judgment. In Torgerson's revised and more complete classification system for the model of comparative judgment case II is called class II. Luce explicitly warns that his theory applies to single organisms, not to aggregates over groups of them, and adds: "This does not mean that group studies can never be used in connection with this theory, but they must be chosen with care so as not to do violence to the basic ideas." (1959, p. 8.)

If preferential choice behavior is generated by a joint space like that postulated by unfolding theory, the "basic ideas" of Luce's theory are violated. The reason for this is provided by the discussion of inconsistency of preferences in Section 9 of Chapter 5. In brief, strong stochastic transitivity is violated by pairwise probabilities because an effect called laterality arises when an individual has an ideal point between stimulus points. The B.T.L. model and Thurstone's case V imply strong stochastic transitivity. In the remainder of this chapter, then, we shall not consider suitable either of these models as social welfare functions but shall consider a social welfare function based only on ordinal utilities and leading only to an ordinal social utility, that is, an ordinal group scale.

Majority decision suggests itself as such a social welfare function, and in fact is in daily use. This mechanism consists of taking the majority preference on every pair, and, if the preferential choices so determined are transitive, then the resulting rank ordering is a social utility scale. The transitivity condition here is that of weak stochastic transitivity. Thus the Thurstone and B.T.L. models, leading to cardinal social utility, require strong stochastic transitivity; but majority choice, leading to ordinal social utility, requires only weak stochastic transitivity. Unfortunately, majority decision, even under very reasonable conditions, will not in general satisfy even weak stochastic transitivity, as was shown by Arrow. He and Black have shown, however, that if the domain of individual preference orderings is restricted to those generated by SPF's, majority rule will satisfy weak stochastic transitivity and is a satisfactory social welfare function.

This result has a particular interpretation from the point of view of unfolding theory, which suggests that this restriction of admissible preference orderings is not incompatible with a free society. The discussion of this is the concern of the next section.

3. MAJORITY DECISION FROM THE POINT OF VIEW OF UNFOLDING THEORY

The theorems of Arrow and Black on SPF's correspond in unfolding theory to the case in which the preference orderings of the individuals all unfold into a common *qualitative* J scale. If a set of individual preference orderings satisfies a common qualitative J scale, we know from their results that majority decision necessarily yields a transitive ordering of alternatives. The total variety of admissible individual orderings is 2^{n-1} under this condition. Let us consider a still more restrictive case, that in which the individual preference orderings are generated from a common quantitative J scale. As we saw in Section 1 of Chapter 9, these orderings correspond to SPF's which are strictly monotonic and symmetric but not necessarily the same for all individuals. Under this condition the variety of admissible individual preference orderings is $\binom{n}{2} + 1$, that is, the number of regions between midpoints.

Under these conditions the order of the midpoints on the J scale is the same for all individuals, and the social ordering obtained by majority rule is the preference ordering of the median individual in the group. This follows because the majority choice on every pair will always include the median individual, so his preference ordering coincides with the stochastic ordering.

Under still stronger assumptions, this social ordering may be interpreted as a *least disliked* social utility. For example, if, in addition, the SPF's are all *linearly* descending, the disutility of an alternative for an individual is the absolute distance between his ideal point and the stimulus point. This distance, if it were known, would be a measure of the disutility. To average these values for a stimulus over all the individuals is to compute the mean absolute deviation of all the individuals about that stimulus point as an arbitrary origin. It is a well-known theorem that the mean absolute deviation of a distribution is a minimum about the median of the distribution. If, in addition, the distribution of individuals is symmetric, then the further the arbitrary origin from the median, the greater the mean absolute deviation.

Hence, under some very special conditions majority rule yields a least disliked social welfare function in that the alternatives would be ordered on the basis of the average absolute deviation of all the individual ideal points about each stimulus point as an arbitrary origin. Successive alternatives would be, in order, successively further away, on the average, from everyone.

The conditions under which this would hold, however, are quite strict:

(1) a common unidimensional J scale;
(2) SPF's that are linearly descending and symmetric;
(3) a symmetric distribution of individual ideals on the J scale.

The second condition calls for some discussion. The slopes at which the two arms of the SPF descend have either of two equivalent interpretations. In the first place the slopes may be interpreted in terms relevant to an individual's unit of measurement for disutility on the J scale and in the second place as relevant to the weighting of the individual in making the composite for the group. The condition that all SPF's be everywhere identical when superimposed at their peaks (their ideals) is equivalent to the condition that all individuals have a common unit of measurement on the J scale and be weighted equally in forming the social ordering.

To change an individual's unit of measurement is to multiply his disutilities by some scalar which is equivalent to weighting him differently in forming the composite. So, by majority decision, we weight all individuals equally and hence effectively assume they have a common unit of measurement. Therefore the *existence* of a common unit of measurement for utility is required for a least disliked social utility which weights individuals equally; but we only require it to exist, not to be estimable or computable for arithmetic purposes. It is interesting to note that there is no requirement of a common origin for all individual utility scales; adding a constant does not affect the social ordering. So this is a somewhat weaker requirement than that of interpersonally comparable utility. In fact, the requirement is that of interpersonal comparability of *changes* in utility.

These three conditions are sufficient to yield an ordinal social utility by majority rule which weights strength of preference and is a least disliked social utility.

These conditions may, of course, be considerably weakened, as shown by Arrow and by Black, and majority rule will still yield an ordinal social utility; but if the conditions are weakened the utility may not in general be characterized as a least disliked utility.

We do not generally expect such strong conditions to be met in any significant real world application. We cannot even test exactly whether they have been met, because the unfolding technique will generate a common quantitative J scale with SPF's which are strictly monotonic and symmetric but not necessarily linear. This means that the unfolding of I scales into a common quantitative J scale does not reveal the existence of a common unit of measurement and hence cannot reveal the existence of an interpersonally comparable utility.

My interest in pursuing this problem from the point of view of unfolding theory is in the psychological implications. I am inclined to assume that the existence of common J scales is, generally speaking, a consequence of cultural homogeneity (see Chapter 16, Section 1) rather than a product of a common biological heritage. If that is so, the implication is that majority decision, in order to yield what might be called collective rationality (by avoiding the voting paradox), depends on the existence of a common basic reference frame for the evaluation of social states.

I hasten to point out that the foregoing analysis by no means implies that the members of a society should have the same attitude (ideal) or must necessarily agree on their relative utilities for the alternative social states. Indeed, individuals at opposite ends of the J scale have preferences which are in reverse order. But it implies that they do agree that the attribute represented by the J scale is the relevant one for evaluative purposes.

Arrow's condition 1, as revised by Blau, allows all possible preference orderings. As we saw in Chapter 7, from the point of view of unfolding theory, this implies that the preference orderings are generated in a space of dimensionality one less than the number of alternatives. Arrow's general possibility theorem says that under such a condition neither majority rule nor any variation of it is satisfactory. At the other extreme, if the preferences are generated in one dimension, then majority rule yields a unique transitive ordering. In fact, if some additional conditions are met, majority rule is characterized as a least disliked social utility. It is an interesting problem to note the effect of spaces of intermediate dimensionality. If preferences are generated in a common J space of 2, 3, and so on, dimensions, but still less than $n - 1$, does majority rule necessarily yield a unique transitive ordering? The answer is no. If the dimensionality is two or greater, any three stimulus points in general position define a circle and all permutations of all subsets of three stimuli occur as a central set of permutations around the center of that circle (see Chapter 7). So a suitable distribution of voters can lead to an intransitive social ordering by majority choice.

In general, a common cultural reference frame for communication and evaluation has the effect of reducing the variety of preference orderings that can occur, and therein lies some of the significance of this problem for the social psychologist.

4. AN ALTERNATIVE TO THE HARE SYSTEM

Among the common mechanisms for aggregating individual preference orderings are the averaging of rank orders and the Hare system. Their value lies in the fact that they will arrive at a decision when majority rule

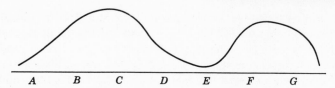

Fig. 18.2   A hypothetical distribution of voters and candidates.

will not. A major objection is that they violate the axiom of independence from other alternatives.

Consider a J scale of alternatives with a population of voters distributed as in Fig. 18.2.

If preferences are generated by SPF's, majority rule will be transitive and the ordering will be the same as that of the median individual's with D and E probably first and second.

The method of averaging rank orders will approximate the solution obtained by majority rule; but because it violates the axiom of independence from other alternatives it can, with an appropriate distribution of candidates, yield a different result from that of majority choice. Averaging rank orders may be regarded as an attempt to take strength of preference into account. An individual who has the preference ordering $X\,Y\,Z$ is presumed to prefer Y more strongly than an individual with the preference ordering $X\,Z\,Y$. The presumption may be incorrect.

Consider next the Hare system in the election situation presented in Fig. 18.2 when only one candidate is to be elected. No candidate will receive a majority of first-place votes, and the one with the fewest first-place votes will be eliminated. The midpoints that are working here are those between adjacent alternatives, that is, the number of first-place votes each candidate receives corresponds to the area under the curve between each candidate's midpoints with his two adjacent opponents. Clearly candidate E will be eliminated first. His "electors" will then be divided by the midpoint between D and F and will join D's electors or F's electors. Probably A will be eliminated next, throwing A's electors in B's group.

This process of successively eliminating the candidate with the smallest number of first-place votes leads to the formation of a coalition (implicit) until a majority is obtained for some candidate. This method is not independent of other alternatives. If candidates E, F, and G were not available, D would win on the first ballot.

Another mechanism that has quite different properties from the Hare system is the following. We start out as in the Hare system, but if no candidate has a majority of first-place votes we eliminate the candidate *with the most last-place votes.* The people who voted for him as their first choice then have their ballots redistributed according to their second choice.

If this method is applied to the *J* scale situation, there is only one midpoint working and that is the midpoint between the first and the last element on the *J* scale, in this case, Fig. 18.2, *A* and *G*. The position of the median individual on one side or the other of this midpoint will determine which of the two endpoints is to be retained. If *A* is retained, *G* is eliminated and the midpoint between *A* and *F* is the next working midpoint. If the median person is on the *F* side of the *AF* midpoint, *A* is eliminated and the next working midpoint is that between *B* and *F*.

This process continues until there is a majority of first-place votes for one candidate. As this majority will always include the median person, his choice will correspond to the majority and the candidate elected will be one nearest the middle of the distribution.

I have not explored this method very fully but it does present some interesting contrasts to the Hare system. I think, but this is only a conjecture, that it would satisfy at least a weak form of the axiom of independence from other alternatives. As a social welfare mechanism it leads to a compromise position or solution which has the flavor of a "least disliked" choice for the group as a whole. It will always yield the same choice that majority decision will yield if the latter is transitive.

The Hare system would, on the other hand, lead to a choice which has the flavor of a "most liked" choice for a majority subgroup. Perhaps the difference can be described by saying that the Hare system moves toward the choice of a modal group and this other system moves toward the choice of the median individual.

In a situation in which an elected candidate would need the support of a coalition I would suspect the Hare system would be more effective in that a candidate is selected who is highly prized by a majority. Under the alternative system a candidate is selected on the grounds that the total opposition is weakest, but it would not follow that the support would be strong.

In the simple one-dimensional case the new method will yield the same result as majority rule. The Hare system will not necessarily do so because of its lack of independence from other alternatives. Any candidate can be eliminated under the Hare system by bracketing him sufficiently closely with a candidate on each side of him.

Just what characteristics these systems have when preferences are not generated by SPF's or are multidimensional are unsolved problems.

5. SUMMARY

The chapter introduces the topic of social welfare functions as a means of amalgamating individuals' preference patterns into a single preference pattern. Although the problem has been of primary interest to economists, it is much concerned with the problem of interpersonal comparability of utility, which is interesting to psychologists. Indeed, some of psychology's methods for processing data are, at least formally, potential social welfare functions. These include, for example, averaging ratings, Thurstone's model for comparative judgment, and the B.T.L. model for choice behavior.

Economists and others have tended to avoid the assumption of inter-personally comparable utility and have sought social welfare functions based only on individuals' ordinal utilities. In the second section we discussed Arrow's general possibility theorem on social welfare functions, as modified by Blau, and some aspects of majority rule as a social decision function. Arrow showed that any social welfare function which met certain seemingly reasonable and desirable properties must either be imposed or dictatorial. This being an undesirable outcome, we seek ways of modifying the "seemingly reasonable and desirable properties" in order to avoid it.

The property to which we gave our attention is the requirement that the social welfare function be able to resolve *all possible combinations* of individual preference orderings into a single social utility ordering. That this is possible is shown by Arrow and also by Black when the individual preference orderings are confined to those generated by SPF's, that is, a common qualitative *J* scale.

This linkage between social welfare functions on the one hand and the unfolding theory of preferential choice on the other, led us to examine the problem in the context of scaling theory and seek a psychological inter-pretation of the result. In Section 2 the mapping of preferential choice *behavior* into *QIIIa data* was discussed in detail. The same *behavior* may be mapped into *QIa data*, and if certain constraints are satisfied the preference orderings can be unfolded in one dimension to generate a *J* scale of individuals and alternatives. To map the behavior into QIIIa and analyze it by a QIIIa model is to construct a stimulus scale with only the alternatives on it, not the individuals.

We saw that the value of a stimulus for an individual under a QIIIa interpretation is the *distance* of the stimulus point from his ideal point. These distances were called *disutilities*. To apply a QIIIa model is to aggregate the disutilities for each alternative. Another comparison was drawn between a QIa interpretation and a QIIIa interpretation of behavior in terms of a branch in a tree listing all possible choice behaviors. If the paths are nonrandomly chosen, a QIa interpretation is relevant and significant. A QIIIa interpretation is always relevant and significant. Our interest here lies in the special interpretation that a QIIIa analysis has when a QIa analysis is relevant.

The aggregating of preferential choice behavior by either the Thurstone or the B.T.L. model is incompatible with the analysis of the same behavior as QIa data. The reason for this is that the Thurstone case V and the B.T.L. model imply strong stochastic transitivity of choice behavior, whereas unfolding theory implies moderate stochastic transitivity. Preferential choice behavior, then, generated by SPF's, should not be aggregated into a social utility by either the Thurstone or the B.T.L. model.

We then discussed majority decision as a social welfare function under the restriction of SPF's and interpreted the social ordering in terms of psychological scaling theory. The theorems of Arrow and Black reveal that preferences generated from a *qualitative J* scale satisfy weak stochastic transitivity and hence majority rule is suitable as a social welfare function. If a further step is taken to require that the preferences be generated by a common *quantitative J* scale and that the distribution of individuals be symmetric on the *J* scale, then the social ordering by majority rule may be interpreted as a least disliked social utility. The ordering obtained by majority rule is identical with the *I* scale of the median individual, so the group scale is a folded *J* scale.

To weight individuals equally in this social utility requires that all individuals' SPF's be linearly descending, symmetric, and identical everywhere if superimposed at the locus of the ideals, the peak. This requirement is equivalent to assuming the existence of interpersonally comparable utility for changes, as it corresponds to requiring a common unit of measurement but not a common origin; however, the requirement is that a common unit of measurement *exist*, not that it be estimable or arithmetically processed.

The unfolding technique for the analysis of preference orderings is capable of distinguishing between SPF's which are and are not symmetrical. If not symmetrical, the result is a qualitative *J* scale. If symmetrical, the result is a quantitative *J* scale. Given a quantitative *J* scale, however, there is no way, as yet, of saying whether the SPF's are linearly descending or not. Hence there is no way, even given a quantitative *J* scale, of insuring that individuals are weighted equally, that is, of testing for the existence of a common unit of measurement for an interpersonally comparable utility.

The final section discusses the method of averaging rank orders and the

Hare system as social welfare functions and then offers an alternative to the Hare system. The new method would reject the candidate with the most last-place votes instead of the one with the fewest first-place votes as in the Hare system. This method would yield the same result as majority rule in the one-dimensional case with SPF's and would, I conjecture, satisfy at least a weak form of the axiom of independence from other alternatives.

Finally we might point out that the problem of arriving at a group scale by majority decision is, in principle, the same problem as arriving at an individual's I scale when he is inconsistent under replication. An individual at different times may be thought of as a lot of individuals, and the problem is to aggregate "their" choices. The problem in this context is discussed in Section 10 of Chapter 5, where we compared weak stochastic transitivity and expected matrices as possible models for arriving at an *individual's* aggregate I scale.

REFERENCES

Arrow, K. J., 1951, *Social choice and individual values*, John Wiley and Sons, New York.

Black, D., 1948a, On the rationale of group decision making, *J. pol. Econ.*, **56**, 23–34.

Black, D., 1948b, The decisions of a committee using a special majority, *Econometrica*, **16**, 245–61.

Blau, J. H., 1957, The existence of social welfare functions, *Econometrica*, **25**, 302–313.

Huntington, E. V., 1938, A paradox in the scoring of competing teams, *Science*, **88**, 287–88.

Kemeny, J. G., 1959, Mathematics without numbers, *Dædalus*, **88**, 577–91.

Luce, R. D., 1959, *Individual choice behavior*, John Wiley and Sons, New York.

Luce, R. D., and H. Raiffa, 1957, *Games and decisions*, John Wiley and Sons, New York.

Milnor, J., 1954, "Games against nature," Chapter 4 in *Decision processes*, edited by R. M. Thrall, C. H. Coombs, and R. L. Davis, John Wiley and Sons, New York.

Riker, W. H., 1958, The paradox of voting and congressional rules for voting on amendments, *Amer. pol. Sci. Rev.*, **52**, 349–66.

Riker, W. H., 1961, Voting and summation of preferences: an interpretive bibliographical review of selected developments during the last decade, *Amer. pol. Sci. Rev.*, **55**, 900–911.

Vickery, W., 1960, Utility, strategy, and social decisions rules, *Quart. J. Econ.*, **74**, 507–35.

CHAPTER 19

QIIIb Data and Models

1. THE NATURE OF THE DATA

The data for QIIIb are proximity relations on pairs of points from the same set. Of all the various kinds of data (octants), this is one of the youngest in terms of its formal study and models for its analysis.

This kind of data appeared on the scene as early as 1916 among the methods used by Henning (1916) in the study of odors. In one method the subject was presented with a number of odors, instructed to smell a particular one, and then pick from the remainder the one most similar to it. This kind of observation may be interpreted as a proximity relation on the corresponding pair of points, QIIIb data. In Henning's method the subject then went on to find a third odor which was the most similar to the second, and so on, through long chains of odors. In still another method the subject's task was to assign a name to each odor as it was presented (that is, to identify the stimulus). These data were studied in terms of how often a given stimulus was confused with each other stimulus, the inference being that a stimulus would most often be confused with stimuli that were close to it in the psychological space.

Henning did not construct any formal method for analyzing this kind of data but apparently followed an intuitive process to arrive at a multidimensional configuration. Henning's data collection methods give rise to a particular kind of nonsymmetric QIIIb data, a kind which is classified as a *conditional proximity matrix.*

Although QIIIb data were recognized early as an appropriate form of observation for the study of stimuli differing in several attributes simultaneously, it was much later that the formal study of such data appeared.

It has been hardly more than a decade since the publication of Goodman's *The Structure of Appearance* in 1951, in which this kind of data was first given the serious and significant consideration it deserves. Consequently there is no established tradition of kinds of *behavior* mapped into this kind of data, nor is there a stable of tested models for its analysis.

The kind of behavior which would be mapped into QIIIb data might be described generically as "matching" behavior, "same-different" judgments, or "confusions." There are two kinds of such data, both in QIIIb, and they must be carefully distinguished. One may be called *symmetric* proximity data and the other *conditional* proximity data. Most of the remainder of this section is concerned with the distinction between the two.

A QIIIb data matrix is square, $n \times n$, and each stimulus is associated with a row and the corresponding column. A cell of the matrix contains a (response) measure pertaining to the degree to which the corresponding pair of stimuli were judged similar, confused, and so on, as the case may be. The critical distinction between the symmetric and the conditional proximity matrices is that the (j, k) cell in the symmetric proximity matrix necessarily has the same entry as the (k, j) cell, whereas in the conditional proximity matrix the entries in the (j, k) cell and the (k, j) cell may differ.

Suppose we present a subject with a pair of cigarettes which he smokes and then judges whether they are the same brand or not. If he did this many times, we could construct a matrix with each brand designating a row and corresponding column, and a cell, including the diagonal cells, would contain the proportion of times the corresponding pair of brands were judged to be the same. We would have the same entry in the (j, k) cell and the (k, j) cell if the data were collected in such a manner as to control for any serial effect in smoking a pair of cigarettes. In such a case we would have a symmetric proximity data matrix.

Suppose we collect our proximity data differently. We take an experienced cigarette smoker and tell him that we have cigarettes belonging to some particular set of brands. We ask him to smoke each cigarette and identify the brand. We let the row correspond to the brand being smoked and the column identify the brand the subject reports he is smoking. We may now expect that the proportion of times he reports brand B when smoking brand A will not be the same as the proportion of times he reports brand A when smoking brand B. So we have conditional proximity data.

Proximity matrices, either symmetric or conditional, do not need to be probabilistic matrices. Other kinds of response measures such as latency or amplitude might be used. The response by no means needs to be a verbal judgment, and there are many varieties of experimental contexts,

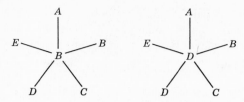

Fig. 19.1 Figurative cartwheels for a conditional data matrix.

but the formal pattern is clear. There is a set of stimuli mapped into corresponding stimulus points, and the observed behavior is interpreted to signify that a particular pair of points are "near" each other or not.

In symmetric proximity data the pair of points is an *unordered* pair. In conditional proximity data the pair of points is an *ordered* pair. This distinction bears on their respective interpretations when the cell entries are transformed into distances. For the symmetric proximity matrix the distances measured are *absolute* distances and are comparable between all cells in the matrix.

For the conditional proximity matrix the distances measured are *relative* distances and are only comparable in the same row of the matrix. For example, the proportion of times that stimulus A is identified as stimulus B is related to the distance from stimulus A to stimulus B *relative to the distances of all the other stimuli from A*. So the conditional probability, $p(B \mid A)$, is comparable to $p(C \mid A)$, that is, an entry in the same row, but not to $p(A \mid B)$, that is, an entry in another row.*

Another way of looking at the data in a conditional proximity matrix is to imagine that the stimuli are being presented in the form of a cartwheel, spokes only, with the row-stimulus at the hub and *all* the column-stimuli on the rim. With five stimuli, for example, Fig. 19.1 illustrates two presentations. In each such cartwheel the subject is instructed to pick the rim stimulus most like the hub. Each such cartwheel, replicated many times, yields a row of a conditional proximity matrix.

It should be intuitively evident that the percentage of times B is identified as a D in the cartwheel on the left will not necessarily be the same as the percentage of times that D is identified as a B in the cartwheel on the right. The conditional probability matrix is obtained from cartwheels in which the method of collecting the data consists of replications of 'pick $1/n$.' The experimenter presents the hub stimulus and the subject picks the rim stimulus, and this response is interpreted as a proximity relation

---

* We might make a corresponding argument leading to comparability only between entries in the same column. The point is that the data are relative proximity measures and the experimenter has to decide to what they are relative.

on the corresponding pair of stimulus points. The probabilities in a given row may be interpreted as the relative frequencies with which the column-stimuli are a "best" match to the row-stimulus, the hub of the cartwheel. These conditional probabilities, then, reflect the relative magnitudes of the distances from the row-stimulus to the several column-stimuli.

Another interpretation may be given to conditional proximity matrices; it is to regard them as QIVa similarities data. When an individual is presented with a stimulus and asked to identify it he may be regarded as picking the smallest among a set of conjoint distances, the spokes of the cartwheel. These are similarities data, being order relations on distances. But they are data collected by the method 'pick $1/n$'; and just as in QIa we found it necessary to transfer such data to QIIb to obtain a scale, so here in QIVa we find it necessary to transfer such data to QIIIb.

Formally, the observational equation for QIIIb data may be written in "distance" terms as follows:

$$|q_{hij} \ominus q_{hik}| = |p_{hi,jk}| \leq \epsilon_{hi,jk} \Leftrightarrow j \, M \, k \qquad (19.1)$$

where q_{hij} and q_{hik} are the points corresponding to stimuli j and k at the moment h for individual i. If and only if the absolute distance between them is less than some criterion or threshold quantity, ϵ, at that moment for that individual for that pair of stimuli, then the two stimuli are said to match each other.

The essential character of QIIIb data may be put in terms of vectors and vector displacements.* Each stimulus point, being an r-tuple, may simply be thought of as a vector, and the distance between two points may be thought of as a vector displacement. In the case of a symmetric proximity matrix, the data pertain to the *absolute magnitude of a vector displacement*. In the case of a conditional proximity matrix, the data pertain to the relative magnitudes *of vector displacements from a common point*.

In brief, proximity data may be either absolute or relative; the former yield symmetric matrices, the latter conditional. Further clarification of the nature of QIIIb data may be obtained by contrasting them with the data of QIIIa. In QIIIa the data consist of information about the algebraic difference between two points on a line, which, of course, may be positive or negative (see expression 17.1). In other words, the data in QIIIa included the *direction* of a vector displacement along a line, whereas in QIIIb the data pertain to the magnitude of a vector displacement between two points anywhere in a multidimensional space. The QIIIb data may pertain to absolute magnitude of displacement (symmetric proximity data) or relative magnitude of vector displacement (conditional proximity data).

* A suggestion of John Tukey, personal communication.

An example of a symmetric proximity matrix is contained in the study of Rothkopf (1957), in which pairs of Morse code signals were presented to Air Force cadets and each judged whether the signals in a pair were the same or different. The square data matrix is bordered by the signals, each cell contains the proportion of cadets who reported that pair of signals as the same, and hence the matrix is symmetric. A correlation or covariance matrix is also a good example of a symmetric proximity matrix. These measures, just like probabilities, latencies, and amplitudes, may be converted to measures of distances between pairs of points.*

Examples of conditional proximity matrices are contained in Green and Anderson (1955), Miller and Nicely (1955), and Shepard (1958).

In closing this discussion of the nature of QIIIb data I would like to turn to some further contrasts with QIIIa and point out some of the psychological implications. In Section 1 of Chapter 17 the nature of QIIIa data was discussed, and the point was made that if an experimenter wishes to classify or measure stimuli with respect to *some particular attribute*, the data and models of QIIIa are very appropriate. All models for QIIIa require that the data being analyzed involve the comparison of stimuli with respect to some common attribute, be it brightness of lights, strength of opinion, utility of commodities, or distance between pairs of points. Models for the analysis of QIIIa data all yield unidimensional stimulus scales.† The reason for this is that the task set for the subject is to compare two stimuli as to which has more of the attribute in question—an asymmetric predicate.

Goodman (1951, Section 2, Chapter 9) discusses the relative merits of various basic predicates for the purpose of discovering which aspects of stimuli are important.‡ He makes it clear that an asymmetric predicate such as that of QIIIa—"· · · has more of x than · · ·"—begs the question of what the psychological attributes underlying perceptual judgment are. Evaluating colors with respect to every a priori attribute we can think of is not the way to discover that hue, saturation, and brightness are or are not the important aspects. After discussing several possible predicates he arrives at "matches" as having superior advantages; in particular, it involves no prejudgment of what the aspects are to be and is applicable to all modalities. Unfortunately, use of the symmetric predicate involves some special problems of its own which will become apparent by the end of the chapter.

We turn first to a discussion of the models for each of the various

---

* See Chapter 24 for a more detailed discussion.
† A detailed discussion of this issue is contained in Hefner (1958).
‡ Galanter (1956), taking his inspiration from Goodman, discusses these same matters in a context more familiar to psychologists.

matrices; then to some limitations on matching data, including some experimental results; and finally, to an interpretation of sociometric matrices, relating them to QII and QIII.

Models for the analysis of QIIIb data are relatively few and may be

Table 19.1

Response Measure

	Discrete; for example, (1, 0)	Continuous; for example, Probability
Symmetric proximity matrix	1. Goodman-Galanter model for ordinal scales of stimuli	2. Ordinal scales of distances 3. Hefner's model for ratio scales of distances
Conditional proximity matrix	4. Triangular analysis for ordinal scales of distances	5. Shepard's model for ratio scales of distances

simply organized in a fourfold table, as in Table 19.1. Models for the symmetric proximity matrix will be discussed first and then those for the conditional proximity matrix.

2. SYMMETRIC PROXIMITY MATRICES

The Goodman-Galanter Model

This model is a set theoretic model leading in the simplest case to ordinal scales of stimuli. The data matrix is square with 1 or 0 elements in the cells indicating that the matching predicate holds between the corresponding stimuli or does not, so the matrix is symmetric. If an ordinal scale obtains, a permutation of the matrix exists such that the 1's form a diagonal parallelogram in many ways similar to the parallelogram analysis of QIIb data.

It is convenient here to adopt Galanter's notation. Stimuli are designated by lower-case letters, a, b, c, and so on. The *manor* of a stimulus a is defined as a set, A, of all stimuli that match a. Capital letters will designate the manor that corresponds to a stimulus. The cells in a row of the data matrix containing a 1, then, designate the manor of that row-stimulus. The objective is, in the terms of Goodman's book, to "plot on a map" (1951, p. 240) the relative positions of the stimulus points.

Goodman and Galanter make the reasonable assumption that matching elements are nearer each other than are nonmatching elements and then go on to define three additional concepts useful in constructing a linear array. These concepts, all very simple, are *betweeness*, *besideness*, and the term *clan*. The basic idea of *betweeness* is that a stimulus between two others is nearer either of them than they are to each other. They then use the assumption that matching elements are nearer than are nonmatching elements to define betweeness in terms of the relations between the three manors. If we let $a/b/c$ signify the statement that b is between a and c, the formal definition requires that the three stimuli match each other pairwise and that the symmetric difference* of A and C, that is, $(A \dagger C)$, be cardinally greater than the symmetric difference of either with B, that is,

$$a/b/c = a\,M\,b,\ b\,M\,c,\ a\,M\,c,\ A \dagger C > A \dagger B,\ A \dagger C > B \dagger C$$

Besideness is simply defined for two distinct elements, say a and b, in that they match and no element exists which is between them.

A clan is such that, however it is partitioned into two subsets, some element of one of the subsets will match some element of the other. A *clan* of stimuli, then, is a set of stimuli such that there is an M path between any two elements. This concept corresponds to the similar notion of *connectedness* in graph theory and is basic to the notion of a linear array.

These concepts are sufficient under certain circumstances to arrive at a linear array of the stimuli. One of these circumstances is whether the manors of the stimuli are cardinally constant or vary in size. The problem here is easily seen in the context of parallelogram analysis. It was seen in Chapter 4 that if stimuli satisfied an ordinal scale it was readily recovered by parallelogram analysis if the data were 'pick k/n,' with k a constant. Whereas, in Chapter 15, where the data are 'pick any/n' (that is, k not constant), parallelogram analysis was seen to lead to indeterminacies in the order of stimuli or of individuals.

There is a very close relation between parallelogram analysis and this model of Goodman and Galanter, even though the former is for two distinct sets of points and the latter for only one.‡ The relation may be seen in terms of the relations between their data matrices. Imagine a square symmetric (1, 0) data matrix of QIIIb data. Divide the stimuli into two disjoint subsets which we will now call individuals and stimuli. For example, cross out the odd-numbered rows and the even-numbered columns. Then the cells that remain will be QIIb data, and may be analyzed by parallelogram analysis.

---

* The symmetric difference $\dagger$ of two sets is their union minus their intersection, that is, $A \dagger B = A \cup B - A \cap B$.

‡ This also suggests that their model may be readily extended to (1, 0) conditional proximity matrices, which are nonsymmetric.

Usually, of course, in the case of QIIIb data, we would not expect the manors to be cardinally constant. This leads Goodman and Galanter to a procedure which they call "regularizing" an array. This amounts to interpolating hypothetical points, that is, adjusting the spacing between points on the "ordinal" scale, in order that there will always be more stimulus points between nonmatching pairs than between matching pairs. This permits them to introduce something equivalent to a "just noticeable difference" and thereby introduce at least the aura of a metric. Galanter remarks, however, that the entire theory of map adjustment is yet to be worked out, especially in the multidimensional case.

Many, if not most, data matrices will not satisfy a linear order, and Goodman discusses some types of nonlinear arrays. The necessity for a theory of nonlinear arrays is apparent when a data matrix reveals an element which has more than two others beside it. A linear array admits an element to have at most two others beside it. More than two requires increasing the dimensionality of the configuration or map. Goodman's discussion is limited to a few special configurations, and much further work needs to be done before the theory will be generally useful in the multidimensional analysis of a data matrix.

Ordinal Scales of Distances

A rank order of the interpoint distances is very easily obtained from a symmetric proximity matrix if the assumption is made that the more often two stimuli are confused the nearer they are. If there is a strictly monotone function relating probability of confusion to psychological distance, the rank order of the probabilities from largest to smallest corresponds to the rank order of the interpoint distances from small to large. As Stevens (1958, pp. 187-88) points out, this assumption may not always hold.

An analysis of a probabilistic symmetric proximity matrix is presented in Chapter 22, in which the assumption is made that the more often two stimuli are confused the nearer they are.

Hefner's Model for Ratio Scales of Distances

As discussed in the first section, the data with which we are concerned here are contained in a square matrix with the same set of stimuli designating both the rows and the columns. A cell of the matrix contains the proportion of times the corresponding pair of stimuli were judged to be *different*—the complement of the proportion of times they were judged the *same*.

It is important for Hefner's model that the diagonal elements of this matrix be experimentally determined. This requires the presentation of pairs of identical stimuli. The reason for this, as will be clearer shortly, is to determine the individual's criterion distance for judging stimuli to be different.

The problem is to transform each probability in the data matrix into an absolute distance between the corresponding pair of points. When this is accomplished, the distances may be analyzed by the Young-Householder procedure as modified and described by Torgerson (1958, Chapter 11). The objective is to process these QIIIb data on probability of matching into QIVa data on *degree of similarity*, that is, measures of interpoint distances, and then to use a multidimensional model of QIVa for the recovery of the stimulus space.

Hefner (1958) extended Thurstone's model of comparative judgment to adapt it to this problem. He showed that under certain assumptions, in the spirit of Thurstone's case V, the distribution of the discriminal processes for a squared distance is noncentral χ^2 with r degrees of freedom, where r is the dimensionality of the space. The noncentrality parameter is the square of the distance between the means of two r-variate normal distributions. The parameter r may be estimated by an iterative process.

We first show that the distribution of the discriminal processes for a squared distance is noncentral χ^2; we then discuss its application to the transformation of the probabilistic symmetric proximity matrix to a distance matrix; and we finish with a discussion of some special aspects of the computing routine.

The assumptions made are that there is a multivariate normal distribution of values of the discriminal process associated with each stimulus. This is to say that the point corresponding to a stimulus varies randomly in this manner. The space is of unknown dimensionality, r; the discriminal process is uncorrelated over dimensions; and the variability of every stimulus point in every dimension is the same. In geometrical terms we might think of each point as surrounded by concentric circles (hyperspheres) whose radii correspond to probabilities of confusion. These are the assumptions which I described as being in the spirit of Thurstone's case V but extended to an r-dimensional space. The problem is to estimate the parameter r and the coordinates of the means or modal points of the n multivariate normal distributions from the data.

When two stimuli are presented to the subject it is assumed that each gives rise to a point drawn at random from its distribution of discriminal processes. If the Euclidean distance between that pair of points is greater than some criterion distance, the subject judges them to be different; otherwise he judges them to be the same.

We wish to prove that the distribution function of the square of the distance between pairs of points drawn at random from two r-variate normal distributions with equal variance in all dimensions, and uncorrelated over dimensions, is noncentral χ^2 with r degrees of freedom.

Let X and Y be r-variate normal distributions with normal projections on each dimension, $N(\bar{X}_d, \sigma^2)$ and $N(\bar{Y}_d, \sigma^2)$ respectively. A point drawn at random from each distribution will have the following projections:

$$X_d = x_d\sigma + \bar{X}_d, \qquad Y_d = y_d\sigma + \bar{Y}_d$$

where x_d and y_d are random deviates drawn from a population that is $N(0, 1)$.

The difference between the projections on each dimension of such a set of points is

$$X_d - Y_d = \sigma(x_d - y_d) + \bar{X}_d - \bar{Y}_d$$

Letting $\delta_d = (x_d - y_d)/\sqrt{2}$, a random deviate drawn from a population that is $N(0, 1)$, and $c_d = (\bar{X}_d - \bar{Y}_d)/\sigma\sqrt{2}$, we have

$$X_d - Y_d = \sqrt{2}\sigma(\delta_d + c_d)$$

The square of the distance between the pair of points in the total space $D_{XY}{}^2$, is

$$D_{XY}{}^2 = \sum_{d=1}^{r} (X_d - Y_d)^2 = 2\sigma^2 \sum_{d=1}^{r} (\delta_d + c_d)^2$$

The unit of measurement being arbitrary, we may set $\sigma^2 = \frac{1}{2}$ and we have

$$D_{XY}{}^2 = \sum_{d=1}^{r} (\delta_d + c_d)^2 \tag{19.2}$$

and
$$c_d = \bar{X}_d - \bar{Y}_d$$

Equation 19.2 is the equation of a noncentral χ^2 with r degrees of freedom. The noncentrality parameter λ is

$$\lambda = \sum_{d=1}^{r} c_d{}^2$$

which is the square of the distance between the means of the two r-variate normal distributions, that is, $D_{XY} = \sqrt{\lambda_{XY}}$.

We are now in a position to transform the symmetric proximity matrix into a distance matrix. We recognize that there are n diagonal elements for the n identical pairs which can be used to determine the criterion distance. There are $n(n - 1)/2$ offdiagonal elements which can be used to estimate the corresponding number of distances. Then there is the unknown parameter r, the dimensionality of the space, to be determined.

The method of analysis that Hefner developed is an iterative one. First assume $r = 1$, compute the interpoint distances, and test to see if they satisfy a one-dimensional space; if not, assume $r = 2$, redetermine the interpoint distances, test; and continue as necessary. Unfortunately, tables of noncentral χ^2 with more than one degree of freedom are not available.* In the case of $r = 1$, $D_{XY} = \sqrt{\lambda_{XY}}$ is distributed normally and a table of the unit normal may be used. A hypothetical example in one dimension, taken from Hefner, will be used to illustrate the procedure which readily generalizes to $r > 1$. When adequate tables become available this method will be quite feasible.

Table 19.2   Hypothetical Probabilistic Symmetric Proximity Data:
Proportion of Times Judged *Different*

	A	B	C	D	E
A	.05				
B	.23	.05			
C	.60	.27	.05		
D	.75	.29	.07	.05	
E	.77	.33	.08	.052	.05

Table 19.2 contains hypothetical data for five stimuli. The numbers in the cells are p_{jk}, the proportion of times stimuli j and k were judged to be *different*; note that the empirical values of p_{jj} are included.

The first problem is to determine the criterion distance, assuming that the $\epsilon_{hi,jk}$ of equation 19.1 is a constant for all pairs (j, k). Differences between two stimuli j and k in one dimension will be normally distributed. An individual's judgment that the pair j and k are the same or different is equivalent to drawing a "difference" from this distribution and comparing it in absolute magnitude with the criterion distance, $\epsilon_{hi,jk}$.

To determine this criterion distance we use the distribution of differences between pairs of points which are assumed to be independently drawn from the *same* normal distribution. Hence two identical stimuli will sometimes appear different just as a difference drawn from this distribution of differences will sometimes be extreme. Note that the variance of this distribution of differences is 1 since the variance of the stimulus distributions has been set equal to $\frac{1}{2}$.

---

* Patnaik (1949) points out that noncentral χ^2 has been used almost exclusively to evaluate the power function of the χ^2 test, and to develop the noncentral F-distribution to evaluate the power function of the F test. For these purposes most interest has been centered on a few values (Fix, 1949). Patnaik also discusses various approximations to noncentral χ^2 which are not simple and Hefner believes are probably not accurate enough for this purpose.

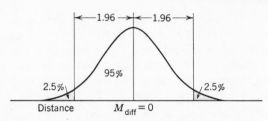

Fig. 19.2 Distribution of differences between identical stimuli for determining criterion distances.

In these hypothetical data we have an individual who 5 % of the time judges two identical stimuli to be different. In Fig. 19.2 we show a normal distribution of differences with a mean of *zero* and a variance of *one*. All differences within ±1.96 of the mean lead to judgments of *same* and all differences greater than this lead to judgments of *different*. In general, with dimensionality one the percentage of times two identical stimuli are judged *different* is the area under the two symmetric tails of a normal distribution. The point of truncation in sigma units (absolute value) is the criterion difference.

Each diagonal entry leads to an independent estimate of this criterion distance. With fallible data they will not be alike. If they do not differ significantly, the estimates may be averaged. If they do differ significantly, the criterion distance is not a constant, and this must be taken into account in analyzing the data. Hefner provides a procedure for this which is described in the next section. In a footnote (1958, p. 38) he has this to say about the problem:

In general we would expect the subject to vary the criterion distance to suit various situations. It is presumed that we can hold the (criterion distance) constant for a given experiment by holding constant the following parameters:
P_s, the *a priori* subjective probability of the stimuli being the same;
U_1, the value to the subject of judging "same" when the stimuli are the same;
U_2, the value to the subject of judging "same" when the stimuli are different;
U_3, the value to the subject of judging "different" when the stimuli are different;
U_4, the value to the subject of judging "different" when the stimuli are the same.

In the next section we present some experimental work of Hefner's which indicates that the stability of a criterion distance is a serious problem. With these hypothetical data, however, we are remarkably free of any difficulties of this kind and are able to illustrate without complications the next step in the transformation of probabilities into distances.

Converting an offdiagonal probability into a distance may be visualized as sliding or translating a normal distribution with unit variance along

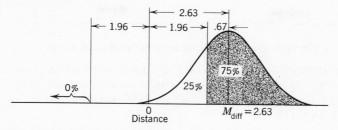

Fig. 19.3 Distribution of differences for stimuli A and D: $p_{\text{diff}} = .75$.

the real line so that the area of the distribution over the line segment between ±1.96 (or whatever the criterion distance may be) corresponds to the proportion of "same judgments." The mean of the distribution is the required distance D_{jk}. Two examples are shown in Figs. 19.3 and 19.4. Figure 19.3 is for the pair of stimuli A and D from Table 19.2 and illustrates

Table 19.3 Distances Corresponding to the Probabilities of Table 19.2

	A	B	C	D	E
A	0				
B	1.21	0			
C	2.21	1.00	0		
D	2.63	1.42	0.42	0	
E	2.72	1.5	0.51	0.09	0

a case in which only one tail of the distribution is substantially outside the line segment defined by the criterion distance. Figure 19.4 illustrates the case for stimuli D and E in which both tails have significant amounts of area outside the criterion interval.

Table 19.3 contains the distances obtained in this manner from the probabilities contained in Table 19.2, assuming $r = 1$. Figure 19.5 gives the configuration of points which satisfy these interpoint distances.

The hypothetical data in Table 19.2 were selected so that the interpoint distances of Table 19.3 would satisfy unidimensionality. In practice, this

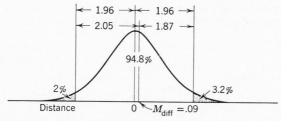

Fig. 19.4 Distribution of differences for stimuli D and E: $p_{\text{diff}} = .052$.

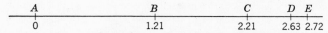

A   B   C   D   E

0   1.21   2.21   2.63 2.72

Fig. 19.5 Stimulus scale for hypothetical data, Table 19.2.

matrix of interpoint distances would be converted to scalar products and factored; and this procedure would check the dimensionality which was initially assumed. The details of this procedure are presented in Torgerson (1958, Chapter 11).

Some Limitations of Probabilistic Symmetric Proximity Data

Although symmetric same-different data have certain real advantages over the data of QIIIa for discovering the "structure of appearance," they also have some limitations. In particular, there are two which Hefner's experimental work points up and which will be discussed here. These limitations are (1) that the criterion distance for the judgment "different" may not be a constant for all pairs in a given data matrix, and (2) that the method of collecting data runs into difficulties with highly discriminable or very different stimuli. Judgments of "different" 0% or 100% of the time cannot be translated into a distance; even percentages in the neighborhood of 0% or 100% need to be based on many trials to be sufficiently reliable.

Hefner studied both of these issues. The stimuli he used were five Munsell gray values: 7, 6, 5, 3.5, and 3, in order from light to dark. One and one-half inch squares of these papers were cemented to 4 × 6 inch white cards and were tachistoscopically exposed, pairwise, through 1-inch circular holes in a frame at the rear of the tachistoscope. Because these stimuli were relatively discriminable he used a procedure of degrading the stimuli by using a brief exposure interval. The two subjects in the experiment were run individually.

His instructions to the subject were as follows (1958, pp. 64-65):

In this portion of the experiment you will be observing two stimuli. Your task is to tell me whether the two stimuli are the "same" or "different." Of all the pairs that you see, one-third will actually be physically the same and two-thirds will be different in varying degrees—some very close and some very different. There are four possible kinds of judgments that we can diagram in the following way:

Proportion	Physical Situation The Pairs Are	Your Judgment The Pairs Are	
$\frac{1}{3}$	Same	Same	(correct)
		Different	(wrong)
$\frac{2}{3}$	Different	Same	(wrong)
		Different	(correct)

Note that there are two ways of being correct—by saying "same" for pairs that are actually the same and by saying "different" for pairs that are actually different. I want you to regard all of these possible outcomes as equally weighted; that is, one kind of error is just as serious as the other kind, and one way of being correct is just as desirable as the other. Another way of saying the same thing would be to assume that I had money to pay you for each response. If I said that I would pay you ten cents for each correct response, and if you had to pay me ten cents for each wrong response, then all four responses would be "equally important" or "equally weighted."

In a pretest he determined a suitable exposure interval for each subject in the context of these instructions which would make the stimuli relatively

Table 19.4 Proportion of "Different" Judgments—$S1$

	7	6	5	3.5	3
7	.562	.647	.896	.962	.924
6		.548	.607	.776	.808
5			.426	.454	.579
3.5				.336	.287
3					.312

Table 19.5 Proportion of "Different" Judgments—$S2$

	7	6	5	3.5	3
7	.514	.769	.925	.918	.972
6		.615	.639	.611	.663
5			.463	.402	.448
3.5				.435	.370
3					.491

indiscriminable. For $S1$ the interval used was 0.0407 seconds and for $S2$ the interval was 0.0199 seconds. Each pair of stimuli was replicated at least 100 times.

The symmetric proximity matrix for each subject is presented in Tables 19.4 and 19.5.

The diagonal elements of these two symmetric proximity matrices strongly suggest that the assumption of constant criterion distance and/or equal variance has been violated. Consequently Hefner computed the criterion distance for each offdiagonal pair by averaging the proportions in the two corresponding diagonal elements. He points out that this is an approximate solution to the multidimensional analogue of case III of Thurstone's model for comparative judgment.

Any negative estimate of a distance was arbitrarily set equal to zero. The resulting matrix of interpoint distances was analyzed by the usual procedure for the Thurstone model of comparative judgment.

Stimulus
7
6
5
3.5
3
Scale value
0.00
0.85
1.70
2.40
2.46

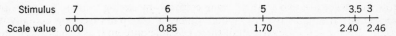

Fig. 19.6 Stimulus scale for subject 1.

Tables 19.6 and 19.7 give the interpoint distances obtained in this manner, and Figs. 19.6 and 19.7 give the resulting stimulus scales for the two subjects.

Table 19.6 Interpoint Distances for *S*1

	7	6	5	3.5	3
7	0	0.73	1.92	2.53	2.21
6		0	0.76	1.49	1.63
5			0	0.57	1.03
3.5				0	0
3					0

Table 19.7 Interpoint Distances for *S*2

	7	6	5	3.5	3
7	0	1.34	2.08	2.04	2.58
6		0	0.86	0.76	0.98
5			0	0	0
3.5				0	0
3					0

The data reveal that even in this simple stimulus context of gray papers the criterion distance is probably not constant, but Hefner has provided an approximate method for solution. The adequacy of the procedure is perhaps indicated by the comparison of the results with those obtained by other methods. Data which lent themselves to a QIIIa analysis by case V of Thurstone's model for comparative judgment were collected on the same stimuli, and a separate set of data was also collected by cartwheel methods (case 2). In the former instance each subject was presented with each pair of stimuli and judged which was brighter, replicated at least 100 times, and in the latter case each triple was presented, permuting hubs, and replicated at least 80 times with each hub. In this case the subject is judging which of two stimuli is more like the hub stimulus, so this is a pair comparison of distances, that is, similarities data.

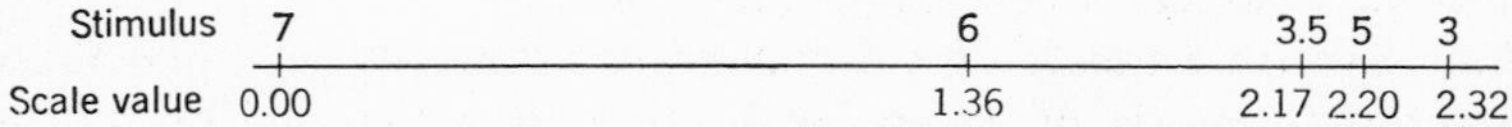

Stimulus
7
6
3.5
5
3
Scale value
0.00
1.36
2.17
2.20
2.32

Fig. 19.7 Stimulus scale for subject 2.

Each of these experiments leads to a probability data matrix. The first is on pairs of the n stimuli (the grays themselves), and the second is on pairs of the n' stimuli (the interpoint distances). Each data matrix leads to a set of distances between all pairs of points which may be compared with those obtained from the same-different data. There is no need to report the results in detail; a summary suffices. The interpoint distances obtained by Hefner in this analysis of the same-different data are linearly related to each of the others. The relation is especially close, for each subject, with the distances obtained from pair comparison data on brightness analyzed by case V of the comparative judgment model. The relation

Table 19.8   Proportion of "Different" Judgments—$S3$

	$A, 4/6$	$B, 4/10$	$C, 5/8$	$D, 5/12$	$E, 6/6$	$F, 6/10$	$G, 7/4$
$A, 4/6$	.207	.315	.252	.528	.810	.903	1.00
$B, 4/10$		.216	.202	.245	.842	.908	1.00
$C, 5/8$			.307	.339	.760	.788	.953
$D, 5/12$				.337	.771	.845	.981
$E, 6/6$					.462	.383	.667
$F, 6/10$						.416	.615
$G, 7/4$							.188

is very poor, for one subject, with the distances obtained by a case V analysis of the similarities data.

At this point the model appears very promising at least for the analysis of same-different data in the one-dimensional case, and experimental impoverishment of the stimuli appears to have accomplished its purpose. Difficulties arise, however, in the multidimensional case. Hefner duplicated the procedure he used to collect same-different data on the gray stimuli with a set of Munsell red-colored papers, the same ones used by Torgerson (1951) in his thesis. They were all Munsell 5R (red) but differed in value and chroma. The value and chroma numbers, respectively, for the seven stimuli, were $A, 4/6$; $B, 4/10$; $C, 5/8$; $D, 5/12$; $E, 6/6$; $F, 6/10$; $G, 7/4$. According to the Munsell system they are located in a plane, a two-dimensional color space.

Instructions to subjects were exactly the same as before except that the subjects were told "one half of the pairs will actually be physically the same and one half will be different" instead of the previous $\frac{1}{3}:\frac{2}{3}$ ratio. Two subjects were used, $S3$ and $S4$. Degradation to achieve a desired degree of inconsistency was determined by the pretest; the exposure time used for $S3$ was 0.0324 and for $S4$ it was 0.0510 seconds.

The proportions of judgments "different" obtained from each subject are given in Tables 19.8 and 19.9.

The diagonals here clearly reveal the violation either of a constant criterion distance or of constant variance as assumed in the model or both. An approximate method could be used, however, such as the one Hefner devised for the previous set of data, except that here the dimensionality is two and tables of noncentral χ^2, as previously mentioned, are not available.

Under these circumstances, what Hefner did was to transform these proportions into a *rank order* of the distances and analyze the rank order by Hays's nonmetric multidimensional model for similarities data (see Chapter 21).

Table 19.9 Proportion of "Different" Judgments—S4

	A, 4/6	B, 4/10	C, 5/8	D, 5/12	E, 6/6	F, 6/10	G, 7/4
A, 4/6	.028	.029	.119	.302	.920	.991	1.000
B, 4/10		.028	.135	.187	.914	.982	.990
C, 5/8			.163	.182	.817	.935	.990
D, 5/12				.267	.942	.896	.991
E, 6/6					.568	.657	.750
F, 6/10						.540	.725
G, 7/4							.249

Hefner assumed that distances between pairs of stimuli are monotonically related to the proportion of judgments "different" for each pair when the proportion for identical stimuli is constant. When this condition is not satisfied he proposed to take it into account by applying the following transformation on the proportions:

$$D_{jk} = 1 - \frac{(1 - P_{jk})(1 - P_{kj})}{(1 - P_{jj})(1 - P_{kk})}$$

where P_{jk} is the proportion of judgments "j different from k." The transformation has the property of assuring that the distance from any stimulus to itself is zero. It also relates the proportion of judgments "different" for each stimulus pair to the proportion of judgments "different" for each stimulus with itself. He recognizes that this is not the only possible transformation. What is desired is the rank order of the distances, and he assumes that the rank order of the D_{jk} given by the transformation is a better approximation than the rank order of the P_{jk} themselves.

The multidimensional analysis of the rank order of the distances for each subject is a process by which we "take out" a dimension at a time, each time accounting for as much of the data as possible. The latter phrase means the following:* Each triple of points defines a triangle in

* We are here anticipating what will be discussed in some detail in Part 5.

the space and the distance relations among the three sides are known. The three corners of a triangle, or, better yet, the three sides of a triangle, will project on any dimension through the space. If the orientation of a triangle to an axis is such that the relative magnitude of the projections of the sides is identical with the relative magnitude of the lengths of the sides themselves, that triple of distances is considered satisfied.

Hefner's analysis of his data for each of the two subjects revealed that the first dimension satisfied 31 out of the 35 triples for $S3$ and 30 out of 35 for $S4$. The few data remaining, the unsatisfied triples, are insufficient to determine a second dimension and may represent error. The significant thing is that the first dimension for both subjects was perfectly monotonically related to the brightness dimension of the Munsell system, the implication being that the experimental impoverishment of the stimuli by brief time exposure changed them qualitatively in that the subjects responded primarily to brightness differences. It is as if there were "brightness receptors" and "color receptors" and the latter's response time were longer than the former's and greater than the exposure intervals.

These results indicate that the use of same-different data for multidimensional analysis of stimulus spaces is quite difficult. If the stimuli are not to be impoverished they must be nearly indiscriminable, and if they are impoverished they may be qualitatively changed. The problem of the lack of constancy of the criterion distance is also a serious one but at least can be patched up in special ways for special cases.

3. CONDITIONAL PROXIMITY MATRICES

We first discuss the construction of ordinal scales of interpoint distances from conditional proximity matrices, which is more complicated than the construction for symmetric proximity matrices, and then we briefly discuss Shepard's model for constructing ratio scales of interpoint distances from such data.

Triangular Analysis for Ordinal Scales of Distances

As was pointed out in Section 1, the cell entries of a probabilistic conditional proximity matrix are conditional probabilities and are only comparable within a row and not between rows, in contrast to symmetric proximity matrices. We shall assume that the conditional proximity measures in a row of the matrix are inversely related to distances. Then the rank order of the measures in a given row (from largest to smallest) is the same as the rank order of the distances (from smallest to largest) to the corresponding column-stimuli from that row-stimulus.

Suppose, for example, we have a conditional proximity matrix as in Table 19.10 based on hypothetical data. In the first row the rank order of stimuli going away from A is $A\ B\ C\ D$ because $p(A \mid A) > p(B \mid A) > p(C \mid A) > p(D \mid A)$. Such a rank order is analogous to the I scales of Part 2

Table 19.10   A Conditional Proximity Matrix (Hypothetical Data)

	A	B	C	D
A	.80	.10	.06	.04
B	.15	.70	.05	.10
C	.08	.02	.85	.05
D	.04	.06	.02	.88

in that it is the rank order of the stimuli in order of increasing distance from a point. In this case the ideal point is another stimulus point. It will be convenient to call such a scale a "stimulus I scale" or just an I scale. A separate term would be desirable, such as S scale, but this could be confused with the stimulus scales of QII or QIII. So rather than continue to multiply neologisms, we shall use the term I scale here again.

Table 19.11 presents the stimulus I scales corresponding to the four rows of Table 19.10.

Table 19.11   Stimulus I Scales from Table 19.10

$$A\ B\ C\ D$$
$$B\ A\ D\ C$$
$$C\ A\ D\ B$$
$$D\ B\ A\ C$$

The next step is to test these distance relations for transitivity. The problem may be most simply put in the following terms. Consider any triple of points, say A, B, and C, in a multidimensional space. The conditional probabilities in row A give the relative distances of stimuli B

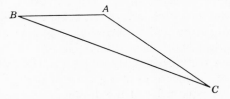

Fig. 19.8   Three stimulus points on a plane.

and C from A, so let us suppose we find that B is nearer to A than C is to A. We might think of these three points as defining a triangle, as in Fig. 19.8. From row C let us suppose we find that A is nearer to C than B is.

If the space in which these points lie is a metric space, the distances are symmetric and transitive. Thus the distance *from A to B* must be the same as the distance *from B to A*. So we may now write

$$A\text{'s } I \text{ scale} \Rightarrow \overline{AC} > \overline{AB}$$
$$C\text{'s } I \text{ scale} \Rightarrow \overline{BC} > \overline{AC}$$

Hence
$$\overline{BC} > \overline{AB}$$

The data in row B, being experimentally independent, provide a test of whether these distances are transitive and the hypothesis of a metric space is sustained. If transitivity holds, A should be nearer to B than C is to B, so the stimulus B should be more often "recognized" as an A than as a C, and B's I scale should be B A C.

This condition of transitivity must be tested for and satisfied by all triples of points, and furthermore for all triples of distances, within the limits of the reliability of the data. A convenient way of testing for this is to see if a partial order of distances can be formed from the several I scales. A procedure for finding out is to use triangular analysis as discussed in Chapter 17, Section 3. The discussion there of constructing ordinal scales of interpoint distances deals with the problem of merging stimulus I scales obtained from cartwheel methods of collecting the data. If the stimulus I scales have been obtained from a conditional proximity matrix, as they have here, however, the method of analysis presented in Chapter 17 is applicable. In fact, these same data are analyzed in Table 17.4.

Usually only a partial order will be formed because disjoint distances will not necessarily be ordered. A conditional proximity matrix contains information on the order relations of disjoint distances only by inference, not by observation. Here, for example, we find (Chapter 17, Section 3) that $\overline{CD} > \overline{AB}$, not by direct observation, but as a consequence of the observations that $\overline{CD} > \overline{AD}$ and that $\overline{AD} > \overline{AB}$.

If a triangular analysis reveals intransitivities, they may be pinpointed as shown in the discussion in Chapter 17. The manner in which intransitive cycles are broken to remove the intransitivities is a problem to be solved by the experimenter for his particular matrix. In Chapter 22 an analysis of a conditional proximity matrix which contains intransitive distance relations is presented and a procedure for resolving them is illustrated.

The analysis of these order relations on interpoint distances, whether from a symmetric or a conditional proximity matrix, or any other source, is a problem for a QIVa model and is discussed in the next several chapters.

Shepard's Model for Ratio Scales of Distances

Shepard, in his excellent thesis on stimulus and response generalization (1957, 1958, 1960), had a more profound intent than the metric analysis of conditional proximity matrices, but this analysis is at least an incidental contribution if not the major one. The problem here, the analysis of a conditional proximity matrix, he has embedded in a more general problem of multiple stimulus-response situations. A brief look at this more general problem will make clear its relevance to the analysis of a conditional proximity matrix.

He considers a situation in which there is a set of stimuli and exactly the same number of responses in one-to-one correspondence with the stimuli. Assume the subject's task is to learn the paired associates. In the course of learning he makes errors. Shepard assumes that errors arise because the stimulus presented is confused with another stimulus because they are similar, or the response called for is replaced by another because they are similar. If either the stimuli or the responses are clearly and unambiguously differentiated and discriminable, or if by experimental procedure the confusions among one of the sets may be controlled, then errors are attributable to confusions among the elements of the other set. The degree of confusion, a frequency measure, is interpreted as a measure of similarity, a distance, and thereby leads to a scale of the stimuli (or the responses, as the case may be).

Two big theoretical steps are required to reach a symmetric matrix of interpoint distances. One is a choice of a function to transform each conditional probability into a distance, and then a resolution of the two estimates of each distance obtained from two different cartwheels, like those illustrated in Fig. 19.1.

Shepard assumes an exponential decay function for the former on the basis of various generalization studies, and simply averages the two estimates of the same distance to obtain a symmetric matrix. I think the latter step is vulnerable to the following criticism. If the measures in a conditional proximity matrix reflect the *relative* distances of the column points from the row point, as I have argued here, then averaging the two estimates of the distance $\overline{jk}$ obtained from the (j, k) cell and the (k, j) cell is incorrect.

The distance matrix that Shepard constructs is assumed to contain measures of the distances on a ratio scale, so these data then are mapped into QIVa as similarities data and analyzed by Torgerson's method.

4. SOCIOMETRIC CHOICE BEHAVIOR FROM THE POINT OF VIEW OF DATA THEORY

A discussion of sociometric choice is a very appropriate topic with which to bring our treatment of QIII to a close. It has the virtue of illustrating not only the relation between QIIIa and QIIIb data but also the relation between QIII data and those of QII.

Matrix theory and graph theory have been used in models for making inferential classifications from sociometric choice behavior. The data with which they deal may readily be seen to be, in its formal properties, the data of QII and QIII.

If each member of a task group is asked whom he bosses, a matrix may be formed in which a 1 in a cell indicates that the row-individual says he bosses that column-individual. We would expect the symmetric cell* in the matrix to have a 0 entry or we would have two individuals bossing each other. Such a sociometric matrix contains QIIIa data. As far as the data matrix is concerned, it could represent the judgment that one weight is heavier than another.

If the members of a fraternity are asked with whom they go to movies, a matrix may be formed in which a 1 in a cell indicates that the individual of that row said he goes to the movies with the individual of that column. If instructions are clear, memory is perfect, and reporting is honest, the symmetric cell would also have a 1 in it, as in a symmetric proximity matrix.

If the members of a fraternity are asked with whom they *would like* to go to movies, a matrix may be formed in which a 1 in a cell indicates that that row-individual chooses that column-individual. Here the symmetric cell may or may not have a 1 in it, and in general such a matrix would be nonsymmetric, as in a conditional proximity matrix.

The study of such matrices by either graph theory or matrix algebra involves manipulating the matrix to study the structure and pattern of interrelations in a group, such as tendencies to form cliques, measurement of influence, cohesion, and a great variety of matters of interest in the study of groups. The papers of Cartwright and Harary (1956), Harary and Ross (1957), Katz and Powell (1957), and Glanzer and Glaser (1959) are representative of the variety of approaches and problems.

Sociometric models are mostly concerned with (1, 0) data matrices and nominal classification in contrast to so-called measurement models which are mostly concerned with more refined data matrices (for example, probabilistic) and levels of classification and structure higher than nominal.

---

* That obtained by transposing row and column designations.

The sociometric models anchor one end of a broad band or spectrum of logical systems for the inferential classification of stimuli and people on the basis of behavior.

The context of sociometric choice also provides a way of illustrating the distinction between the data of QII and the data of QIII as well as the role of the scientist in phase 2, making data out of observations. The formal difference between QIII and QII data is that QIII data have one set of points whereas QII have two. Suppose we ask the members of a fraternity with whom they would like to play tennis. We might readily map these data into QIIIb by imagining each individual as a point in a space of "tennis ability" and liking to play with individuals of similar general capability. The Goodman-Galanter model would seem called for in that each row-individual is being "matched" to his "manor" of column-individuals.

As one possible alternative to this, we might feel that the point which corresponds to an individual as a respondent, his ideal point, might be a different point from that which corresponds to him as a stimulus to others. Some individuals may "see themselves as other see them" and the same point will serve both purposes, that is, as stimulus point and as ideal point. Other individuals may have an exaggerated opinion of themselves or merely like to play with players better than themselves, and others may be more modest or like to win more often. The point is this: *If the experimenter chooses to assume that the individual in the two different roles may be two different points he makes QII data out of the matrix* and analyzes it accordingly. In this case he may make it QIIb data and use a latent class model, for example. *If the experimenter chooses to assume that the individual is essentially only one point, he makes QIIIb data out of it.*

The important lesson in all of this, it seems to me, is that the models for inferential classification designed for quite different contexts, in these examples sociometric choice and scaling theory, are seen to deal with identical relations. The problems and techniques in each content area are, at least in principle, transferable from one to the other. Surely workers in either content area would gain new tools and new insights by recognizing the correspondences and reinterpreting the work in one context in terms of the other context.

5. SUMMARY

The nature of QIIIb data is discussed in detail. It was recognized at least as early as 1916 as an appropriate form of observation for the study of stimuli which may differ from each other in terms of more than one attribute. It was Goodman (1951), however, who presented a careful and logical analysis of "matching" as a predicate, which yields the data of QIIIb. Generically the data may be described as proximity data.

The importance that Goodman recognizes in such data is that they do not prejudge the problem of what are the subjective dimensions or perceived aspects of stimuli. The data of QIIIa do, in that the asymmetric predicate involves the subject judging which of the stimuli has more of some explicit attribute x. In contrast, the symmetric predicate of QIIIb— "Do the stimuli match or not?"—permits the simultaneous interaction of any number of attributes regarded as relevant by the subject.

The data of QIIIb may be contained in a data matrix with the same labels for rows as for columns since there is only one set of points. The cells may contain only a 1 or a 0 to indicate match or not match, or they may contain probabilities or other proximity measures. There are two kinds of proximity data in QIIIb, one is called symmetric proximity data and the other conditional proximity data.

In a symmetric proximity matrix of probabilities, the cell entries are joint probabilities. The row-stimulus and the column-stimulus represent an unordered pair, and the observations reflect that they match or do not match in some simultaneous and symmetric sense. In a conditional proximity matrix of probabilities the cell entries are conditional probabilities and the matrix is nonsymmetric. The row-stimulus and the column-stimulus are an ordered pair, and the observations reflect that they match or do not match in some nonsymmetric sense, that is, the row-stimulus has or has not been identified as, recognized as, or otherwise confused with the column-stimulus, but the reverse is not necessarily true.

Probabilities are not the only response measure that may appear in the cells of these matrices. They have been used for illustrative purposes because of their common occurrence, but other measures, such as latency and amplitude of response, may also be interpreted as proximity measures.

The data of QIIIb may be processed with either of two objectives in mind: (1) to construct a stimulus scale directly or (2) to convert the data into measures of degree of similarity, making QIVa data out of them, which can then be analyzed by a QIVa model to arrive at a multidimensional stimulus space.

A model for the first objective, the Goodman-Galanter model, is incompletely developed, especially if multidimensional solutions are required. It requires only the (1, 0) data matrix, however. The model is set theoretic, and its basic concepts are summarized. It has a close relation to parallelogram analysis of QIIb and QIa data.

The second objective involves obtaining an ordinal or a ratio scale of interpoint distances from a symmetric proximity matrix or from a conditional proximity matrix. The symmetric proximity matrix is discussed first; Hefner's model for constructing a ratio scale of distances is presented after a brief discussion of the simple problem of getting an ordinal scale from such data. His model is a multidimensional extension of Thurstone's model for pair comparisons. He shows that if the stimuli project multivariate normal distributions in an r-dimensional space the transformation of percentage "matches" into psychological distance requires the integral of the noncentral χ^2 distribution with r degrees of freedom. In one dimension this is no problem but for $r > 1$ the values of the function have not been adequately tabled. If, however, the probabilities can be transformed into an index which will permit just a rank order of the distances, then a nonmetric model is applicable, such as that discussed in Chapter 21.

The transformation of such same-different data into actual distances requires the estimation of the subject's criterion distance for judging same or different. Some experimental work of Hefner's is reported in which he finds that the criterion distance is not constant for all pairs of stimuli in his experiment (or the case V assumption of constant variability is violated), and he suggests an approximation procedure for bypassing this difficulty. Another limitation of same-different data is the difficulties they run into if the stimuli are highly discriminable. This is no problem with Goodman's set theoretic model in the one-dimensional case, but the multidimensional case is still unsolved.

The use of a model like Hefner's on stimuli which are very different leads to the idea of degrading the stimuli by brief tachistoscopic exposure. Hefner also studied this experimentally and found that there were accompanying *qualitative* changes in the stimuli he used (color patches).

Discussion of the analysis of conditional proximity matrices takes up the construction of ordinal scales of distance, and then we present Shepard's model for ratio scaling of distances. Shepard's model is constructed in the context of a theory of stimulus and response generalization, but when lifted out of this context it is a general model for probabilistic conditional proximity matrices. He assumes an exponential decay function relating a conditional probability to a psychological distance. Ratio scale estimates of distances are thereby obtained, which, if nonsymmetric for a given pair, are averaged.

As in the case of a symmetric proximity matrix, the conditional probabilities in a row of the conditional proximity matrix may, with weaker assumptions, yield a rank order of the distances of all the column-stimuli from that row-stimulus. Transitivity of distance must be tested, and, if it is satisfied, certain of the conditions for a metric space are sustained and a nonmetric multidimensional analysis is not excluded. A method for testing transitivity of distances and for constructing a partial order of the distances, triangular analysis, was discussed and illustrated in Chapter 17.

The chapter closes with a discussion of sociometric choice behavior as QIII and as QII data. Sociometric matrices if skew-symmetric are QIIIa and if symmetric or nonsymmetric are QIIIb. If an individual is regarded by the experimenter as possibly different points in his two roles as stimulus and as respondent, however, the same behavior becomes QIIa or QIIb, respectively. The topic is discussed because it not only points up, again, the creative role of the scientist in making data out of observations, but also awakens us to the possible correspondences between the matrix and graph theory approach to sociometric matrices on the one hand and the scaling theory approach to so-called measurement data on the other.

Sociometric and scaling models are seen as lying in opposite corners of a two-dimensional space: Sociometrics is primarily concerned with nominal classification based on relatively weak data information [for example, (1, 0) data matrices], and scaling is primarily concerned with stronger levels of classification, like ordinal and ratio scales, based on relatively stronger data information (for example, probabilistic data matrices).

They are all inferential classification systems for analyzing data and certain correspondences are clearly suggested when the models are looked at from the point of view of data theory.

REFERENCES

Cartwright, D., and F. Harary, 1956, Structural balance: a generalization of Heider's theory, *Psychol. Rev.*, **63**, 277–93.

Fix, E., 1949, Table of non-central χ^2, *Univer. California Publ. Statist.*, **1**, 15–19.

Galanter, E. H., 1956, An axiomatic and experimental study of sensory order and measure, *Psychol. Rev.*, **63**, 16–28.

Glanzer, M., and R. Glaser, 1959, Techniques for the study of group structure and behavior: I. Analysis of structure, *Psychol. Bull.*, **56**, 317–32.

Goodman, N., 1951, *The structure of appearance*, Harvard University Press, Cambridge, Mass.

Green, B. F., Jr., and Lois K. Anderson, 1955, The tactual identification of shapes for coding switch handles, *J. appl. Psychol.*, **39**, 219–26.

Harary, F., and I. Ross, 1957, A procedure of clique detection using the group matrix, *Sociometry*, **20**, 205–15.

Hefner, R. A., 1958, Extensions of the law of comparative judgment to discriminable and multidimensional stimuli, unpublished Ph.D. dissertation, University of Michigan.

Henning, H., 1916, *Der Geruch*, Barth, Leipzig.

Katz, L., and J. H. Powell, 1957, Probability distributions of random variables associated with a structure of the sample space of sociometric investigations, *Ann. math. Statist.*, **28**, 442–49.

Miller, G. A., and P. E. Nicely, 1955, An analysis of perceptual confusion, *J. acoust. Soc. Amer.*, **27**, 338–52.

Patnaik, P. B., 1949, The non-central χ^2 and F-distributions and their applications, *Biometrika*, **36**, 202–32.

Rothkopf, E. Z., 1957, A measure of stimulus similarity and errors in some paired-associate learning tasks, *J. exp. Psychol.*, **53**, 94–101.

Shepard, R. N., 1957, Stimulus and response generalization: a stochastic model relating generalization to distance in psychological space, *Psychometrika*, **22**, 325–45.

Shepard, R. N., 1958, Stimulus and response generalization: test of a model relating generalization to distance in psychological space, *J. exp. Psychol.*, **55**, 509–23.

Shepard, R. N., 1960, "Similarity of stimuli and metric properties of behavioral data," Chapter 4 in *Psychological scaling: theory and applications*, edited by H. Gulliksen and S. Messick, John Wiley and Sons, New York.

Stevens, S. S., 1958, Problems and methods of psychophysics, *Psychol. Bull.*, **55**, 177–96.

Torgerson, W. S., 1951, A theoretical and empirical investigation of multidimensional scaling, unpublished Ph.D. dissertation, Princeton University.

Torgerson, W. S., 1958, *Theory and methods of scaling*, John Wiley and Sons, New York.

PART 5

SIMILARITIES DATA

Parts 4 and 5 are concerned with the construction of stimulus spaces, unlike Parts 2 and 3, which are concerned with joint spaces. In Part 4 we took up the variety of models available in such spaces when the data consist of relations on the stimulus points; for example, whether one was "higher" than another (QIIIa) or whether two of them were close together (QIIIb). We saw that QIIIa data lead naturally to the construction of unidimensional stimulus spaces and not to multidimensional ones (this may not be a necessary limitation; see Chapter 24, Section 2). We saw that QIIIb data, in contrast, have the potentiality for generating multi-dimensional stimulus spaces but that models are not yet sufficiently developed.

We turn now in Part 5 to QIV data, which consist of relations on stimulus *differences*. In QIVa we ask whether the members of one pair are more alike (or different) than the members of another pair, that is, whether the distance between the stimulus points comprising one pair is less (or greater) than the distance between those comprising the other pair. In QIVb we ask whether the similarity of one pair is distinguishably different from that of another pair, that is, whether the corresponding pair of distances match. Our attention is directed exclusively to QIVa data, for which considerable progress has been made on models which yield multidimensional stimulus spaces. Since we can collect similarities data from a single individual, the way is laid open for the study of an individual's perceptual and cognitive structures.

CHAPTER 20

Introduction to QIVa

1. NATURE OF THE DATA

Let us return for a moment to the candidates, colors, and candies of Chapter 1 and reconsider an hypothesis which we abandoned when we analyzed preferential choice behavior by QIa methods. The hypothesis we abandoned then was that the stimuli might "really" be subjectively different for different people. Peanut brittle may be mostly salty and chewy to some people and sweet and crunchy to others; candidate A may seem like an entirely different person to one voter from the one he appears to be to another voter. Our interest may be in trying to discover just what these relevant aspects into which stimuli are analyzable are; that is, what the structure of appearance is. We may know the properties of the stimuli from a real world, physical point of view. That is all well and good, in fact very useful to the experimental psychologist, but it is neither necessary nor sufficient for the determination of the subjective aspects in terms of which stimuli are perceived and evaluated. We might say that we wish to discover aspects of the stimuli from the way *people behave* with respect to them and not from the way the *stimuli "behave"* under physical operations.

We conceive, then, of a psychological space with one set of points in it corresponding to the set of stimuli, and with the relations among these points to correspond, in some sense, to the relations among the stimuli as given by behavior. In particular, we conceive of a distance between every pair of points in the space which is a measure of the *similarity* of the corresponding stimuli. Perhaps *dissimilarity* would be better (just as *disutility* was a convenient term in treating preferential choice behavior as

433

QIIIa data), but there should be little danger of confusion in what follows if we use either term at will.

QIVa data consist of information about these distances. This information, for current models, is useful only if it consists of measures of the distances at the level of an ordinal scale or of a ratio scale. Models are available which we can apply to QIVa data to construct a stimulus space. For example, there is a model which utilizes only order relations on interpoint distances to construct a configuration of the points in a multi-dimensional space. The solution is in the form of the rank order of the projections of the stimuli on each dimension. We call such a model a nonmetric model.

Shepard (1962) has developed a computer program to generate the metric configuration for a set of stimulus points given only order relations on interpoint distances. For data which consist of ratio scale measures of the distances, there are the procedures developed by Young, Householder, and Torgerson (see Torgerson, 1958, Chapter 11), which also yield a set of Cartesian coordinates for the stimuli.

All these are models for analyzing QIVa similarities data. They differ in various ways, for example, in the amount of information required of the data and the size of the matrix that can be conveniently analyzed. With the limited experience so far available Shepard's method seems to get the most for the least. Here, however, we confine our attention to a nonmetric method which has never been presented in detail and which has certain advantages, especially for smaller matrices to be analyzed without a computer.

The absolute distance between any pair of stimulus points (j, k) or (l, m) is

$$|p_{hi,jk}| = |q_{hij} \ominus q_{hik}|$$
$$|p_{hi,lm}| = |q_{hil} \ominus q_{him}| \tag{20.1}$$

where the symbol $\ominus$ signifies some distance function such as the Euclidean or city-block model.

The information in the data may be defined as

$$|p_{hi,jk}| - |p_{hi,lm}| \leq 0 \Leftrightarrow (j, k) < (l, m) \tag{20.2}$$

That is, if and only if the distance between the pair of stimuli (j, k) is less than the distance between the pair (l, m), then the pair (j, k) is more similar than the pair (l, m). The phrase ". . . is more similar than . . ." is a generic term for a great variety of real world observations and may capture all of them. In fact the sources of such data are so varied that a later section of this chapter is devoted to their discussion and illustration.

The pairs of stimuli (j, k) may be ordered or unordered pairs; this is part of the basis for the distinction between symmetric and conditional proximity matrices (respectively) in the last chapter. In the language of distances, a symmetric proximity matrix contains information about absolute distances, whereas the conditional proximity matrix contains information about relative distances; for example, about the distance from j to k *relative to* the distances of all stimuli from j. Another way of putting it is that the information in a conditional proximity matrix has to do with the *relative* magnitude of distances from a common terminus, that is, conjoint distances only. The information in a symmetric proximity matrix, on the other hand, has to do with the absolute magnitude of all distances.

I remarked at the beginning of this section that similarities data are appropriate for the study of a single individual's perceptual or cognitive structure for a set of stimuli. This merely requires that the information in expression 20.2 be obtained from a single individual. Group data may also be used, however. The only requirement is one imposed by the models available for the analysis of the data. This is the requirement that in a group experiment each stimulus point be relatively stable for the data obtained in any given experiment, that is, over subjects.

It is conceivable, for example, that even in an experiment with a single individual this condition may not be met. Administration of a drug to the subject in the course of an experiment, to take just one possible example, may change the psychological space of the stimuli for him. If this occurs, the models require that he be considered a different subject under the different drug conditions. Conversely, if different subjects may be regarded merely as independent and random replications of each other, then their data may be pooled and a single space obtained. If the stimuli are color patches, however, a color-blind subject is not a random replication of a subject with normal color vision. Their psychological spaces for the appearance of colors are significantly different, and their data should not be pooled. The models neither know nor care what the source of the data is. If certain conditions are met by any given body of data, the models will yield, within the basic structure which each postulates, a configuration of points which conforms to the data.

In the next section we digress somewhat to point out some of the theoretical implications and psychological significance of similarities data. The third section is concerned with pointing out the variety of sources of QIVa data, and the fourth section will discuss how the chapters in Part 5 are related to each other. The final section is, of course, a summary.

2. IMPORTANCE OF SIMILARITIES DATA

At the beginning of Chapter 19 the discussion centered on the importance of "matching" data for the purpose of determining the subjective aspects into which stimuli are analyzable, that is, the structure of appearance. Nelson Goodman (1951, Chapter 9) very ably discusses this same point but rejects similarity as a possible basic predicate in favor of matching. He rejects judgments of whether one pair of stimuli are more similar than another because the predicate is too complex. I suppose he feels that the task is too difficult for a subject to perform. There is no doubt, however, that if it were possible to get such data it would fulfill the requirements for studying the structure of appearance at least as well as matching data.

One role, then, that similarities data may play in psychology is the study of certain aspects of the cognitive structure of individuals. This is a relatively new role; only recently have models been available for making inferential classifications of stimuli from such data.

Another role that similarity plays, however, makes its study important in psychology, and this is the fact that the concept has been used so widely as an explanatory principle. I shall not repeat here the brief but excellent discussion of this subject by Fred Attneave (1950, pp. 516–19). He points out the relevance of the concept of similarity as an explanatory principle in perceptual organization; in association theory of retention and recall; and in transfer phenomena such as stimulus generalization and retroactive inhibition.

The use of the concept as an explanatory principle in these several areas gives rise to the question of what shall be the basic operational definition, if any, of similarity. This is perhaps more a psychological problem than a logical one.

On the one hand, we may construct a "similarity" space for a set of stimuli for each of many behavioral processes and measures, for example, discrimination time, substitution errors, and amplitude of response. These spaces would probably not all be alike, and we would then seek transformations from one to another. These are merely mathematical problems.

On the other hand, we might choose for psychological reasons to settle on an operational definition of similarity, and then each behavioral process would correspond to an appropriate function on this basic similarity space; just as we related preferential choice to a latent attribute by a SPF.

This is essentially a problem in phase 1—deciding what behavior to observe (see Section 1 of Chapter 1)—in order to construct a measure of similarity. It has always seemed self-evident to me that the observations should be *verbal judgments* of similarity. We could, of course, utilize a transfer experiment and observe changes in amplitude or latency and use such observations to measure similarity. Even if this were done, however, the ultimate criterion for accepting the measure as a measure of similarity would be subjective. It seems to me that verbal judgments should be used to construct a measure of similarity, and then psychological theory would revolve around the functions that would relate similarity to other behavior phenomena.

I must point out that these remarks have nothing to do with the models that follow for the analysis of similarity data; the models do not care whether the observations are judgments or something else. The models analyze the data, and the data are order relations on pairs of dyads, all from the same set. In other words the models are concerned with phase 3, which comes after recorded observations have been converted into data in phase 2.

This section is introduced only because, as Attneave points out, the concept of similarity is very important in psychology and yet widely neglected. I think this neglect has been due to the lack of methods for analyzing such data, but this limitation is rapidly being overcome.

3. SOURCES OF SIMILARITIES DATA

The variety of the sources of similarities data calls for comment. Whereas QIVa models are concerned with the construction of a stimulus space from measures of the interpoint distances, these measures must first be procured. Measurement of interpoint distances may be achieved in a great variety of ways, in terms of the kind of data and also in terms of the model used to infer the distances. Whereas the n stimuli are mapped into points in an r-dimensional space, the $n' = \binom{n}{2}$ interpoint distances are themselves points on a unidimensional scale of distance. Models are available in QIVa for the construction of a stimulus space if the measures of the interpoint distances are elements of either an ordinal scale or a ratio scale. Hence methods which can be used to construct unidimensional stimulus scales are potentially available (with suitable adaptation) for measuring interpoint distances and then analyzing these by a QIVa model.

Clearly, then, any of the methods of QIIa, QIIb, QIIIa, and QIIIb which will yield at least an ordinal scale can be used in this intermediate step of constructing similarity measures. This is the reason I made as much of a point as I did of methods for constructing ordinal scales in QII and QIII. In general, ordinal stimulus scales are uninteresting, but when the stimuli are interpoint distances the picture changes, because an ordinal scale of interpoint distances can be used to construct a multi-dimensional stimulus space.

There are examples in the literature using methods from all four of the octants of QII and QIII to measure interpoint distances. I shall briefly survey a few of these for illustrative purposes.

Measuring Distances in QII

QII methods have been used to scale distance stimuli by Messick (1956), Mellinger (1956), Helm (1960), Abelson (1954), Ekman (1954), and others. The observations consist of mapping pairs of stimuli into a set of response categories. The names used for these methods include rating scales, method of successive intervals, method of categorical judgment, and the multidimensional method of successive intervals. The latter term simply refers to the fact that the stimuli being evaluated are distance stimuli. The actual instructions to the subject usually refer to evaluating the degree of similarity of the pair of stimuli.

The models used for analyzing the data convert the ratings of degree of similarity into measures of the distances between pairs of stimuli. These models range over QIIa and QIIb. Some studies, like Ekman's, treat numerical ratings like the method of equal appearing intervals (QIIb) and merely average the ratings. Others, like Helm's, map the observations into method-of-successive-intervals data without the assumption of equal intervals. The analysis, then, may be by any of several methods which scale the distances on a joint scale with the category boundaries (QIIa).

These methods all lead to measures of the interpoint distances on an interval or ratio scale. The zero point on the ratio scale of distances may be an outright assumption or may be built into the method of collecting the data. The latter is illustrated by Abelson's study in which the method of equal appearing intervals was used with one (extreme) category representing identity of the two stimuli. Construction of a real Euclidean space from the interpoint distances by the Young-Householder-Torgerson model requires that the measures of distance be elements of a ratio scale, so an additive constant needs to be determined to convert interval scale measures to ratio scale measures. This problem is discussed by Messick and Abelson (1956) and Torgerson (1958).

Another QIIb method was used by Indow and Uchizono (1960) for measuring interpoint distances between stimuli. They adapted Stevens' direct method of magnitude estimation to the measurement of distances between color patches. In its essentials their procedure was as follows. The subject was given one color to serve as standard, placed on the left side of a table, and was instructed to place each of 21 color patches a distance to the right to correspond to their apparent differences from the standard. Each color served as standard in turn. The physical distances on the table were interpreted as subjective distances on a ratio scale. They attempted to use a pair of grays to provide a unit of measurement; but I infer from reading their article that they must have obtained a non-symmetric distance matrix, since they corrected the cell entries to a common unit of measurement to obtain symmetry. Their procedure appeared to yield a conditional proximity matrix* in which the cell entries were *response amplitudes* (linear distances on the table).

Indow and Uchizono call their method multiple-ratio judgment, because the distances of a number of stimuli from the same standard are "simultaneously" estimated on a ratio scale. This may, and probably does, make the set of estimates relative and hence different for different standards—and hence like a conditional proximity matrix rather than a symmetric proximity matrix.

Measuring Distances in QIII

There are three principal methods for the measurement of distance stimuli in QIII. These are the application of a modified version of Thurstone's model for comparative judgment to QIIIa data on the distance stimuli, the analysis of symmetric proximity matrices in QIIIb, and the analysis of conditional proximity matrices, also in QIIIb.

The method most widely used is the application of Thurstone's model for comparative judgment to the pair comparison data on pairs of distances. The data for such an analysis may be collected, in principle, by any method of the searchingness structure but this is not usually feasible because the number of stimuli, n, becomes $n' = \binom{n}{2}$, the number of interpoint distances. The routine application of Thurstone's model to the scaling of these distances, then, could require an exorbitant amount of experimental effort. For example, for $n = 10$ stimuli there are $n' = 45$ distances and hence 990 *pairs* of distances, and these pairs need to be replicated to obtain probabilistic data.

The method of cartwheels was developed for precisely this reason. For any of the five cases of the method of cartwheels the judgments on any presentation may be decomposed as discussed in Chapter 2, and accumulated over presentations to yield the probabilistic data matrix. The solution of this matrix yields measures of the interpoint distances on an

* See Chapter 19.

interval scale and so an additive constant needs to be estimated. Torgerson (1958) discusses a procedure for analysis of such a probabilistic data matrix in some detail.

Thurstone's model, however, does not transfer in a simple manner to the analysis of such cartwheel data in which the stimuli being compared are interpoint distances. As Hefner has shown (Chapter 19), distances between pairs of points from multivariate normal distributions are distributed as noncentral χ^2 with r degrees of freedom where r is the dimensionality of the space. Even in the one-dimensional case, in which the distribution reduces to the normal distribution, laterality considerations enter in. The effect of this variable is discussed in detail in Chapter 23.

We may measure the interpoint distances by application of Hefner's model to a symmetric proximity matrix of QIIIb data. Although this method bypasses the problem of an additive constant, it has a problem of its own, that of estimating a criterion distance. This, however, will not be a serious stumbling block if data are collected on pairs of identical dyads. A temporary practical difficulty is the lack of adequate tables for noncentral χ^2 at a number of different degrees of freedom.

Finally, we may measure the interpoint distances by application of Shepard's model to a conditional proximity matrix (see Chapter 19).

These models, of course, by no means exhaust the possibilities. Others are the adaptation of the B.T.L. QIIIa model to distance stimuli (Luce, 1961) and the development of entirely new models for such data as well as for the symmetric and the conditional proximity matrices of QIIIb.

Furthermore, both QII and QIII data may be analyzed in their respective octants by weaker models which yield only ordinal scale measures of the interpoint distances. This is particularly true for QIII data. In the case of QIIIa, weak stochastic transitivity on pairs of dyads is sufficient to yield a simple order of the distances, from data collected by cartwheels or any other method of the searchingness structure.

In the case of QIIIb, weaker assumptions than Hefner's and Shepard's are sufficient to permit inference of order relations on distances from symmetric proximity and from conditional proximity matrices respectively, as discussed in Chapter 19. For example, in the case of a symmetric proximity matrix, if we merely assume that the nearer a pair of stimulus points the more often that pair of stimuli are confused or judged the same, the joint probabilities of the symmetric proximity matrix lead directly to a simple order of the absolute distances.

The case of the conditional proximity matrix in QIIIb is similar. If we assume the existence of a single-peaked, symmetric, strictly monotonic function relating the conditional probabilities to psychological distances, this is sufficient to order the stimulus points in a space in order of increasing distance from each stimulus, thereby yielding for each stimulus an ordinal scale analogous to an I scale. This suggests that the set of n I scales may be analyzed by an appropriate modification of the unfolding technique.

The remaining chapters of Part 5 are concerned with just such data, order relations on interpoint distances, and the construction of stimulus spaces from such information. The analysis of ratio scale measures of interpoint distances is well advanced and is well presented in Torgerson (1958). But nonmetric multidimensional scaling is just emerging. Sufficient progress has been made so that the method is operational and worth presenting, although considerable improvements are to be anticipated in the future, ranging from its foundations to its mechanics.

4. RELATION OF CHAPTERS IN PART 5

The purpose of this introductory chapter is to prepare the ground for the chapters which follow on a model and its applications. The model discussed is basically an adaptation of the QIa unfolding technique to QIVa similarities data. The next chapter deals with both theory and technique in the case of the unidimensional stimulus scale and in the general multidimensional case. The final chapter presents two applications of the multidimensional model in detail and a third in summary.

5. SUMMARY

In this chapter we introduce the idea of a multidimensional stimulus space to reflect the behavior of a single individual or a group of individuals with respect to the stimuli. Similarities data consist of information about the relative magnitude of the distances between the stimulus points in this space, and the models are designed to process this information to yield the proposed space. The models require that this information on inter-point distances consist of measures at the level of either an ordinal or a ratio scale.

The importance of similarities data to theoretical psychology is briefly discussed in terms of two roles which they play: (1) as a means of studying the structure of appearance, an aspect of cognitive structure, and (2) as an explanatory principle for certain psychological processes like association and transfer of training.

The major part of the chapter is devoted to the sources of similarities data. Analysis of similarities data by a QIVa model requires a prior scaling of the interpoint distances. These interpoint distances may themselves be regarded as points, and hence observations on similarities may be interpreted as data in the appropriate octants of QII and QIII, which deal with pairs of points. Having processed the observations on interpoint distances by an appropriate model in QII or QIII, the relations (or measures) on distances may be transferred to QIVa and analyzed to yield a stimulus space. There are two completely separate steps here: to infer the distances from the observations, and then to infer the space from the distances. Here in QIVa we are concerned only with the second step.

As a matter of fact, we should now be able to see that the same is true of QIa data. Again, there are two steps. The first is to infer the distances of the stimulus points from each individual point, corresponding to constructing I scales, and the second is to infer the space from these distances, corresponding to unfolding a set of I scales. As with QIVa, any method of QII or QIII can, at least in principle, be used to infer the distances which may then be thought of as transferred to QIa and analyzed to yield a joint space.

So, while QIVa is concerned with analyzing information about interpoint distances to construct a stimulus space, a brief review has been made of the prior step of inferring the interpoint distances. Examples are presented in which methods from QII and QIII have been used. Generally speaking, the methods of QII used for this purpose are ratings, category scaling, or magnitude estimation; the methods of QIII that have been used or proposed are Thurstone's model for comparative judgment, as adapted by Torgerson for cartwheel data, the analysis of symmetric proximity matrices by Hefner's model, and the analysis of conditional proximity matrices by Shepard's model.

We then discussed the use of weaker models to arrive at ordinal scales of distances, which is sufficient for a nonmetric multidimensional analysis. This approach is particularly applicable in the case of QIII data on distances. A QIIIa probabilistic matrix that satisfies weak stochastic transitivity leads to an ordinal scale of distances under weaker assumptions than either Thurstone's or the B.T.L. model. In a similar manner, a symmetric proximity matrix or a conditional proximity matrix can lead to ordinal scales of distances on the basis of weaker assumptions than are required by the currently available metric models for these matrices, that is, Hefner's and Shepard's respectively.

The remaining chapters of Part 5 are concerned with the unfolding analysis of similarities data. Chapter 21 is concerned with the general theory of multidimensional unfolding of similarities data to yield a stimulus space; and Chapter 22 presents two applications, the analysis of a symmetric proximity matrix and the analysis of a conditional proximity matrix.

REFERENCES

Abelson, R. P., 1954, A technique and a model for multidimensional attitude scaling, *Publ. Opin. Quart.*, **18**, 405–18.
Attneave, F., 1950, Dimensions of similarity, *Amer. J. Psychol.*, **63**, 516–56.
Ekman, G., 1954, Dimensions of color vision, *J. Psychol.*, **38**, 467–74.
Goodman, N., 1951, *The structure of appearance*, Harvard University Press, Cambridge, Mass.
Helm, C., 1960, A successive intervals analysis of color differences, Educational Testing Service Technical Report, November 1960.
Indow, T., and T. Uchizono, 1960, Multidimensional mapping of Munsell colors varying in hue and chroma, *J. exp. Psychol.*, **59**, 321–29.
Luce, R. D., 1961, A choice theory analysis of similarity judgments, *Psychometrika*, **26**, 151–64.
Mellinger, J., 1956, Some attributes of color perception, unpublished Ph.D. dissertation, University of North Carolina.
Messick, S. J., 1956, The perception of social attitudes, *J. abnorm. soc. Psychol.*, **52**, 57–66.
Messick, S. J., and R. P. Abelson, 1956, The additive constant problem in multidimensional scaling, *Psychometrika*, **21**, 1–15.
Shepard, R. N., 1962, The analysis of proximities: multidimensional scaling with an unknown distance function I, *Psychometrika*, **27**, 125–40.
Torgerson, W. S., 1958, *Theory and methods of scaling*, John Wiley and Sons, New York.

CHAPTER 21

Nonmetric Multidimensional Psychological Scaling

The term nonmetric multidimensional psychological scaling refers to models which, given order relations on the interpoint distances among a set of points (similarity relations), may be used to construct a space the axes of which are only recovered at the level of a rank order. Hays, after developing the multidimensional unfolding of preferential choice data, adapted that model in 1954 to the unfolding of similarities data. He has never been fully satisfied with the foundations or the procedures, but some of us have been venturesome in attempting to apply the principles and develop the procedures further. In the course of such explorations some changes and contributions to the model have been made. To give documented credit to all those who have so contributed is now impossible. From memory, however, I can certainly testify to the contributions of David Cross, Robyn Dawes, Frank Goode, Andrew Karoly, and Joseph Zinnes.

The method as it now stands is an application of a series of insights into inferring spatial relations when some order relations on distances between points are known. The procedures are not completely routine. We have not designed them with the intent to program a computer, although we would eventually like to do that. The results obtained by these procedures would be very similar to the results that would be obtained by any other procedures using the same insights.

Several applications have justified a tentative confidence in this method, and so it is presented here in some detail. I shall first discuss the basic concepts and summarize the rationale, then the analytical procedure, and finally present examples in one and two dimensions.

444

1. BASIC CONCEPTS AND PROCEDURE

I shall present a heuristic description of the procedure to provide a framework in order that the details of the analytic procedure, presented in the next section, may be more clearly seen in reference to the whole.

We have n points in a Euclidean space of unknown dimensionality, r, and at least a partial order of the interpoint distances. The intent is to put a reference frame in this space, consisting of r axes or lines, and to determine the rank order of the projections of the points on each of these lines. Every pair of points in the space defines a line, and each of these lines is a potential axis of the space. We wish to select a minimal subset of these lines and to determine the order of projections on each in such a manner as to "satisfy" the given partial order on interpoint distances. The criterion for selecting these lines, proposed by Hays, is in the spirit of a principal components factor analysis, that is, a least squares fit to the space.

A line of least squares fit to any triangle is one on which the longest side of the triangle has the largest projected distance. If in the triangle ABC, for example, the line from A to C, A–C, is the longest side of that triangle, a line of least squares fit to that triangle will show these three points projecting in the order $A\ B\ C$ on that line. This is only a necessary condition for a least squares fit, of course, not a sufficient one, a limitation occasioned by the fact that the interpoint distances are measured on an ordinal scale rather than on a cardinal scale.

A line in the space on which a triangle projects so that the longest side of the triangle has the longest projection will be spoken of as "fitting" that triangle, and the triangle will be spoken of as being "satisfied" by that line.

In order to approximate a line of least squares fit to the space, then, we want a line such that the rank order of the projections of the points on that line will satisfy as many triangles as possible, with priority or preference given to fitting the largest triangles.

If we take as the line defining the first dimension the line defined by the two stimuli which are furthest apart in the space, then all the other points must project between them, as may be illustrated in two dimensions by Fig. 21.1. In the figure, the line X–Y is taken to be the longest line between any two stimuli in the space. Every other stimulus point in the space, then, must be inside the hatched area. This hatched area is the intersection of the two circles drawn with X and Y respectively as centers and with the distance $\overline{XY}$ as radius.

With the longest line in the space defining the first dimension, we insure that the largest triangles in the space will be fitted because the third point

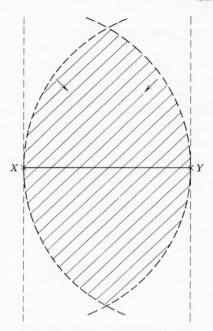

Fig. 21.1   The region containing all stimulus points where $X–Y$ is the longest line.

in each such triangle will project *between* X and Y. The next step is to determine the actual order of the projections of the other points between X and Y.

This is done by fitting as many of the remaining triangles as possible, especially those which have either X *or* Y as a corner. Here is a helpful basic concept. Consider any four points A, B, C, and D and the line defined by A and B, as in Fig. 21.2. If the order of the points in distance

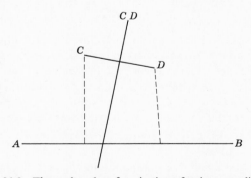

Fig. 21.2   The rank order of projection of points on a line.

from A is $A\ C\ D\ B$ and from B is $B\ D\ C\ A$ (the mirror image), then the boundary hyperplane, CD, intersects the line A–B between A and B and the order of projection on A–B is $A\ C\ D\ B$. This is immediately evident because A must be on one side of the CD hyperplane and B on the other.

Good use may be made of this fact in determining the rank order of projections between X and Y, the first dimension, by comparing X's and Y's I scales. The rank order of the projections between X and Y is known immediately for any pair of points which are reversed in order on the two I scales. Comparing these two I scales, then, leads to a partial order of the projections between X and Y.

For example, suppose the line X–Y is the longest line in some set of data and so we choose it to define the first dimension. We combine their I scales into a common partial order. Suppose their I scales are:

X's I scale: $X\ E\ B\ C\ D\ G\ Y$

Y's I scale (reversed*): $X\ B\ D\ C\ E\ G\ Y$

These two I scales, then, may be seen to generate the following partial order:

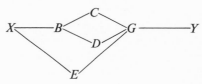

Thus, for example, B and C project in that order between X and Y because on X's I scale they are in the order $X\ B\ C\ Y$ and on Y's I scale their order is $Y\ C\ B\ X$. The stimulus E, on the other hand, precedes B, C, and D on X's I scale and also on Y's I scale, so in the common partial order E is not ranked with respect to B, C, and D.

By insuring that the rank order of projections on the first dimension satisfies this partial order we will have insured fitting all triangles whose longest side is the longest line in the space and also fitting a number of triangles which have either X or Y as one corner.

The next step is to resolve this partial order into a simple order. This may be accomplished for any unordered pair in the partial order by examining all the triangles involving that pair and taking as their order the one that fits the most triangles.

For example, the pair C, D is unordered in the partial order. So the triple they form with B and the triple they form with G will be examined.

* It is convenient for this purpose to write one of the I scales in reverse order and to look for pairs of stimuli which are not reversed.

Suppose the triangle formed by B, C, and D has as its longest side $\overline{BD}$. Then it will be desirable to have the order of projections on the line $X\text{-}Y$ to be $X\,B\,C\,D\,Y$. Suppose the triangle formed with G had as its longest side $\overline{CG}$. Then it would be desirable to have the order of projections on the line $X\text{-}Y$ to be $X\,C\,D\,G\,Y$. These can both be satisfied at the same time with the order $X\,B\,C\,D\,G\,Y$. If these two had not been mutually compatible in this way, the question of whether $\overline{BD}$ or $\overline{CG}$ is the longer line determines which triple it is better to fit.

To locate a single point like E in the rank order we examine all the triples involving E and choose the position that fits the most triples. At this point, the attempt to take both size of triangles and number of triangles into account is apt to lead to uncertainties and no decision. I have preferred to use these criteria in a lexicographic way; after fitting the largest triangles, I then try to fit as many more as possible.

The order in which the incomparabilities in the partial order are resolved may affect the result. Hence this is a means of obtaining alternative solutions.

In this manner we may construct an axis through the space which has some of the characteristics of a first principal component or major axis of the space. We have fitted as many triangles as possible with priority given to the largest ones. If all the triangles have been fitted by this procedure, the result is a one-dimensional solution in the form of an ordered metric stimulus scale.

The one-dimensional case, however, is simpler than this procedure suggests, in that the I scales of the end points of the longest line are mirror images of each other and so the rank order of projections is given immediately.

With empirical data it may not always be certain which pair of stimuli are furthest apart, as will be the case, for example, in the real applications presented in the next chapter. My practice in such a case is to take all upper bounds in the partial order of distances as trial first dimensions in turn and postpone the decision as to which is to be selected. The final decision will be based on the number of triangles fitted and on the interpretability of the alternative solutions.

As a matter of fact it might be well to point out here that while this method of nonmetric multidimensional analysis has no formal process of rotation in itself, as in metric methods of factor analysis, the process of directly constructing alternative solutions is a substitute.

If the first dimension does not satisfy all the triples, the existence of a second dimension is implied. This involves choosing a pair of stimuli, U and V, to define the line which will be the second dimension. Two criteria, not necessarily compatible, may be used to select U and V.

(1) Among those triangles left unsatisfied by the first dimension determine the longest line and count the number of unsatisfied triangles for which it is the longest line.

(2) The line defining the second dimension should be reasonably orthogonal to that of the first dimension in the sense that the stimulus pair defining the second dimension should be adjacent in their rank order on the first dimension, and ultimately the pair defining the first axis will project next to each other on the second axis.

These criteria are not necessarily compatible, and hence alternative solutions which satisfy one but not the other may sometimes be constructed.

Having selected a trial pair of stimuli to define the line for the second dimension we proceed to locate the projections of the stimulus points on the line. Attention is now confined to those triples of points not satisfied by the first dimension. The procedure for the second dimension may follow closely that for the first dimension, that is, we may use the I scales of the defining points for the second axis to construct a joint partial order and resolve this partial order by fitting as many of the unfitted triangles as possible. An alternative to this procedure is to avoid use of the I scales of the defining points and instead work directly with the unsatisfied triangles, embedding a maximal number of them in a common ordering.

This modification is merely an abbreviated version of the more complete method. My experience has been that if the defining points for the new dimension define a line reasonably orthogonal to previous dimensions and there is a large number of unsatisfied triangles to work with, using the I scales of the defining points is an advantage. If either of these two conditions does not hold, we should work with the unsatisfied triangles directly.

In the case of the second (and later) dimensions, it is not necessary that all points project between the defining points. We converge on a solution in a succession of steps. The third stimulus in all the unsatisfied triangles in which the line $U\text{--}V$ is the longest line must project between them on the second dimension. Their order is resolved by using the remaining unsatisfied triangles.

For example, suppose we have the following unsatisfied triangles:

$$UAV, \quad UBV$$

$$UAB, \quad VAB$$

$$AVC, \quad BAC$$

We see from the top two that both A and B project between U and V. We see from the next two that their order from U and their order from V are contradictory and we cannot satisfy both of these triangles, but of course we can satisfy one of them. If $\overline{UB} > \overline{VB}$, the order $U\,A\,B\,V$ is preferable to the order $U\,B\,A\,V$. Here, however, a certain arbitrariness enters in and alternative solutions may be generated. For example, we have the unsatisfied triangle AVC, which implies that C projects on the line U–V to the "right" of V.

The unsatisfied triangle that still remains is BAC. This triangle will be satisfied if the order is $U\,B\,A\,V\,C$ and will not be satisfied if the order is $U\,A\,B\,V\,C$. Consequently we have two alternative solutions:

(1) $U\,B\,A\,V\,C$, which fits all the unsatisfied triangles but UAB;

(2) $U\,A\,B\,V\,C$, which fits all the unsatisfied triangles but VAB and BAC.

If, then, UAB is the largest in the sense that $\overline{UB}$ is greater than either $\overline{VB}$ or $\overline{BC}$, the criteria suggested here do not determine which of the alternative solutions is preferred. The problem is much like that of choosing between rotations in factor analysis, but criteria like simple structure may be inapplicable and irrelevant. Interpretability seems to me a useful criterion in such a case, but others which may also lay a claim to consideration may be constructed.

If the second dimension leaves triples still unsatisfied, the existence of a third dimension is implied. Any triangle will be satisfied by one or both of two orthogonal axes in the plane of the triangle. In fact, the largest angle between two axes which is possible without one of them fitting the triangle is the size of the second largest angle in the triangle, which is always less than 90°.

The procedure for constructing the third dimension (and all later ones) is exactly the same as that for the second, but we use in each case only the unsatisfied triples that remain.

2. SUMMARY OF ANALYTICAL PROCEDURE

The routine of the analytical procedure may be summarized as follows:

(1) The analysis begins with a partial order of the interpoint distances and with the stimulus I scales as given.*

(2) List all triples in a column on a work sheet in such a manner as both to index them and to indicate which is the longer side of the triangle. I have found it useful to index them as if each triangle were in alphabetical order and then its order in the list were determined lexicographically, but to record each one so that the order of projection is indicated.

* Symmetric proximity matrices yield both directly. Conditional proximity matrices yield the stimulus I scales directly, and the partial order of interpoint distances needs to be constructed and provides a test of transitivity of distance. See the analysis in the next chapter for an example. Cartwheels may yield one or both depending on which case is used to collect the data.

NONMETRIC MULTIDIMENSIONAL SCALING

For example, the triangle defined by the points A, B, and C is recorded first, then A, B, and D; A, B, and E; and so on. But any given triangle, like A, B, and C, may be written in such a way as to indicate which side is longest. If the side $\overline{AB}$ is longest, as indicated by the partial order of interpoint distances, the triangle is recorded as ACB to indicate that there must be a line in the space on which the point C projects between the points A and B if this triangle is to be fitted. If the side $\overline{BC}$ is the longest, the triangle is recorded as BAC to indicate that there must be a dimension on which A projects between B and C. A column, then, may look as follows:

$$ABC$$
$$ADB$$
$$ABE$$
$$BAF$$
$$BAG$$
$$A(BH)$$

The column is interpreted as follows:

In the Triangle	The Longest Side Is
ABC	$\overline{AC}$
ADB	$\overline{AB}$
ABE	$\overline{AE}$
BAF	$\overline{BF}$
BAG	$\overline{BG}$
$A(BH)$	$\overline{AB} = \overline{AH}$

(3) Choose the two stimuli to define the first dimension, for example, the two which define the longest line, given by the partial order on interpoint distances.

(4) Construct the partial order that is satisfied by the I scales of the two stimuli that define the longest line. If the two I scales are complete mirror images of each other, a simple order which constitutes the rank order of the projections on the first dimension is obtained. If not, as is apt to be the case, the partial order must be resolved.

(5) The partial order is resolved by examining all the triples involving an incomparable pair and choosing the order that fits the most triangles.

(6) On the data sheet containing the column of triples, a tally should be made of those triangles which are fitted by the dimension.

(7) If some triangles have not been fitted, a second dimension is called for. Either of two procedures may be followed:

(*a*) If a large number of unfitted triangles remain, a procedure essentially similar to that followed for the first dimension is followed. Tabulate the longest line in such unsatisfied triples and see how often the same line appears as the longest line of an unsatisfied triangle. Choose from among these lines the one to be the second dimension. It should have appeared relatively frequently as the longest line of an unsatisfied triangle, it should be defined by stimuli which project closely together on the first dimension, and it should be as long a line as possible within these constraints. Return to step 4 and iterate steps 4 to 7.

(*b*) If the number of unfitted triangles is not large, we may work with them directly, seeking an ordering which satisfies as many as possible.

(8) Step 7*a* or 7*b* is continued until too few triangles remain unfitted to define another dimension.

We turn now to two examples with hypothetical data to illustrate the analytical procedure.

3. EXAMPLES

We shall work through two hypothetical examples in detail. The first is a simple one in one dimension, the second is in two dimensions. A third example is a one-dimensional case with real data.

A Unidimensional Case

We begin with either a simple order of the distances or a set of stimulus *I* scales, depending on how the data may have been collected. In this example we begin with a simple order of the distances and in the next example with a set of stimulus *I* scales. We do not, of course, know that the data will be satisfied by one dimension; this is a consequence of the analysis. We might have good reason to anticipate it in certain experimental contexts, but it is not an assumption that will be imposed.

Suppose we have a simple order on the interpoint distances as given in Table 21.1, with the largest distance at the top and the smallest at the bottom. In a real example there may be ties or only a partial ordering of these distances, but such instances offer no serious difficulties, as will be seen in the real applications in the next chapter.

Given an ordering like that in Table 21.1, the first step is to get the stimulus *I* scales. These may be read off directly for any stimulus, by reading off in turn the stimuli paired with the stimulus of interest beginning at the bottom of the chain ordering. Thus to obtain *A*'s *I* scale we find that the stimulus paired with *A* nearest to the bottom of the chain is *B*, indicating that *B* is nearer *A* than any other stimulus is to *A*. Going up the chain, the next stimulus paired with A is C, then comes D, and finally E. So A's I scale is $A\ B\ C\ D\ E$.

Take stimulus C as another example. The stimulus nearest to C is B, then D, A, and E. So C's I scale is $C\ B\ D\ A\ E$.

Table 21.1   Order Relations on Interpoint Distances (Hypothetical Data)

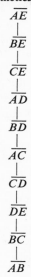

$$\overline{AE}$$
|
$$\overline{BE}$$
|
$$\overline{CE}$$
|
$$\overline{AD}$$
|
$$\overline{BD}$$
|
$$\overline{AC}$$
|
$$\overline{CD}$$
|
$$\overline{DE}$$
|
$$\overline{BC}$$
|
$$\overline{AB}$$

Table 21.2 lists the stimulus I scales read off in this manner from Table 21.1.

From our study of the unfolding technique* in Chapter 5, it is immediately evident that this set of stimulus I scales satisfies one dimension, with the stimuli ordered from A to E, and with the metric relations given in Table 21.1.

Table 21.2   Stimulus I Scales from Table 21.1

$$A\ B\ C\ D\ E$$
$$B\ A\ C\ D\ E$$
$$C\ B\ D\ A\ E$$
$$D\ E\ C\ B\ A$$
$$E\ D\ C\ B\ A$$

We could, of course, carry out the routine steps of the analytical procedure of the previous section, but there is nothing more to be learned. That analytical routine becomes useful only if the distance relations are not satisfied by one dimension.

* See also Coombs (1954).

When a one-dimensional solution is adequate, the result is an ordered metric stimulus scale. For the most part, ordinal stimulus scales are rarely of interest because they are frequently known a priori. Ordered metric scales, however, can be of real interest—particularly in studying individual differences in the structure of an attribute—as suggested in the study of academic ranks mentioned in Chapter 17, Section 3.

I have carried out similar studies, primarily as laboratory exercises, using as stimuli military ranks, adjectives describing comeliness, line drawings of faces which differ only in curvature of the mouth from frown to smile, and other sets of stimuli. Individual differences in the scale structure always seem to appear (for example, see Goldberg and Coombs, 1963) and it would be most interesting to pursue them in relation to other variables. In many experimental contexts the problem of interest may be the changes in metric relations among stimuli as a result of training, for example. This method permits the study of such changes for each individual.

An interesting example of a somewhat different kind is presented next.

A Real Example in One Dimension

I take this example from a book by Milton Rokeach (1960, Chapter 16). He was interested in the cognitive organizations of the adherents of six major Christian sects. His description of the procedure follows.

Subjects are presented with a mimeographed list of religions in alphabetical order as follows:

> Atheist
> Baptist
> Catholic
> Episcopalian
> Jewish
> Lutheran
> Methodist
> Mohammedan
> Presbyterian

A number of blank lines follow this list. The subject is simply asked to write the name of his own religion on the first line, the name of the religion most similar to his own on the second line, and so on. The least similar religion is written on the last line.*

We do not define what we mean by "similarity." Each subject decides this for himself.

* A tenth group, ex-Catholic, was also on the list. But this turned out to mean so many different things to different subjects that we dropped it from further study.

The mean similarity rank assigned to each of the nine religions was determined separately for six groups of college students: Catholics, Episcopalians, Presbyterians, Lutherans, Methodists, and Baptists. The reason these six groups of subjects were used and no other is simply that they are the denominations most frequently found in our samples. Other Christian denominations, Jews, etc., were found too infrequently to warrant separate study.

Table [21.3] may be read as follows: The Catholics, on the average, judged the Episcopalians to be most similar to themselves, followed by the Lutheran, Presbyterian, Methodist, and Baptist denominations. Then follow the Jews, Mohammedans, and Atheists.

Table 21.3 The Similarity Matrix

Rank Order of Similarity

Group	Number	1	2	3	4	5	6	7	8
Catholic	120	Epis.	Luth.	Pres.	Meth.	Bapt.	Jew	Moham.	Ath.
Episcopalian	38	Cath.	Luth.	Pres.	Meth.	Bapt.	Jew	Moham.	Ath.
Lutheran	57	Pres.	Meth.	Epis.	Bapt.	Cath.	Jew	Moham.	Ath.
Presbyterian	100	Meth.	Bapt.	Luth.	Epis.	Cath.	Jew	Moham.	Ath.
Methodist	116	Pres.	Bapt.	Luth.	Epis.	Cath.	Jew	Moham.	Ath.
Baptist	26	Meth.	Pres.	Luth.	Epis.	Cath.	Jew	Moham.	Ath.

Inspection of the similarity matrix shows the following:

(1) All six Christian groups are unanimous in ranking as least similar to themselves Jews, then Mohammedans, then Atheists.

(2) If we stay within the Christian fold, we note that the rank order of similarity for Baptists is the exact reverse of that for Catholics.

(3) The similarity continuum for Episcopalians is identical with that for Catholics, except that Catholics rank Episcopalians as most similar, and Episcopalians rank Catholics as most similar.

(4) With the exception of the Episcopalians, all other Protestant denominations judge Catholics as the least similar of the Christian faiths to their own.

(5) The similarity continua found cannot be attributed to similarities in social status, but to cognitive similarity of belief systems. For example, it is a widely known sociological fact (e.g., Barber, 1957) that Catholics are, generally speaking, relatively low in social status, while Episcopalians are relatively high. Despite this sociological fact, it is seen in Table [21.3] that Catholics judge Episcopalians, and Episcopalians judge Catholics, to be most similar to each other.

(6) If we take the Catholic continuum as a point of departure, it becomes apparent that the similarity continua of the remaining groups are but variations of it, the variations arising from the fact that each denominational group views the continuum from its own position.

To determine more precisely whether the similarity matrix involving the Christian faiths is indeed reducible to one basic scale, we applied an "unfolding method" technique similar to that developed by Coombs (1950). All six similarity continua can be reproduced from one scale, as shown in Fig. [21.3].

Table 21.3 is a conditional proximity matrix which they analyzed with the assistance of Frank Restle to obtain Fig. 21.3.

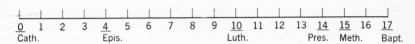

Fig. 21.3 Scale positions of similarity for six Christian denominations, as constructed by Rokeach.

They constructed Fig. 21.3 by trial and error. I reanalyzed the data by constructing the I scales from Table 21.3, merging them by triangular analysis as described in Chapter 17, constructing a partial order of the distances, and then constructing a numerical scale from this partial order under the constant Δ assumption (Chapter 5). The result is shown in Fig. 21.4 and is exceedingly close to the one they obtained by trial and error. This is merely an illustration of the remarkably high degree of constraint an ordered metric scale places on its numerical representation.

Just what interpretation this continuum might best be given is not absolutely clear, but a possibility is that it represents a scale of *degree of prescribed ritual*, diminishing from left to right, as perceived by these college students.

The question naturally arises as to just what value such a scale has—is it related to other behavior or just judgments of similarity? Rokeach examined church records in Lansing, Michigan, from two churches in each of five denominations. He found that the relative migration of new members to a church from others and the relative migration from a church to other denominations are functions of their similarity as measured on the similarity scale. He also studied interfaith marriages and found that the frequency of interfaith marriage varies directly with judged interfaith similarity. These results support the contention that similarity analysis may be used to reveal the cognitive and perceptual structure of individuals in significant areas of behavior.

A Multidimensional Case

In this case we begin with the stimulus I scales as given. It is as if the data were obtained by judgments on cartwheels, case 2 (see Chapter 2) or from a conditional proximity matrix (see Chapter 19).

The I scales with which we begin, then, are as given in Table 21.4.

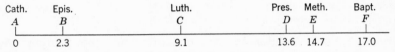

Fig. 21.4 The cognitive similarity scale under the constant Δ assumption.

The first step is to construct a partial order of the distances. From each I scale we have immediately the rank order of a subset of interpoint distances, the subset consisting of distances having a common terminus, that is, conjoint distances. Thus A's I scale yields the rank order: $\overline{AE} > \overline{AF} > \overline{AB} > \overline{AD} > \overline{AC}$.

Every pair of I scales has one distance in common. Thus, C's I scale yields the rank order $\overline{CE} > \overline{CB} > \overline{CD} > \overline{CF} > \overline{CA}$; and the distance

Table 21.4   Stimulus I Scales
(Hypothetical Data)

$$A\ C\ D\ B\ F\ E$$
$$B\ D\ E\ A\ F\ C$$
$$C\ A\ F\ D\ B\ E$$
$$D\ B\ F\ E\ A\ C$$
$$E\ D\ B\ F\ A\ C$$
$$F\ D\ C\ E\ B\ A$$

$\overline{AC}$ must be the same as the distance $\overline{CA}$, having assumed a metric space. The problem, then, is to merge all these rank orders into a common partial order of the interpoint distances.

A procedure for doing this is triangular analysis as described in Chapter 17. In this case the triangular pattern is shown in Table 21.5.

Having obtained a perfect triangular pattern, the order of the rows (and columns) yields the partial order of the distances directly. The partial order on distances that corresponds to Table 21.5 is given in Fig. 21.5. In

Table 21.5   Triangular Analysis of the Stimulus I Scales Listed in Table 21.4

	$\overline{CE}$	$\overline{BC}$	$\overline{AE}$	$\overline{AF}$	$\overline{CD}$	$\overline{BF}$	$\overline{AB}$	$\overline{EF}$	$\overline{BE}$	$\overline{AD}$	$\overline{CF}$	$\overline{AC}$	$\overline{DE}$	$\overline{DF}$	$\overline{BD}$
$\overline{CE}$	—	1	1	—	1	—	—	1	1	—	1	1	1	—	—
$\overline{BC}$		—	—	—	1	1	1	—	1	—	1	1	—	—	1
$\overline{AE}$			—	1	—	—	1	1	1	1	—	1	1	—	—
$\overline{AF}$				—	—	1	1	1	—	1	1	1	—	1	—
$\overline{CD}$					—	—	—	—	—	1	1	1	1	1	1
$\overline{BF}$						—	1	1	1	—	1	—	—	1	1
$\overline{AB}$							—	—	1	1	—	1	—	—	1
$\overline{EF}$								—	1	—	1	—	1	1	—
$\overline{BE}$									—	—	—	—	1	—	1
$\overline{AD}$										—	—	1	1	1	1
$\overline{CF}$											—	1	—	1	—
$\overline{AC}$												—	—	—	—
$\overline{DE}$													—	1	1
$\overline{DF}$														—	1
$\overline{BD}$															—

the partial order a line is drawn only between pairs of distances which have a common terminus. Thus $\overline{CE}$ is above both $\overline{AE}$ and $\overline{BC}$ but these latter two are not directly comparable. Disjoint pairs of distances may sometimes be ordered in magnitude through a chain of transitive distance relations. An example of comparability by virtue of transitivity of distance may be seen from the fact that $\overline{BC}$ is greater than $\overline{AD}$ in the partial order because $\overline{BC} > \overline{CD}$ and $\overline{CD} > \overline{AD}$.

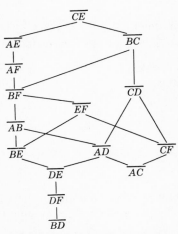

Fig. 21.5 Partial order on distances from Table 21.5.

Step 2 is to list each triple in such a way as to indicate the required order for the projections of each triangle. We have done this in Table 21.6.

The construction of this table follows readily from the partial order. The first triple to be listed, decided on a lexicographical basis, is that involving the points A, B, and C. We note in Fig. 21.5 that $\overline{BC} > \overline{AB} > \overline{AC}$, so we record this triangle as BAC to indicate that A must project between B and C on some dimension to satisfy a least squares fit to that triple. Note that the same information would be conveyed by recording the triangle as CAB, and we do not distinguish between these two modes of recording.

For step 3 we observe in Fig. 21.5 that the longest line is C–E, so we take it to define the first dimension.

For step 4 we observe from Table 21.4 that the two I scales of C and E are

C's I scale: $C \; A \; F \; D \; B \; E$
E's I scale (reversed): $C \; A \; F \; B \; D \; E$

The partial order that satisfies both of them is

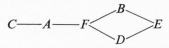

Step 5 calls for resolving all incomparabilities in the partial order. In this case only B and D are incomparable, so we examine all triples involving both B and D. For convenience they are listed in Table 21.7 with the implication of each noted for the order of B and D on the line from C to E.

**Table 21.6 Lexicographic Ordering of Triples Indicating
Desired Projection of Each Triangle**

BAC

ADB

ABE

ABF

CAD

CAE

ACF

ADE

ADF

AFE

BDC

CBE

BFC

BDE

BDF

BEF

CDE

CFD

CFE

EDF

For example, consider the triple *ADB*. To fit this triangle, *D* should project between *A* and *B*. In view of the partial order that this projection must fit, the order of the projections of *D* and *B* between *C* and *E* should be *C D B E*. This is what is indicated in the table. We take one other example, the triple *BDE*. To fit this triangle, *D* must project between *B* and *E*, which implies that on the line from *C* to *E* the order of projection should be *C B D E*.

We note from Table 21.7 that three triangles will be fitted by the order *C D B E* and only one if the order *DB* is reversed. The fact that the triples *BDC* and *BDE* have contradictory implications is the reason that *B* and *D* are incomparable in the partial order in the first place. So, in actuality, we are using the remaining triples to decide which order will fit the most triangles. This leads us to adopt as the solution for the first dimension the order

$$C \, A \, F \, D \, B \, E$$

Table 21.7 Triples Involving the Pair *B* and *D* and the Implied Order

$$ADB \Rightarrow DB$$
$$BDC \Rightarrow DB$$
$$BDE \Rightarrow BD$$
$$BDF \Rightarrow DB$$

Step 6 is completed by tallying on the data sheet of Table 21.6 the triples that have been satisfied by this first dimension. The tally is presented as Table 21.8.

This involves checking that the order of the triple as given in Table 21.8 is embedded in the order of projections on the first dimension. It does

Table 21.8   Triples Satisfied by the First Dimension

Satisfied Triples

BAC	1	BDC	1
ADB	1	CBE	1
ABE	1	BFC	1
ABF		BDE	
CAD	1	BDF	1
CAE	1	BEF	
ACF		CDE	1
ADE	1	CFD	1
ADF		CFE	1
AFE	1	EDF	1

not matter, of course, whether a triple in Table 21.6 is written as it is or in reverse order. The significant relation is the *betweenness* relation, that is, that one stimulus projects between the two defining the longest side.

We find in Table 21.8 that 15 of the 20 triples are satisfied by the first dimension.

In step 7 we proceed to select a pair of stimuli to define the second dimension. From the unsatisfied triangles in Table 21.8 we tabulate the longest line. I have done this in a separate table, Table 21.9, to make the step clear.

Table 21.9   Tally of Longest Line in Unsatisfied Triples

Unsatisfied Triple	Longest Line
ABF	A–F
ACF	A–F
ADF	A–F
BDE	B–E
BEF	B–F

The line *A–F* is indicated as most often unsatisfied. We check in Table 21.5 and note that it is also a longer line than either *B–E* or *B–F*.

Finally we check with the order on the first dimension and find that *A* and *F* project next to each other, so we may accept the line *A–F* as reasonably orthogonal to *C–E*, the line of the first dimension.

There is no necessary "pecking order" on these criteria and their combinations. The first two criteria are suggested because they define an axis on which the rank order of projections is more readily determined, that is, these criteria lead to "computational" simplicity. They are likely to be related in the sense of yielding the same decision. The third criterion is motivated by psychological considerations, in that the considerations are more esthetic than logical. I do not consider it vital to establish a pecking order on these criteria because alternative solutions are desirable since the capability to rotate is desirable.

We return, then, to step 4.

The unsatisfied triples are

$$ABF$$
$$ACF$$
$$ADF$$
$$BDE$$
$$BEF$$

The first three triples involve the defining pair of stimuli for this axis (A and F) and some third stimulus point which must project between them. So we see that the partial order for this dimension based on the three triples involving A and F is

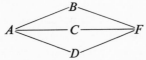

Step 5 calls for resolving this partial order. We proceed by examining the incomparable pairs.

In this particular case there are two remaining unsatisfied triples, BDE and BEF. It is immediately clear that in the partial order E must come between B and F and, also, that D must come between B and E. So we have resolved the partial order to the following:

$$A\text{---}B\text{---}D\text{---}E\text{---}F$$
$$\diagdown C \diagup$$

There are not sufficient data in the unsatisfied triples to locate the projection of C on the second dimension.

As a matter of interest, I constructed this problem by picking 6 points on a plane and computing the I scales which led to Table 21.4. The arrangement of the 6 points originally chosen is shown in Fig. 21.6. The reader can check for himself the order of projections on the line C–E and the line A–F and compare with the corresponding solutions obtained in the analysis.

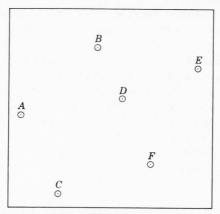

Fig. 21.6   Original configuration for the two-dimensional problem.

4. SUMMARY

Nonmetric multidimensional psychological scaling is defined as the problem of constructing a stimulus space from order relations on inter-point distances, the solution being in the form of a set of simple orders. The insights underlying the method are due to William Hays, who adapted his solution for multidimensional unfolding of preferential choice data to the multidimensional unfolding of similarities data.

The basic concepts and procedures are presented in Section 1 leading up to a summary of the analytical procedure in Section 2. The analytical procedure is illustrated with two applications to one-dimensional data, one hypothetical and the other involving real data, and one application to hypothetical data in two dimensions.

In the next chapter we take up some further applications to real data which are on a larger scale than these simple illustrative examples.

REFERENCES

Coombs, C. H., 1954, A method for the study of interstimulus similarity, *Psychometrika*, **19**, 183–94.
Goldberg, D., and C. H. Coombs, 1963, Some applications of unfolding theory to fertility analysis, paper no. 5 at Milbank Memorial Fund Roundtable on Emerging Techniques in Population Research, New York, Fall, 1963.
Rokeach, M., 1960, *The open and closed mind*, Basic Books, New York.

CHAPTER 22

Some Applications
of Nonmetric Multidimensional
Psychological Scaling

This chapter presents an example in full detail of the application of the model and algorithm presented in Chapter 21, and several other applications are summarized. It concludes with some comments relating this approach to Torgerson's metric model for multidimensional psychological scaling and to factor analysis.

1. ANALYSIS OF A CONDITIONAL PROXIMITY MATRIX FOR PSYCHOLOGICAL JOURNALS

The Data

Similarities and differences among psychological journals are always a subject of interest to psychologists. The first problem in analyzing them was to decide what observations would be appropriate from which interpoint distances could be inferred. The observations chosen have an internal test of validity as well as an a priori one and are applicable to most scientific journals. The observations consist of a count of the number of references made in each journal to each of the journals being analyzed. The data were obtained from the entire output of ten psychological journals in 1960. A tabulation was made for each journal of the number of references made in its articles to each of the ten journals.

This seems to me on a priori grounds to be a reasonable criterion of similarity. This is very literally a count of the extent to which a journal "uses" another journal. The more one journal uses another the more like it it must be. If we were trying to determine whether physiological psychology was becoming more pharmacological or more neurophysiological, a position based on the references the journal makes to the journals

Table 22.1   Psychological Journals Selected for Similarity Analysis

A	American Journal of Psychology	AJP
B	Journal of Abnormal and Social Psychology	JASP
C	Journal of Applied Psychology	JAP
D	Journal of Comparative and Physiological Psychology	JCPP
E	Journal of Consulting Psychology	JCP
F	Journal of Educational Psychology	JEdP
G	Journal of Experimental Psychology	JExP
H	Psychological Bulletin	PB
I	Psychological Review	PR
J	Psychometrika	Pka

in these two fields would provide a pretty definitive argument. Another way of looking at it is this. If we submitted a paper to the *Journal of Abnormal and Social Psychology* which leaned heavily on psychometrics, it might be returned with the suggestion that it would be more suitable for some other journal. The data and their analysis, however, will provide internal evidence of the reasonableness or unreasonableness of the criterion.

I selected eight journals from the list of APA publications and added two non-APA journals (*American Journal of Psychology* and *Psychometrika*) which particularly interested me. Those selected are listed in Table 22.1 in alphabetical order, with the letters which identify them in subsequent tables and figures.

The data matrix* of Table 22.2 contains the count of the number of references *in* each row-journal *to* each column-journal. The column

Table 22.2   Number of References *in* Row-Journal *to* Column-Journal, 1960

	A	B	C	D	E	F	G	H	I	J	Other
A	122	4	1	23	4	2	135	17	39	1	319
B	23	303	9	11	49	4	55	50	48	7	1200
C	0	28	84	2	11	6	15	23	8	13	432
D	36	10	4	304	0	0	98	21	65	4	744
E	6	93	11	1	186	6	7	30	10	14	843
F	6	12	11	1	7	34	24	16	7	14	358
G	65	15	3	33	3	3	337	40	59	14	531
H	47	108	16	81	130	14	193	52	31	12	1095
I	22	40	2	29	8	1	97	39	107	13	437
J	2	0	2	0	0	1	6	14	5	59	221

* I am indebted to Mr. Michael Levine of Stanford University for the tabulation contained in this data matrix.

labeled "Other" contains the count of the number of references in each row-journal to journals not included in this study and to any other publications, such as books.

We note that a single year of publication provides a smaller sample of data for some journals than for others. This is particularly true of *Psychometrika*, in which no references at all were made in 1960 to three of the ten journals, one reference was made to another, and two references were made to each of two others.

This matrix is a bit too large for a simple presentation of the method of analysis I wish to illustrate. For $n = 10$ journals we have $n' = \binom{10}{2} = 45$ interpoint distances, which means that the triangular analysis of interpoint distances to construct a partial order of the distances involves a matrix of order 45×45. Consequently I eliminated two journals, the *Psychological Bulletin* and the *Psychological Review* (*H* and *I* respectively), as the indications were that they, especially the *Psychological Bulletin*, would seriously violate certain of the conditions for a metric space. This gives us $n = 8$ and hence a matrix for the triangular analysis of distances that is 28×28, a matrix sufficiently large to illustrate the method of analysis in some detail but still not too complicated for reasonable clarity.

The original data matrix, Table 22.2, is a conditional proximity matrix, and when reduced to an 8×8 matrix is still a conditional proximity matrix. We could analyze this 8×8 matrix as it stands, but in this particular instance a substantive question arises which makes it desirable to transform this matrix into a residual matrix and to analyze the latter.

The problem is this. Journals differ in the degree to which they make citations and also in the sheer number of articles they publish to which citations may be made. These "bulk" effects, or main effects, may distort the relative interactions of the journals. Thus, journal *A* may make 20 references to journal *B* and 10 to journal *C*, which may suggest that *A* is relatively more similar to *B* than to *C*. However, if *B* has a "pool" of 500 articles to be referred to and *C* has a smaller pool of 200, the opposite implication is suggested.

Consequently I subtracted the main effects attributable to row and column means and constructed the residual matrix of interactions, Table 22.3.

Basic Assumptions and Analysis

We wish to map each journal into a point in a multidimensional Euclidean space. We assume that Table 22.3 is a conditional proximity matrix. We assume that a single-peaked generalization surface is associated with each row-journal point and that the gradient falls off symmetrically and strictly monotonically and reflects the relative inter-action of that row-journal with each of the column-journals. With these assumptions we may construct the I scale for each row-stimulus and proceed with step 1 of the multidimensional analysis.

Table 22.3   Residual Matrix: the Matrix of Interactions

	A	B	C	D	E	F	G	J
A	89.623	-54.000	-14.500	-23.750	-28.375	-4.875	50.500	-14.625
B	-30.500	223.875	-27.625	-56.875	-4.500	-24.000	-50.625	-29.750
C	-15.750	-13.375	85.125	-28.125	-4.750	15.750	-52.875	14.000
D	-16.875	-68.500	-32.000	236.750	-52.875	-27.375	-7.000	-32.125
E	-30.375	31.000	-8.500	-49.750	149.625	-4.875	-81.500	-5.625
F	-3.500	-23.125	18.375	-22.875	-2.500	50.000	-37.625	21.250
G	10.000	-65.625	-35.125	-36.375	-52.000	-26.500	229.875	-24.250
J	-2.625	-30.250	14.250	-19.000	-4.625	21.875	-50.750	71.125

Step 1: I Scales and Partial Order on Distances. For each row-journal in Table 22.3 we may rank order the column-journals from the most similar to the least similar, that is, that column-journal with the largest interaction in the row is first on that row-journal's I scale and the rest of the column-journals are taken in order of decreasing interaction. This provides the first test of whether the data matrix will satisfy the conditions for a metric space. From the assumption of the single-peaked generalization surface *a journal should interact more with itself than any other journal* which is equivalent to the condition that a point cannot be nearer any other point than it is to itself.

We see in row A, for example, that the diagonal entry is the largest, so A's I scale begins with A, as it should. For each row we see that the largest entry is in the diagonal, so each row I scale begins with the corresponding row-journal.

The row I scales constructed from Table 22.3 called the "original stimulus I scales," are presented in Table 22.4.

We now need to test whether the distance relations implied by these several I scales are consistent, that is, transitive. If not, corrections need to be made in order to construct a partial order of the distances. Tri-angular analysis, as described in Chapter 17, is useful for this purpose. With $n = 8$ we have 28 distances.

A perfect triangular pattern means that the distance relations are transitive and we can immediately write down the partial order on the distances implied by the order of the columns (or rows) on the basis of which distance "covers" another, as described in Chapter 17. Failure to obtain a perfect triangular pattern means that intransitivities exist and the data cannot be analyzed until these intransitivities are removed.

If there is one or more intransitive cycles embedded in a partial order, then depending on where we "cut" these cycles different partial orders

**Table 22.4   Original Stimulus *I* Scales; the Rank Order
of the Column-Journals from Each Row-Journal**

$$A\ G\ F\ C\ J\ D\ E\ B$$
$$B\ E\ F\ C\ J\ A\ G\ D$$
$$C\ F\ J\ E\ B\ A\ D\ G$$
$$D\ G\ A\ F\ C\ J\ E\ B$$
$$E\ B\ F\ J\ C\ A\ D\ G$$
$$F\ J\ C\ E\ A\ D\ B\ G$$
$$G\ A\ J\ F\ C\ D\ E\ B$$
$$J\ F\ C\ A\ E\ D\ B\ G$$

may be constructed, each of which violates at least one relation in the data. A cycle of k intransitive elements can be made transitive by cutting it at any one of the k links, and the problem is to choose the link that in some sense will least violate the data.

This may be done in the following manner. An entry of 1 below the diagonal represents the link in an intransitive cycle which will be broken if the order of the columns of that triangular pattern is accepted. To break the cycle at that link will violate the order between the two corresponding entries in the residual matrix. The difference between those two entries, then, is treated as if it were zero. The sum of all the differences which are so treated is a rough measure of the degree to which the data are violated. I looked for the triangular pattern that minimized this sum.

One triangular pattern arrived at in the analysis of these journal data is presented in Table 22.5. The intransitive cycles may be conveniently identified by constructing the partial order on distances based on the order of the columns, as shown in Fig. 22.1. In this figure the dashed lines correspond to the 1's below the diagonal and represent the links that would be cut.

To each of the 1's below the diagonal there corresponds a difference between two residuals which must be reduced to zero, that is, violated. For example, the cell ($\overline{DJ}$, $\overline{DG}$) has a 1 in it. In D's row of Table 22.3, the $\overline{DJ}$ residual is -32.125 and the $\overline{DG}$ residual is -7.000. Thus a difference of 25.125 will be disregarded if this triangular pattern is accepted. We

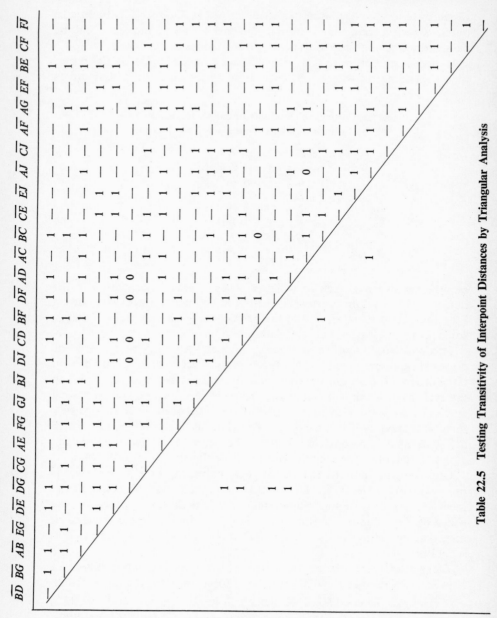

Table 22.5 Testing Transitivity of Interpoint Distances by Triangular Analysis

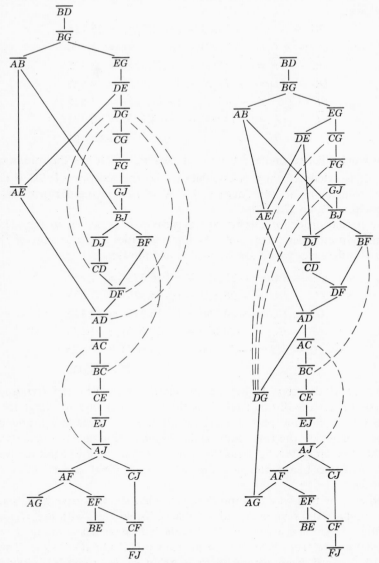

Fig. 22.1 Partial order on distances, from Table 22.5.

Fig. 22.2 Final partial order on distances, from Table 22.6.

may list all residual differences which will be disregarded and sum them as follows:

$$\overline{DG} - \overline{DJ} = -7.000 - (-32.125) = 25.125$$
$$\overline{DG} - \overline{CD} = -7.000 - (-32.000) = 25.000$$
$$\overline{DG} - \overline{DF} = -7.000 - (-27.375) = 20.375$$
$$\overline{DG} - \overline{AD} = -7.000 - (-16.875) = 9.875$$
$$\overline{BF} - \overline{BC} = -24.000 - (-27.625) = 3.625$$
$$\overline{AC} - \overline{AJ} = -14.500 - (-14.625) = 0.125$$
$$\Sigma = 84.125$$

We would like to find the triangular pattern which has the minimum sum. It is evident from this calculation that the location of $\overline{DG}$ is the prime contributor to this large sum. A revised triangular pattern is presented in Table 22.6.

The partial order for this triangular pattern is presented in Fig. 22.2.

This partial order yields only 24 intransitivities and the sum of the residual differences which are violated is as follows:

$$\overline{CG} - \overline{DG} = -35.125 - (-36.375) = 1.250$$
$$\overline{FG} - \overline{DG} = -26.500 - (-36.375) = 9.875$$
$$\overline{GJ} - \overline{DG} = -24.250 - (-36.375) = 12.125$$
$$\overline{BF} - \overline{BC} = -24.000 - (-27.625) = 3.625$$
$$\overline{AC} - \overline{AJ} = -14.500 - (-14.625) = 0.125$$
$$\Sigma = 27.000$$

This concludes step 1, but let us summarize. We used triangular analysis to test the distance relations for transitivity and to merge the I scales into a common partial order of distances. We found a triangular pattern for which the total sum of the residual differences violated was 27.000. I accepted this figure as the minimum that could be achieved with these data and hence accepted Fig. 22.2 as the final partial order on distances.

Perhaps the best way to appreciate just what changes have been made is to compare the revised stimulus I scales, Table 22.7, with the original in Table 22.4. The arrow in A's I scale indicates that stimulus J was moved forward from behind C to in front of C. On B's I scale C was moved forward from behind F to in front of F. On G's I scale D was moved from behind C to in front of J.

Step 2: Projection of Triangles. A lexicographic ordering of the triangles is contained in Table 22.8 where each triangle is listed so as to indicate its longest side. A solution consists of finding one or more simple orders

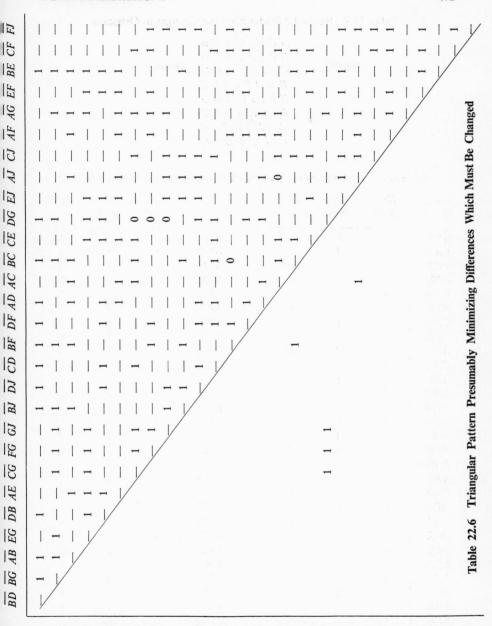

Table 22.6 Triangular Pattern Presumably Minimizing Differences Which Must Be Changed

Table 22.7   Revised *I* Scales Showing Changes in Originals

$$A\,G\,F\,J\,C\,D\,E\,B$$
$$B\,E\,C\,F\,J\,A\,G\,D$$
$$C\,F\,J\,E\,B\,A\,D\,G$$
$$D\,G\,A\,F\,C\,J\,E\,B$$
$$E\,B\,F\,J\,C\,A\,D\,G$$
$$F\,J\,C\,E\,A\,D\,B\,G$$
$$G\,A\,D\,J\,F\,C\,E\,B$$
$$J\,F\,C\,A\,E\,D\,B\,G$$

Table 22.8   Lexicographic Ordering of Triangles Indicating Longest Side

	$K^{(1)}$ B–D	$K^{(1)}$ B–G	$K^{(2)}$		$K^{(1)}$ B–D	$K^{(1)}$ B–G	$K^{(2)}$
ACB	1	1	0	BJD	1	1	0
BAD	1	1	1	BEF	1	1	0
AEB	1	1	0	BEG	1	1	0
AFB	1	1	0	BEJ	1	1	0
BAG	1	1	1	BFG	1	1	0
AJB	1	1	0	BFJ	1	1	1
CAD	1	1	0	BJG	1	1	0
ACE	1	1	1	DCE	1	1	1
AFC	1	1	0	CFD	1	1	0
CAG	1	1	0	CDG	0	1	1
AJC	1	1	0	DCJ	0	0	1
DAE	1	1	0	CFE	0	0	1
DAF	1	1	0	ECG	1	1	1
AGD	1	0	1	CJE	0	0	1
DAJ	1	1	0	CFG	1	1	0
AFE	1	1	1	CFJ	1	1	1
EAG	1	1	0	CJG	1	1	0
AJE	1	1	1	DFE	1	1	1
FAG	1	1	0	EDG	0	1	1
AFJ	0	0	1	DJE	1	1	1
GAJ	1	1	0	FDG	0	1	1
BCD	1	1	0	DFJ	0	0	1
BEC	1	1	0	GDJ	0	1	1
BCF	1	1	1	EFG	1	1	1
BCG	1	1	0	EFJ	1	1	0
BCJ	1	1	1	EJG	1	1	1
BED	1	1	0	FJG	1	1	0
BFD	1	1	0	Number	47	49	26
BGD	1	0	1	fitted			

of all the stimulus points such that the ordering of each triple of points as given in this table will be embedded in at least one of these simple orders.

If one simple ordering of the points can accommodate all the triples, a one-dimensional solution obtains at the level of an ordered metric scale. If more than one simple ordering is required, the solution is multi-dimensional.

Step 3: Selection of the First Dimension. From the partial order in Fig. 22.2 we see that B–D is the longest line and B–G the second longest line. I tested each of these as alternative axes for the first dimension.
Steps 4 to 6: Solution for Each Trial First Dimension. For each of the two trial dimensions we shall go through steps 4 to 6 in their entirety.

  B–D as Trial First Dimension. We first construct the joint partial order of B's and D's I scales (Table 22.7).

B's I scale:	$B E C F J A G D$
D's I scale (reversed):	$B E J C F A G D$

Their common partial order is

$$B \; E \; C \; F \; A \; G \; D$$
$$J$$

To resolve the partial order we need to locate J relative to C and F. So we consider all triples of points involving the pair CJ and the pair FJ and examine their implication for the ordering of J. The relevant triples are listed in Table 22.9. For example, we have the triple AJC which, in

Table 22.9   Triples Involving J with C or F and Their Implications

CJ	FJ
$AJC \Rightarrow CJ$	$AFJ \Rightarrow JF$
$BCJ \Rightarrow CJ$	$BFJ \Rightarrow FJ$
$DCJ \Rightarrow JC$	$CFJ \Rightarrow FJ$
$CJE \Rightarrow JC$	$DFJ \Rightarrow JF$
$CFJ \Rightarrow CJ$	$EFJ \Rightarrow FJ$
$CJG \Rightarrow CJ$	$FJG \Rightarrow FJ$

$$\therefore CFJ$$

order to be satisfied, requires that J project between A and C. For this order to be embedded in the partial order, J must project to the right of C, as indicated.

It is apparent from this table that the largest number of triangles will be fitted if J projects to the right of F. So we have as the solution to this trial first dimension the partial order

$$B\ E\ C\ F\ J\ A\ G\ D$$

We next tally in Table 22.8 the triangles fitted by this line as the first dimension. In the column of that table labeled $K^{(1)}$, $B–D$, a 1 indicates a triangle whose projection is satisfied by this solution and a 0 indicates an unfitted triangle. We see that the line $B–D$ satisfies 47 out of the total of 56 triangles, or 84%.

B–G as Trial First Dimension. We first construct the joint partial order of B's and G's I scales (Table 22.7).

B's I scale: $B\ E\ C\ F\ J\ A\ G\ D$
G's I scale (reversed): $B\ E\ C\ F\ J\ D\ A\ G$

Their common partial order is

$$B\ E\ C\ F\ J\ A\ G$$
$$\diagdown$$
$$D$$

To resolve the partial order we need to locate D relative to A and G. So we consider all triples of points involving the pair AD and the pair DG and examine their implications for the ordering of D. The relevant triples are listed in Table 22.10. For example, to embed the triple BAD in the partial order would require that D project to the right of A, as indicated.

Table 22.10   Triples Involving D with A or G and Their Implications

AD	DG
$BAD \Rightarrow AD$	$BGD \Rightarrow GD$
$CAD \Rightarrow AD$	$CDG \Rightarrow DG$
$DAE \Rightarrow AD$	$EDG \Rightarrow DG$
$DAF \Rightarrow AD$	$FDG \Rightarrow DG$
$AGD \Rightarrow AD$	$AGD \Rightarrow GD$
$DAJ \Rightarrow AD$	$GDJ \Rightarrow DG$
$\therefore\ ADG$	

It is apparent from this table that the largest number of triangles will be fitted if D projects between A and G. So we have as the solution to this trial first dimension, the simple order

$$B\ E\ C\ F\ J\ A\ D\ G$$

We tally in Table 22.8 the triangles fitted by this line, $B–G$, as the first dimension. In the column of that table labeled $K^{(1)}$, $B–G$, a 1 indicates a triangle whose projection is satisfied and a 0 indicates a triangle that is not. We see that the line B–G satisfies 49 of the 56 triangles, 87.5%.

Although the line B–G misses two of the triangles that the line B–D fitted, one of them involving the distance $\overline{BD}$, which is the largest distance, it hits four other triangles that the line B–D missed, all of them relatively large. There are few grounds for choice between them, and they are very closely related as they differ only in the order of the last two elements. I chose the line B–G as first dimension.

Step 7: Selection of the Next Trial Dimension. There are only seven unsatisfied triples remaining:

$$AGD, \quad AFJ, \quad BGD, \quad DCJ, \quad CFE, \quad CJE, \quad DFJ$$

The easiest thing to do is to seek an ordering or partial order which will satisfy as many of these as possible. We note that the two triples AGD and BGD involve the same pair, DG, so for these two triples the partial order is

```
A
  \
   >G—D
  /
B
```

From DCJ and DFJ we have

```
    C
   / \
  D    J
   \ /
    F
```

From the triple AFJ, the first partial order must adjoin the second as follows:

```
A          C
  \       / \
   >G—D<     >J
  /       \ /
B          F
```

The triple CJE requires that E follow J; the triple CFE orders C and F; and we have, finally, the solution:

$$(A\ B)\ G\ D\ C\ F\ J\ E$$

which fits all the seven triples. The tally in the third column of Table 22.8 indicates the triangles fitted by this dimension. (The tie between A and B represents a minor problem. They could be in either order, and so for the purpose of this tally I regarded B as being to the left of A because that would fit two more triangles.)

To summarize, then, the second dimension fits all 7 of the remaining triples and, in addition, 19 of those already fitted by the first dimension, a total of 26.

Interpretation

The two dimensions obtained in this analysis of the interactions of eight psychology journals are summarized in Table 22.11, and the configuration as it might appear in two dimensions is shown in Fig. 22.3. The figure does not adequately reflect the metric relations nor the relative lengths of the two dimensions.

Table 22.11   The Final Two Dimensions

$K^{(1)}$		$K^{(2)}$	
B	JASP	A	AJP
E	JCP	B	JASP
C	JAP	G	JExP
F	JEdP	D	JCPP
J	Pka	C	JAP
A	AJP	F	JEdP
D	JCPP	J	Pka
G	JExP	E	JCP

The first dimension might have any one of a number of possible interpretations: soft-hard, real-artificial, field-laboratory, significant-rigorous, and so on. The second dimension has an even less satisfactory or obvious interpretation: the first four are ordinarily associated with academic psychology and the last four more with service and application, so we might tentatively label it academic-applied.

Quite aside from these weakly supported interpretations, I was surprised at the outcome of this analysis—that only two dimensions were required and that the first so dominated the interaction of these journals. When these procedures are programmed for a computer it will be interesting to apply them to a larger data matrix of this nature.

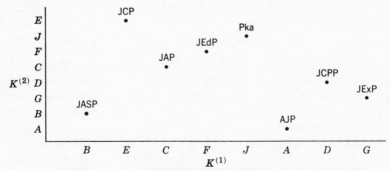

Fig. 22.3   A configuration for the journals in two dimensions.

Coincidence or Not? Before leaving this analysis of the residual matrix derived from a conditional proximity matrix I wish to point out an interesting possibility. In a conditional proximity matrix elements in different rows are not comparable. But after removing main effects, leaving only the interaction matrix, it would seem that column I scales might also be analyzed. These would, in a sense, reflect the relative extent to which a journal was "used" by other journals, in contrast to the row I scales which reflect the relative extent a journal "uses" the other journals.

Table 22.12   Column I Scales from Table 22.3

$$A\ G\ J\ F\ C\ D\ E\ B$$
$$B\ E\ C\ F\ J\ A\ G\ D$$
$$C\ F\ J\ E\ A\ B\ D\ G$$
$$D\ J\ F\ A\ C\ G\ E\ B$$
$$E\ F\ B\ J\ C\ A\ G\ D$$
$$F\ J\ C\ (AE)\ B\ G\ D$$
$$G\ A\ D\ F\ B\ J\ C\ E$$
$$J\ F\ C\ E\ A\ G\ B\ D$$

With this in mind, I constructed the column I scales based on the residual matrix, Table 22.3. They are listed in Table 22.12.

The remarkable thing is the close resemblance of these column I scales to the revised row I scales of Table 22.7. We wonder if this is merely a coincidence or if the process of removing main effects from a conditional proximity matrix will tend to make it a symmetric proximity matrix. I have no rational grounds for such a conjecture.

Supplementary Analysis

There are, needless to say, other important relations among these journals not revealed by this analysis. To reveal some of these I constructed several indices inspired by an informational analysis of some similar data by Osgood and Wilson (1957).

These indices bear on the extent to which a journal is a "self-feeder," the extent to which it feeds on "core"* psychology journals relative to feeding outside this core (an inside/outside ratio), and the extent to which a journal is a "producer for" relative to being a "consumer of" the other core psychology journals (a producer/consumer ratio). Indices are all based on the original data matrix of Table 22.2.

Two indices of "self-feeding" were constructed: (1a) the proportion of

* In Table 22.1 the *American Journal of Psychology* and *Psychometrika* are added to eight of the official APA publications, and I have rather arbitrarily identified these 10 as "core" psychology journals. They are, at least, the core journals which at the same time span the breadth of psychology.

references a journal makes to itself compared with references to the other 9 journals; and (1*b*) the proportion of references a journal makes to itself compared with references to any other source. This latter is self-feeding in the strictest sense.

After "self-feeding," where else does a journal feed, relatively speaking— on the core psychology journals or outside of them? The "inside/outside" ratio attempts to capture this by dividing the number of references a journal makes to the other 9 journals by the number it makes to all other sources.

When we know something about where a journal feeds it is interesting

Table 22.13   Values for Three Indices for Each Journal and Their Rank Order

		Self-Feeder				2. Inside/ Outside		3. Producer/ Consumer	
		1*a*		1*b*					
		Index	Rank	Index	Rank	Index	Rank	Index	Rank
A	AJP	0.540	7	0.224	4	0.708	1	0.916	6
B	JASP	1.184	4	0.208	5	0.213	8	1.211	3
C	JAP	0.792	6	0.156	7	0.245	7	0.555	8
D	JCPP	1.277	3	0.310	2	0.320	5	0.761	7
E	JCP	1.045	5	0.182	6	0.211	9	1.191	4
F	JEdP	0.347	9	0.075	9	0.274	6	0.378	10
G	JExP	1.434	2	0.440	1	0.443	4	2.681	2
H	PB	0.082	10	0.030	10	0.577	2	0.400	9
I	PR	0.426	8	0.143	8	0.505	3	1.084	5
J	Pka	1.967	1	0.235	3	0.136	10	3.067	1

to compare this with its role as a source for other journals. Is it an "innovator" in the sense of producing things other journals make use of or is it primarily a consumer of what others produce? An index designed to reflect the balance of these functions for a journal is the "producer/consumer" index: the number of references made to the journal by the other nine journals divided by the number of references it makes to the other nine.

In Table 22.13 are the values of each index for each journal with their rank order indicated in each column to facilitate interpretation.

We see that the *Journal of Experimental Psychology*, the *Journal of Comparative and Physiological Psychology*, and *Psychometrika* are the three strongest self-feeders on the basis of both the 1*a* and 1*b* self-feeder indices; and we see that the *Psychological Review*, the *Journal of Educational Psychology*, and the *Psychological Bulletin* are successively the weakest self-feeders by both indices. The first three may perhaps be said to represent the highest degree, in psychology, of technical and specialized development and have the most restricted clientele. The last three draw on the most diffuse sources and represent the work of the most varied clientele.

On the basis of the inside/outside index we see that the *American Journal of Psychology*, the *Psychological Bulletin*, and the *Psychological Review* are the most dependent on the core psychology journals; and the *Journal of Abnormal and Social Psychology*, the *Journal of Consulting Psychology*, and *Psychometrika* are much more dependent on sources outside the core psychology journals. If we look at the data of Table 22.2 in more detail, particularly the first row of the table, it is apparent that the high index for the *American Journal of Psychology* is due to its heavy dependence on the *Journal of Experimental Psychology*, which is actually greater (in 1960) than its dependence on itself. The three journals with the lowest inside/outside ratio are all journals which are seeking their inspiration and their support outside these core journals. They are journals which tend to widen the horizons of psychology by bringing material obtained elsewhere to the core.

This latter interpretation is important in the light of the interpretation of the producer/consumer index. A value of this index greater than 1 represents a journal which is used by the core psychology journals more than it uses them. A value less than 1 represents a journal which uses the core journals more than it is used by them. Five have indices greater than 1, five have less.

We see here that the three journals in the core which draw proportionately the most from outside the core are amongst the top four in their producer/consumer ratio. In other words, these three journals, *Psychometrika*, the *Journal of Abnormal and Social Psychology*, and the *Journal of Consulting Psychology* present a profile or pattern of bringing to psychology articles from outside which the core journals use.

We see that the *Journal of Applied Psychology*, the *Psychological Bulletin*, and the *Journal of Educational Psychology* are primarily consumers of the core journals and are lightly used by them in return. This is in spite of the fact that the *Journal of Applied Psychology* and the *Journal of Educational Psychology* are relatively heavy outside feeders as well.

Table 22.14 shows the intercorrelations of the various indices and their correlations with the dimensions obtained in the nonmetric multidimensional analysis. It is evident that self-feeders tend to be producers. This is in part accounted for by the fact that the number of references made by a journal to the other nine in the core is the denominator of the producer/consumer index, part of the denominator of self-feeding 1*b*, and all of the denominator of self-feeding 1*a*.

The dominant dimension $K^{(1)}$ of the nonmetric analysis of the journals appears unrelated to any of these indices, whereas the second dimension, $K^{(2)}$, is significantly related to the inside/outside index. If the first dimension is correctly interpreted as soft-hard and the second as academic-applied, these correlations with the indices are not unreasonable after the fact. A

Table 22.14   Correlations (τ Coefficients) among Indices and Dimensions

	1b	2	3	$K^{(1)}$	$K^{(2)}$
1a	.78	.02	.69	.00	.21
1b		.16	.56	−.14	.29
2			.07	−.07	.64
3				.14	.21
$K^{(1)}$					.11

soft-hard dimension is inherently unrelated to these indices, whereas journals high in an academic-applied dimension might be expected to be higher on an inside/outside index.

2. SUMMARY OF AN ANALYSIS OF A SYMMETRIC PROXIMITY MATRIX FOR MORSE CODE SIGNALS

The Data

The source of the data to be analyzed here is a study by Rothkopf (1957). He used Morse code signals, presenting the stimuli for one symbol (a letter or numeral) and then after 1.4 seconds the signal for another symbol. The time interval between pairs was 3 seconds, and a tone speed of 20 words per minute was used. Subjects were asked to judge whether the two signals were the same or different.

The 26 letters and 10 numerals make up 36 signals or 1260 pairs of signals. They were randomly divided into 4 groups of 315 and then randomly divided a second time into 4 more groups of 315. To each of these 8 groups of 315 the 36 pairs of "same" signals were added, making each group contain 351 pairs of signals.

Subjects for the experiment consisted of 598 airmen awaiting basic training at Lackland Air Force Base. The number was composed of 8 separate marching units ranging in size from 51 to 120 men. Subjects who reported Morse code experience were not used. Each marching unit was assigned to a different list of stimulus pairs.

The original data matrix is 36 × 36 and I chose to analyze for illustrative purposes the 10 × 10 submatrix for the 10 numerals because they made a neat package. The percentage of "same" judgments for each of the 45

Table 22.15 Percentage of "Same" Judgments

	A*	B	C	D	E	F	G	H	I	J
A	84									
B	62	89								
C	16	59	86							
D	06	23	38	89						
E	12	08	27	56	90					
F	12	14	33	34	30	86				
G	20	25	17	24	18	65	85			
H	37	25	16	13	10	22	65	88		
I	57	28	09	07	05	08	31	58	91	
J	52	18	09	07	05	18	15	39	79	94

* The letters A to J designate the Morse code signals 1 to 0, in order.

pairs of numerals is presented in Table 22.15. This matrix satisfies the definition of a symmetric proximity matrix.

The Analysis

We assume that each stimulus may be represented by a point in multi-dimensional Euclidean space and that there exists a strictly monotone transformation of the percentage of "same" judgments into psychological distance, that is, the more often a pair is judged to be the "same" the closer they are together.

The latter assumption is sufficient to lead directly to an ordering of the interpoint distances and the construction of the stimulus I scales. The ordinal scale of interpoint distances is obtained from a symmetric proximity matrix by ordering the percentages of "same" judgments from small to large. This order corresponds to the order of the interpoint distances from large to small. The I scales follow immediately and are presented in Table 22.16. A glance at the I scales is sufficient to reveal that a

Table 22.16 Stimulus I Scales, from Table 22.15

A B I J H G C (E F) D
B A C I (G H) D J F E
C B D F E G (H A)(I J)
D E C F G B H (I J) A
E D F C G A H B (I J)
F G D C E H J B A I
G (F H) I B D A E C J
H G I J A B F C D E
I J H A G B C F D E
J I A H (B F) G C D E

Table 22.17 Lexicographic Ordering of Triangles Indicating Longest Side

	E–I	E–J	C–G		E–I	E–J	C–G
ABC	1	1	1	CBH	1	1	1
ABD	1	1	0	CBI	1	1	1
BAE	0	0	1	CBJ	1	1	1
ABF	1	1	0	BDE	1	1	0
ABG	1	1	0	BDF	0	0	1
BAH	1	0	1	BGD	1	1	0
BAI	1	1	1	DBH	1	1	0
BAJ	1	1	1	DBI	1	1	0
ACD	1	1	0	DBJ	1	1	0
ACE	1	1	0	BFE	1	1	0
ACF	1	1	0	BGE	1	1	0
AGC	1	1	0	BHE	0	0	0
C(AH)	1	1	0	EBI	1	1	0
CAI	1	1	1	EBJ	1	1	0
CAJ	1	1	1	BGF	1	1	0
AED	0	0	1	BHF	0	0	1
AFD	1	1	0	FBI	1	1	0
AGD	1	1	0	BJF	0	0	1
AHD	0	1	0	B(GH)	0	0	0
AID	0	0	1	BIG	0	0	1
AJD	0	0	1	GBJ	1	1	0
A(EF)	0	0	0	BIH	0	0	1
AGE	1	1	1	BHJ	1	1	0
EAH	1	0	0	BIJ	0	1	1
EAI	1	1	0	CDE	1	1	0
EAJ	1	1	0	CDF	0	0	1
AGF	1	1	0	CDG	0	0	1
AHF	0	1	1	DCH	1	1	0
FAI	1	1	0	DCI	1	1	0
AJF	0	0	1	DCJ	1	1	0
AHG	0	1	1	CFE	1	1	0
AIG	0	0	1	CEG	0	0	1
GAJ	1	1	0	ECH	1	1	0
AIH	0	0	1	ECI	1	1	0
AJH	0	0	1	ECJ	1	1	0
AIJ	0	1	1	CFG	0	0	1
BCD	1	1	0	CFH	0	0	0
BCE	1	1	0	FCI	1	1	0
BCF	1	1	0	CFJ	0	0	0
CBG	0	0	1	CGH	1	1	0

Table 22.17 (*Continued*)

	E–I	E–J	C–G
CGI	1	1	0
CGJ	1	1	0
CHI	1	1	0
CHJ	1	1	0
C(IJ)	1	1	1
EDF	1	1	1
EDG	1	1	1
EDH	1	1	1
EDI	1	1	0
EDJ	1	1	0
DFG	1	1	1
DFH	1	1	0
DFI	1	1	0
DFJ	1	1	0
DGH	1	1	0
DGI	1	1	0
DGJ	1	1	0
DHI	1	1	0
DHJ	1	1	0
D(IJ)	1	1	1
EFG	1	1	1
EFH	1	1	0
EFI	1	1	0
EFJ	1	1	0
EGH	1	1	0
EGI	1	1	0
EGJ	1	1	0
EHI	1	1	0
EHJ	1	1	0
E(IJ)	1	1	1
FGH	1	1	0
FGI	1	1	0
GFJ	0	0	1
FHI	1	1	1
FHJ	1	1	1
FJI	1	0	1
GHI	1	1	1
GHJ	1	1	1
GIJ	0	1	0
HIJ	0	1	0

one-dimensional space will not satisfy the data because the I scales end in more than two different stimuli.

A lexicographic ordering of the triangles is presented in Table 22.17, where each triangle is listed so as to indicate the longest side of that triangle.

The longest line in the space corresponds to the smallest percentage in Table 22.15; we see that the lines E–I and E–J are tied for that honor. Each of them was explored here as a trial first dimension.

Table 22.18 gives a summary of the analysis of E–I as a trial $K^{(1)}$, and Table 22.19 summarizes E–J as a trial $K^{(1)}$.

A tally of the triangles fitted by each of these trial dimensions is contained in Table 22.17. Tallying triples with ties represents a minor problem. I counted a triple like $C(AH)$ as being satisfied by the line E–I because the tied elements project next to each other; triples like $A(EF)$ and $B(GH)$ are not counted as being satisfied. The degree of fit indicated in the tables is a lower bound to the amount of data actually satisfied because these dimensions fit most of the largest triangles.

The two alternate trial first dimensions are obviously highly correlated; the τ coefficient is .91.

Because of the better fit, the line E–J was tentatively adopted as the preferred solution for $K^{(1)}$.

The line C–G was chosen to define the second dimension on the basis of several criteria: It is the longest line in more unsatisfied triangles and it is reasonably orthogonal to the line E–J in that C and G project next to each other on that line.

For the second and all further dimensions, however, it is not necessary that all stimulus points in the space project between the two points which define the axis. Also, we want to give primary attention to the triangles not yet fitted so if there are not too many of them we may work directly with them.

Table 22.18 The Line E–I as Trial First Dimension

E's I Scale

$$E\ D\ F\ C\ G\ A\ H\ B\ (I\ J)$$

I's I Scale (Reversed)

$$E\ D\ F\ C\ B\ G\ A\ H\ J\ I$$

Their Common Partial Order

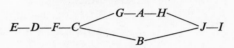

Resolution of B with GAH

BG	AB	BH
$ABG \Rightarrow GB$	$ABC \Rightarrow BA$	$BAH \Rightarrow BH$
$CBG \Rightarrow BG$	$ABD \Rightarrow BA$	$CBH \Rightarrow BH$
$BGD \Rightarrow GB$	$BAE \Rightarrow AB$	$DBH \Rightarrow BH$
$BGE \Rightarrow GB$	$ABF \Rightarrow BA$	$BHE \Rightarrow HB$
$BGF \Rightarrow GB$	$ABG \Rightarrow BA$	$BHF \Rightarrow HB$
$B(GH) \Rightarrow$	$BAH \Rightarrow BA$	$B(GH) \Rightarrow$
$BIG \Rightarrow$	$BAI \Rightarrow BA$	$BIH \Rightarrow$
$GBJ \Rightarrow GB$	$BAJ \Rightarrow BA$	$BHJ \Rightarrow BH$
	$\therefore\ GBAH$	

Solution

$$E\ D\ F\ C\ G\ B\ A\ H\ J\ I$$

Fit

Satisfies 89/120 triples, 74.2%

All triples involving C and G immediately tell us which stimuli project between them and which may project outside one of them. Here we have immediately from CG's triples that B, D, E, and F must project between C and G, and there is no triple indicating that a stimulus should project outside. For example, if CGH had been an unsatisfied triangle with side $\overline{CH}$ as longest side, this would indicate that H should project on the line C–G to the right of G.

The procedure from here on is a cut-and-try procedure to find which ordering of the stimuli will satisfy a maximum number of these unsatisfied

Table 22.19   The Line E–J as Trial First Dimension

E's I Scale

$E\ D\ F\ C\ G\ A\ H\ B\ (I\ J)$

J's I Scale (Reversed)

$E\ D\ C\ G\ (B\ F)\ H\ A\ I\ J$

Their Common Partial Order

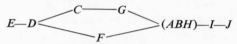

Resolution of CFG

CF	FG
$ACF \Rightarrow FC$	$AGF \Rightarrow FG$
$BCF \Rightarrow FC$	$BGF \Rightarrow FG$
$CDF \Rightarrow$	$CFG \Rightarrow FG$
$CFE \Rightarrow FC$	$DFG \Rightarrow FG$
$CFG \Rightarrow CF$	$EFG \Rightarrow FG$
$CFH \Rightarrow CF$	$FGH \Rightarrow FG$
$FCI \Rightarrow FC$	$FGI \Rightarrow FG$
$CFJ \Rightarrow CF$	$GFJ \Rightarrow GF$

$$\therefore\ FCG$$

Resolution of (ABH)

AB	AH	BH
$ABC \Rightarrow BA$	$BAH \Rightarrow$	$BAH \Rightarrow$
$ABD \Rightarrow BA$	$C(AH) \Rightarrow (AH)$	$CBH \Rightarrow BH$
$BAE \Rightarrow AB$	$AHD \Rightarrow HA$	$DBH \Rightarrow BH$
$ABF \Rightarrow BA$	$EAH \Rightarrow AH$	$BHE \Rightarrow HB$
$ABG \Rightarrow BA$	$AHF \Rightarrow HA$	$BHF \Rightarrow HB$
$BAH \Rightarrow$	$AHG \Rightarrow HA$	$B(GH) \Rightarrow$
$BAI \Rightarrow BA$	$AIH \Rightarrow HA$	$BIH \Rightarrow$
$BAJ \Rightarrow BA$	$AJH \Rightarrow$	$BHJ \Rightarrow BH$

$$\therefore\ BHA$$

Solution

$E\ D\ F\ C\ G\ B\ H\ A\ I\ J$

Fit

Satisfies 94/120 triples, 78.3 %

triangles. It is unreasonable, of course, to consider all possible permutations and count the number of triangles fitted. A little intelligent control reduces the amount of effort considerably. I found two solutions here in less than an hour.

One solution is the order $C B A I J H E D F G$, which leaves five triangles still unfitted: EAH, $A(EF)$, $B(GH)$, CFH, and CFJ.

Another solution is $C B A I J E D H F G$. This order leaves six triangles still unfitted; they are $A(EF)$, EAH, BHE, $B(GH)$, CFH, and CFJ. Although this second solution fits only 21 of the 27 unfitted triangles whereas the first solution fits 22 of them, I prefer the second because it leads to a more reasonable interpretation of the axis.

The still unsatisfied triples are too few in number to define a third dimension adequately.

Interpretation

The two dimensions obtained are presented in Table 22.20 with the Morse signals indicated.*

It would seem from the rationale of the method that there are no

Table 22.20 Order of Projection on the Two Dimensions

$K^{(1)}$		$K^{(2)}$	
E	· · · · ·	C	· · - · -
D	· · · · -	B	· · · - -
F	- · · · ·	A	· - · - -
C	· · · - -	I	· · - - ·
G	- - · · ·	J	· - - - -
B	· · - - -	E	· · · · ·
H	- - - · ·	D	· · · · -
A	· - - - -	H	- - - · ·
I	- - - - ·	F	· · - · ·
J	- - - - -	G	- - · · ·

a priori grounds why these dimensions should have a psychological interpretation. The criteria used for selecting them gave primary emphasis to fitting the data and to being mutually orthogonal. That they should have a psychological interpretation can only be a consequence, it seems to me, of a dominating effect of some psychological variables.

---

* The results reported here for the second dimension are somewhat different from those reported in Coombs (1958). This is due in part to an error in the previous analysis discovered by David Cross and to slight changes in the analytical procedures.

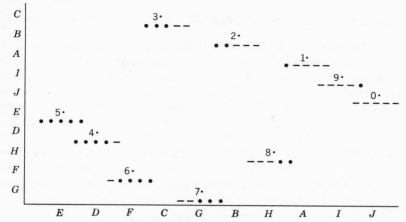

Fig. 22.4 A possible configuration for the Morse code data.

The first dimension clearly ranges from number of dots to number of dashes. The second dimension has a much less clear interpretation, but a possible interpretation is that it ranges from signals with dots first to signals with dashes first. I would feel a little more confident of such an interpretation if I and D were exchanged on $K^{(2)}$. I tested such a solution and found that it failed to satisfy 10 triples, whereas the dimension as given fails to satisfy only 6. Whether such differences are significant is a moot question.

Perhaps a better way to see the implications of this analysis is to make a two-dimensional plot of the stimuli. With only ordinal scales for the two axes, distances between points are somewhat arbitrary, but having in mind that the first dimension is the long axis of the space the configuration is like that in Fig. 22.4. It is clear from this figure that if stimuli D and I were interchanged on the second dimension the stimuli would appear on the circumference of an ellipse with the stimuli running along the top of the ellipse from left to right with decreasing number of dots in the beginning of the signal and along the bottom of the ellipse from left to right with decreasing number of dots at the end of the signal. Such a solution is very intuitively compelling.

Of considerable interest to me is the apparent fact that auditory patterns made up of two sequences of dots and dashes, as these are, may be thought of as perceived by untrained subjects mainly in terms of just two attributes which appear to have simple physical descriptions.

It should be possible by such methods as this to study problems like the primary dimensions of smell and problems in which functional (behavioral) relations may be captured in a structural configuration.

3. ON THE RELATION OF METRIC AND NONMETRIC MODELS

This nonmetric model for multidimensional psychological scaling is essentially a nonmetric equivalent of Torgerson's metric model. It makes less strong assumptions and the conclusions are weaker. Torgerson's model requires that interpoint distances be measured on a ratio scale, and his model yields a real Euclidean space. This model requires only order relations on interpoint distances and yields a set of simple orders which span a product space.

Naturally the question arises, which should we use? It is not easy to give a fair answer. I feel, at least intuitively, that the data typically have more information in them than just a simple order on interpoint distances, as in the case of probabilistic data matrices, for example. To use just the order relations, then, is to throw information away.

To capitalize on the additional information in the data, however, requires making some further assumptions, as Hefner, Shepard, and Torgerson have done for various probabilistic matrices. We buy knowledge with the assumptions we make; all knowledge is paid for; if the assumptions are correct, we have a bargain.

My inclination, not necessarily my recommendation, would be to do both analyses. The nonmetric analysis would provide some useful information about the dimensionality of the space and would provide a minimum base of knowledge about the space to which a metric analysis would add much more but less securely.

Helm (1960) has made an empirical study of the consequences of certain biases in a metric analysis. His study was stimulated by an earlier study of Mellinger's (1956). Mellinger used multidimensional successive intervals* to scale similarities among a set of color patches which varied in hue, saturation, and brightness, and analyzed the interpoint distances by Torgerson's model. He obtained six dimensions rather than the three-dimensional solution to be expected on the basis of color theory.

Helm then made an analysis of a presumed two-dimensional color space and obtained twelve. An examination of the interpoint distances on which his analysis was based suggested to him that the extra dimensions were due to a distortion of the interpoint distances, and in particular, that "big" distances were underestimated. Consequently, he transformed the interpoint distances by an exponential transformation,† and an analysis of the transformed distances yielded a two-dimensional space. He applied the same transformation to Mellinger's interpoint distances and reported

---

* See Chapter 20, Section 3.

† A rationale for the exponential transformation is discussed in Helm, Messick, and Tucker (1961).

that a "reanalysis yielded very nearly a three-dimensional multidimensional scale" (1960, p. 23). He concludes with the statement "it seems apparent that with 'deformed' distances, the Young-Householder analysis [see Torgerson 1958, Chapter 11] will generate a Euclidean space whose dimensionality is determined by the number of points considered."

That distortion of interpoint distances leads to extra dimensions is further borne out by a nonmetric reanalysis I made of a metric analysis reported by Ekman (1954). I shall report my reanalysis here as it serves as another illustration of the technique.

Table 22.21 Ekman's Similarity Matrix

		A		B	C		D			E	F		G	H	
		434	445	465	472	490	504	537	555	584	600	610	628	651	674
wave	434		.86	.42	.42	.18	.06	.07	.04	.02	.07	.09	.12	.13	.16
length	445	.86		.50	.44	.22	.09	.07	.07	.02	.04	.07	.11	.13	.14
	465	.42	.50		.81	.47	.17	.10	.08	.02	.01	.02	.01	.05	.03
	472	.42	.44	.81		.54	.25	.10	.09	.02	.01	.00	.01	.02	.04
	490	.18	.22	.47	.54		.61	.31	.26	.07	.02	.02	.01	.02	.00
	504	.06	.09	.17	.25	.61		.62	.45	.14	.08	.02	.02	.02	.01
	537	.07	.07	.10	.10	.31	.62		.73	.22	.14	.05	.02	.02	.00
	555	.04	.07	.08	.09	.26	.45	.73		.33	.19	.04	.03	.02	.02
	584	.02	.02	.02	.02	.07	.14	.22	.33		.58	.37	.27	.20	.23
	600	.07	.04	.01	.01	.02	.08	.14	.19	.58		.74	.50	.41	.28
	610	.09	.07	.02	.00	.02	.02	.05	.04	.37	.74		.76	.62	.55
	628	.12	.11	.01	.01	.01	.02	.02	.03	.27	.50	.76		.85	.68
	651	.13	.13	.05	.02	.02	.02	.02	.02	.20	.41	.62	.85		.76
	674	.16	.14	.03	.04	.00	.01	.00	.02	.23	.28	.55	.68	.76	

Ekman had 31 students rate on a scale from 0 to 4 ("no similarity at all" to "identity") all pairs of 14 colors. The similarity ratings for each pair of colors were averaged, linearly transformed to a scale from 0 to 1, and the resulting matrix factored by the group centroid method. Hence he regarded his similarity measure as a scalar product or correlation but provided no rationale for such an interpretation. He obtained five factors which he identified with violet, blue, green, yellow, and red. As these results are incompatible with classical color theory, it seemed worthwhile to make a nonmetric analysis of the same data and compare the results. His original similarity matrix is presented in Table 22.21.

Not wishing to analyze a 14 × 14 matrix, I arbitrarily selected 8 of the 14 stimuli, which included the 5 stimuli that spanned his 5 dimensions, to analyze by Hays's nonmetric model. The 8 stimuli selected are labeled A to H in Table 22.21. The stimuli identified with a particular color name are A = violet, B = blue, D = green, F = yellow, and H = red.

Their similarity ratings (a symmetric proximity matrix) lead directly to a weak ordering of the interpoint distances, as shown in Fig. 22.5. The

Weak Ordering of Interpoint Distances from Table 22.21	Transformed Rating of Similarity
$\overline{BF}$, $\overline{BG}$, $\overline{CG}$	.01
$\overline{AE}$, $\overline{BE}$, $\overline{CF}$, $\overline{DG}$, $\overline{BH}$, $\overline{CH}$, $\overline{DH}$	.02
$\overline{AF}$	.04
$\overline{CE}$, $\overline{AD}$	.07
$\overline{BD}$	.10
$\overline{AG}$	.11
$\overline{AH}$	.13
$\overline{DF}$	.14
$\overline{EH}$	.20
$\overline{AC}$, $\overline{DE}$	.22
$\overline{EG}$	.27
$\overline{CD}$	.31
$\overline{FH}$	.41
$\overline{AB}$	.44
$\overline{FG}$	.50
$\overline{BC}$	.54
$\overline{EF}$	.58
$\overline{GH}$	.85

Fig. 22.5 Similarity ratings and ordering of D instances.

ordering is paralleled by a column showing the actual transformed ratings of the interpoint distances. The largest distances, most dissimilar, are at the top of the figure. The stimulus I scales, read directly from the weak ordering, are given in Table 22.22. The longest lines are B–F, B–G, and C–G, as may be seen from Fig. 22.5. I shall only report the analysis for C–G, as this turns out to be the preferred line for the first dimension.

Table 22.22 Stimulus *I* Scales from Fig. 22.5

$$A\ B\ C\ H\ G\ D\ F\ E$$
$$B\ C\ A\ D\ (E\ H)\ (F\ G)$$
$$C\ B\ D\ A\ E\ (F\ H)\ G$$
$$D\ C\ E\ F\ B\ A\ (G\ H)$$
$$E\ F\ G\ D\ H\ C\ (B\ A)$$
$$F\ E\ G\ H\ D\ A\ C\ B$$
$$G\ H\ F\ E\ A\ D\ (B\ C)$$
$$H\ G\ F\ E\ A\ (B\ C\ D)$$

The solution for the line *C–G* is immediate because *C*'s and *G*'s respective *I* scales are both satisfied by the same simple order.

C's *I* scale: $C\ B\ D\ A\ E\ (F\ H)\ G$

G's *I* scale (reversed): $(B\ C)\ D\ A\ E\ F\ H\ G$

These yield the following rank order of projections on the line *C–G*:

$$C\ B\ D\ A\ E\ F\ H\ G$$

which satisfies 36 of the 56 triples as shown in Table 22.23.

To select a line for the second dimension, we tally the number of triangles whose longest lines are unsatisfied by $K^{(1)}$. This tally is given in Table 22.24. The line *A–E* is seen to be more frequently the longest line of an unfitted triangle, and it is relatively orthogonal to $K^{(1)}$ as *A* and *E* project next to each other on the line *C–G*, so we select it as our second dimension.

To get the order of projection on this line we examine *A*'s and *E*'s *I* scales:

A's *I* scale: $A\ B\ C\ H\ G\ D\ F\ E$

E's *I* scales (reversed): $(A\ B)\ C\ H\ D\ G\ F\ E$

These satisfy the weak ordering

$$A\ B\ C\ H\ (D\ G)\ F\ E$$

As all the triples involving the pair *D* and *G* are satisfied by $K^{(1)}$ (see Table 22.23) there is no ground for breaking the tie between them.

The triples fitted by the line *A–E* are tallied in Table 22.23. We see that it fits 29 triples of which 17 are among the 20 not fitted by $K^{(1)}$, leaving 3 triples still unsatisfied. The 3 left unsatisfied are $B(EH)$, $B(FG)$, and $H(CD)$.

Figure 22.6 presents a plot of the rank orders for $K^{(1)}$ and $K^{(2)}$ against each other. The two dimensions have been plotted as if they were

Table 22.23   Projection of Triples

	$K^{(1)}$ C–G	$K^{(2)}$ A–E		C–G	A–E
ABC	1	1	BEF	1	0
ABD	0	1	BEG	1	0
(AB)E	0	1	B(EH)	0	0
BAF	1	0	B(FG)	0	0
BAG	1	0	BHF	0	1
BAH	1	0	BHG	1	1
ACD	0	1	CDE	1	1
ACE	0	1	CDF	1	1
CAF	1	0	CDG	1	0
CAG	1	0	(CD)H	0	0
CAH	1	0	CEF	1	0
ADE	0	1	CEG	1	0
ADF	0	1	CEH	1	0
DAG	1	0	CFG	1	0
DAH	1	0	C(FH)	1	0
AFE	0	1	CHG	1	1
AGE	0	1	DEF	1	0
AHE	0	1	DEG	1	0
AFG	0	1	DEH	1	0
AHF	0	1	DFG	1	0
AHG	1	1	DFH	1	0
BCD	0	1	D(GH)	1	0
BCE	0	1	EFG	1	1
BCF	0	1	EFH	1	1
G(BC)	1	1	EGH	0	1
H(BC)	1	1	FGH	0	1
BDE	1	1	Total		
BDF	1	1	number		
BDG	1	0	fitted	36	29
H(BD)	1	0			

Table 22.24   Tally of Longest Distances Unsatisfied

$\overline{AD}$	2	B(EH)	1
A(BE)	1	B(FG)	1
$\overline{AE}$	5	H(CD)	1
$\overline{AF}$	3	$\overline{EH}$	1
$\overline{BD}$	1	$\overline{FH}$	1
$\overline{BE}$	1	$\overline{FH}$	1
$\overline{BF}$	2		

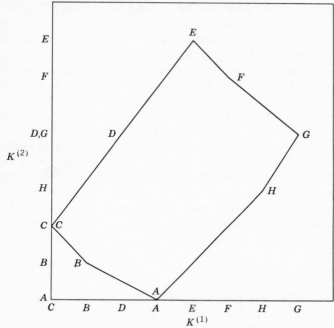

Fig. 22.6 Configuration obtained for Ekman's data.

orthogonal. The configuration is drawn to appear approximately rectangular with the two dimensions representing the diagonals of the rectangle.

There is no reason to doubt that a complete analysis of all 14 stimuli would yield a similar picture, and it is very doubtful that a five-dimensional structure is necessary. It would seem much more reasonable to use Helm's findings on the effect of underestimating large distances on dimensionality. This is strengthened further when we realize that a pair of stimuli which are complementary colors can, in this method of collecting data, be rated hardly more dissimilar than a pair of stimuli which correspond to nearly orthogonal vectors in the color space. In other words, this method of collecting data would almost certainly lead to underestimating large distances.

I would anticipate that a similar analysis of Mellinger's data would yield results similar to Helm's reanalysis and reveal that six dimensions are not necessary.

This analysis of Ekman's study and Helm's reanalysis of Mellinger's reveal the supporting relation that a nonmetric analysis of similarities data has to a metric analysis. It would seem that the solution obtained by the metric analysis should correspond in rank orders to the solution obtained by the nonmetric analysis. The nonmetric analysis will yield the dimensionality and an ordering of the projection of the stimuli on each dimension, which will provide an approximate picture of the configuration. If more than this is needed, a metric analysis will give more.

An advantage that the metric analysis has over the nonmetric model is the relative ease of rotation so that alternative solutions may be examined if we seek axes which are interpretable. Another principal advantage of metric analysis lies in the number of stimuli it can handle, although there is no reason why a nonmetric method should not be programmed for a computer also, in which case larger numbers of stimuli could be studied.

This method, however, new as it is, may already be superseded by a method that Roger Shepard (1962) has developed for analysis of similarities data. His method involves an iterative procedure, is programmed for a computer, and yields a metric space. An advantage of the method presented here is that it can be readily carried out by hand on a moderate number of stimuli and makes somewhat weaker assumptions.

4. SUMMARY

We first presented an analysis of a conditional proximity matrix in some detail because the algorithm for this matrix is more involved than that for a symmetric proximity matrix. It is possible, for example, to test whether some of the necessary conditions for a metric space are satisfied. The data matrix used here consists of the references made in each of ten psychological journals to all the others including itself. A nonmetric multidimensional scaling analysis was made on an 8 × 8 submatrix with main effects removed. A two-dimensional solution was obtained.

Because of a substantive interest in the study, a supplementary analysis of a different kind was made of the original 10 × 10 matrix.

An analysis of a symmetric proximity matrix is presented in more summary form. The data matrix is a 10 × 10 matrix for Morse code signals which were presented pairwise and judged same or different. Here also a two-dimensional solution was obtained.

The third section of the chapter discusses the relation between metric and nonmetric analyses of similarities data. A study of Helm's reveals that distortion of interpoint distances leads to serious effects on the metric solutions, Helm having obtained twelve dimensions for one set of distances and two dimensions after a monotone transformation of these distances. Ekman reports similarities data which he factor analyzed and obtained five dimensions. A nonmetric analysis of the same data is reported here which requires only two dimensions. The suggestion is that large distances are severely underestimated in Ekman's data and that this distortion accounts for the additional dimensions required by the metric analysis. The nonmetric model yields less information but is not subject to this effect.

REFERENCES

Coombs, C. H., 1958, An application of a nonmetric model for multidimensional analysis of similarities, *Psychol. Reps.*, **4**, 511–18.

Ekman, G., 1954, Dimensions of color vision, *J. Psychol.*, **38**, 467–74.

Helm, C., 1960, A successive intervals analysis of color differences, Educational Testing Service Technical Report, Princeton, N.J., November 1960.

Helm, C. E., S. Messick, and L. R. Tucker, 1961, Psychological models for relating discrimination and magnitude estimation scales, *Psychol. Rev.*, **68**, 167–77.

Mellinger, J., 1956, Some attributes of color perception, unpublished Ph.D. dissertation, University of North Carolina.

Osgood, C. E., and K. Wilson, 1957, Some terms and associated measures for studying human communication, Institute of Communications Research, University of Illinois (unpublished).

Rothkopf, E. Z., 1957, A measure of stimulus similarity and errors in some paired-associate learning tasks, *J. exp. Psychol.*, **53**, 94–101.

Shepard, R. N., 1962, The analysis of proximities: multidimensional scaling with an unknown distance function I, *Psychometrika*, **27**, 125–40.

PART 6

_____

INTERRELATIONS

Chapters 23–25 have to do with *interrelations*: interrelations among quadrants, among data matrices, among various response measures, and among various methods of collecting data.

Chapter 26 summarizes certain features of an earlier formulation of a theory of data as presented in Festinger and Katz (1953). This earlier formulation still has some virtue; although it is intimately related to the present formulation, it is more closely related to the real world of behavioral observation. Sometimes a less abstract approach is more immediately comprehensible; then it may serve as a bridge.

CHAPTER 23

Thurstone's Comparative Judgment Model with Laterality Effects

In Section 9 of Chapter 5 the Amsterdam experiment on inconsistency of preferences is reported. The unfolding theory has certain implications for the stochastic properties of preferential choice behavior, and that experiment provides a test of these implications. In particular, the theory implies that moderate stochastic transitivity will be satisfied but that strong stochastic transitivity, in general, will not. The experiment reported there sustains these predictions. The variable which is important in these considerations is called laterality.

In order to apply Thurstone's model for comparative judgment to data containing laterality effects certain modifications are necessary. These modifications are the subject of this chapter. In particular, the problems to which the considerations of this chapter apply are (1) the construction, at the level of an interval scale, of unidimensional joint scales directly from preferential choice data and the construction of unidimensional stimulus scales directly from cartwheel data; (2) the construction of a social utility* scale of preferability; and (3) the measurement of interpoint distances in a stimulus space from cartwheel data.

Fundamentally, all these problems are centered around the analysis of data which consist of order relations on distances—similarities data (QIVa) and its special case† preferential choice data (QIa).

The laterality variable enters into the comparison of distances in preferential choice behavior in the following way. If the distributions of discriminal processes of the stimuli are both on the same side of, that is,

---

* See Chapter 18 also.
† See Chapter 24.

unilateral to, the individual's distribution of ideal points, we will see that the inconsistency of judgment may be much less than if the distributions are on opposite sides (bilateral). The consequence of this, in brief, is that *two* data matrices must be constructed: One contains the proportion of times *j* is greater than *k* when *j* and *k* are a unilateral pair, and the other contains the proportion of times *j* is greater than *k* when *j* and *k* are a bilateral pair.

Because the relation of inconsistency to psychological distance is different for these two matrices, the comparative judgment model for each is different and hence gives rise to a unilateral equation for the unilateral matrix and a bilateral equation for the other.

The partitioning of preferential choice behavior into two data matrices, as required by the laterality variable, is clearly relevant to the construction of a stimulus scale of preference in QIIIa and to an interval *J* scale in QIa. The relevance of the laterality variable to scaling similarities data from cartwheels in QIIIa is less obvious. But consider an individual judging which of two stimuli is more similar to a third, as in case 2 of the cartwheel methods (Section 2 of Chapter 2). The individual may be thought of as having a temporary ideal at the stimulus point for the third stimulus and judging which of the other two stimulus points is nearer. Any variability of a stimulus point then becomes variability of an ideal when that stimulus point is playing the role of the ideal point. Exclusive attention is here given to the one-dimensional case. In this instance a pair of stimuli are either exactly unilateral to an individual's ideal point (or hub stimulus) or exactly bilateral to it. If the pair of stimuli is exactly unilateral, the laterality effect is zero; if the pair of stimuli is exactly bilateral, the laterality effect is maximal. These extremes are the only two possibilities in the one-dimensional case. In higher dimensions the same extremes may occur but intermediate degrees may also be present.

Consider a vector originating at an individual point and terminating at a stimulus point. The laterality effect is a function of the angle between pairs of such vectors originating at the same point. In the one-dimensional case such vectors are all collinear as the angle is $0°$ for a unilateral pair and $180°$ for a bilateral pair, corresponding to the extremes of the laterality effect. In the multidimensional case these angles all lie between $0°$ and $180°$, corresponding to intermediate effects of laterality.

In the following section the formal development for the analysis of the two data matrices, the unilateral and the bilateral, is presented, and in the final section some of the implications for and difficulties in application are considered.*

---

* This material also appears in Coombs, Greenberg, and Zinnes (1961).

1. UNILATERAL AND BILATERAL EQUATIONS

The unfolding theory of preferential choice postulates the existence of a space consisting of ideal points for individuals, denoted by c's, and points corresponding to stimuli, denoted by q's. The signed distance on a J scale from the ideal point of individual i to the stimulus j, at the moment h, is then defined as

$$p_{hij} = c_{hij} - q_{hij} \qquad (23.1)$$

In terms of this model, individual i will prefer stimulus j to stimulus k at the moment h, if and only if

$$|p_{hij}| - |p_{hik}| \leq 0 \qquad (23.2)$$

Alternatively, we can say that the preferential choice of an individual at a given moment signifies which stimulus point is nearer his ideal point. Furthermore, the percentage of times that we observe stimulus j preferred to stimulus k, then, is the percentage of times that 23.2 holds. From equation 23.1 we may write

$$|p_{hij}| - |p_{hik}| = |c_{hij} - q_{hij}| - |c_{hik} - q_{hik}| \qquad (23.3)$$

It is assumed in the following discussion that when an individual is judging a pair of stimuli at a given moment only one ideal point is involved. Thus, for stimuli j and k

$$c_{hij} = c_{hik} = c_{hi} \qquad (23.4)$$

The development of these equations may be pursued in the context of case I of Thurstone's model for comparative judgment (replications on a single individual) or case II (replications over individuals). Because the possible applications of this development will more likely be in the context of case II, the assumption is made in what follows that each of a number of individuals has responded once to every pair of stimuli. Adaptation to case I or to a combination of cases I and II, in which each of a number of individuals responds a number of times to each pair, is relatively straightforward and adds little to the theoretical implications from case II alone. Hence in what follows the subscript h is dropped so that individually replicated judgments will not be explicitly considered.

It is necessary to distinguish between those pairs of stimuli which are unilateral with respect to a given individual and those which are bilateral. A stimulus pair (j, k) is unilateral to the subject located at c_i if *both* stimuli have scale values q_{ij} and q_{ik} less than or greater than c_i. More simply, we can say that both stimuli lie on the same side of c_i. Formally, stimuli j and k are unilateral to c_i if and only if

$$(q_{ij} \lessgtr c_i) \Leftrightarrow (q_{ik} \lessgtr c_i) \qquad (23.5)$$

Stimuli j and k are bilateral to c_i if and only if

$$(q_{ij} \lesseqgtr c_i) \Leftrightarrow (q_{ik} \gtreqless c_i) \tag{23.6}$$

The unilateral equations will be developed first.

It is evident that if $q_{ij} > c_i$ and $q_{ik} > c_i$, the individual is to the left of both stimuli; this is called condition L. (If $q_{ij} < c_i$ and $q_{ik} < c_i$, we have condition R.)

Consider first condition L. It is immediately evident that since c_i is less than q_{ij} and q_{ik}, equation 23.3 reduces to

$$|p_{ij}|^L - |p_{ik}|^L = (q_{ij} - c_i{}^L) - (q_{ik} - c_i{}^L) = q_{ij} - q_{ik} \tag{23.7}$$

and similarly, for c_i to the right of this unilateral pair, we have

$$|p_{ij}|^R - |p_{ik}|^R = q_{ik} - q_{ij} \tag{23.8}$$

Equations 23.7 and 23.8 indicate that the preferential choice of an individual for one of two unilateral stimuli is mediated by the difference between the scale values of the stimuli on the joint scale. This immediately suggests that the preferential choices of those individuals unilateral to a pair of stimuli can be used to scale the stimuli on the joint scale.

To simplify matters we shall make the well-known case V assumptions, that is, that the stimuli project normal distributions on the J scale with equal variances,

$$q_{ij} \quad \text{is} \quad N(q_{.j}, \sigma_q{}^2) \tag{23.9}$$

and that the correlation, over individuals, between each pair of stimuli is a constant

$$\underset{i}{\text{Correlation}} \, (q_{ij}, q_{ik}) = r_{qq} \qquad \text{for all pairs } j, k \tag{23.10}$$

The unilateral model for comparative judgment may then be written as

$$|p_j|^L - |p_k|^L = X_{kj}{}^L \sigma_q \sqrt{2(1 - r_{qq})} \tag{23.11}$$

where $X_{kj}{}^L$ denotes the normal deviate corresponding to the proportion of unilateral-left persons preferring stimulus j to k and $|p_j|^L$ is the mean value over individuals of $|p_{ij}|^L$.

Of course, an equivalent expression may be written for the R condition. In equation 23.11 we have the quantity $\sigma_q \sqrt{2(1 - r_{qq})}$, the square of which we shall call the unilateral comparatal variance, $\sigma_u{}^2$. So

$$\sigma_u{}^2 = 2\sigma_q{}^2(1 - r_{qq}) \tag{23.12}$$

The development of the comparative judgment equation for the bilateral case parallels the unilateral treatment. If the individual's ideal point is between the stimulus points (we may assume $q_{ij} < c_i < q_{ik}$ without any loss of generality), equation 23.3 may be written as

$$|p_{ij}|^R - |p_{ik}|^L = (c_i^{R_jL_k} - q_{ij}) - (q_{ik} - c_i^{R_jL_k}) \qquad (23.13)$$

$$= 2c_i^{R_jL_k} - q_{ij} - q_{ik}$$

where $c_i^{R_jL_k}$ denotes the c_i of those individuals who are to the right of stimulus j and to the left of stimulus k.

A comparison of equation 23.13 with equation 23.7 or 23.8 makes evident the source of the essential difference between unilateral and bilateral preference judgments. In the unilateral case preference is mediated by the difference between the two scale values of the stimuli, completely independent of the c_i's. In the bilateral case, on the other hand, we see that the c_i's enter in a significant way, and, in particular, it is evident that the variance of the differences $|p_{ij}|^R - |p_{ik}|^L$ includes among its components the variance of the $c_i^{R_jL_k}$.

To simplify a good deal of tedious algebra, we shall make the same case V-like assumptions previously introduced into the unilateral case (see equations 23.9 and 23.10) and in addition assume $r_{c_iq_{ij}} = r_{c_iq_{ik}} = r_{cq}$. The variance of the differences* on the left-hand side of equation 23.13, called the bilateral comparatal variance, may be written

$$\sigma_{jk}^2 = 4\sigma_c^2 - 8r_{cq}\sigma_c\sigma_q + 2\sigma_q^2(1 + r_{qq}) \qquad (23.14)$$

where σ_c^2 is the variance of all the c_i for which the pair of stimuli j and k are bilateral. This bilateral comparatal variance is distinctly different from the unilateral comparatal variance under the same assumptions, as may be seen by comparing it with equation 23.12.

The bilateral equation for comparative judgment with case V assumptions may then be written as

$$|p_j|^R - |p_k|^L = X_{kj}^B\sqrt{4\sigma_c^2 - 8r_{cq}\sigma_c\sigma_q + 2\sigma_q^2(1 + r_{qq})} \qquad (23.15)$$

If σ_u^2 is set equal to 1 for the unit of measurement in the unilateral case, the bilateral comparatal variance may have some value quite different from 1. The bilateral pairwise percentages not only are generated on the

---

* In passing the following observation is of interest. In developing equation 23.14 the expression for $r_{(c_i-q_{ij})(c_i-q_{ik})}$ needs to be determined. Under case V-like assumptions,

$$\sigma_{c_i} = \sigma_{q_{ij}} = \sigma_{q_{ik}} = \sigma \quad \text{and} \quad r_{c_iq_{ij}} = r_{q_{ij}q_{ik}} = r$$

in which case

$$r_{(c_i-q_{ij})(c_i-q_{ik})} = \frac{\sigma^2(1-r)}{2\sigma^2(1-r)} = \frac{1}{2}$$

The implication is that under certain conditions the correlation between gain scores of two matched groups will necessarily be $r = .50$.

basis of a different unit of measurement but, as may be seen by comparing equation 23.13 with equation 23.8, are estimates of a different variable than unilateral pairwise percentages. Unilateral and bilateral pairwise preferential choices should therefore not be combined in the same probability matrix.

This brings us to the relevance of this development to practical applications.

2. IMPLICATIONS*

Equations 23.11 and 23.15, for unilateral and bilateral judgments respectively, constitute what was called the double law of comparative judgment in our original paper on this problem. It is clear from these equations that according to the unfolding model of preferential choice the inconsistency measures for unilateral and bilateral pairs of stimuli must be differently translated into psychological distance. Furthermore, it is clear that the inconsistency measures represent different variables in that the right-hand side of equation 23.7 (or 23.8) represents the unilateral variable and the right-hand side of equation 23.13 represents the bilateral variable.

Several conventional procedures are affected by these developments. I shall organize my discussion of these in terms of three general problems: (1) the problem of constructing one-dimensional J scales and stimulus scales, (2) the problem of measuring a social utility, and (3) the problem of measuring interpoint distances in a stimulus space.

The problems of constructing one-dimensional J scales and stimulus scales from QIa and QIVa data respectively are intimately related. This becomes evident from noting that the presentation of a pair of stimuli to an individual to collect QIa data is like a case 2 cartwheel which instead of having a stimulus at the hub has an ideal point. This relation of QIa to QIVa data is brought out in considerable detail in the next chapter. For our purposes here we merely note the similarity of the model for an individual's preferential choices among stimuli on a J scale and the model for the judgments of similarity of the stimuli on a stimulus scale to a particular stimulus.

I shall discuss the problem in terms of constructing a J scale and then point out the equivalences for the case of a stimulus scale.

The usual procedure for constructing a J scale at the level of an interval scale involves scaling the stimuli first by categorical (QIIa) or pair comparison (QIIIa) methods in one operation and then, in a completely

---

* This discussion of implications is an elaboration of that in the original paper (Coombs et al., 1961) and corrects certain errors of interpretation made there.

independent operation, finding out where the people are by asking them what items they endorse (QIIb). From the consideration of laterality effects it now seems feasible to construct a J scale directly from pair comparison preferential choice data.

The initial step in the analysis of the data involves finding the approximate order of the stimuli on the J scale. If this order is not known from a priori considerations, it can be obtained by utilizing the unfolding technique. The need for this approximate ordering resides in the need to distinguish, for each individual, whether a given pair of stimuli is a unilateral pair or not, because only the unilateral equation will be used to construct the J scale. The entries in the unilateral matrix are obtained as follows. Let the number of individuals to the left of both stimuli j and k be N^L and let the number of these who say they prefer j to k be $n_{jk}{}^L$. Similarly, there are N^R individuals to the right of both stimuli j and k, and $n_{kj}{}^R$ prefer k to j.

An individual to the left of both j and k who prefers j over k is, in effect, judging k to be greater than j. An individual to the right of both j and k who prefers k over j is, in effect, judging k to be greater than j. A combined estimate of the proportion of individuals who judge k to be greater than j is

$$\text{pr.}\,(k > j) = \frac{n_{jk}{}^L + n_{kj}{}^R}{N^L + N^R} \qquad (23.16)$$

If X_{kj} represents the normal deviate corresponding to the proportion in 23.16, it is clear (from equations 23.8, 23.11, and 23.12) that

$$q_{\cdot k} - q_{\cdot j} = X_{kj}\sigma_u \qquad (23.17)$$

Thus case V of the unilateral equation for comparative judgment may be applied to scale the stimuli on the J scale.

The location of the individuals on the J scale, then, may be approximated in any of a variety of ways. One way follows. Each individual's preferential choices will satisfy a partially ordered I scale. A partially ordered I scale will be bounded on the J scale by a pair of midpoints, the pair which bounds the segment of the J scale that corresponds uniquely to that partial order. The individual may then be arbitrarily assigned to the central point of that segment.

Now the modifications in these procedures required for the case of the one-dimensional stimulus scale are probably pretty obvious. An approximate order of the stimuli on the scale must be determined, which may readily be done by unfolding, and then those cartwheels or cartwheel segments that involve a pair of stimuli unilateral to a hub stimulus provide the data for the unilateral matrix. Only the application of the unilateral equation is called for, just as with the J scale, but this yields the complete solution. There is no need of the further step of locating individuals, as there is with the J scale, which has two sets of points.

The problem of measuring a social utility is the second general problem area for which the laterality effects have implications. This is the problem of constructing a scale of preferability for the stimuli, from most to least preferred, and has been discussed at length in Chapter 18. The further discussion here serves only to point out that the comparative judgment model also runs up against a problem which is essentially equivalent to the problem of interpersonal comparability of utility.

The usual procedure that psychologists use to construct a social utility scale of preferability is to use Thurstone's model for comparative judgment on the pairwise probabilities of choice, or some close relative of the model like Torgerson's model for categorical judgment. The procedures involve mapping preferential choice behavior into stimulus comparison data (QIIIa). This implies making no distinctions between individuals and constructing a scale on which only the stimuli correspond to points. From the point of view of unfolding theory and laterality effects this procedure is clearly incorrect.

The problem of arriving at a social utility scale of preferability from the point of view of unfolding theory is the problem of averaging the distances of the individuals from each stimulus. The "disutility" of each stimulus is its average absolute distance from all individuals. The comparative judgment model provides, at best, a method for estimating the difference between these values for every pair of stimuli.

Consider first the case in which the J space generating preferences is a one-dimensional J scale. By use of equation 23.11 the difference in the disutility of a pair of stimuli for those individuals for whom that pair of stimuli are unilateral left may be estimated. The expression equivalent to equation 23.11 for condition R provides an estimate of the difference in disutility for the same pair of stimuli for those individuals for whom that pair is unilateral right.

The difficulties arise when we consider those individuals for whom the same pair of stimuli are bilateral. The difficulties arise because of some difficult estimation problems and/or strong assumptions that appear necessary to find a solution. From equation 23.15 we see that the comparatal variance for every pair of bilateral stimuli is different because the expression involves the variance of those ideal points for which a given pair of stimuli are bilateral.

We might assume that $r_{cq} = r_{qq} = 0$, and letting $\sigma_c = m\sigma_q$, equation 23.15 for a particular bilateral pair of stimuli j and k becomes

$$|p_j|^R - |p_k|^L = X_{kj}{}^B \sigma_q \sqrt{2} \sqrt{2m^2 + 1} \tag{23.18}$$

Setting $\sigma_q\sqrt{2} = 1$ to define the unit of measurement in the unilateral case requires that the parameter m be estimated in order to find a solution for the difference in the disutilities of a given pair of stimuli for those individuals for whom that pair of stimuli is bilateral. At present only crude methods for estimating it are available, and none is recommended.

The final step in the solution, then, for the social utility scale of preferability would involve a weighted average of the differences in disutility obtained for each pair of stimuli from the unilateral left cases, the unilateral right cases, and the bilateral cases. This procedure is not recommended; it serves primarily to indicate how very different this problem is from that assumed in the conventional procedure of scaling pairwise probabilities of preferences by Thurstone's model for comparative judgment. That this problem is so intractable reflects the fact that it essentially involves a solution to the problem of interpersonal comparability of utility, which seems obtainable only with very strong and unpalatable assumptions.

The case that has just been considered is that in which the preferences were generated by a one-dimensional J scale. The seriousness of the implications for the difficulty of the problem in this case is just a prelude to the more general case in which the preferences are generated in a multidimensional J space. This case is more complicated because the laterality effect may be different for every pair of stimuli.

In the undimensional case the vectors to the stimulus points with origin at an individual's ideal point are always collinear. The angle between them is either 0° or 180°. When the angle is 0° we have a unilateral pair of stimuli and when 180° we have a bilateral pair of stimuli. The variance of the ideal point contributes nothing to the comparatal variance of a unilateral pair and contributes maximally to the variance of a bilateral pair.

In the multidimensional case we must allow, in principle, for a contribution to the comparatal variance from the variance of the ideal to range continuously from zero to the maximal effect. The degree of the contribution will be a function of the angle between the vectors to the stimuli with origin at the ideal point. This strikes me as a very unpromising approach to the problem. My present inclination, if a procedure is demanded, is to solve for the joint space first by factor analysis (Chapter 8) and then compute the projections of the stimuli on the extra dimension, which I called the social utility dimension for just that reason.

We turn now to the third problem area, that of measuring the interpoint distances in a stimulus space. The one-dimensional case has already been discussed along with the one-dimensional J scale. The problem that remains, then, is that of measuring the distances between stimulus points in a multidimensional space. The data are typically cartwheel data in which we have the proportion of times the distance between one pair of stimuli is judged greater than the distance between another pair.

A model such as Torgerson's (1958, pp. 263–68) modification of Thurstone's comparative judgment model seeks to process such data to estimate the differences between distances, that is, scale the interpoint distances on an interval scale. The model involves the transformation of probabilities on pairs of distances by use of a normal curve transformation. I would make two criticisms of this procedure: (1) It is incompatible with the usual assumption in the Thurstone model that the discriminal processes for each stimulus are themselves normally distributed, and (2) it does not take laterality effects into account.

With respect to the first criticism if the stimulus points themselves are multivariate normal, the squared distance between a pair of points is noncentral χ^2 with r degrees of freedom, as Hefner (1958) has shown (Chapter 19), in which case the probability distribution of differences between pairs of distances drawn from two such distributions is not known.

With respect to the second criticism, laterality effects would enter into all comparisons of pairs of conjoint distances in a manner formally identical to the laterality effects in a multidimensional joint space of preferential choice data. The angle between the vectors from a stimulus to each of two others is directly related to the amount of laterality effect.

As a result of these criticisms I see no way as yet of measuring interpoint distances at the level of an interval scale by this comparative judgment model except when the stimulus points themselves are in one dimension.

3. SUMMARY

A theoretical analysis of pairwise preferential choices is made in the spirit of Thurstone's model for comparative judgment but from the point of view of the unfolding theory of preferential choice behavior. The unfolding theory of preferential choice has the implication that a variable called laterality will seriously affect the stochastic properties of pairwise choice probabilities. The implications were borne out in the Amsterdam study (Chapter 5, Section 9) and so we consider certain modifications of Thurstone's model for pair comparison data to accommodate this variable.

The analysis reveals that for every pair of stimuli the subjects must be partitioned into those who are (1) to the left of both stimuli on the J scale, (2) between them, and (3) to the right of both. The comparatal variance is seen to be different for (2) from the variance for (1) and (3). So two equations are constructed. One is for the matrix of probabilities based on unilateral judgments, the other is for the matrix of probabilities when the judgments are on bilateral pairs of stimuli.

These equations reveal that the variance of the individual's ideal does not enter into unilateral inconsistency but does enter into bilateral inconsistency. They also reveal that the variable being estimated by the unilateral equation is a difference between the scale values of two stimuli on the J scale; whereas the variable being estimated by the bilateral equation is a difference between two differences.

These considerations are relevant to three practical applications: (1) the construction of a one-dimensional J scale or stimulus scale at the level of an interval scale, (2) the construction of a scale of social utility, and (3) the scaling of interpoint distances from cartwheel data.

With respect to the first problem, it is seen how the unilateral equation may be used to locate the stimuli on a J scale directly from pair comparison preferential choice data instead of the usual two-phase process of first scaling the stimuli by a QIIIa model and then the individuals by collecting QIIb data.

A deeper analysis and more complete development of a probabilistic unfolding theory than that presented here is contained in Zinnes (1959). He points out that a major factor limiting the adequacy of a probabilistic unfolding theory is the relatively small amount of data which can be incorporated into the method of solution.

The relevance of this discussion for the problem of constructing a unidimensional stimulus scale is pointed out.

The second and third problems are intimately related because a pair comparison preferential choice is a pair comparison of two distances, just as in similarities data. The problem of constructing a social utility is discussed first for the case in which preferential choices are generated by a one-dimensional J scale and then for the case of a multidimensional J space. The one-dimensional case is seen to be tractable up to a point but the bilateral equation gives rise to serious difficulties which only exceedingly strong assumptions can overcome. I suppose this should not seem remarkable because the effect is equivalent to solving the problem of interpersonal comparability of utility.

The multidimensional case is even less tractable, in that the laterality effect varies in degree depending on the relative orientation of the stimulus points to the ideal point in the space.

The third problem of constructing stimulus spaces involves the measurement of interpoint distances in an r-dimensional space. It is seen that any extension of Thurstone's model to such a problem is not yet feasible, because the laterality effect cannot be estimated and the probability distribution for differences between pairs of distances is not sufficiently known.

REFERENCES

Coombs, C. H., M. Greenberg, and J. L. Zinnes, 1961, A double law of comparative judgment for the analysis of preferential choice and similarities data, *Psychometrika*, **26**, 165–71.

Hefner, R. A., 1958, Extensions of the law of comparative judgment to discriminable and multidimensional stimuli, unpublished Ph.D. dissertation, University of Michigan.

Torgerson, W. S., 1958, *Theory and methods of scaling*, John Wiley and Sons, New York.

Zinnes, J. L., 1959, A probabilistic theory of preferential choice, unpublished Ph.D. dissertation, University of Michigan.

CHAPTER 24

Some Interrelations among Data Matrices and among Methods

One very simple way to bring out some of the interrelations between quadrants is in terms of the relations between the kinds of data matrices that characterize them. Inasmuch as there seem to be only three basic kinds of data matrices in psychological measurement, plus a certain kind of submatrix of each, this approach is a very simple one. The three kinds of matrices are what might be called a dominance matrix, a symmetric proximity matrix, and a conditional proximity matrix.

The next two sections introduce these matrices; the first section is concerned solely with the correlation matrix as an instance of a symmetric proximity matrix but interesting in its own right. The remaining sections are concerned with other interrelations, including interrelations of response measures and of methods of collecting data. The fourth section takes up alternative response measures, with special emphasis on latency, and reports some experimental work. The fifth section summarizes an intensive experimental comparison of several methods of collecting data.

1. CORRELATION MATRICES

In this section I want to look at a set of n correlated variables from two points of view and relate them. One point of view is as follows. For any two of these variables there are differences and a variance of these differences. This variance of the differences between two variables may be interpreted as a distance between a pair of corresponding points; we might go by such a route to a multidimensional configuration of points.

The second and more familiar point of view is to factor analyze the covariance or the correlation matrix, and this viewpoint also leads to a multidimensional configuration of points. Obviously, these two approaches should be intimately related, as was first pointed out by Young and Householder (1938).

Consider a correlation matrix with n variables. Such a matrix is usually secured after a succession of transformations of the original basic observations, but we are not concerned here with where it came from; rather, we care about what may be done with it.

In some forms of factor analysis a correlation coefficient is given a geometrical interpretation as the scalar product of two vectors:

$$r_{jk} = h_j h_k \cos \alpha_{jk} \tag{24.1}$$

where h_j and h_k are the lengths of the two vectors in the common factor space and never greater than 1, and α_{jk} is the angle between them.

Let us consider a more general case, the factor analysis of covariances. The covariance between two tests, cov (jk), is given by:

$$\text{cov}(jk) = \sigma_j \sigma_k r_{jk} \tag{24.2}$$

The cov (jk) may also be given a geometrical interpretation as the scalar product of two vectors, in which case σ_j and σ_k are their respective lengths and r_{jk} is the cosine of the angle between them.

We may now relate this to a distance model, that is, we may convert a covariance matrix into a matrix of distances between pairs of points. According to the law of cosines,

$$d_{jk}^2 = d_j^2 + d_k^2 - 2d_j d_k \cos \alpha_{jk} \tag{24.3}$$

where d_j and d_k are the lengths of the vectors and d_{jk} is the distance between the termini of the two vectors. Hence we may write

$$d_{jk}^2 = \sigma_j^2 + \sigma_k^2 - 2\sigma_j \sigma_k r_{jk} \tag{24.4}$$

which says that the distance between a pair of points is simply the standard deviation of the differences between the corresponding variables.

If the variables are expressed in standard scores with variances equal to 1, then (absorbing a $\sqrt{2}$ in the unit of measurement)

$$d_{jk} = \sqrt{1 - r_{jk}} \tag{24.5}$$

which is a monotone transformation of the correlations. The higher the correlation the closer two points are together.

Equation 24.4 and its special case, equation 24.5, permit the conversion of a correlation matrix into a matrix of interpoint distances. A correlation is then interpreted as a measure of the proximity of a pair of points from the same set (that is, as a measure of the degree to which a pair of points match), so I would interpret the matrix as QIIIb data. Because the correlation coefficient (and the covariance) is a symmetric measure of proximity, I call such a matrix an instance of a symmetric proximity matrix.

If the correlation matrix is converted to a matrix of interpoint distances by equation 24.4, we may analyze it by QIVa methods.

Another transformation of a correlation matrix into interpoint distances has been suggested by Joseph Levin (1961) and by Henry Kaiser (1962) for the particular case of a Guttman simplex. A simplex is defined as a correlation matrix with the following property:

$$r_{ik} = r_{ij} r_{jk} \quad \text{for} \quad i < j < k \tag{24.6}$$

Taking logarithms we have

$$\log r_{ik} = \log r_{ij} + \log r_{jk} \tag{24.7}$$

so the logarithm of the correlation between two variables in a simplex may be interpreted as the distance between the two variables on a one-dimensional scale.

In general, in the factor analysis of correlation or covariance matrices the models imply a monotone transformation between correlation (or covariance) and interpoint distance—the higher the correlation between two stimuli the less the distance between the corresponding points. Hence an ordinal scale of interpoint distances follows immediately from the correlation matrix and may be analyzed by any nonmetric multidimensional scaling model, such as that illustrated in Chapter 22. Such an analysis is a nonmetric factor analysis of a correlation or covariance matrix.

In making such a nonmetric analysis we are throwing away information about the actual numerical distances as given by equation 24.4 or equation 24.5, but on the other hand we have a solution that would be valid for all distance functions which would yield this same order of interpoint distances. Something has been lost in specificity and power, but something has been gained in generality. I am not proposing here that we make nonmetric factor analyses of correlation matrices. In instances, however, where the distance transformation is uncertain but may be assumed to be monotonic, nonmetric analysis has some utility.

It is instructive now to partition a correlation matrix and to see what the consequences are. Let us take the n variables and partition them into two disjoint subsets and consider the correlation submatrix which has the variables of one of these subsets as rows and those of the other as columns.

We might call such a submatrix an offdiagonal submatrix (see Chapter 11, Fig. 11.5). In order to bring out most forcibly the relations with which we are concerned here, let me call the row elements "individuals" and the column elements "stimuli."

If we assume the existence of a function relating correlation to distance, such as that given by equation 24.4 or 24.5, we may "measure" all distances. However, and this is the important point, a distance is always between an element of one set and an element of a distinct set, for example, between an individual point and a stimulus point.

It is evident that we have QIIb data here, a correlation being interpreted as a measure of a proximity relation on a pair of points from distinct sets. Since it is a measure of the degree of proximity, however, we are able to order the distances of the stimulus points from each individual, that is, construct I scales. So these have become QIa data; but they are of a kind that we have had no occasion to deal with before.

In Chapter 3 we made a distinction between $A \times A$ data and $\bigcup_i (A_i \times A_i)$ data. The former consist of order relations on all pairs of distances between elements of distinct sets and the latter of order relations on only those pairs of distances that have a point in common, for example, an individual point. In $\bigcup_i (A_i \times A_i)$ data we know, for each individual, which stimulus is nearer him. In $A \times A$ data we also know whether stimulus j is closer to individual 1 than stimulus k is to individual 2. In preferential choice data, this would imply or require interpersonal comparability of utility, but in an offdiagonal correlation matrix it would merely require that the same distance function be applied to all correlations.

I said in Chapter 3 that we have no model for analyzing $A \times A$ data. The nearest that I can come to it is the following. In each row we can order the column-stimuli for that row-individual's I scale. Thus the rows will yield a set of I scales which may be analyzed by the unfolding theory discussed in Part 2. Now, identically the same thing may be done for each column. That is, the row-individuals may be ordered on each column-stimulus's I scale. These will also contribute a set of I scales which may be analyzed by unfolding theory. The problem is that the two analyses must match, and I know of no way, as yet, to ensure this or bring it about. The problem, however, is certainly solvable.

To appreciate the difference between $A \times A$ data and $\bigcup_i (A_i \times A_i)$ data, we recognize that there are $m \times n$ cells in the offdiagonal matrix for the m row-individuals and the n column-stimuli. If the matrix contains $A \times A$ data, there are $\binom{mn}{2}$ comparisons to be made (that is, between all cells); and if the matrix contains $\bigcup_i (A_i \times A_i)$ data, there are $m \binom{n}{2}$ comparisons

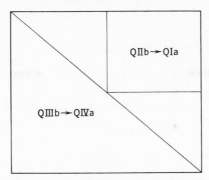

Fig. 24.1 Relation between the kinds of data in a symmetric correlation matrix and in its offdiagonal submatrix.

(that is, between cells in the same row). The ratio of these numbers is approximately $1/m$. So with $m = 100$ subjects, the $\bigcup_i(A_i \times A_i)$ matrix would have about 1% of the comparisons that could be made in the corresponding $A \times A$ matrix.

We may now see a parallel between the analysis of the intact matrix and the analysis of the offdiagonal submatrix. The intact correlation matrix was interpreted as QIIIb data, converted into QIVa by one inferential system, and would be analyzed by a QIVa model, another inferential system, to yield a classification of the stimuli in a stimulus space. The offdiagonal submatrix was interpreted as QIIb data and converted into QIa data, to be analyzed by a model appropriate for such data, which would yield a joint space of the two sets of points (see Fig. 24.1).

We see here that there is a sense in which the data for QI and QII are a particular kind of subset of the data of QIII and QIV, respectively.

We shall see in Section 2 that these relations hold more generally, and this analysis of correlation matrices provides something of a paradigm for the consideration of such problems in general.

2. THE BASIC DATA MATRICES

As well as I can tell, psychology seems to have been able to distinguish three types of basic data matrices and to build corresponding inferential classification systems for their analyses, including the analyses of their respective offdiagonal submatrices. Two of these we have met in Chapter 19, the symmetric proximity matrix and the conditional proximity matrix. The third we met in Chapter 17 in the discussion of the Thurstone and B.T.L. models. The latter type of matrix was not distinguished by name at that time, but it will be convenient to have a name for it here, so let us call it a dominance matrix.

The cell entry most commonly occurring in these matrices is either a dichotomous index such as 1 or 0 or a fine grained index such as a probability. Other response measures are possible; some of them are discussed in Section 4. In this section, however, I shall confine my examples to the (1, 0) and the probabilistic data matrices for simplicity and concreteness.

The Dominance Matrix

By a dominance matrix we mean a matrix in which a cell entry signifies an order relation between the row and the column element. A probabilistic dominance matrix is one in which the cell entry is a probability that the row element will dominate, exceed, be judged greater than, and so on, the column element.

The square $n \times n$ matrix in which the same elements label both the rows and the columns we readily recognize as a QIIIa dominance matrix for which both the Thurstone and the B.T.L. models (Chapter 17) are appropriate. If we consider an offdiagonal submatrix we have two distinct sets of points. A cell entry of 1 or 0 indicates the order relation between the corresponding row and column element, as in a QIIa Guttman-type matrix. A cell entry with a probability indicates the probability of an element of one set dominating an element of the other set. This also is a QIIa data matrix and is the kind for which Torgerson's model for categorical judgment is explicitly designed.

The relation between the intact dominance matrix and its offdiagonal submatrix is portrayed in Fig. 24.2 (see also Fig. 11.5).

A QIIIa dominance matrix is usually assumed to be inherently capable of yielding only a one-dimensional space. Support for this point of view comes from Goodman's analysis (see Chapter 19) and from the fact that the models (Thurstone's and the B.T.L.) are only capable of yielding one-dimensional scales.

The submatrix, however, which maps into QIIa, may lead directly to multidimensional spaces (Chapter 12). This leads me to suspect that there is nothing inherent in a dominance matrix (even in QIIIa) that limits it to one-dimensional solutions but rather that this is a consequence of the predicates commonly used and the experimental context in which they are used. It is conceivable, at least in principle, to observe some kind of behavior which could be interpreted as dominance relations among a set of stimuli and which would not compel us to infer that the stimuli were simply ordered or points on a real line.

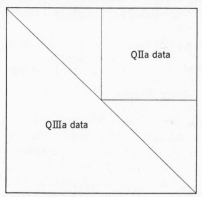

Fig. 24.2 The kinds of data in the dominance matrix and in its offdiagonal submatrix.

A possible example is a round-robin tennis tournament. Each player corresponds to a point in a multidimensional space and each match yields an order relation on the corresponding pair of points. The possibility exists that the match between one pair of players may involve a different combination of weighted attributes than the match between another pair. Such circumstances could lead to intransitivities and calls for the development of new models involving, for example, making the composition

Table 24.1   Varieties of Dominance Matrices

Response Measure

	Discrete; for Example, $(1, 0)$	Continuous; for Example, Probabilities
QIIIa Intact Matrix	Illustrated by round-robin tournament. Only one-dimensional models available, such as triangular analysis (Chapter 17).	Illustrated by pair comparison of loudness of tones. Models for probabilistic data include Thurstone's and the B.T.L. (Chapter 17).
Offdiagonal Submatrix (QIIa)	Illustrated by answers to arithmetic problems. Variety of models include Guttman's, Lazarsfeld's, and Coombs and Kao's (Chapters 11 and 12).	Illustrated by threshold detection data and categorical judgment. Models include Torgerson's categorical judgment (Chapter 11).

function or the subset of relevant dimensions a function of the particular pair of stimuli.

The principal varieties of dominance matrices are summarized in Table 24.1.

The Symmetric Proximity Matrix

The symmetric proximity matrix has been discussed at some length in Chapters 19, 20, and 22, and in this chapter the correlation matrix as a particular instance of it. It only remains to point out certain relations among quadrants that hold for it. It will be recalled that the $(1, 0)$ symmetric proximity matrix is interpreted as same-different data, a proximity relation on a pair of points from the same set, QIIIb. A probabilistic symmetric proximity matrix provides measures of the degree of proximity, which lead in a natural way, then, to QIVa data.

Consider an offdiagonal submatrix of a $(1, 0)$ proximity matrix. Let us again call the row elements "individuals" and the column elements "stimuli," as they belong to distinct sets. For each individual we have a proximity relation between his point and each stimulus point with unity in the corresponding cell of his row. Such data are QIIb data. Because this is a submatrix of a *symmetric* proximity matrix, however, it may also be said that for each stimulus we have a proximity relation between its point and each individual point with unity in the corresponding cell of its column.

This kind of data is not common. At first blush we might think that an individual's endorsements of attitude statements would yield such a data matrix until we realize that an endorsement of a stimulus by the individual *does not* also represent a mutual endorsement by the stimulus of the individual's position. So we see that such data are conditional proximity data, to be discussed later. A possible example of a $(1, 0)$ offdiagonal submatrix of a symmetric proximity matrix might be the observations of who dances with whom at a fraternity-sorority party.

Now suppose the cell entries, instead of $(1, 0)$ data, are probabilities in the offdiagonal submatrix. The data are still QIIb but now we have available a measure of the degree of proximity of each stimulus point to the individual point. By assuming a monotone function inversely relating probability to distance, these QIIb data may be converted into QIa data so that each individual's rank order I scale over the stimuli immediately follows.

We have here, again, a case like that previously discussed for correlation matrices, in that all elements of the symmetric proximity matrix are comparable and we have $A \times A$ data. Hence we may also use the columns of the submatrix to construct the stimulus I scales over the individuals.

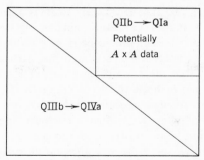

Fig. 24.3 The kinds of data in the symmetric proximity matrix and in its offdiagonal submatrix.

Each of these two collections of I scales can be analyzed by unfolding theory separately, but there is no model for analyzing them as a single set of data.

Figure 24.3 illustrates the relation between the kinds of data in the symmetric proximity matrix and in its offdiagonal submatrix.

Table 24.2   Varieties of Symmetric Proximity Matrices

Response Measure

	Discrete; for Example, (1, 0)	Continuous; for Example, Probabilities
QIIIb Intact Matrix	Illustrated by mutual sociometric choice as in "Whom do you play tennis with?" Analysis of structure by graph theoretic models, matrix theory models, and the Goodman-Galanter model (Chapter 19).	Illustrated by relative proportion of "same-different" judgments. May be converted to QIVa data (Chapter 19) and analyzed multi-dimensionally (Chapters 21 and 22).
Offdiagonal Submatrix (QIIb)	Illustrated by who dances with whom at a fra-ternity-sorority party. No model explicitly takes symmetry into account, but Lazars-feld's latent class model and parallelogram analysis could be adapted.	Illustrated by the number of times each young man and young lady dance together. May be converted to QIa, $A \times A$ data, and both boys' I scales and girls' I scales may be analyzed by unfolding.

A caution needs to be inserted here. Even though the probabilistic symmetric proximity matrix is itself symmetric, it does not necessarily follow that the order relations on all pairs of probabilities are the same as (but inversely) the order relations on the corresponding pairs of distances. For example, to say that the more often a pair of stimuli is confused the shorter the distance between the corresponding pair of points requires that the criterion distance for a same-different decision not differ significantly for different pairs of stimuli. Hefner's research on this, discussed in Chapter 19, is relevant here. If this condition is not met, the probabilities need to be modified in some manner such as that suggested by Hefner before they can be converted to a rank order of distances.

The principal varieties of symmetric proximity matrices are summarized in Table 24.2.

The Conditional Proximity Matrix

The conditional proximity matrix has also been discussed at some length previously (Chapters 19, 20, and 22). It suffices here merely to recall that a unity in a cell of the (1, 0) conditional proximity matrix signifies that the row element has been identified as, recognized as, or otherwise confused with the column element. The matrix is nonsymmetric. Unity in a cell is interpreted here as a proximity relation of the row element to that column element relative to the other column elements. This is a QIIIb datum.

The probabilistic conditional proximity matrix provides a more detailed measure of this proximity relation and hence it leads naturally to QIVa data. In exactly the same manner as with the symmetric proximity matrix, an offdiagonal submatrix of the conditional proximity matrix yields QIIb data and then leads naturally to QIa data.

The big difference between the conditional proximity submatrix compared with the symmetric proximity submatrix is that the former yields only $\bigcup_i (A_i \times A_i)$ data whereas the symmetric proximity submatrix yields $A \times A$ data. This comes about because in the symmetric proximity matrix the probabilities are joint probabilities, the matrix is symmetric, and all cells of the matrix are comparable if the criterion distance for all same-different decisions is a constant. The conditional proximity matrix, on the other hand, is based on data obtained on ordered pairs. Generally the data may be described in this way: Given one stimulus, what is the probability that it will be taken to be another stimulus? That is, we have conditional probabilities. Hence, for each row element, the probabilities in that row are comparable and we can construct each "individual's" I scale. The data are strictly $\bigcup_i (A_i \times A_i)$; a column of the submatrix will not yield a stimulus's I scale over the individuals, because the conditional probabilities in a column are not comparable under this interpretation.

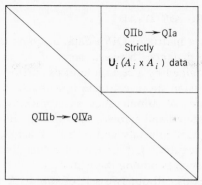

Fig. 24.4 The kinds of data in the conditional proximity matrix and in its offdiagonal submatrix.

The relation between the kinds of data in the conditional proximity matrix and in its offdiagonal submatrix is portrayed in Fig. 24.4.

The principal varieties of conditional proximity matrices are summarized in Table 24.3.

Table 24.3   Varieties of Conditional Proximity Matrices

Response Measure

	Discrete; for Example, (1, 0)	Continuous; for Example, Probabilities
QIIIb Intact Matrix	Illustrated by identification or recognition data and unilateral sociometric choice. Analysis of structure by digraph theory and matrix models.	Illustrated by number of references one journal makes to another. May be converted to QIVa data (Chapters 17 and 19), and analyzed multidimensionally (Chapters 21 and 22).
Offdiagonal Submatrix (QIIb)	Illustrated by "Which radio programs do you listen to?" or "Which items do you endorse?" Models for analysis include Lazarsfeld's and parallelogram analysis (Chapter 15).	Illustrated by relative frequency with which individuals smoke various brands of cigarettes. May be converted to QIa, $\bigcup_i (A_i \times A_i)$ data, and analyzed by unfolding theory.

3. DATA ON PAIRS OF DYADS

We next consider a matrix of QIVa data, a square matrix, bordered by elements which are distances between pairs of points, and consider the varieties of data obtained by a certain kind of partitioning of this matrix. To make the discussion more concrete imagine that on the real world level we have two sets of stimuli, such as brightness of lights and pitch of tones, or the feathered and arrowed lines of the Müller-Lyer illusion, or a list of psychological journals and a list of articles which might be submitted for publication. Let us consider the kinds of data that we might collect on distances among these stimuli.

For simplicity, let us call our two sets of stimuli X and Y and form all pairs of x's, all pairs of y's, and all pairs (x, y). Let us further imagine that the observations we make are interpreted as order relations on pairs of these dyads. It does not really matter whether the data are (1, 0) or probabilities, but it will be more general to imagine them to be probabilistic.

All the data, then, are contained in a square matrix, as in Fig. 24.5, bordered by the pairs of x's, (x, x), the pairs of y's, (y, y), and the pairs (x, y), as both rows and columns. Let us partition this matrix to divide the rows (and the columns) so as to separate out the pairs of x's, the pairs (x, y), and the pairs of y's, as indicated.

Corresponding cells on opposite sides of the main diagonal contain probabilities which are complementary, so we need only consider one side

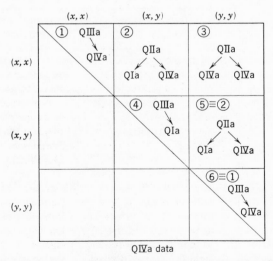

QIVa data

Fig. 24.5 A matrix of data consisting of order relations on pairs of dyads, partitioned into six submatrices.

of the diagonal and forget the redundant half. Each of the six distinct submatrices is numbered to permit ready reference in the text. In each submatrix the kind of data is indicated in the figure at two "levels." The upper level indicates the classification of the data when the interpoint distances themselves are mapped into points to be scaled. The lower level is the kind of data that could then be made out of the scaled distances in order to recover the original stimulus points themselves. This distinction between the two levels must be kept in mind throughout the ensuing discussion. Let us take each of the six submatrices in turn and discuss them in more detail.

In submatrix 1 we have order relations on pairs of dyads in which all points are from the same set; for example, the stimuli may all be lights. The first step would be to scale the distances, so we could classify the data as order relations on pairs of points where each point is a "distance" between a pair of lights. The distance points are themselves all members of the same set as they are all paired with each other. With this interpretation in mind, this submatrix would be classed as QIIIa data on interpoint *distances*. A model in QIIIa would then be applied for the purpose of scaling the distances.

With the distances between all pairs of lights scaled in QIIIa we may then map the data into QIVa since the scaling of distances now yields the relative similarity of all the stimuli to each of them in turn. A QIVa model may then be applied to analyze the distance relations and arrive at a classification of the lights in a stimulus space.

Now let us consider submatrix 2. The data consist of order relations on pairs of dyads, that is, pairs of distances, and the dyads are from two distinct sets. One set of distances is between pairs of points from the same set, for example, lights, feathered lines, or journals. The other set of distances is between pairs of points from distinct sets, for example, distances between a light and a tone, a feathered line and an arrowed line, a journal and an article.

The row elements for submatrix 2 are distances between pairs of points from the same set, that is, pairs of x's. The column elements are distances between pairs of elements from different sets, that is, (x, y) pairs. The basic observation in the $(1, 0)$ matrix is that the row pair is a better (1) or a poorer (0) match than is the column pair. A cell entry in a probabilistic data matrix might be the proportion of times such a judgment was made. An interpretation of such observations is that the distance between a pair of journal points is greater or less than the distance between a journal point and an article point. The first step is to scale these distances.

Here we have two sets of distances. Each row element is a distance between a pair of journal points, and these distances are never compared with each other. Each column element is a distance between a journal point and an article point, and these distances are also never compared with each other. The data in the submatrix are order relations between pairs of distances (pairs of points) where the distances are from distinct sets; hence we have QIIa data which are analogous to individuals passing and failing arithmetic problems. An individual is always compared with an arithmetic problem, and from such observations we wish to make inferences about comparisons between individuals and comparisons between arithmetic problems.

These data, the distances, may be scaled on a joint scale by a QIIa method. Having constructed such a scale, however, we now have two sets of distances, one a set of distances between pairs of journals, the other of distances between journal-article pairs.

The distances on journal pairs are between elements of one set, all x's, so these data can be classified as QIVa and analyzed to yield a stimulus space of journals (lights, or feathered lines, as the case may be).

The other set of distances, however, is something different. We now have the distances (as, say, elements of an ordinal scale at least) from every journal to every article, but never the distances between a pair of journals or between a pair of articles. Here we have QIa data. It is possible, for example, to order the distances of all the journal points from each article point, that is, construct an article's I scale. It is also possible to order all the article points from each journal point, that is, construct a journal's I scale. In fact, it is possible to do even more; we can order *all* the distances between journal-article pairs.

We may illustrate such data in the context of preferential choice as follows. Besides being able to construct the preference ordering of each individual over a set of stimuli, it is simultaneously possible to construct the preference ordering of each stimulus over the individuals. Furthermore, it is possible to say whether one individual likes one stimulus more or less than some other individual likes some other stimulus and to say, even, whether some stimulus likes some individual more than some other stimulus likes some other individual.

This kind of data simply does not exist in the real world context of preferential choice data, although we might come close to it. If, for example, we had a set of boys and a set of girls and each individual gave us his preference order for the members of the other set, we would only lack observations of the sort, "Henry likes Helen more than Jim likes Jane."

In the case of the journal-article pairs, however, we have the kind of data that were described in Chapter 3 as $A \times A$ data; for which no models have been constructed which clearly take advantage of all the information in the data. The only model we have is the unfolding theory for $\bigcup_i (A_i \times A_i)$ data, that is, data which consist of the I scales of the journals or the data which consist of the I scales of the articles. Each of these two sets of I scales may be analyzed by unfolding theory, and each analysis would yield a joint space of journals and articles. But there is no theory or method yet constructed which takes advantage of all the information in $A \times A$ data and constructs a common joint space. This issue previously arose in this chapter in connection with symmetric proximity matrices.

In submatrix 3 we have order relations on pairs of dyads in which the row elements are pairs of lights, for example, and the column elements are pairs of tones. The probability in a given cell may have been obtained from the proportion of times a pair of lights has been judged more alike than a pair of tones. We may interpret the basic observation as an order relation on a pair of distances in which the two distances are elements of distinct sets. The first step would be to scale the distances. With the distances mapped into points, the data are order relations on pairs of points from distinct sets, QIIa data. So some model, such as Guttman scalogram analysis or Torgerson's categorical judgment model, for example, could be used.

When the distances have been scaled we have two sets of distances, those between the lights and those between the tones. Each of these sets of distance measures may be mapped into QIVa data and analyzed by a QIVa model to yield a stimulus space for the lights or the tones as the case may be. Note that these would be two distinct spaces; there is nothing to tie them together. At no time is a distance between a light and a tone observed. This may not seem unreasonable, but suppose the two sets of stimuli had been feathers and arrows or journals and articles. We might hope that the two sets in either of these cases would map into one space. The point is that data such as those in submatrix 3 would not be informative on this question.

We turn now to submatrix 4. This matrix is different from any of the others. The row and the column elements are the same, but each element is a distance between a pair of points from distinct sets, for example, a light and a tone, an arrowed line and a feathered line, a journal and an article. The data consist of order relations on pairs of such dyads. An interpretation is that the distance between one pair of points is less than that between another pair of points. As the distances being compared are all elements of a single set, the data are identified as QIIIa data. An appropriate QIIIa model will lead to a scale of the distances at the level of an ordinal, interval, or ratio scale.

The data on distances may then be mapped into QIa data as $A \times A$ data; and the discussion of the QIa data in submatrix 2 applies here identically. These four submatrices of Fig. 24.5 represent all distinct kinds. Submatrix 5 corresponds identically to submatrix 2 except that dyads of (y, y) elements have been substituted for dyads of (x, x) elements. Similarly, it is evident that the discussion of submatrix 1 applies identically to submatrix 6.

In review we may note that the diagonal submatrices are all QIIIa and the offdiagonal submatrices are all QIIa in so far as the scaling of interpoint distances is concerned. Interpoint distances are themselves always scaled in QII or QIII, and then these interpoint distances are analyzed in QI or QIV to recover the space for the points.

4. ALTERNATIVE RESPONSE MEASURES

Psychologists have given much of their attention to the analysis of choice behavior, particularly verbal judgments about stimuli, for example, judgments about which stimulus is greater, statements of preferential choice, psychophysical detections, magnitude estimations, and so on. The content of such judgments provides the information which is then processed to yield a classification of stimuli and people.

Other characteristics besides the content of an individual's responses to stimuli are, of course, also utilized as sources of information to be processed for the same purpose. Speaking very generally, or generically, these other response measures include consistency, latency, and amplitude. Each of these response measures has been used to provide information about psychological distance. Consistency, the stochastic property of response, has been the most intensively exploited. Probability models now exist for every kind of data. Amplitude as a response measure has been widely used in the study of generalization gradients. Latency has only begun to come into its own as a source of information about psychological distance.

We might, with some distortion, identify a basic psychological process with each quadrant. From QI to QIV, I would identify them as preference, detection, discrimination, and similarity. To each of these processes there corresponds behavior which has content, consistency, latency, and amplitude. Models for inferential classification of stimuli and people are more or less well advanced for analyzing content and consistency for each one of these four processes. Models for latency and amplitude lag well behind (but see Shepard, 1960).

The problem is not to be formulated in terms only of transforming these response measures to construct psychological spaces, but rather of transforming them to construct interlocking systems which mutually relate the response measures to each other so that we would obtain the same metric space from each. The models for processing these several measures should be mutually compatible in the sense of yielding at least the same metric relations.

These different response measures may not necessarily yield the same information. We may think of a response as having a direction and a distance, like a vector. A data matrix may contain information about only one or about both. A (1, 0) data matrix contains only directional information on the basis of a convention, such as a 1 indicating that the row point dominates the column point. This is the content of the response. Probability, latency, and amplitude measures, in the absence of content, convey no information about direction but only about magnitude of difference.

Nevertheless, in a QIIIa probability matrix, for example, all the information about differences is contained in the entries on one side of the diagonal; the other side is redundant.* In contrast to this is the latency QIIIa data matrix in which a cell on one side of the diagonal contains the latency of the judgments $j \rangle k$ and on the other side the latency of judgments $k \rangle j$. These are experimentally independent observations and so might be providing information different from that provided by the probabilistic data matrix.

Some careful and intensive experimental work is called for to explore the relations of these several response measures to each other and to psychological distance. Experimental work like that of Dember (1955, 1957) and Greenberg (1961) is much to be desired.

Dember's Experiment on Decision Time

Dember was concerned with exploring decision time as a potential source of metric information in both QI and QIV data. He carried out three experiments and reanalyzed data from an early study by Dashiell (1937). The first two experiments involved QIVa data and the last two experiments QIa data.

For the first experiment the stimuli were five patches of Munsell gray paper; the stimuli of the second experiment were five words: "always," "often," "rarely," "seldom," and "never." In each of these two experiments the subjects were given pair comparisons of interpoint distances, that is, the subjects were asked to choose the pair whose members were more alike. These judgments yielded sufficient information to order the five stimuli in each experiment and the distances between them.

* The directional information is contained in the convention that the probability in any cell reflects the proportion of judgments of row greater than column.

The third experiment, as well as Dashiell's, obtained pair comparison preferential choice data, QIa. Dember's third experiment used as stimuli the seven adjectives: "excellent," "very good," "good," "fair," "poor," "bad," and "very bad." The subject chose from each of the twenty-one pairs of adjectives the adjective which more nearly described his opinion of a recent movie. In the experiment by Dashiell, the stimuli were seven colors, presented pairwise, and the subject indicated his aesthetic preference on each pair.

In the three experiments that Dember did, each subject judged each pair exactly once and the latency of each such choice was obtained. In the fourth experiment, Dashiell's, there were nine subjects and the decision time on each pair for a given subject was an average of six replications.

In each experiment the choices made by each subject (the content) were analyzed to obtain order relations on the distances between pairs of points. In the QIV experiments, the order relations were on the distances between the stimuli on the stimulus scale. In the QI experiments, order relations were obtained on the distances between stimuli on the I scale. These latter relations were those that follow naturally given just the rank order of the stimuli on the I scale. The order relations on distances were compared with the order relations on the corresponding latencies. A significant correlation suggests a monotone function relating latency to psychological distance, that is, the less the difference the longer the decision time.

Results: The metric relations for each subject in the first two experiments are in the form of a partial order. To compute (Kendall's) τ coefficients, Dember took, through each partial order, the longest unbroken path, or paths when there was more than one (of the same length). For each such path, a τ coefficient was computed between the rank order of the distances and the rank order of the corresponding latencies. The high, median, and low correlation coefficients for each of the subjects in experiments 1 and 2 are reported in Table 24.4. All are significant except the coefficient with the value of .24.

Experiments 3 and 4, the QIa experiments, indicate that a more complicated relation exists between latency and psychological distance in the case of preferential choice data. For each subject four τ coefficients could be computed. These are for the four paths through the partial order of the distances on an I scale correlated with the rank order of the preferential choice latencies. All these coefficients are reported in Table 24.5. The p values associated with these τ coefficients are as follows: $\tau = 1.00, p = 0$; $\tau = .87, p = .01$; $\tau = .73, p = .03$; $\tau = .60, p = .07$; $\tau = .47, p = .14$;

Table 24.4   Coefficients Between Rank Orders of Decision Times and of Distances for QIVa Data

		Experiment 1				Experiment 2, S 1
		S 1	S 2	S 3	S 4	
	high	.63	.76	.75	.68	.57
τ Coefficient	median	.56	.64	.73	.62	.47
	low	.56	.24	.68	.59	.40

$\tau = .33$, $p = .24$; $\tau = .20$, $p = .36$; $\tau = .07$, $p = .50$. The results are ambiguous; some subjects exhibit a significant relation between decision time and psychological distance for preferential choice behavior and some do not.

Dember discusses some of the possible explanations for the differences in the relations between latency and psychological distance found in QIVa data as compared with QIa data. The τ coefficients are less reliable for the QIa data, being based on rank orders of length 6. In addition, in experiment 3 the stimuli, which were words, differed in length and the latencies include reading time. Then Dember discusses sources of the differences that might be anticipated from theory, that is, decision time may be a function of distance on the J scale rather than on the I scale and variability of an ideal point may enter into QIa latencies, whereas it would not in QIVa.

In review, Dember's thesis suggests that for QIVa data latencies are monotonically related to psychological distance, even for single observations. This has considerable practical potential because the alternative of transforming probabilities into distances requires experimentally independent replications, which may not be possible, and requires probabilities other than 1 or 0, that is, inconsistency. An advantage of latency data is

Table 24.5 τ Coefficients between Rank Orders of Decision Time and of Distances of QIa Data

Subjects in Experiment 3			Subjects in Experiment 4								
1	2	3	1	2	3	4	5	6	7	8	9
.47	.60	.20	.73	.73	.20	.60	.87	−.07	.87	.60	.87
−.20	.60	.20	.73	.33	.20	.73	.20	.47	.20	.73	.47
.73	.20	.33	1.00	.33	.33	.87	.47	.07	.73	.60	.73
.60	.87	.07	.60	.47	.20	.73	.20	.47	.60	.60	1.00

that they contain metric information for completely consistent behavior and for unreplicated behavior.

Indications of a Pilot Study

An interesting relation of latency in preferential choice behavior to the stochastically dominant or nondominant choice was observed in the intensive pilot study mentioned in Section 1 of Chapter 2. Latencies were obtained in the pair comparison data. The approximately 100 replications obtained on each pair were divided in 2 subsets according to the preferential choice of the subject, that is, those instances when he preferred j to k and those when he preferred k to j. Median latencies for each of these subsets were computed for each pair of stimuli. For the 66 pairs, for each of the 2 subjects, the median latency of the more frequent decision was less than that for the stochastically nondominant decision.

Soon after observing these results Warren Torgerson and I hit on a reasonable hypothesis from the point of view of Thurstone's probabilistic model for comparative judgment. Thurstone hypothesizes a normal distribution of differences for each pair. The mean of this distribution is the average distance between the members of the pair; the areas in the two portions of the distribution where it is truncated at zero difference correspond to the two probabilities of the two responses. The absolute values of the means of these two truncated portions are the corresponding average differences when the individual makes one or the other judgment. The average difference for the stochastically dominant choice will always be greater. If there is a monotone function relating latency to distance, the stochastically dominant choice should on the average be made quicker. Actually a good deal more than this can be done to relate the theory and data, but we have not yet had the time to pursue it.

Greenberg's Experiment on Decision Time

Dember's thesis indicated that in preferential choice data latency is not as simply related to distance as it seems to be in stimulus comparison data. Preferential choice data involve the comparison of distances, as in similarity data, and we may well expect other considerations to enter in.

Suppose, for example, we have a J scale, with stimuli in the order A, B, C, and so on, and an individual's I scale which is the J scale folded. On a priori grounds we might anticipate that there are at least three variables mediating the latency of a preferential choice:

(1) the *distance* between a pair of stimuli on the I scale;

(2) the *laterality* of the two stimuli, that is, whether they are a unilateral or a bilateral pair (see Chapter 23);

(3) the *remoteness* of the distance on the I scale from the ideal point. This last variable needs further explication. Consider the distance on the J scale between a pair of stimuli like A and B, and an individual with his ideal in the neighborhood of stimulus C. For this individual, the distance between A and B, which is to be discriminated by his preferential choice, is relatively near to him compared with an individual whose ideal is near stimulus F. The latter individual has also to discriminate the distance between A and B, but from a more remote ideal. We define remoteness, then, to be the average distance of the two stimuli from the ideal point. This is the distance on the I scale from the ideal point to a point midway between the two stimuli.

Marshall Greenberg (1961, 1963) in his thesis gave particular attention to the relation of this variable, remoteness, to latency. He compared three models: the absolute difference model, the ratio model, and the two-stage model.

The Absolute Difference Model: As we saw in Chapter 23 (equations 23.7 and 23.8), in the case of a unidimensional J scale, an individual's preferential choice on a unilateral pair of stimuli is mediated by the difference between the two stimuli on the J scale. If this is the case, the remoteness of c_i should be irrelevant to the latency of the choice between the stimuli.

The Ratio Model: If we postulate that the individual responds to the ratio $|p_{hij}|/|p_{hik}|$ rather than the difference $|p_{hij}| - |p_{hik}|$, we have

$$\frac{|p_{hij}|}{|p_{hik}|} \leq 1 \Leftrightarrow j \cdot \rangle k$$

Consider, then, a J scale with an individual at X and an individual at Y:

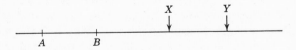

Then we would have

$$1 < \frac{Y - A}{Y - B} < \frac{X - A}{X - B}$$

If the smaller the ratio the more difficult the decision, then latency should increase with remoteness.

The Two-Stage Model: The individual is presumed first to judge whether the pair of stimuli is unilateral left, unilateral right, or bilateral. Then, for a unilateral pair,* he judges which stimulus is greater or less, independently of c_i, as in the absolute difference model.

The first stage is presumed to be more difficult the less the remoteness, so latency of this stage should be inversely related to remoteness. The second stage corresponds to the absolute difference model according to which remoteness of c_i is irrelevant to latency, so the latency of this stage is independent of remoteness. Taken together, then, the two stages of this model would predict that latency should decrease with remoteness.

Procedure: Greenberg used six shades of gray as stimuli and presented them pairwise with four variations in the instructions, labeled as follows: B, "Which is darker?"; A_1, "Which is the better representative of a good *light* gray?"; A_2, "Which is the better representative of a good *medium* gray?"; A_3, "Which is the better representative of a good *dark* gray?"

Each subject carried through all four instructions in one of two sequences: B, A_2, A_1, A_3; and B, A_3, A_1, A_2. Stimulus pairs were projected on a screen, and the subject indicated his choice by punching a key. His response and its latency were automatically punched on an IBM card.

Each subject was run in five 2-hour sessions, to obtain fifty replications on each pair of stimuli under each of the four instructions. The entire sequence was presented in each session. Space errors and experimental sequential dependencies were controlled for by randomizing procedures. There were four subjects. Subjects 1 and 2 were given the sequence B, A_2, A_1, A_3, and subjects 3 and 4 were given the sequence B, A_3, A_1, A_2.

Results: The relations obtained between latency and stochastic dominance were interestingly different from those reported in the pilot study discussed in Chapter 2, Section 1 and Chapter 5, Section 9. Greenberg's results are reported in Table 24.6. If the proportion of times j is preferred to k, proportion $(j > k)$, is greater than .5, then that choice is called the stochastically dominant choice. In the table the mean latency of the stochastically dominant choice is designated ML_D and the mean latency of the stochastically nondominant choice is designated ML_{ND}. The number of pairs of stimuli is reported for each subject under each instruction for which $ML_D > ML_{ND}$ and vice versa.

For subject 1 the results are significant at the .02 level, and for all the other subjects the results are significant beyond the .01 level.

---

* Bilateral pairs are not considered further in this context because they confound remoteness and distance.

The interesting result is that subjects 1 and 2 yield the same relation as we had obtained in our pilot study and subjects 3 and 4 reveal exactly the reverse relation.

To study the effect of remoteness on latency, the subjects' I scales under instructions A_1, A_2, A_3 were obtained, and hence the laterality of the stimuli was determinable. For each subject there were four unilateral pairs with respect to which the subject had a less remote and a more remote ideal. For example, the stimulus pair A, B was unilateral under

Table 24.6 Relation between Mean Latency and Stochastic Dominance*

	$ML_D > ML_{ND}$	$ML_D < ML_{ND}$	$ML_D > ML_{ND}$	$ML_D < ML_{ND}$
	$S1$		$S2$	
B	1	5	0	4
A_2	1	12	1	9
A_1	4	5	2	9
A_3	3	1	0	2
Total	9	23	3	24
	$S3$		$S4$	
B	7	2	2	2
A_3	11	4	12	3
A_1	8	3	8	5
A_2	8	1	7	0
Total	34	10	29	10

* Total numbers differ because there is no determinable latency for a nondominant choice on those pairs in which a subject made one choice consistently.

A_2 and A_3 instructions for all subjects; and was less remote under A_2 instructions and more remote under A_3 instructions.

In Table 24.7 the latencies in hundredths of a second are reported for each subject for the four unilateral pairs from a less remote and more remote ideal.

Fourteen of these sixteen instances indicate a longer latency for the less remote ideal. The two contrary instances are subject 2 in the fourth column of the table and subject 4 in the third column. So the indication is that latency *decreases* with remoteness.

That latency is a very sensitive measure of psychological distance, even for completely consistent judgments, is indicated by an analysis of the judgments under instruction B, "Which is darker?" Each subject was 100% consistent in correctly judging each of the stimuli from B to F as

Table 24.7   Mean Response Latencies for Unilateral Pairs as Related to Remoteness. (Reported in hundredths of a second.)

		Unilateral pairs			
		1	2	3	4
S 1	less remote	64	81	66	111
	more remote	50	63	42	93
S 2	less remote	67	77	62	87
	more remote	56	67	48	96
S 3	less remote	49	52	51	52
	more remote	35	50	45	44
S 4	less remote	44	51	44	44
	more remote	35	50	45	41

Table 24.8   Relation of Latency to Distance under 100% Consistent Judgments

		$S1$	$S2$	$S3$	$S4$
	$B > A$	47	53	43	36
	$C > A$	41	51	41	34
Judgment	$D > A$	39	43	39	32
	$E > A$	38	43	39	32
	$F > A$	37	41	37	32

darker than A. The mean latency of these decisions, in hundredths of a second, is reported in Table 24.8 for each subject.

As may be seen, there is not a single reversal although there are a number of ties.

Discussion: The relations obtained between latency and stochastic dominance are very puzzling. Greenberg proposes that the difference between subjects 1 and 2 on the one hand and 3 and 4 on the other may reflect a difference in set with regard to speed versus accuracy in their judgments. Subjects 1 and 2 had the sequence in which a "medium gray" ideal (A_2) preceded A_1 and A_3; whereas 3 and 4 had the sequence in which a "dark gray" ideal (A_3) preceded A_1 and A_2.

Greenberg argues that the sequence A_2, A_1, A_3, being more difficult, establishes a set for accuracy and that the sequence A_3, A_1, A_2 establishes a set for speed. He presents supporting evidence in terms of more errors, more inconsistency, and faster responses for subjects 3 and 4.

An accuracy orientation leads to a lesser latency for the stochastically dominant choice because a discrimination is being made and the stochastically dominant choice is an easier one (à la interpretation by Torgerson and me in terms of a truncated normal distribution of differences; see p. 530).

A speed orientation leads to longer decision time for the stochastically dominant choice in that the longer decisions under a speed orientation will tend to be the accurate ones and will tend to coincide with the stochastically dominant choice. The shorter decision times will be associated with judgments in which less discrimination is being made, will contain more error, and will tend to be in the nondominant subset of judgments.

If a speed-versus-accuracy set underlies the relation of latency to stochastic dominance, it is a very significant empirical result. It will be useful in checking up on subjects in laboratory experiments of judgment and choice and will be an important consideration in behavioral model building.

The result indicating that latency decreases with remoteness supports the two-stage model. The two-stage model adds a "time to determine laterality" to the decision time of the absolute difference model to make up the total latency of the judgment.

That latency is a very sensitive response measure and potentially very significant in the analysis of behavior is clearly evident. Much additional and very careful experimental work will be required, however, to determine the empirical scope, including the boundary conditions governing its interpretation.

5. BEARDSLEE'S EXPERIMENTAL COMPARISON OF QIIIa AND QIVa METHODS

One of the most intensive studies of the microstructure of scaling data was carried out by Beardslee (1957). The questions and problems he addressed himself to included:

(1) Are there differences in the data obtained by cases 2 and 3 of the

method of cartwheels (see Fig. 24.6)? Can cartwheels be freely decomposed into paired judgments of distances?

(2) A stimulus scale may be obtained by (a) applying Thurstone's model for comparative judgment to a dominance matrix (see Section 2) of QIIIa data; (b) Torgerson's application of Thurstone's model to the scaling of the interpoint distances from cartwheel data of QIVa; and (c) analysis of cartwheel data by unfolding the stimulus I scales. Are these several sources of metric information, from different data and analyzed by different models, consistent with each other?

The existence of individual differences in metric relations among stimuli might obscure some of these issues, so complete data were obtained on each of two subjects and analyzed separately. Each subject is a separate experiment.

Selection of stimuli was a delicate matter because, on the one hand, they had to yield sufficiently inconsistent data on the pair comparisons of the stimuli themselves and also on the pair comparisons of their interpoint distances (the cartwheel data) to permit analysis by the probabilistic models of Thurstone and Torgerson, and, on the other hand, the cartwheel data had to be sufficiently consistent to permit the construction of the stimulus I scales by weak stochastic transitivity.

The stimuli finally selected were pairs of vertical lines, each $\frac{3}{16}$ inch high and $1\frac{1}{2}$ millimeters wide, with a horizontal distance or "gap" between them. These gaps were the actual stimuli being judged. For subject 1 the stimuli were seven in number, labeled A to G, and the distances were, respectively, in millimeters, 72.0, 72.5, 73.2, 74.6, 75.2, 76.0, 77.0. For subject 2, only the six stimuli A to F were used.

The instructions to the subjects were:

(1) for the dominance matrix of QIIIa data, "Which pair of lines is further apart?"

(2) for case 2 cartwheels, "Which of the outer pairs of lines is most like the pair in the center in distance apart?"

(3) for case 3 cartwheels, "Which of the outer pairs of lines is most like the pair in the center in distance apart and which of the outer pairs of lines is least like the pair in the center in distance apart?"

The stimuli were presented in a variety of spatial arrangements to test for space errors. Two sessions of $1\frac{1}{2}$ to 2 hours each were held each day, whenever possible, with at least 2 hours intervening. In each session judgments were obtained by all three methods of data collection. Each subject was run for about a total of 100 hours of testing time after more than 20 hours of pre-experimental practice. A sequential method of data collection and analysis was used so that more judgments could be obtained on those pairs with highest inconsistency.

Results on QIIIa Pair Comparison Data

Differences in Accuracy between Sessions: Error scores were obtained for each subject for each session. The between-session variance is significant for each subject at the 5% level. About 10% of each subject's variance is between sessions, the rest, 90%, is within sessions.

Both subjects showed a significant long-term trend in accuracy over the course of the experiment (there was no feedback on correctness of judgments), subject 1 showing an increase in accuracy, subject 2 a decrease. Changes in accuracy appear to affect all pairs equally.

Subject 1 showed a significant "warm-up" effect within single experimental sessions, that is, his accuracy improved through the session. Subject 2 showed no such effect. There were no significant effects due to time of day, between the two experimenters, nor associated with complaints of eyestrain.

Constant Errors: There is a very significant constant error associated with the spatial arrangement of the stimuli, but the *importance* of this significant position error is slight. Using McGill's (1954) analysis we can calculate the percentage of information received which is information about position. For subject 1 the positional effect contributes 1.4% of the total information; for subject 2, 12.0%.

Positional effects were completely balanced for pair comparisons experimentally, so the effect is averaged out. For the cartwheel data, randomization rather than balancing was used to control positional effects, so it is a source of variability.

Each stimulus was drawn on duplicate cards which were used interchangeably. Significant differences between the two cards for certain stimuli were found for each subject, but the effects were idiosyncratic to the subjects and small in importance.

Comparisons of Case 2 and Case 3 Cartwheel Data

The most important question here is whether cartwheels like those of case 3 can be freely decomposed by the decomposition model discussed in Chapter 2 into the component pair comparisons as presented in case 2. Is there a possible interactional effect of being embedded in a larger set of stimuli which leads to different proportions of judgments than are obtained on the component judgments individually as in case 2?

Beardslee tested by χ^2 the homogeneity of proportions derived from case 3 with those obtained by case 2. For subject 1, 1 χ^2 out of 43 is significant at the 5% level for unilateral* judgments and 4 out of 33 for bilateral, a total of 5, where $3.8 = 5\%$ of 76 is the chance expectation. For subject 2, the corresponding figures are 3 out of 32 and none out of 19, a total of 3, where $2.55 = 5\%$ of 51 would be the chance expectation.

The percentages estimated from case 2 and case 3 were compared to see if one tended to be biased toward consistency (that is, percentages of 0 and 100) relative to the other. There was no evidence that this was the case.

The probabilities from case 3 for a given pair are obtained by summing over all the cartwheels in which that pair is embedded. For example, in the case 3 cartwheel (see the accompanying sketch), the proportion of

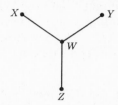

times the distance $\overline{WX}$ is judged greater than the distance $\overline{WY}$ is obtained by counting over the sets of 4 in which only the stimulus in position Z is varied. Although these percentages were homogeneous with the corresponding ones obtained from case 2 (in which there is no stimulus in position Z), it is possible that the judgment on the pair WX versus WY in case 3 may be different as the fourth stimulus, Z, varies.

To test this possibility Beardslee included instances in which a pair of distances like $\overline{WX}$ and $\overline{WY}$ was judged about 50 times with each of two different stimuli as the fourth stimulus. For each subject there were 15 instances of such pairs of proportions in which the proportions differed only in being derived in the context of a different fourth stimulus.

The instances include some unilateral and some bilateral pairs of distances, and include both highly consistently judged pairs and pairs whose percentages approach 50%. For neither subject were any of the 15 χ^2's significant at the 5% level.

With these stimuli, then, any differences in the proportions obtained from the two cartwheel cases are sufficiently below the error in repeated judgments not to be revealed by such analysis, even with rather large amounts of data, and as far as these data go no context effects or interactions are due to the varying fourth stimulus in case 3 cartwheels.

---

* Unilateral and bilateral judgments in cartwheels refer to whether a pair of stimuli on the rim are unilateral or bilateral to the hub stimulus. Such similarity judgments are made analogous to preferential choice judgments by interpreting the hub stimulus as a temporary ideal.

Because of the close agreement between the pairwise probabilities obtained from the case 2 cartwheels and the corresponding ones obtained by decomposing the case 3 cartwheels the data were combined to estimate the pairwise probabilities utilized in the later comparisons between models.

Beardslee also studied two hypotheses for the relation between pairwise probabilities from case 2 and the probabilities of the different rankings of these stimuli in case 3. For example, Fig. 24.6 shows three case 2 cartwheels and one case 3 cartwheel all with the same hub. The problem is: Given the probabilities for the judgments on each of the case 2 cartwheels, can we predict the probabilities of the six alternative rankings that may be made to the case 3 cartwheel? This is the problem of the proper decomposition model to be used with cartwheels and is closely related formally to the same problem for preferential choice data, as discussed in Chapter 2.

The case 3 cartwheel yields a rank order of three distances, $\overline{AB}$, $\overline{AC}$, and $\overline{AD}$. This rank order decomposes into three pair comparisons, the same three represented by the case 2 cartwheels. We might hypothesize that the probability of a given ordering from the case 3 cartwheel would be the product of the probabilities of the component pair comparisons from the case 2 cartwheels. This latter procedure, however, also yields probabilities for two intransitive combinations of the case 2 cartwheels which are not admissible for case 3. What should be done with these?

Beardslee explored two hypotheses. The first (suggested by James Chabot) was that the proportion of judgments which would have been intransitive if the judgments had been obtained separately is distributed over the six transitive rankings in proportion to the frequency of those six rankings. The second hypothesis was that the proportion of intransitive judgments predicted by the judgments on the case 2 cartwheels is distributed equally over the six rankings. This would correspond psychologically to the organism responding "at random" when confronted by an intransitive percept.

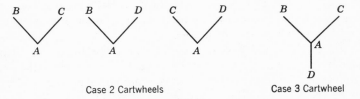

Case 2 Cartwheels   Case 3 Cartwheel

Fig. 24.6 Illustrating the three case 2 cartwheels used to predict the case 3 cartwheel.

The same fifteen case 3 cartwheels used to test for the effect of context were used to test these composition functions. The component pair comparisons were presented as case 2 cartwheels for at least 50 judgments each.

Beardslee computed the expected proportion of each rank order for the case 3 cartwheels from the observed proportions on the case 2 cartwheels according to both the proportional hypothesis and the equal distribution hypothesis. These expected frequencies were then compared with the observed frequencies for the case 3 cartwheels. Neither hypothesis fitted the data well. For subject 1 there were 36 cases where the observed frequency was closer to the frequency expected on the proportional hypothesis, 35 where it was closer to the frequency expected on the equal distribution hypothesis, and 1 tie. For the second subject the corresponding figures were 41, 48, and 1 tie.

Comparison of Metric Information from the Different Procedures

A systematic trend during the course of the experiment occurred in subject 1's judgments on the case 3 cartwheels. Significance tests on the percentages obtained at the beginning of the experiment and at the end for the same pairs of distances indicated that 2 of 70 unilateral and 5 of 35 bilateral pairs of distances differed at the .05 level, a total of 7 where 5.02, equal to 5 % of 105, would be the pure chance expectation. For subject 2, 3 of 40 unilateral and 3 of 20 bilateral pairs showed significant differences, a total of 6 where 3 would be the chance expectation. For the first subject the changes reflected a change in the metric relations, so some of his data were analyzed separately for the first and second halves of the experiment.

The principal methods to be compared are three: (1) a Thurstone case V analysis of the QIIIa data; (2) a Torgerson analysis of the cartwheel data to scale the interpoint distances; (3) an unfolding analysis of the cartwheel data. These three methods are referred to as methods 1, 2, and 3 in the subsequent discussion.

For method 2, the cartwheel data were not analyzed separately for the first and second halves of the experiment for subject 1 because some of the proportions would be based on too little data and a number of probabilities of 1 and 0 arise which are not usable.

Since methods 1 and 2 yield interval scales, the interpoint distances obtained by the two methods can be correlated. For subject 1, the product moment correlation is .995 and the rank order correlation ρ is .989. For subject 2 the corresponding correlations are .979 and .975. So the agreement within subjects, between scales, is very high.

The correlations between subjects within scales are lower. For method 1 the correlations of interpoint distances between the subjects are .955 and .989 (product moment r and rank order ρ, respectively). For method 2 the corresponding correlations are .939 and .956. Thus there is an indication of more intra-individual agreement across different methods of collecting data and different methods of analysis than there is inter-individual agreement within a given method of collecting data and a given method of analysis.

Method 3 yields only an ordered metric scale so to compare this method with methods 1 and 2 we look to see if the metric relations obtained by methods 1 and 2 confirm those obtained by unfolding. Subject 2 shows essentially no disagreements of method 3 with methods 1 or 2 in ranking the interpoint distances. Subject 1, however, shows several disagreements between methods 1 and 3. On the data from the first half of the experiment there are 7 disagreements in ranking, and on the second half there are 4. This is out of nearly 200 comparisons possible from each half's partial order on metric given by the unfolding technique, so the agreement is very substantial.

In comparing method 3 with method 2 the agreement is found to be closer than it is between methods 1 and 3. For each half of the data analyzed by method 3, there are two disagreements in the ranking of interpoint distances with the ranking obtained by method 2. Of course, these two methods are being compared on the same data except that method 2 was applied to all the data whereas method 3 was applied to each half separately. So it is not so surprising, perhaps, that these two methods are in such close agreement.

In general the findings are that the methods essentially agree, that there are no gestalt-like interactions with these stimuli, and that case 2 and case 3 cartwheels when decomposed yield similar estimates of probability.

6. SUMMARY

Correlation matrices, probability matrices, and data on pairs of dyads are discussed in ways which are designed to bring out the relations between the data of the different quadrants.

The conversion of a correlation matrix into a matrix of interpoint distances is discussed, leading to QIVa data and their analysis by a nonmetric model, which reveals how this model may be interpreted as nonmetric factor analysis.

We then discussed the kind of data we would have if we had only an offdiagonal submatrix of the correlation matrix. Whereas the complete correlation matrix was interpreted as QIIIb data and converted into a

QIVa matrix of interpoint distances, an offdiagonal correlation matrix may be interpreted as QIIb data and converted into a QIa matrix of interpoint distances.

We see, however, that the data are $A \times A$ data in that all pairs of dyads are comparable instead of just $\bigcup_i(A_i \times A_i)$ data. Unfolding theory as discussed in Part 3 has been developed only for analysis of $\bigcup_i(A_i \times A_i)$ data, which is a small fraction of the total in $A \times A$, about $1/m$, where m is the number of individuals. While real world preferential choice behavior does not yield $A \times A$ data, we see that there are contexts in which such formal data may arise and $A \times A$ models will be useful.

In the second section of the chapter the three basic types of data matrices are discussed. The first is called the dominance matrix of QIIIa data containing, for example, the probabilities that stimulus j is judged greater than stimulus k. An offdiagonal submatrix of the dominance matrix contains QIIa data. This throws doubt on the previous convictions of many, including myself, that QIIIa data are of necessity one-dimensional. The doubt arises when we recognize that a *submatrix* of these data is QIIa and subject to multidimensional analysis (see Chapter 12). The problem is discussed but not illuminated.

The other two types of probability matrices are discussed next. They are the symmetric proximity matrix and the conditional proximity matrix, both QIIIb data. The symmetric proximity matrix is seen to be the more general form, of which the correlation matrix is a particular instance, of QIIIb data which may be converted into QIVa while any offdiagonal submatrix is QIIb data which may be converted into $A \times A$ data in QIa. The conditional proximity matrix parallels this exactly except that the mapping into QIa yields $\bigcup_i(A_i \times A_i)$ data rather than $A \times A$.

The fourth section of the chapter discusses data matrices on pairs of dyads. By beginning with two sets of points (as with two sets of stimuli; for example, lights and tones, feathered and arrowed lines, journals and articles), we may construct the total matrix of all pairs of dyads and partition it into six distinct submatrices. Each of these submatrices has the data on pairs of dyads that lead to measures of interpoint distances, which may then be analyzed to obtain a "map" of the points themselves.

Four of the six submatrices are quite distinct and are discussed in some detail. In each case, the first level of data analysis is scaling the interpoint distances. For the submatrices along the diagonal this is done in QIII; for the offdiagonal submatrices it is done in QII. The second level of data analysis is to analyze the interpoint distances to obtain the configuration of the points themselves. This is done in either QI or QIV as indicated for each submatrix.

Section 4 introduces the subject of alternative response measures which are crudely classified as content, consistency, amplitude, and latency. As a psychological speculation, I would identify a basic psychological process with each quadrant: QI, preference; QII, detection; QIII, discrimination; QIV, similarity. For each process and response measure, as a pair, we would like to build a system by which we go from the response measures to the inferential classification of stimuli and people. Ultimately, of course, these systems must all interlock.

Systems are already well advanced for the analysis of content and consistency for each one of the four processes. Models for latency and amplitude lag behind. Experimental studies by Dember and Greenberg are reported which are important for the interpretation of decision time in QI and QIV. A possible relation between decision time and consistency is also pointed out.

The last section reports an intensive experimental comparison of certain methods of collecting and analyzing data in QIIIa and QIVa. This is a study by Beardslee in which he compared Thurstone's model for comparative judgment data (QIIIa), Torgerson's model for similarities data (QIVa), and the unfolding analysis of QIVa data. He also compared case 2 and case 3 cartwheels as methods of collecting data and two alternative hypotheses for the decomposition of cartwheels.

There are many interesting problems in this crucial area of comparative studies of methods. There are the relations between methods dealing with the same formal relations on points, the methods within a given octant. These within-octant methods may include methods designed for any of the several kinds of response measures. Then there are the relations between methods dealing with different formal relations on points, that is, methods from different octants, but dealing with the same response measure.

It is my opinion that such studies are not "studies in pure methodology" but are the most direct routes through which psychological measurement and scaling become a part of behavioral theory. To many, the area of psychological measurement and scaling is merely a handmaiden in the investigation of interesting psychological problems. The area is certainly devoted to and plays that role to its maximum capability. This must not lead us to overlook the fact that the models in psychological measurement and scaling are themselves miniature theories of behavior. They provide the building blocks for more comprehensive theory as well as being useful tools in the study of more complex behavior.

REFERENCES

Beardslee, D. C., 1957, An empirical study of the measurement of psychological distance, unpublished Ph.D. dissertation, University of Michigan.

Dashiell, J. F., 1937, Affective value-distances as a determinant of esthetic judgment-times, *Amer. J. Psychol.*, **50**, 57–67.

Dember, W. N., 1955, Decision-time and psychological distance, unpublished Ph.D. dissertation, University of Michigan.

Dember, W. N., 1957, The relation of decision-time to stimulus similarity, *J. exp. Psychol.*, **53**, 68–72.

Greenberg, M., 1961, Response latency as a test of mathematical models for preference behavior, unpublished Ph.D. dissertation, University of Michigan.

Greenberg, M., 1963, *J* scale models for preference behavior, *Psychometrika*, **28**, 265–71.

Kaiser, H., 1962, Scaling a simplex, *Psychometrika*, **27**, 155–62.

Levin, J., 1961, A least square fit to a simplex, paper read at Amer. Psychol. Ass., New York, September, 1961.

McGill, W. J., 1954, Multivariate information transmission, *Psychometrika*, **19**, 97–116.

Shepard, R., 1960, "Similarity of stimuli and metric properties of behavioral data," Chapter 4 in *Psychological scaling: theory and applications*, edited by H. Gulliksen and S. Messick, John Wiley and Sons, New York.

Young, G., and A. S. Householder, 1938, Discussion of a set of points in terms of their mutual distances, *Psychometrika*, **3**, 19–22.

CHAPTER 25

The Scale Grid

In this chapter* we discuss a way of distinguishing and organizing various kinds of psychological data in terms of the presence or absence of both sets of points. This organization of data is distinct from that provided by the theory of data and has some interesting implications for the relations between models and their areas of application.

1. JOINT SPACES

A joint space is one in which the data consist of relations on pairs of points the members of which are identified with distinct sets of objects. These are the data of QI and QII. Typically the distinct sets of objects are people and stimuli; for convenience we shall use this terminology. I hardly need to point out, by now, that the two sets of objects need not be people and stimuli; it should no longer be misleading to talk in these terms. We are discussing here, then, all methods and models which, from the observed behavior, seek to make an inferential classification of two distinct sets of objects (points) in a common or joint space.

Let us consider some of the ways in which such spaces may differ from each other. The variety of ways may, of course, be very numerous, for example, in dimensionality, in distance function, and so on, but for my purpose here I wish to pinpoint only certain characteristics, those which have to do with the variability of the points in the space.†

Consider, then, that we have two sets of objects, say individuals and

* This chapter is a revision of an earlier paper (Coombs, 1956).
† An early analysis of the scale grid in algebraic terms and in more detail is contained in Coombs (1952).

stimuli, and the individuals "behave" with respect to the stimuli according to instructions. The point associated with an individual may be conceived of as relatively stable, as the individual successively responds to the several stimuli, or the point may be variable. It is sufficient for certain purposes merely to categorize the variability of an individual point as essentially zero or greater than zero. If the individual point is variable, this variability may be broken down into components, one component being the variability of an individual point identified as a "within-stimulus" component, another being identified as a "between-stimulus" component.

We have, presumably, a number of individuals and hence a number of corresponding points, to each of which there corresponds a variability which might be dichotomously classified as zero or greater. If, in the entire set of points, there is at least one which has a nonzero variability, we speak of the entire set of data as having variability of the individual points.

Now, everything that has been said here about the individual points may be said, *mutatis mutandis*, about the stimulus points. They may or may not have variability as different individuals respond to them, and if they do, this variability may have a "within-individual" and a "between-individual" component.

In these terms, then, we may speak of joint spaces, or their corresponding sets of data, as differing from each other in terms of two dimensions: (1) whether the individual points do or do not have variability and (2) whether the stimulus points do or do not have variability. These two dimensions generate the classes of data shown for joint spaces in Fig. 25.1.

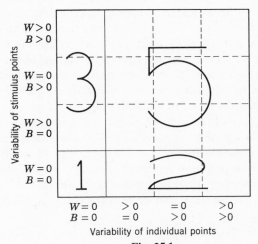

Fig. 25.1

In the figure the ordinate and abscissa are each divided into four categories. The abscissa categories pertain to the variability of individual points, the ordinate categories to the variability of stimulus points. The categories are generated by the two components of within and between variance.

The figure is embedded in a larger figure (see Fig. 25.3), which accounts for the apparently odd numbering of classes of data as 1, 2, 3, and 5. Class 1 data are seen to be those in which there is no variability of any of the points. This kind of data exists almost exclusively in idealized, hypothetical, data matrices. It is useful for teaching purposes but is rarely encountered outside the classroom.

Class 2 data are the kind we have in joint spaces in which the stimulus points are stable, both within and between individuals, but the individual points vary. Class 2 may be further partitioned on the basis of the components as indicated in the figure. The first subclass, in which only the within-stimulus component is greater than zero, is one of the kinds of data that lead to less than perfect reproducibility in scalogram and parallelogram analysis; for example, a kind that is sometimes called "unreliable" or "lacking in precision."

The second and third subclasses of class 2 are quite different. Here there is variability of individual points between stimuli. This is the kind of data we have in omnibus mental tests as in the Army General Classification Test used in the first half of World War II. This test has vocabulary, arithmetic, and box-counting items, emphasizing verbal, numerical, and spatial abilities. Each item corresponds to a point relatively stable over individuals, but an individual's point may vary significantly as he passes from a vocabulary item to a box-counting item.

The term homogeneity is sometimes used to refer to data in joint spaces, and the various classes of Fig. 25.1 bring out the ways in which data may lack it. In the second and third subclasses of Class 2, for example, the stimuli may be said to be homogeneous over people, in that each stimulus point varies not at all whereas the individuals are heterogeneous over stimuli in that an individual point may shift in a significant manner between stimuli. Such might be the data we would have, for example, from a mixture of opinion statements taken from different attitude continua. The following is an attempt at a laboratory demonstration of this kind of class 2 data which I call the temperature-moisture experiment.

I took the verbal stimuli A, hot; B, warm; C, cool; D, cold; E, dry; F, humid; G, damp; H, wet and presented them pairwise to obtain preferential choices. Each student was asked, first, to select an activity he enjoyed, such as boating, skiing, tennis, fishing, or picnicking, and then, for each pair of weather conditions (stimuli), to choose the kind of weather he would prefer for that activity. What would we expect? I anticipated that the stimuli A, B, C, and D would constitute one continuum; and E, F, G, and H another; that each individual would have two ideals for his activity, one on each continuum; that he would have a preference order, an I scale, for the eight stimuli, but that this would be a merger of two I scales from two distinct J scale continua.

I expected, then, that this would be class 2 data in that each stimulus would correspond to a reasonably stable point for the different individuals but an individual's point would be different for some stimuli than for others.

These expectations were borne out. One individual, for example, whose activity ideal was "fishing," had the preference ordering $F G H B C E D A$, a merger of $B C D A$ and $F G H E$. Another, for golfing, had the I scale $B C E A F D G H$, made up of $B C A D$ and $E F G H$. By separating each individual's I scale into two I scales, the two sets could be unfolded to obtain the J scales for temperature and moisture.*

In this situation, then, a stimulus point is relatively stable over individuals but an individual point is variable between stimuli.

Class 3 data are analogous to class 2 in the sense that one is a transpose of the other; that is, the individual points in class 3 data are stable and the stimulus points vary. The first subclass is that in which only the within-individual component is nonzero, that is, the loci of the stimulus points are unreliable or lack precision. The other two subclasses may be characterized as instances in which a stimulus is heterogeneous over individuals but an individual is homogeneous over the stimuli.

Such data might arise if the individuals were drawn from culturally different backgrounds or populations and were evaluating the same stimuli but in terms of different aspects. For example, we might have a group of Republicans and Democrats indicating their preferences among a set of statements about foreign issues. For the Republicans, the issues may be distributed along a J scale (or J space) different from that along which the Democrats distribute them. The two groups are folding different J scales. A given statement corresponds to one stimulus point on the Republicans' J scale and a different stimulus point on the Democrats' J scale.

Such data would be relatively easy to analyze compared with the corresponding class 2 data, because here the total collection of I scales could be partitioned into two sets, those generated by folding one J scale

---

* The demonstration worked exceedingly well as far as the temperature continuum was concerned but the moisture continuum was something of a problem. In the first place almost every activity ideal that people chose tended to be near the "dry" end of the continuum and, in the second place, there is not even a common qualitative J scale for these four adjectives; a substantial number of individuals put "humid" between "damp" and "wet" on the J scale, while for others it was between "damp" and "dry."

and those generated by folding the other. I expect that class 3 data are not uncommon in the areas of attitude and personality measurement but quite rare in areas of ability and achievement measurement.

Finally we come to class 5 data, which are partitioned into nine subclasses. I will not pursue these in detail but will make some general remarks. The subclasses of class 5 that border classes 2 and 3 in Fig. 25.1 are the subclasses of data in which both sets of points, the stimulus points and the individual points, are varying. In these subclasses of class 5 the variability of at least one of the sets of points is classifiable as unreliability. These are the subclasses of class 5 which are most amenable to analysis, in the sense that methods now exist for analyzing such data and recovering the joint space. Such methods are essentially those discussed with reference to classes 2 and 3 but applied to data collected by more powerful methods from the searchingness structure in order to control inconsistency.

The remaining subclasses of class 5 comprise the square block of four in the upper right-hand corner of Fig. 25.1. These are classes of data in which both sets of elements are varying *between* elements of the other set. In effect each stimulus may be a different point for different individuals, and, similarly, each individual may be a different point for different stimuli. Perhaps the best way to describe such data is to say that it is as if different stimuli had the same label and different individuals had the same name and we did not know which of the several "Henrys" responded to which of the several stimuli labeled *B*. These are the subclasses of data in which a stimulus point may be in different spaces for different individuals and an individual point may be in different spaces for different stimuli. There are no algorithms available for such data which lead to a geometrical configuration for the inferential classification of stimuli and people.

A significant characteristic of joint spaces is that they are constructed by putting together pieces from different individuals (and/or from different stimuli). The relations of an object in one set to the elements in the other set provide one view, one perspective, one image, one transformation, of the total space. A model specifies what this transformation is and provides an algorithm by means of which a common space may be generated.

The loci of the elements of one of these sets of objects needs to be relatively stable to provide a lever or handle by means of which a joint space may be constructed. We saw how this might be done for class 2 or class 3 data, in which the handle was provided by the stimuli for class 2 and by the individuals for class 3. When both stimuli and individuals vary between the elements of the other set (the four subclasses in the upper right-hand section of class 5) there is nothing to provide this handle and I see no way to construct a joint space from such data.

2. STIMULUS SPACES

Whereas in joint spaces, as stated, we obtain a partial or limited picture of the space from each individual and construct a composite space from the pieces, in stimulus spaces we obtain a total picture from each individual and merge these into a "best" common picture. A stimulus space is one in which the data consist of relations on pairs of points, the members of which are all identified with a single set of elements called stimuli. The individuals are not, themselves, mapped into points in the space: only the stimuli are; and each individual or each replication ideally tells you exactly the same thing as every other. These are the data of QIII and QIV.

The data may be replicated observations from a single individual as in case 1 of Thurstone's model for comparative judgment, or replications may be obtained by using different individuals as in Thurstone's case 2. In the first case the model seeks a stimulus space that "best" captures, in some sense, the predominant character of the individual's behavior: a space which is the "structure of appearance" of the stimuli within the limitations imposed by the experimenter's instructions. In the second case, the model seeks the common or predominant behavior characterizing all the individuals.

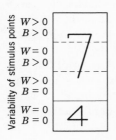

Variability of stimulus points

$W > 0$
$B > 0$

$W = 0$
$B > 0$

$W > 0$
$B = 0$

$W = 0$
$B = 0$

Fig. 25.2

Inasmuch as we have only one set of points, the stimulus points, the various spaces differ from each other in the components of the variance of the elements of only this one set. Hence in Fig. 25.2 we see stimulus spaces categorized in two general classes, class 4 and class 7, with class 7 further subdivided into three subclasses. The one-way classification of stimulus spaces is in terms of the components of the variance of the stimulus points as indicated in the ordinate of Fig. 25.2.

Class 4 data comprise the subclass in which there is no detectable variability of the stimulus points. Such would be the data we might expect if individuals were judging weights of 1, 5, 10, and 20 pounds by pair comparisons as to which member of each pair was the heavier. We would probably find that everyone's behavior could be perfectly captured by a common ordinal scale of the stimuli.

If the same stimuli were presented as cartwheels and an individual judged the relative similarity in felt-heaviness of each pair to a third several times, the data might well fall in the first subclass of class 7, in which each stimulus point is variable in only a random way over the succession of judgments.

If, however, the stimuli were statements of opinion on some issue and different individuals from different subcultures were judging their relative strengths, then, quite conceivably, the loci of particular statements might be significantly different for different individuals. These differences might range from being merely differences in the metric relations among the stimuli on the same common ordinal scale to differences in the order relations among the stimuli themselves or even in the dimensionality of the stimulus space. For example, the study of grade expectations reported in Section 5 of Chapter 5 indicated that individuals had different metric relations on the same common ordinal scale of the course grades from A+ to C.

At the other extreme of class 7 data, consider the example of collecting from these same students QIVa cartwheel data in which they judged the relative similarity of fields of psychology. We would expect that the stimulus spaces of the different individuals would be different even to the extent of having different numbers of dimensions. Such data if analyzed separately for each individual would perhaps be in class 4 or in the first subclass of class 7, whereas if pooled the data would probably be in the second or third subclass of class 7.

In review, class 4 and the first subclass of class 7 data can yield stimulus spaces which would faithfully reflect the data to a high degree. The second and third subclasses of class 7 can only be faithfully represented, perhaps, by weaker levels of measurement such as partial orders and ordinal scales of the stimuli.

3. POPULATION AND FIELD SPACES

In our discussion of joint and stimulus spaces we categorized the data in each of these in terms of the components of variance in the loci of the points, one dimension being the components of the variance of the stimulus points and the other dimension being the components of the variance of the individual points. But now let us consider how these two kinds of spaces, joint and stimulus spaces, differ from each other.

Obviously they differ from each other in terms of whether the points are identified with elements of two distinct sets (stimuli and individuals), as in joint spaces, or with elements of a single set (stimuli only), as in stimulus spaces. Let us call this a third dimension of the scale grid, that is, whether individual points are present or absent. Immediately a fourth dimension is suggested which is dualistically isomorphic to the third, that is, whether stimulus points are present or absent.

These two dimensions constitute respectively the abscissa and the ordinate of Fig. 25.3 and generate what are labeled in that figure as

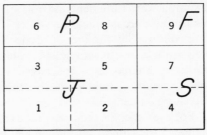

Fig. 25.3

population spaces and field spaces. If there are data which to be accommodated seem to require spaces with both stimulus points and individual points, and if there are data which call for spaces which seem to require only stimulus points, are there kinds of data which would seem to require only individual points (population spaces) and, *reductio ad absurdum*, spaces which require no points at all?

I now propose that this is not a *reductio ad absurdum* but leads to meaningful psychological insights and interrelations among the methodologies associated with various areas of psychological research.

4. AN INTERPRETATION

The Duality between Stimulus and Population Spaces

Let us consider how data which are interpreted as QIII or QIV data and which then lead to stimulus spaces are collected. An experimenter has a number of stimuli and from the behavior of individuals with respect to these stimuli he wishes to make an inferential classification of the stimuli. The observed behavior is to be "explained" entirely in terms of the characteristics of the stimuli. The individuals, if there are more than one, are merely replications of each other as far as any one set of data and the stimulus space it gives rise to are concerned.

The stimuli are presented to the subject in an experimental context which is intended to constrain and define the attribute space in which the behavior is generated. In the simplest case the experimenter instructs the subject to compare the stimuli with respect to some attribute—heaviness, brightness, strength of opinion, or aesthetic merit, for example. The instructions to the subject and the experimental procedure are designed to eliminate as much "noise" as possible in the specification of the attribute space. The reason for this is that generally stimuli may be evaluated with respect to many attributes, and individuals are, generally, capable of evaluating them with respect to many different characteristics.

For the experimenter to classify the stimuli, then, it is desirable that each stimulus correspond to a reasonably stable point in a space that is the same for all individuals or for the same individual under replication. Hence, in all instances of collecting data to generate a stimulus space the experimental controls and instructions to the subject are designed to constrain the space in which the stimulus points are to be localized. In a lifted weight experiment the experimenter's instructions on how to grasp and lift the weights, and so on, correspond, in an experiment on the scaling of aesthetic merit, to his attempt to delineate just what the attribute means. The correspondence between these examples lies in the intent of the experimenter to cut down the variability of a stimulus point over replications, particularly over individuals.

As we can see from the scale grid, the data for population spaces correspond in every way to the data for stimulus spaces, except that the characteristics and the function of the stimuli and the individuals are exchanged.* This means that in the experimental context we must reverse the roles of stimuli and people as they are found in stimulus spaces in order to obtain population spaces. In a stimulus space only the stimuli are identified with points, so in the population space only the individuals are to be identified with points. In the stimulus space, the experimenter-subject pair determines the attribute space in which the stimulus points are to be localized; so in the population space, the experimenter-stimulus pair determines the attribute space in which the individual points are to be localized. Do we ever collect such data? Of course, whenever we use open-end questionnaires, interviews, and essay examinations.

The individual comes into these situations with many characteristics; he is an r-tuple in a space of many dimensions, just as our attitude statement or painting may have been when we wanted to classify it on some characteristic. The experimenter-item pair must now come to the individual and constrain the attribute space within which the behavior is elicited, just as the experimenter-subject pair constrained and defined the space that was to represent attitude toward the British or aesthetic merit.

The editing of items and questions in mental tests and in surveys corresponds to the experimental controls in running a rat in an alternation experiment to ensure that he is affected only by the stimulus changes of interest to the experimenter.

---

* A duality between stimuli and individuals was first perceived, as far as I know, by Charles I. Mosier (1941). He interpreted this duality as a relation between psychophysics and mental test theory in the sense that the first seeks to measure the stimuli and the latter seeks to measure the individuals. The duality he was dealing with is between mental test theory and that section of psychophysics dealing with threshold measurement and signal detection, both in joint spaces (actually, in QIIa).

To abbreviate things somewhat, in stimulus spaces the individual comes to the experimental situation with an attribute in mind and the behavior reflects where the stimulus is. In population spaces the stimulus comes to the individual with an attribute in "mind" and the behavior reflects where the individual is.

It immediately follows, then, that all the experimental procedures, controls, and lore and all the models for making inferential classifications in one of these spaces are immediately transferable, at least in principle, to use in generating the other space. And to bring this transference about requires only that the roles (in the experimental context) and the symbols (in the models) for stimuli and individuals be exchanged.

A possible instance of such a transference of a model is provided by Thurstone's model for comparative judgment. The model is designed to process individuals' pairwise judgments of stimuli to secure a stimulus scale. The dual of this, then, would be to have stimuli make pair comparison judgments of individuals. This is what might be said to happen in a round-robin tennis tournament or in any competition between two individuals (or teams, for example, Mosteller, 1951). When two individuals play a tennis match, the stimulus, a game, may be said to make a pair comparison between the two individuals.

Another consequence of the duality between stimulus and population spaces is the following interpretation. We saw in Chapter 24 that Torgerson's model for categorical judgment is a model for handling a particular subset of the data for which Thurstone's model is designed. Hence, if there is a dual interpretation of Thurstone's model there should be a dual interpretation of Torgerson's. In Torgerson's original interpretation individuals sorted stimuli into ordered categories and the model scales the stimuli and the category boundaries.

The dual interpretation would be data in which stimuli have sorted individuals into ordered categories. This is exactly what is presumed when Likert-type items are used. The alternatives to a Likert-type item are monotonically ordered with respect to the attribute by definition. Each individual responds by choosing an alternative—so the item may be said to have sorted the people into piles, corresponding in number to the alternatives. (This use of Torgerson's model is discussed in Chapter 15.)

Models built for population spaces would also have their duals for stimulus spaces. Thus Lazarsfeld's latent structure analysis is designed in the context of population spaces but is potentially a model for the psychophysical laboratory. In the context of population spaces the model takes the responses of a large number of individuals to a relatively few stimuli and puts the individuals into latent classes, as Gibson's study reported in

Chapter 15 bears witness. By associating the operating characteristic with individuals rather than with items, the same model may be used to classify stimuli in latent classes. Why should it seem so strange that, to carry through the duality, we would take a large number of stimuli and relatively few people?

In general, the data usually collected to construct population spaces tend to be the single stimulus data of QII which, as we saw in Chapter 24, constitute a special kind of subset of QIII data. The reason for this limited source of data for population spaces lies in the very difficulty of having a stimulus compare two individuals. We sometimes have a stimulus compare two individuals indirectly by having each individual respond to the stimulus, as in an essay examination question or open-end questionnaire, and then taking the protocols of the different individuals and treating them as stimuli and constructing a "stimulus" space.

In order to draw a comparison between individuals from single stimulus data it is necessary that the experimenter-item pair arouse the same attribute space for all responding individuals in order that their protocols may be classified in the same stimulus space. A case in point is the use of play with negro and white dolls to arrive at individuals' attitudes toward negroes. Here the experimental situation and stimuli are all designed to arouse the same attribute space in the children so their behavior will reflect their attitude toward negroes. Otherwise, the comparison of different children's protocols on this attribute will not necessarily reflect the corresponding individuals' attitudes on the attribute.

In review of this duality between stimulus and population spaces, we find that the models and the experimental methodology in each have a dual interpretation in the other. From the duality between these two spaces in the scale grid we also see that models for joint spaces, QI and QII data, which make a distinction in these roles of individuals and stimuli, can be turned into dual models in which the roles are reversed. This is what we did above with Torgerson's model for categorical judgment and Lazarsfeld's latent structure analysis system.

Field Spaces

In joint spaces both people and stimuli are points and either or both may define and constrain the attribute space within which the behavior is generated. When we move in the scale grid from joint spaces to stimulus spaces the individuals cease to be points but are required to define the attribute space, as the stimuli do not. When we move from joint spaces to population spaces, the stimuli cease to be points but are required to define the attribute space, as the individuals do not. If, now, we make both moves at once, we have neither stimuli nor individuals as points in the space and neither is designed or instructed to define the attribute space.

How would we go about creating such an experimental situation?

We would want stimuli so amorphous that in combination with the rest of the experimental situation there would be no constraint or even suggestion of an attribute space by the experimenter-stimulus pair. We would want the subject to come to the experimental situation totally uninstructed to evaluate stimuli on any particular attribute space. How could we do this? Present the subject with an idealized "ink-blot," one that looked like nothing in experience, in an experimental situation in which interaction with either the stimulus or the experimenter would not constrain or be suggestive of some attribute space.

If either the experimenter or the stimulus constrained the attribute space we would have a population space. For example, if the experimenter aroused the subject by his manner or appearance, or if the ink blot was suggestive of some object, the effect would be to constrain the attribute space and to move toward a population space. The argument is that, if the experimenter or the stimulus tends to select an attribute space because of some characteristic he or it possesses, this tends to be the case for all subjects and their behavior will reflect their locus *in the same space*, and hence a population space.

There are many examples of this technique in which the attribute is presumed to be common (but implicit): Proshansky's Labor TAT, Johnson's Anglo-Spanish TAT, McClelland's Need-Achievement pictures, and so on. An essay examination or a questionnaire is an example in which the attribute space is common but explicit.

The consequence of the attribute space being common is that the individuals are all points in a common space, a population space, and so they may be compared with each other.

If we satisfy the conditions for field spaces, what is different? Here the individual has no one but himself to rely on to choose the relevant attribute space, and his behavior will reflect the attribute space he selects. There is here, then, no reason why different individuals should choose the same attribute space, and so individuals are likely to reflect different spaces and not be comparable. The experimenter is in the position of comparing the answers in the essay examinations of two individuals and *he does not know what the questions were or even if they were the same*.

The problem of the experimenter-clinician is to evaluate a protocol to infer the attribute space, the locus of the individual's point in that space, and then to interpret these inferences. For example, he must detect that the relevant attribute space in one instance is guilt feelings, how much guilt the subject is expressing, and what it signifies that he should express guilt. As difficult as the first two problems are, the latter is even more so. Does a subject reveal the most salient attribute space for him at that moment, or the one in which his point locus is most extreme, or what? What does it mean that a particular attribute space was revealed?

At present I know no answers to these questions. The protocol of a respondent in a field space situation is itself only slightly removed from an ink blot presented to the clinician! Because there was nothing in the experimenter-stimulus complex to permit inferring that a particular attribute space was aroused, the protocol becomes a projective instrument for the interpreter. What the interpreter perceives in a protocol is based on his theory and experience and may reflect him instead of, or at least as well as, the respondent.

The protocol is recorded behavior that has not yet been transformed into data. The behavior in field spaces is not yet data. There are no points or relations on points. The experimenter-clinician is faced with converting the behavior into data (see phase 2 of Fig. 1.1), and this mapping is necessary before any of the logical systems for inferential classification may be used.

Observations (behavior) in field spaces are uniquely different from those in joint, stimulus, and population spaces. In these latter there is a built-in constraint on the attribute space—so we always have interindividual or interstimulus comparability. Only in field spaces do we allow the subject to pick the attribute space freely.

That the kind of behavior observed in field spaces is significant and important for psychology cannot be overemphasized. *It is the only kind of space in which the behavior reflects intra-individual dynamics.* According to the theory of data, an individual's behavior reflects a relation on points in a space of relevant dimensions. If there is nothing in the external stimulus situation guiding the selection of the set of relevant dimensions, the selection has to be made by the subject and this is why the behavior reflects intra-individual dynamics.

In population spaces the behavior yields interindividual comparability on previously selected attributes, though they may be implicit. In stimulus spaces the behavior yields interstimulus comparability on previously selected attributes. In joint spaces we get both interindividual and interstimulus comparability on previously selected attributes. *Only in field spaces is the behavior generated in an attribute space freely selected by the individual. But only in stimulus, population, and joint spaces do we have well-constructed and testable inferential classification systems.*

It might seem that the new methods developed for QIVa multidimensional analysis will permit an experimental attack on the problem of interpreting field space data. A subject, in generating similarities data, is free to choose the attribute space which is relevant because the explicit attribute he is evaluating is "distance": The models then permit us to infer an attribute space. I am not at all sanguine about this. In all instances in which similarities data are collected the attribute space is certainly strongly influenced by the stimuli. Psychologically this stimulus control of the relevant dimensions would have to be eliminated completely to obtain field space behavior.

My feeling is that when psychologists know how to interpret observations in field spaces they will no longer have any other problems. This is not meant to be disparaging nor discouraging but to put the difficulties of our problems in perspective.

5. SUMMARY

This chapter presents another way of organizing or systematizing the various kinds of psychological data in something of a real world context. The system presented here is intended to point up the similarities and differences among the various *substantive* areas of psychological research from the point of view of their methodologies.

The scale grid distinguishes nine different classes of data which are classified as corresponding to four kinds of spaces: joint, stimulus, population, and field spaces.

The first section deals only with joint spaces. The classes of data which are analyzed to yield joint spaces all come from QI or QII and are distinguished from each other in terms of two dimensions. These two dimensions pertain to the components of the variability of the loci of the points in the joint space. One dimension pertains to the variability of the individual points, the other to the variability of the stimulus points. The components of the variance of a set of points are the "within" and "between" components with respect to the elements of the other set.

The classes of data which are found in joint spaces are classes 1, 2, 3, and 5, and each of these is illustrated and interpreted; some of the problems of analyzing the data peculiar to each are discussed.

Joint spaces, in general, are constructed by putting pieces together from different individuals' data corresponding to different "views" of the space in contrast to stimulus spaces where each individual's data gives a picture of the entire space from the same "view" and the problem is to merge them into a "best" single picture.

Stimulus spaces are discussed in Section 2. The classes of data for such spaces are classes 4 and 7, identified with QIII and QIV, distinguished in terms of the components of the variance of stimulus points only. Problems in the methods of analysis peculiar to the classes and their subclasses are discussed.

The distinction between joint and stimulus spaces in terms of the presence and absence of individual points constitutes the third dimension of the scale grid and the presence or absence of stimulus points constitutes the fourth dimension. The conjunction of the third and fourth dimension generates two additional kinds of spaces called population and field spaces. Population spaces have a dual correspondence to stimulus spaces.

The interpretation of field spaces is one of the prime objectives of the chapter. This interpretation is approached by first interpreting stimulus spaces as the product of data obtained by having individuals define the space of relevant attributes in which the stimuli correspond to the points. The duality with population spaces lies in the fact that they are the result of data in which the stimuli (essay questions, open-end questionnaires, interviews, and so on) define the space of relevant attributes in which the individuals correspond to the points. In each case, the elements which define the attribute space do not correspond to points in the space.

The implications of this duality for the correspondences between methodologies and models is pointed out.

Joint spaces are generated from data in which both sets of elements correspond to points and either or both may define the attribute space. As we move through the scale grid through both population and stimulus spaces to reach field spaces, the points for stimuli and individuals drop out and neither set is designed or instructed to constrain and define the attribute space. Then the individual, to react, must select an attribute space. The protocol that emerges reflects this attribute space.

The problem of the experimenter-clinician is to infer this attribute space and the locus of the individual point in it and to interpret these inferences.

The behavior of the subject in field spaces is of prime psychological significance because it reflects his internal dynamic psychology in a way that none of the other kinds of spaces do. But these field spaces are not data, in the sense of the theory of data, in that there are as yet no points and no relations on points. The protocols are recorded observations, in the sense of Fig. 1.1, and have not yet undergone the process of mapping observations into data, phase 2.

These protocols, then, are "ink blots" to the experimenter-clinician, and only his theory and experience leads him to interpret them as data. So the data which are ultimately analyzed may reflect the interpreter as much as the behavior.

The observations of behavior which lead to joint, stimulus, and population spaces are all attribute-constrained, and the interpretations that lead to data permit interpersonal or interstimulus comparisons or both because all points are in the same space.

The behavior that is emitted in field spaces, it is argued, is intrinsically intrapersonal, because nothing in the experimenter-stimulus situation ensures that the different individuals will be in the same space. There is no reason, of 'course, why two protocols cannot be compared on the degree of guilt feelings they express, but the interpretation that this reflects differences between the individuals in guilt feelings is hardly admissible if that attribute space was not relevant for both protocols.

REFERENCES

Coombs, C. H., 1952, A theory of psychological scaling, *Engng. Res. Inst. Bull.*, *No.* 34, University of Michigan Press, Ann Arbor.
Coombs, C. H., 1956, The scale grid: some interrelations of data models, *Psychometrika*, **21**, 313–29.
Mosier, C. I., 1941, Psychophysics and mental test theory: fundamental postulates and elementary theorems, *Psychol. Rev.*, **47**, 355–66.
Mosteller, F., 1951, Remarks on the method of paired comparisons: II. The effect of an aberrant standard deviation when equal standard deviations and equal correlations are assumed, *Psychometrika*, **16**, 203–18.

CHAPTER 26

Relation to an Earlier Formulation of a Theory of Data

1. THE EARLIER FORMULATION

An earlier formulation of a theory of data (Coombs, 1953) may be regarded as an interpretation of this more abstract one. The earlier formulation is closer to the operational and practical world of measurement, so it perhaps will serve as a connecting link between the two. I shall first present the essentials of the earlier formulation and then the correspondences between it and the theory as presented in Chapter 1.

The old theory conceived of all behavioral data as satisfying three dichotomies: (1) task A or task B, (2) relative or irrelative, and (3) involving monotone or nonmonotone stimuli. These dichotomies will be discussed in turn.

The basic idea of the distinction between tasks A and B is that an individual's behavior either reflects the relation of stimuli to himself (task A) or the relation of stimuli to an attribute (task B). If we ask an individual which of several kinds of candy he prefers, we might expect him to relate the stimuli to a reference ideal identified with himself, that is, task A behavior. If, however, we ask an individual which kind of candy is sweeter, we might expect him to relate the stimuli to the attribute, that is, task B behavior.

The idea is that there are only two things an individual can do with stimuli, relate them to an ideal point or relate them to an attribute. Task A refers to the evaluation of a stimulus with respect to an ideal, and task B refers to the evaluation of a stimulus with respect to an attribute.

The terms "evaluative" and "substantive" might have been used instead of the meaningless A and B but I was afraid of surplus meanings. Torgerson

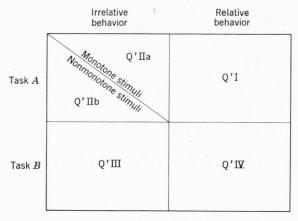

Fig. 26.1

(1958) uses the terms "responses" and "judgments" for tasks A and B respectively,* which I think are even more misleading, particularly as Guilford (1954) uses these terms in the context of a response continuum as an intervening variable between a judgment continuum and a stimulus (physical) continuum.

A second dichotomy which the earlier theory proposed for all behavior is that behavior is either relative or irrelative. In relative behavior the data reflect a relation between two or more stimuli; in irrelative behavior they involve a single stimulus at a time. To ask an individual which of two candidates he prefers is task A, relative. To ask which of two colors is the more saturated is task B, relative. To ask an individual whether he would endorse a particular candidate or not is task A, irrelative. To ask whether a particular color is red is task B, irrelative.

These two dichotomies yield a fourfold table, as illustrated in Fig. 26.1, in which the third dichotomy is also illustrated. The various quadrants so formed are designated with primes in order to avoid confusion with the quadrants in Fig. 1.2.

It will be observed that the Q'II has been divided by a dichotomy between monotone and nonmonotone stimuli. Let us first be clear on what Q'II is. Task A is evaluation of stimuli with respect to an ideal, and irrelative behavior means one stimulus at a time. So this is represented by such things as working arithmetic problems and endorsing statements of opinion. The monotone versus nonmonotone dichotomy may be illustrated as follows.

If an individual responds positively to a monotone item, he will respond

* His reference to Tasks A and B (p. 48) has them reversed.

positively to any item whose scale value is lower. A monotone item with two alternatives, then, dichotomizes a continuum; individuals below some particular point all respond one way and individuals above that point respond another way.

If an individual responds positively to a nonmonotone item he will not necessarily respond positively to items on one side of it. A nonmonotone item with two alternatives trichotomizes a continuum. An intermediate segment of the continuum contains those individuals who respond positively, and the end segments contain those individuals who respond negatively.

For example, if an individual passes an arithmetic problem, will he be as apt to pass an easier one? If the answer is "yes," the stimuli are assumed to be monotone. If an individual endorses a statement favoring athletic scholarships, will he be as apt to endorse it if it is made less extreme? If the answer is "no," the stimulus is assumed to be nonmonotone.

This same distinction has been made many times. Thurstone (Thurstone and Chave, 1929) speaks of two types of tests, "increasing probability" and "maximum probability." Loevinger (1948) uses the terms "cumulative" and "differential." These correspond respectively to what I called "monotone" and "nonmonotone" items and which now correspond to the "order relation-proximity relation" dichotomy in the new theory of data.

2. CORRESPONDENCES BETWEEN OLD AND NEW THEORIES

The correspondences are summarized in Table 26.1.

The notion of task A and task B behavior is captured in the new theory

Table 26.1 Correspondences between Old and
New Theories of Data

Old Theory	New Theory
Q′I	QIa
Q′IIa	QIIa
Q′IIb	QIIb
Q′III	QIIa, QIIb
Q′IV	QIIIa, QIIIb, QIVa, QIVb

with the idea of there being points associated with two distinct sets of objects or one set, respectively. This, in fact, is the reason for my using the labels A and B to denote the set $C \times Q$ and the set $Q \times Q$, respectively, in Chapter 1.

The contrast between irrelative and relative corresponds to the distinction between the method of single stimuli (QII) and the methods of choice which include QI, QIII, and QIV.

The monotone-nonmonotone dichotomy has been captured in the notion of the order or proximity relation in the new theory and applied to all quadrants, not just Q′II. There is nothing in the old theory that corresponds to QIb in the new, but I must admit it has never been missed.

One of the major differences may be described as follows. The old theory divided single stimulus data between two quadrants: Q′II covered single stimulus data in which the individual evaluated stimuli with respect to his ideal point, and Q′III covered methods of absolute judgment, rating scale methods, and category scaling.

We now recognize that in Q′II and Q′III there are two sets of points, and if we neglect their real world identifications we can merge these two quadrants into the new QII. It makes no difference in the formal relations between points whether an individual endorses a statement of opinion or assigns a descriptive adjective to a foreman. In each case we have a proximity relation on a pair of points from distinct sets.

I do not mean to suggest, of course, that the real world distinctions are unimportant; rather, in fact, I wish to take advantage of them by pointing out the formal equivalences of different real world distinctions so that the developments related to one might be utilized by the other.

The other major difference between the old and new theories is in the greater refinement or discrimination to be seen in partitioning the old Q′IV into four different octants of the new theory.

The only advantage the old theory has is its closer association to the actual behavior of subjects in psychological experiments, which makes it more readily grasped but at the same time inhibits it badly. Phase 2, mapping behavior into data, is far less flexible and even less obvious in the old theory. The assumptions being made in the miniature behavior theories that make data out of observations are hidden. The more abstract formulation of the new theory is more general, more flexible, and more discriminating.

3. SUMMARY

This brief and final chapter relates an earlier formulation of the theory of data to the current one as presented in Chapter 1. The old formulation has the advantage of being more concrete and more closely tied to the actual operations of psychological data collecting.

The old theory makes some discriminations that are unnecessary, for example, between the method of single stimuli in which individuals relate stimuli to themselves and the method of absolute judgment in which individuals relate stimuli to categories of an attribute. It fails to make a distinction between what in the new theory are called stimulus comparison data and similarities data.

The more abstract form of the newer theory permits a more ready flow between various areas of psychological research and makes more visible the creative part the scientist plays in making data out of his observations.

REFERENCES

Coombs, C. H., 1953, "Theory and methods of social measurement," Chapter 11 in *Research methods in the behavioral sciences*, edited by L. Festinger and D. Katz, The Dryden Press, New York.

Guilford, J. P., 1954, *Psychometric methods*, second edition, McGraw-Hill Book Co., New York.

Loevinger, Jane, 1948, The technic of homogeneous tests compared with some aspects of "scale analysis" and factor analysis, *Pyschol. Bull.*, **45**, 507–29.

Thurstone, L. L., and E. J. Chave, 1929, *The measure of attitudes*, University of Chicago Press, Chicago.

Torgerson, W. S., 1958, *Theory and methods of scaling*, John Wiley and Sons, New York.

Bibliography

Abelson, R. P., 1954, A technique and a model for multidimensional attitude scaling, *Publ. Opin. Quart.*, **18**, 405–418.

Abelson, R. P., 1958, Purposes of scaling techniques and the choice among them, paper delivered at the American Statistical Association meeting, December, 1958.

Abelson, R. P., and J. W. Tukey, 1959, Efficient conversion of non-metric information into metric information, paper presented at the American Statistical Association, Social Sciences Section, December 1959.

Anderson, T. W., 1954, On estimation of parameters in latent structure analysis, *Psychometrika*, **19**, 1–10.

Anderson, T. W., 1958, *An introduction to multivariance statistical analysis*, John Wiley and Sons, New York.

Arrow, K. J., 1951, *Social choice and individual values*, Cowles Commission Monograph 12, John Wiley and Sons, New York.

Attneave, F., 1949, A method of graded dichotomies for the scaling of judgments, *Psychol. Rev.*, **56**, 334–40.

Attneave, F., 1950, Dimensions of similarity, *Amer. J. Psychol.*, **63**, 516–56.

Bartlett, F. C., 1932, *Remembering: a study in experimental and social psychology*, The Macmillan Co., New York.

Beardslee, D. C., 1957, An empirical study of the measurement of psychological distance, unpublished Ph.D. dissertation, University of Michigan.

Becker, S. W., and S. Siegel, 1962, Utility and level of aspiration, *Amer. J. Psychol.*, **75**, 115–20.

Bennett, J. F., 1956, Determination of the number of independent parameters of a score matrix from the examination of rank orders, *Psychometrika*, **21**, 383–93.

Bennett, J. F., and W. L. Hays, 1960, Multidimensional unfolding: determining the dimensionality of ranked preference data, *Psychometrika*, **25**, 27–43.

Bentley, M., 1950, Early and late metric uses of the term "distance," *Amer. J. Psychol.*, **63**, 619.

Birnbaum, A., 1957a, *Probability and statistics in item analysis and classification problems. On the estimation of mental ability*, Ser. Rep. No. 58-15, USAF School of Aviation Medicine, Randolph AFB, Texas.

Birnbaum, A., 1957*b*, *Probability and statistics in item analysis and classification problems. Efficient design and use of tests of mental ability for various decision-making problems*, Ser. Rep. No. 58-16, USAF School of Aviation Medicine, Randolph AFB, Texas.

Birnbaum, A., 1957*c*, *Probability and statistics in item analysis and classification problems. Further considerations of efficiency in tests of mental ability*, Ser. Rep. No. 58-17, USAF School of Aviation Medicine, Randolph AFB, Texas.

Black, D., 1948*a*, On the rationale of group decision making, *J. pol. Econ.*, **56**, 23–34.

Black, D., 1948*b*, The decisions of a committee using a special majority, *Econometrica*, **16**, 245–61.

Blau, J. H., 1957, The existence of social welfare functions, *Econometrica*, **25**, 302–313.

Boring, E. G., 1950, *A history of experimental psychology*, second edition, Appleton-Century-Crofts, New York.

Boring, E. G., 1953, The role of theory in experimental psychology, *Amer. J. Psychol.*, **66**, 169–84.

Bose, R. C., 1960, "On a method of constructing Steiner's triple systems," Chapter 11 in *Contributions to probability and statistics*, edited by I. Olkin et al., Stanford University Press, Stanford.

Bower, G. H., 1960, Response strengths and choice probability: a consideration of two combination rules, Institute for Mathematical Studies in the Social Sciences, *Stanford Univer. Tech. Rep. No.* 36, December 19, 1960.

Bradley, R. A., 1954, Incomplete block rank analysis: on appropriateness of the model for a method of paired comparisons, *Biometrics*, **10**, 375–90.

Bradley, R. A., and M. E. Terry, 1952, Rank analysis of incomplete block designs: I. The method of paired comparisons, *Biometrika*, **39**, 324–45.

Bruner, J. S., J. J. Goodnow, and G. A. Austin, 1956, *A study of thinking*, John Wiley and Sons, New York.

Brunk, H. D., 1960, Mathematical models for ranking from paired comparisons, *J. Amer. statist. Ass.*, **55**, 503–20.

Campbell, N. R., 1920, *Physics: the elements*, Cambridge University Press, London. Also published in paperback under the title *Foundations of science* by Dover Publications, New York, S372, 1957.

Carmichael, L., H. P. Hogan, and A. A. Walter, 1932, An experimental study of the effect of language on the reproduction of visually perceived form, *J. exp. Psychol.*, **15**, 73–86.

Cartwright, D., and F. Harary, 1956, Structural balance: a generalization of Heider's theory, *Psychol. Rev.*, **63**, 277–93.

Clarke, F. R., 1957, Constant-ratio rule for confusion matrices in speech communication, *J. acoust. Soc. Amer.*, **29**, 715–20.

Cochran, W. G., and G. M. Cox, 1957, *Experimental designs*, second edition, John Wiley and Sons, New York.

Comrey, A. L., 1950, A proposed method for absolute ratio scaling, *Psychometrika*, **15**, 317–25.

Coombs, C. H., 1948, Some hypotheses for the analysis of qualitative variables, *Psychol. Rev.*, **55**, 167–74.

Coombs, C. H., 1952, A theory of psychological scaling, *Engng. Res. Inst. Bull. No.* 34, University of Michigan Press, Ann Arbor.

Coombs, C. H., 1953, "Theory and methods of social measurement," Chapter 11 in *Research methods in the behavioral sciences*, edited by L. Festinger and D. Katz, The Dryden Press, New York.

Coombs, C. H., 1954, A method for the study of interstimulus similarity, *Psychometrika*, **19**, 183–94.

Coombs, C. H., 1956, The scale grid: some interrelations of data models, *Psychometrika*, **21**, 313–29.

Coombs, C. H., 1958a, On the use of inconsistency of preferences in psychological measurement, *J. exp. Psychol.*, **55**, 1–7.

Coombs, C. H., 1958b, An application of a nonmetric model for multidimensional analysis of similarities, *Psychol. Reps.*, **4**, 511–18.

Coombs, C. H., 1960, A theory of data, *Psychol. Rev.*, **67**, 143–159.

Coombs, C. H., M. Greenberg, and J. L. Zinnes, 1961, A double law of comparative judgment for the analysis of preferential choice and similarities data, *Psychometrika*, **26**, 165–71.

Coombs, C. H., and R. C. Kao, 1955, Nonmetric factor analysis, *Engng. Res. Bull. No. 38*, University of Michigan Press, Ann Arbor.

Coombs, C. H., and R. C. Kao, 1960, On a connection between factor analysis and multidimensional unfolding, *Psychometrika*, **25**, 219–31.

Coombs, C. H., and S. S. Komorita, 1958, Measuring utility of money through decisions, *Amer. J. Psychol.*, **71**, 383–89.

Coombs, C. H., and D. Pruitt, 1960, Components of risk in decision making: probability and variance preferences, *J. exp. Psychol.*, **60**, 265–77.

Coombs, C. H., and D. Pruitt, 1961, Some characteristics of choice behavior in risky situations, *Ann. New York Acad. Sci.*, **89**, 784–94.

Coombs, C. H., H. Raiffa, and R. M. Thrall, 1954, Some views on mathematical models and measurement theory, *Psychol. Rev.*, **61**, 132–44.

Cronbach, L. J., and G. C. Gleser, 1953, Assessing similarity between profiles, *Psychol. Bull.*, **50**, 456–73.

Cronbach, L. J., and G. C. Gleser, 1961, Quantal and graded analysis of dosage-effect relations, *Science*, **133**, 1924–25.

Dashiell, J. F., 1937, Affective value-distances as a determinant of esthetic judgement-times, *Amer. J. Psychol.*, **50**, 57–67.

Davidson, D., P. Suppes, and S. Siegel, 1957, *Decision making: an experimental approach*, Stanford University Press, Stanford.

Dawes, R. M., 1964, Social selection based on multidimensional criteria, *J. abnorm. soc. Psychol.*, **68**, No. 1.

Dember, W. N., 1955, Decision-time and psychological distance, unpublished Ph.D. dissertation, University of Michigan.

Dember, W. N., 1957, The relation of decision-time to stimulus similarity, *J. exp. Psychol.*, **53**, 68–72.

Dember, W. N., 1960, *The psychology of perception*, Holt, Rinehart and Winston, New York.

Dember, W. N., and R. W. Earl, 1957, Analysis of exploratory, manipulatory, and curiosity behavior, *Psychol. Rev.*, **64**, 91–96.

Dember, W. N., R. W. Earl, and N. Paradise, 1957, Response by rats to differential stimulus complexity, *J. comp. physiol. Psychol.*, **50**, 514–18.

De Soto, C. B., and J. J. Bosley, 1962, The cognitive structure of a social structure, *J. abnorm. soc. Psychol.*, **64**, 303–307.

Diederich, G. W., S. J. Messick, and L. R. Tucker, 1957, A general least squares solution for successive intervals, *Psychometrika*, **22**, 159–73.

Durbin, J., 1951, Incomplete blocks in ranking experiments, *British J. Psychol., statist. sect.*, **4**, 85–90.

Earl, R. W., 1957, Problem solving and motor skill behaviors under conditions of free choice, unpublished Ph.D. dissertation, University of Michigan.

Easterbrook, J. A., 1959, The effect of emotion on cue utilization and the organization of behavior, *Psychol. Rev.*, **66**, 183–201.

Edwards, A. L., 1952, The scaling of stimuli by the method of successive intervals, *J. appl. Psychol.*, **36**, 118–22.

Edwards, W., 1955, The prediction of decisions among bets, *J. exp. Psychol.*, **50**, 201–14.

Ekman, G., 1954, Dimensions of color vision, *J. Psychol.*, **38**, 467–74.

Eninger, M. U., 1952, Habit summation in a selective learning problem, *J. comp. physiol. Psychol.*, **45**, 604–608.

Festinger, L., and D. Katz, 1953, *Research methods in the behavioral sciences*, The Dryden Press, New York.

Fix, E., 1949, Table of non-central χ^2, *Univer. California Publ. Statist.*, **1**, 15–19.

Ford, L. R., Jr., 1957, Solution of a ranking problem from binary comparisons, *Amer. math. Mon.*, **64**, 28–33.

Galanter, E. H., 1956, An axiomatic and experimental study of sensory order and measure, *Psychol. Rev.*, **63**, 16–28.

Garner, W. R., 1958, Advantages of the discriminability criterion for a loudness scale, *J. acoust. Soc. Amer.*, **30**, 1005–12.

Garner, W. R., 1962, *Uncertainty and structure as psychological concepts*, John Wiley and Sons, New York.

Garner, W. R., and H. W. Hake, 1951, The amount of information in absolute judgments, *Psychol. Rev.*, **58**, 446–59.

Gibson, J. J., 1960, The concept of the stimulus in psychology, *Amer. Psychologist*, **15**, 694–703.

Gibson, W. A., 1955, An extension of Anderson's solution for the latent structure equations, *Psychometrika*, **20**, 69–73.

Gibson, W. A., 1959, Three multivariate models: factor analysis, latent structure analysis, and latent profile analysis, *Psychometrika*, **24**, 229–52.

Glanzer, M., and R. Glaser, 1959, Techniques for the study of group structure and behavior: I. Analysis of structure, *Psychol. Bull.*, **56**, 317–32.

Goldberg, D., and C. H. Coombs, 1963, Some applications of unfolding theory to fertility analysis, paper no. 5 at Milbank Memorial Fund Roundtable on Emerging Techniques in Population Research, New York, Fall 1963.

Goodman, L. A., 1959, Simple statistical methods for scalogram analysis, *Psychometrika*, **24**, 29–43.

Goodman, N., 1951, *The structure of appearance*, Harvard University Press, Cambridge, Mass.

Green, B. F., Jr., 1951, A general solution for the latent class model of latent structure analysis, *Psychometrika*, **16**, 151–66.

Green, B. F., Jr., 1952, Latent structure analysis and its relation to factor analysis, *J. Amer. statist. Ass.*, **47**, 71–76.

Green, B. F., Jr., 1954, "Attitude measurement," Chapter 9 in *Handbook of social psychology*, I. *Theory and method*, edited by Gardner Lindzey, Addison-Wesley Publishing Co., Reading, Mass.

Green, B. F., Jr., 1960, "A technical note on the method of successive categories using category means," Chapter 5 in *Psychological scaling: theory and applications*, edited by H. Gulliksen and S. Messick, John Wiley and Sons, New York.

Green, B. F., Jr., and Lois K. Anderson, 1955, The tactual identification of shapes for coding switch handles, *J. appl. Psychol.*, **39**, 219–26.

Greenberg, M. G., 1961, Response latency as a test of mathematical models for preference behavior, unpublished Ph.D. dissertation, University of Michigan.

Greenberg, M G., 1963, *J* scale models for preference behavior, *Psychometrika*, **28**, 265–71.

Guilford, J. P., 1954, *Psychometric methods*, second edition, McGraw-Hill Book Co., New York.

Gulliksen, H., and L. R. Tucker, 1961, A general procedure for obtaining paired comparisons from multiple rank orders, *Psychometrika*, **26**, 173–83.

Guttman, L., 1944, A basis for scaling qualitative data, *Amer. sociol. Rev.*, **9**, 139–50.

Guttman, L., 1950, Chapters 2, 3, 6, 8, and 9 in *Measurement and prediction*, edited by Stouffer et al., Princeton University Press, Princeton.

Guttman, N., and H. I. Kalish, 1956, Discriminability and stimulus generalization, *J. exp. Psychol.*, **51**, 79–88.

Hanani, H., 1961, The existence and construction of balanced incomplete block designs, *Ann. math. Statist.*, **32**, 361–86.

Hanson, N. R., 1958, *Patterns of discovery*, University Press, Cambridge, England.

Harary, F., and I. C. Ross, 1957, A procedure of clique detection using the group matrix, *Sociometry*, **20**, 205–15.

Hayek, F. A., 1952, *The sensory order*, University of Chicago Press, Chicago.

Hays, D. G., and E. F. Borgatta, 1954, An empirical comparison of restricted and general latent distance analysis, *Psychometrika*, **19**, 271–79.

Hays, W. L., and J. F. Bennett, 1961, Multidimensional unfolding: determining configuration from complete rank order preference data, *Psychometrika*, **26**, 221–38.

Hefner, R. A., 1958, Extensions of the law of comparative judgment to discriminable and multidimensional stimuli, unpublished Ph.D. dissertation, University of Michigan.

Helm, C. E., 1960, A successive intervals analysis of color differences, Educational Testing Service Technical Report, Princeton, November 1960.

Helm, C. E., S. Messick, and L. R. Tucker, 1961, Psychological models for relating discrimination and magnitude estimation scales, *Psychol. Rev.*, **68**, 167–77.

Henning, H., 1916, *Der Geruch*, Barth, Leipzig.

Horst, A. P., 1932, A method for determining the absolute affective value of a series of stimulus situations, *J. educ. Psychol.*, **23**, 418–40.

Householder, A. S., and H. D. Landahl, 1945, *Mathematical biophysics of the central nervous system*, Principia Press, Bloomington, Ind.

Hovland, C. I., O. J. Harvey, and M. Sherif, 1957, Assimilation and contrast effects in reactions to communication and attitude change, *J. abnorm. soc. Psychol.*, **55**, 244–52.

Hull, C. L., 1943, *Principles of behavior: an introduction to behavior*, Appleton-Century-Crofts, New York.

Huntington, E. V., 1938, A paradox in the scoring of competing teams, *Science*, **88**, 287–88.

Hutt, P. J., 1954, Rate of bar pressing as a function of quality and quantity of food reward, *J. comp. physiol. Psychol.*, **47**, 235–39.

Indow, T., and T. Uchizono, 1960, Multidimensional mapping of Munsell colors varying in hue and chroma, *J. exp. Psychol.*, **59**, 321–29.

Johnson, H. M., 1935, Some neglected principles in aptitude-testing, *Amer. J. Psychol.*, **47**, 159–65.

Jones, F. N., and Maxine J. Marcus, 1961, The subject effect in judgments of subjective magnitude, *J. exp. Psychol.*, **61**, 40–44.

Jordan, K., 1947, *The calculus of finite differences*, Chelsea Publishing Co., New York.

Kaiser, H., 1962, Scaling a simplex, *Psychometrika*, **27**, 155–62.

Kamenetzky, J., and H. Schmidt, 1957, Effects of personal and impersonal refutation of audience counterarguments on attitude change, *J. abnorm. soc. Psychol.*, **54**, 200–203.

Katz, L., and J. H. Powell, 1957, Probability distributions of random variables associated with a structure of the sample space of sociometric investigations, *Ann. math. Statist.*, **28**, 442–49.

Kelley, H., 1950, The warm-cold variable in first impressions of persons, *J. Pers.*, **18**, 431–39.

Kemeny, J. G., 1959, Mathematics without numbers, *Dædalus*, **88**, 577–91.

Kemeny, J. G., 1962, Needed: well-rounded colleges, *New York Times Mag.*, March 25, 1962.

Kendall, M. G., 1955, *Rank correlation methods*, second edition, Hafner Publishing Co., New York.

Kershner, R. B., and L. R. Wilcox, 1950, *The anatomy of mathematics*, Ronald Press Co., New York.

Komorita, S. S., 1958, Probability learning under equivalent data collection methods, *J. exp. Psychol.*, **55**, 115–20.

Landahl, H. D., 1945, Neural mechanisms for the concepts of difference and similarity, *Bull. math. Biophys.*, **7**, 83–88.

Lazarsfeld, P. F., 1959, "Latent structure analysis," in *Psychology: a study of a science*, vol. 3, edited by S. Koch, McGraw-Hill Book Co., New York.

Lemaine, J.-M., 1959, Similitude cognitive et relations interpersonnelles, *Psychol. Franç.*, **4**, 102–16.

Levin, J., 1961, A least square fit to a simplex, paper read at Amer. Psychol. Ass., New York, September 1961.

Likert, R., 1932, A technique for the measurement of attitudes, *Arch. Psychol., N.Y.*, No. 140, 55.

Lindzey, G., editor, 1954, *Handbook of social psychology*. Vol. II. *Special fields and applications*, Addison-Wesley Publishing Co., Cambridge, Mass.

Loevinger, Jane, 1948, The technic of homogeneous tests compared with some aspects of "scale analysis" and factor analysis, *Psychol. Bull.*, **45**, 507–29.

Loevinger, Jane, 1957, Objective tests as instruments of psychological theory, *Psychol. Reps., Monogr. Suppl. No. 9.*

Lord, F. M., 1953, An application of confidence intervals and of maximum likelihood to the estimation of an examinee's ability, *Psychometrika*, **18**, 57–77.

Lorge, I., and H. Solomon, 1955, Two models of group behavior in the solution of eureka-type problems, *Psychometrika*, **20**, 139–48.

Luce, R. D., 1959, *Individual choice behavior*, John Wiley and Sons, New York.

Luce, R. D., 1961, A choice theory analysis of similarity judgments, *Psychometrika*, **26**, 151–64.

Luce, R. D., and H. Raiffa, 1957, *Games and decisions*, John Wiley and Sons, New York.

McElwain, D. W., and J. A. Keats, 1961, Multidimensional unfolding: some geometrical solutions, *Psychometrika*, **26**, 325–32.

McGill, W. J., 1954, Multivariate information transmission, *Psychometrika*, **19**, 97–116.

MacKay, D. M., 1950, Quantal aspects of scientific information, *Phil. Mag.*, **41**, 289–311.

McRae, D., Jr., 1956, An exponential model for assessing four-fold tables, *Sociometry*, **19**, 84–93.

Margenau, H., 1959, "Philosophical problems concerning the meaning of measurement in physics," in *Measurement: definitions and theories*, edited by C. W. Churchman and P. Ratoosh, John Wiley and Sons, New York, pp. 163–76.

Mellinger, J., 1956, Some attributes of color perception, unpublished Ph.D. dissertation, University of North Carolina.

Messick, S. J., 1956, The perception of social attitudes, *J. abnorm. soc. Psychol.*, **52**, 57–66.

Messick, S. J., and R. P. Abelson, 1956, The additive constant problem in multidimensional scaling, *Psychometrika*, **21**, 1–15.

Metfessel, M., 1947, A proposal for quantitative reporting of comparative judgments, *J. Psychol.*, **24**, 229–35.

Milholland, J. E., 1953, Dimensionality of response patterns, unpublished Ph.D. dissertation, University of Michigan.

Milholland, J. E., 1955, Four kinds of reproducibility in scale analysis, *Educ. psychol. Measmt.*, **15**, 478–82.

Miller, G. A., E. Galanter, and K. H. Pribram, 1960, *Plans and the structure of behavior*, Holt, Rinehart and Winston, New York.

Miller, G. A., and P. E. Nicely, 1955, An analysis of perceptual confusion, *J. acoust. Soc. Amer.*, **27**, 338–52.

Miller, J., 1939, The rate of conditioning of human subjects to single and multiple conditioned stimuli, *J. gen. Psychol.*, **20**, 399–408.

Milnor, J., 1954, "Games against nature," Chapter 4 in *Decision processes*, edited by R. M. Thrall, C. H. Coombs, and R. L. Davis, John Wiley and Sons, New York.

Mosier, C. I., 1940, A modification of the method of successive intervals, *Psychometrika*, **5**, 101–107.

Mosier, C. I., 1941, Psychophysics and mental test theory: fundamental postulates and elementary theorems, *Psychol. Rev.*, **47**, 355–66.

Mosteller, F., 1949, A theory of scalogram analysis using noncumulative types of items, unpublished manuscript, Laboratory of Social Relations, Harvard University, Reprint no. 9.

Mosteller, F., 1951, Remarks on the method of paired comparisons: II. The effect of an aberrant standard deviation when equal standard deviations and equal correlations are assumed, *Psychometrika*, **16**, 203–18.

Muenzinger, K. F., and M. Fletcher, 1936, Motivation in learning: VI. Escape from electric shock compared with hunger-food tension in the visual discrimination habit, *J. comp. Psychol.*, **22**, 79–91.

Osgood, C. E., and K. Wilson, 1957, Some terms and associated measures for studying human communication, unpublished manuscript, Institute of Communications Research, University of Illinois.

Patnaik, P. B., 1949, The non-central χ^2 and F-distributions and their applications, *Biometrika*, **36**, 202–32.

Polya, G., 1954, *Induction and analogy in mathematics*, Princeton University Press, Princeton.

Powloski, R. F., 1953, The effects of combining hunger and thirst motives in a discrimination habit, *J. comp. physiol. Psychol.*, **46**, 434–37.

Putnam, H., 1959, Review of Hanson's Patterns of discovery, *Science*, **129**, 1666–67.

Ramsey, F. P., 1931, *The foundations of mathematics and other logical essays*, London. Republished in paperback edition by Littlefield, Adams, and Co., in the International Library of Psychology, Philosophy, and Scientific Method, Series No. 214, 1960.

RAND Corporation, 1955, *A million random digits with 100,000 normal deviates*, The Free Press, Glencoe, Ill.

Rasch, G., 1960, *Probabilistic models for some intelligence and attainment tests*, Danish Institute for Educational Research, Copenhagen.

Richardson, M. W., 1938, Multidimensional psychophysics, *Psychol. Bull.*, **35**, 659–60 (abstract).

Riker, W. H., 1958, The paradox of voting and congressional rules for voting on amendments, *Amer. pol. Sci. Rev.*, **52**, 349–66.

Riker, W. H., 1961, Voting and summation of preferences: an interpretive bibliographical review of selected developments during the last decade, *Amer. pol. Sci. Rev.*, **55**, 900–911.

Rokeach, M., 1960, *The open and closed mind*, Basic Books, New York.

Rothkopf, E. Z., 1957, A measure of stimulus similarity and errors in some paired-associate learning tasks, *J. exp. Psychol.*, **53**, 94–101.

Runkel, P. J., 1956*a*, Cognitive facilitation of communication effects, unpublished Ph.D. dissertation, University of Michigan.

Runkel, P. J., 1956*b*, Cognitive similarity in facilitating communication, *Sociometry*, **19**, 178–91.

Runkel, P. J., 1958, Some consistency effects, *Educ. psychol. Measmt.*, **18**, 527–41.

Runkel, P. J., and Dora E. Damrin, 1961, Effects of training and anxiety upon teachers' preferences for information about students, *J. educ. Psychol.*, **52**, 254–61.

Saffir, M. A., 1937, A comparative study of scales constructed by three psychophysical methods, *Psychometrika*, **2**, 179–98.

Sagi, P. C., 1959, A statistical test for the significance of a coefficient of reproducibility, *Psychometrika*, **24**, 19–27.

Schubert, G., 1962, The 1960 term of the Supreme Court: a psychological analysis, *Amer. pol. Sci. Rev.*, **56**, 90–107.

Schucker, R. E., 1959, A note on the use of triads for paired comparisons, *Psychometrika*, **24**, 273–76.

Shepard, R. N., 1957, Stimulus and response generalization: a stochastic model relating generalization to distance in psychological space, *Psychometrika*, **22**, 325–45.

Shepard, R. N., 1958, Stimulus and response generalization: test of a model relating generalization to distance in psychological space, *J. exp. Psychol.*, **55**, 509–23.

Shepard, R. N., 1960, "Similarity of stimuli and metric properties of behavioral data," Chapter 4 in *Psychological scaling: theory and applications*, edited by H. Gulliksen and S. Messick, John Wiley and Sons, New York.

Shepard, R. N., 1962, The analysis of proximities: multidimensional scaling with an unknown distance function I, *Psychometrika*, **27**, 125–40.

Shuford, E. H., L. V. Jones, and R. D. Bock, 1960, A rational origin obtained by the method of contingent paired comparisons, *Psychometrika*, **25**, 343–56.

Siegel, S., 1956, A method for obtaining an ordered metric scale, *Psychometrika*, **21**, 207–16.

Stevens, S. S., 1956, The direct estimate of sensory magnitudes—loudness, *Amer. J. Psychol.*, **69**, 1–25.

Stevens, S. S., 1957, On the psychophysical law, *Psychol. Rev.*, **64**, 153–81.

Stevens, S. S., 1958, Problems and methods of psychophysics, *Psychol. Bull.*, **55**, 177–96.

Stevens, S. S., 1959, The quantification of sensation, *Dædalus*, **88**, 606–21.

Stevens, S. S., 1961, To honor Fechner and repeal his law, *Science*, **133**, 80–86.

Stouffer, S. A., et al., 1949, *The American soldier: combat and its aftermath*, vol. 2, Princeton University Press, Princeton.

Stouffer, S. A., et al., 1950, *Measurement and prediction: studies in social psychology in World War II*, vol. 4, Princeton University Press, Princeton.

Suppes, P., and J. Zinnes, 1963, "Basic measurement theory," in *Handbook of mathematical psychology*, Vol. I, edited by R. B. Bush, E. H. Galanter, and R. D. Luce, John Wiley and Sons, New York.

Tanner, W. P., Jr., and J. A. Swets, 1954, A decision-making theory of visual detection, *Psychol. Rev.*, **61**, 401–409.

Terry, M. E., R. A. Bradley, and L. L. Davis, 1952, New designs and techniques for organoleptic testing, *Food Technol.*, **6**, 250–54.

Thrall, R. M., 1952, A combinatorial problem, *Michigan math. J.*, **1**, 81–88.

Thurstone, L. L., 1947, *Multiple factor analysis*, University of Chicago Press, Chicago.

Thurstone, L. L., and E. J. Chave, 1929, *The measure of attitudes*, University of Chicago Press, Chicago.

Thurstone, L. L., and L. V. Jones, 1957, The rational origin for measuring subjective values, *J. Amer. statist. Ass.*, **52**, 458–71.

Torgerson, W. S., 1951, A theoretical and empirical investigation of multidimensional scaling, unpublished Ph.D. dissertation, Princeton University.

Torgerson, W. S., 1958, *Theory and methods of scaling*, John Wiley and Sons, New York.

Torgerson, W. S., 1960, Distances and ratios in psychological scaling, a paper delivered at the XVI° International Congress of Psychologists, Bonn, Germany, August 2, 1960.

Tucker, L. R., 1951, *A method for synthesis of factor analysis studies*, No. 984, Educational Testing Service, Princeton.

Tucker, L. R., 1952, A level of proficiency scale for a unidimensional skill, *Amer. Psychologist*, **7**, 408 (abstract).

Tucker, L. R., 1960, "Intra-individual and inter-individual multidimensionality," in *Psychological scaling: theory and application*, edited by H. Gulliksen and S. Messick, John Wiley and Sons, New York.

Vastenhouw, J., 1962, *Relationships between meanings*, Mouton and Co., The Hague.

Vernon, M. D., 1955, The functions of schemata in perceiving, *Psychol. Rev.*, **62**, 180–92.

Vickrey, W., 1960, Utility, strategy, and social decision rules, *Quart. J. Econ.*, **74**, 507–35.

von Neumann, J., and O. Morgenstern, 1953, *Theory of games and economic behavior*, Princeton University Press, Princeton.

Warner, W. L., M. Meeker, and K. Eells, 1949, *Social class in America*, Science Research Associates, Chicago.

Warren, J. M., 1953, The additivity of cues in visual pattern discriminations by monkeys, *J. comp. physiol. Psychol.*, **46**, 484–86.

White, B. W., and E. Saltz, 1957, Measurement of reproducibility, *Psychol. Bull.*, **54,** 81–99.
Wolfle, D., 1960, Diversity of talent, *Amer. Psychologist*, **15,** 535–45. Or see, for a similar article, *Science*, **133,** 71 (1961).

Young, G., and A. S. Householder, 1938, Discussion of a set of points in terms of their mutual distances, *Psychometrika*, **3,** 19–22.
Young, P. T., and J. L. Falk, 1956, The relative acceptability of sodium chloride solutions as a function of concentration and water need, *J. comp. physiol. Psychol.*, **49,** 569–75.
Young, P. T., and J. T. Greene, 1953, Relative acceptability of saccharine solutions as revealed by different methods, *J. comp. physiol. Psychol.*, **46,** 295–98.

Zinnes, J. L., 1958, The relationship between two methods for scaling pair comparison data, *Amer. Psychologist*, **13,** 416 (abstract).
Zinnes, J. L., 1959, A probabilistic theory of preferential choice, unpublished Ph.D. dissertation, University of Michigan.

Author Index

Abelson, R. P., 102, 236, 339, 367, 373, 438
Anderson, Lois K., 407
Anderson, T. W., 185, 307, 308
Arrow, K. J., 191, 383–389, 395–397
Attneave, F., 204, 241, 436–437
Austin, G. A., 326

Barber, B., 455
Bartlett, F. C., 326
Beardslee, D. C., 535–541
Becker, S. W., 348
Bennett, Joseph F., 140, 144, 153–155, 163, 179, 181, 199, 200, 203, 246, 254, 257, 259, 267, 271, 277, 280
Bentham, Jeremy, 384
Bentley, M., 213
Birnbaum, A., 238
Black, D., 193, 384, 389, 395, 396
Blau, J. H., 386, 397
Bock, R. D., 274
Borgatta, E. F., 237
Boring, E. G., 327, 345
Bose, R. C., 43
Bosley, J. J., 359
Bower, G. H., 365
Bradley, R. A., 42, 362, 364, 367, 368; see also B. T. L. model in Subject Index
Bruner, J. S., 326
Brunk, H. D., 53

Campbell, N., 362
Carmichael, L., 327
Cartwright, D., 425
Chabot, James, 33, 539
Chave, E. J., 563
Clarke, F. R., 365
Clausen, J. D., 218
Cochran, W. G., 43
Comrey, A. L., 371
Coombs, C. H., 95, 107, 108, 112, 115, 134–136, 181, 251, 259, 264, 280, 331, 348, 359, 379, 450, 454, 456, 486, 500, 504, 517, 545, 561
Cox, G. M., 43
Cronbach, L. J., 226, 248
Cross, David, 41, 112, 115, 444, 486
Cureton, E. E., 246

Damrin, D. E., 328
Dashiell, J. F., 527–529
Davidson, D., 134, 135, 375
Davis, L. L., 42, 364
Dawes, Robyn, 149, 160, 191, 279, 288, 289, 444
Dember, W. N., 45, 131–133, 527–529
DeSoto, C. B., 359
Diederich, G. W., 241
Durbin, J., 42
Dwyer, John, 41, 115

Earl, R. W., 131–133
Easterbrook, J. A., 328

Subject Index

Absolute judgment, 11, 17, 27, 74, 211
Academic ranks, 347
Accounting equations, 307
A data, 18
$A \times A$ data, 62, 514–526
Amplitude of response, *see* Response
Amsterdam experiment, 198, 499
Anglo-Spanish TAT, 556
Army General Classification Test, 547
Attitude measurement, 292, 293, 315
Attitude statements, Likert-type, 554
  Thurstone-type, 309
Average rank order, 52, 398
Axiom of independence from other al-
  ternatives, 40, 53, 56, 351, 384,
  387, 398
Axiom of local independence, 306, 312,
  321

Balanced incomplete block design
  (BIBD), 42, 44, 346
B data, 18
$B \times B$ data, 62, 431*ff.*
Bilateral pair, *see* Laterality
Boundary hyperplane, 142, 151
Box problem, 275–277
Bradley-Terry-Luce (B. T. L.) model,
  54, 364, 371, 373, 394, 440, 516

Cardinality criterion, 144, 150, 153, 159
Cartesian product, 18, 62
Cartwheels, *see* Method of

Central envelope, 163
Central set, 147
Channel capacity, 32, 34, 38, 49
  cartwheels, 46
City block model, 202, 434
Clinical diagnosis, 11, 293
Coefficient of reproducibility, 70–73,
  229, 230, 236, 311
Cognitive structure, 26, 122, 222, 326–
  333, 431, 435–436
Communication system, 51
Comparative judgment model, 54, 117,
  239–241, 363, 364, 374, 375,
  385, 411, 417, 418, 439, 499–
  509, 530, 536, 554
Compensatory composition model, 247,
  250, 259–277, 278, 285, 286,
  288
Composition functions, 245–249
Compound pair comparisons, 374–379
Conative processes, 222
Conditional proximity data, *see* Prox-
  imity matrices
Confusion data, *see* Proximity matrices
Conjoint distances, 44–50, 354, 355,
  406, 435
Conjunctive model, 246–259, 280, 288
Consonance relation, *see* Proximity re-
  lation
Constant ratio, 365
Constant sum method, 371
Contingent pair comparisons, 374–379